Stanley Gibbons

COLLECT
Channel Islands
and Isle of Man
STAMPS

A STANLEY GIBBONS CHECKLIST

2009 Edition

STANLEY GIBBONS LTD
London and Ringwood

*By Appointment to
Her Majesty The Queen,
Stanley Gibbons Ltd., London,
Philatelists*

Published by **Stanley Gibbons Publications**
Editorial, Sales Offices and Distribution Centre:
Parkside, Christchurch Road, Ringwood,
Hants BH24 3SH

25th COMBINED EDITION (2009)

ISBN: 0-85259-703-7

© Stanley Gibbons Ltd 2009

Item No. 2855 (09)

Text assembled and printed in Great Britain by
Piggott Black Bear (Cambridge), Cambridge

Introductory Notes

Scope. The listing of **stamps** for Guernsey and Jersey comprises German Occupation issues, the 1958–69 Regionals and the issues of the Independent Postal Administrations from their inception in 1969. Isle of Man sections cover the 1958–71 Regionals and the issues of the Independent Postal Administration from 1973 onwards.

Information is given on:

- Designers and printers
- The different printings for definitives and postage dues
- Distinctive papers
- Such varieties as imperforates and missing colours
- Phosphors
- Cylinder and plate numbers
- Sheet sizes and imprints
- Quantities sold
- Withdrawal and invalidation dates

The 'Notes' on page 1 may be found helpful in further explanation.

The checklist also covers:

- Miniature sheets
- First-day covers
- Presentation packs and Yearbooks
- Gutter pairs
- Stamp booklets
- Stamp sachets (listed, but unpriced)
- Postal stationery commemorative cards and covers

Items outside the scope and therefore *omitted* are: cylinder and plate varieties; non-postage stamps, such as revenues; and other classes of postal stationery.

Layout. Stamps are set out chronologically by date of issue. In the catalogue lists the first numeral is the Stanley Gibbons catalogue number; the black (boldface) numeral alongside is the type number referring to the respective illustration. The denomination and colour of the stamp are then shown. Before February 1971 British currency was:

£1=20s One Pound = twenty shillings *and*
1s=12d One shilling = twelve pence.

Upon decimalisation this became:

£1=100p One pound = one hundred (new) pence

The catalogue list then shows two price columns. The left-hand is for unused stamps and the right-hand for used.

Our method of indicating prices is:

Numerals for pence, e.g. 5 denotes 5p (5 pence). Numerals for pounds and pence, e.g. 4.25 denotes £4.25 (4 pounds and 25 pence). For £100 and above, prices are in whole pounds and so include the £ sign and omit the zeros for pence.

Size of illustrations. To comply with Post Office regulations illustrations of stamps and booklets are three-quarters linear size. Where illustrations are further reduced (miniature sheets and some booklet covers) actual sizes are given. Illustrations of watermarks are actual size.

Prices. Prices quoted in this catalogue are our selling prices at the time the book went to press. They are for stamps in fine condition; in issues where condition varies we may ask more for the superb and less for the sub-standard. With unused stamps prices are for unmounted mint (though where not available unmounted, mounted mint stamps are often supplied at a lower price). Used prices are normally for stamps postally used but may be for stamps cancelled-to-order where this practice exists. All prices are subject to change without prior notice and we give no guarantee to supply all stamps priced, since it is not possible to keep every catalogue item perpetually in stock. Commemoratives may, at times, only be available in complete sets. Individual low value stamps sold at 399, Strand are liable to an additional handling charge.

The minimum price quoted is 10 pence. For individual stamps prices between 10 pence and 95 pence are provided as a guide for catalogue users. The lowest price *charged* for individual stamps or sets purchased from Stanley Gibbons Ltd is £1.

Perforations. The 'perforation' is the number of holes in a length of 2 cm, as measured by the Gibbons *Instanta* gauge. The stamp is viewed against a dark background with the transparent gauge put on top of it. Perforations are quoted to the nearest half. Stamps without perforation are termed 'imperforate'.

Se-tenant combinations. *Se-tenant* means 'joined together'. Some sets include stamps of different design arranged *se-tenant* as blocks or strips and, in mint condition, these are usually collected unsevered as issued. Where such combinations exist, the individual stamps are priced normally as mint and used singles. The set prices refer to the unsevered combination plus singles of any other values in the set.

First Day Covers. Prices for first day covers are for complete sets used on special covers, the stamps of which bear an official postmark for first day of issue. Where the stamps in a set were issued on different days, prices are for a cover from each day.

Catalogue numbers used. The checklist uses the same catalogue numbers as the Stanley Gibbons *Stamps of the World* catalogue, 2009 edition.

Latest stamps recorded in this edition appeared in November 2008.

Specialist Philatelic Society. Channel Islands Specialists Society. Membership Secretary: Moira Edwards, 86 Hall Lane, Sandon, Chelmsford, Essex CM2 7RQ.

Amendments to the 2008 edition
A number of additions, amendments and corrections have been made to this edition and we would particularly like to thank Ray Dixon for his assistance. Help and information have also been provided by David Gurney, Godfrey Jarand and Richard Monteiro.

CONTENTS

CHANNEL ISLANDS — 1

GUERNSEY
The German Occupation 1940–1945 — 2
Regional Issues — 3
Independent Postal Administration — 4
Postage Due Stamps — 112
Stamp Booklets — 113
Alderney — 122
Stamp Booklets — 153

ISLE OF MAN
Regional Issues — 155
Independent Postal Administration — 156
Souvenir Postal Stationery Postcards — 287
Manx Postal Museum Postcards — 288
Postage Due Stamps — 289
Stamp Booklets — 290

JERSEY
The German Occupation 1940–1945 — 300
Regional Issues — 301
Independent Postal Administration — 302
Commemorative Postal Stationery Envelope — 427
Postage Due Stamps — 427
Stamp Booklets — 429

Catalogue Price or Real Price?

FREE CATALOGUES WORTH £30.00!

If you collect GB, British Empire, Foreign or Thematics, you need these 3 real price auction catalogues worth £10.00 each – posted to you each quarter. OVER 30,000 LOTS Real Price Guide.

Request Your Catalogues Now:

PLEASE MAIL ME YOUR FIRST FREE AUCTION CATALOGUE – WORTH £10.00

NAME...

ADDRESS..

....

Tel:..Postcode............................

Post to: Universal Philatelic Auctions, The Old School, Idbury, Chipping Norton, Oxon. OX7 6RU.

SELLING YOUR STAMPS?

Because 95% of the stamps we sell are sold to collectors – we can afford to pay that bit more than other dealers........and with 4 different selling systems from Mixtures to Approvals to Auction...............

.....WE BUY EVERYTHING!

Please contact our head buyer Andrew McGavin on 01993 831666
email: info@upastampauctions.co.uk

Write to us at:
Universal Philatelic Auctions, The Old School, Idbury, Chipping Norton, Oxon. OX7 6RU. Tel: 01993 831666
(Please make sure to include your telephone number).

Or Visit our website:

www.upastampauctions.co.uk

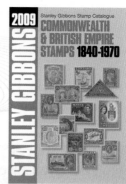

Printings
For definitives and postage due stamps released by the independent Postal Administration we give the dates of the printings as announced, and relate them in the listings to the actual stamps involved. Users will therefore be able to see at a glance how many printings have been made of any particular item.

Cylinder and Plate Numbers
Following the listing of each issue we give the printers' cylinder or plate numbers known to us.

Sheet size
In describing the sheet arrangement we always give the number of stamps across the sheet first. For example, '50 (5×10)' indicates a sheet of fifty stamps in ten horizontal rows of five stamps each.

Paper
Only distinctive types are mentioned. Granite paper can be easily distinguished by the coloured lines in its texture. *Chalky* or *chalk-surfaced* applies to paper which shows a black line when touched with silver.

Perforations
Perforations are normally given to the nearest half and the Instanta gauge is our standard. In this checklist we state if a perforation is by a line (L) or a comb (C) machine. A line machine only perforates one line at a time and consequently it requires two operations to do the horizontal and vertical perforations and where these intersect an irregular-shaped hole often results. A comb machine perforates three sides at a time and therefore produces a single hole at all corner intersections. The differences are easily seen in blocks of four.

The various perforations in this checklist are expressed as follows:

Perf 14:   Perforated alike on all sides.
Perf 14×15: Compound perforation. The first figure refers to top and bottom, the second to left and right sides.

Abbreviations
des = designer, designed
eng = engraver, engraved
litho = lithographed
mm = millimetres
MS = miniature sheet
No. = number
perf = perforated
photo = photogravure
recess = recess-printed
typo = typographed
wmk(d) = watermark(ed)

Channel Islands

C **1** Gathering Vraic   C **2** Islanders gathering Vraic

Third Anniversary of Liberation

(Des J. R. R. Stobie (1d.), or from drawing by E. Blampied (2½d). Photo Harrison and Sons)

1948 (10 MAY). *Wmk Mult* G VI R. Perf 15×14 (C)

C1	C **1**	1d scarlet	25	30
C2	C **2**	2½d ultramarine	25	30
		First Day Cover		35·00

These stamps were primarily intended for use in the Channel Islands although they were also available at eight head post offices in Great Britain.

Cylinder Nos.: 1d 2; 2½d 4

Sheets: 120 (6×20)

Quantities sold: 1d 5,934,000; 2½d 5,398,000

Guernsey

THE GERMAN OCCUPATION 1940—1945

The first German soldiers to arrive in Guernsey set foot on the island on 30 June 1940 and an official notice appeared in the local newspaper the following day announcing the occupation.

The first evidence of the occupation, philatelically, came towards the end of the year when supplies of Great Britain 1d stamps then in use began to dry up. It was decided that the bisecting of 2d stamps for use as 1d's be allowed and this commenced on 27 December. The decision to print 1d stamps locally had been taken in October, but these were not ready and were eventually issued on 18 February 1941. In the meantime the two currently available 2d stamps, the 1937 definitive and the 1940 Postal Centenary, were bisected and used, as were 2d stamps of the reign of George V which were in collectors' hands. Other values are also known to have been bisected and used, and were allowed to pass through the post in most instances without a postage due charge being made.

When the decision to bisect the 2d stamps was taken the German Commandant in Guernsey decided on adding a swastika to each half of the stamp. This overprint was applied to the Postal Centenary stamp and these were submitted to Berlin for approval, but this proposal was turned down. Another proposal, the overprinting of the 1937 1d with a number of small swastikas, would appear to have been dealt with in a similar way. Examples of both items exist though these are very rare.

As previously mentioned, the locally printed 1d stamps were issued on 18 February 1941. The ½d stamp was released on 7 April 1941 and the 2½d on 12 April 1944. This last stamp was issued in an effort to economise on the use of paper as it was found that sealed letters were franked with two 1d stamps and one ½d or a larger number of ½d's, a gross waste in times of shortage. Many printings of these stamps were made, the most notable being on the French bank-note paper in 1942.

Shades of these issues abound, the more outstanding ones being the bluish green (4th) and olive-green (8th) printings of the ½d, and the pale vermilion (11th) printing of the 1d. During the occupation Guernsey stamps were only valid on mail within the Channel Islands. Letters sent overseas were despatched via the German Feldpost system. The stamps continued to be used after the liberation in 1945 until 13 April 1946.

The Swastika Overprints

1940. *Prepared for use but not issued. Stamps of Great Britain overprinted*

(a) 1937 *definitive overprinted with a number of small swastikas*

Cat No.		Unused
SW1	1d scarlet	£900

(b) 1940 *Postal Centenary issue overprinted with a swastika on each half of the stamp*

SW2	2d orange	. . . .	£900

Example of bisected 2d Postal Centenary stamp

The Bisects

1940 (27 DEC).

(a) *Stamps of King George V*

Cat. No.				Price on cover
BS1	1912–22	2d orange	. . . .	£250
BS2	1924–26	2d orange	. . . .	£250
BS3	1934–36	2d orange	. . . .	£275

(b) *Stamps of King George VI*

BS4	1937	1d scarlet	£475
BS5	1938	2d orange	40·00
BS6	1940	Stamp Centenary 1d scarlet . . .	£475
BS7	1940	Stamp Centenary 2d orange . . .	30·00
BS8	1940	Stamp Centenary 2½d ultramarine	£750
BS9	1940	Stamp Centenary 3d violet	

Forged postmarks on fake bisects are known from Guernsey Head Post Office ('2 JA 41'), Market Place ('19 FE 41' or '7 AP 41'), St. Sampson ('27 DE 40') and The Vale ('18 FE 41').

The bisects are priced on philatelic cover. Those which were used commercially are worth more, particularly Nos. BS5 and BS7.

Invalidated: 22.2.41 (last postings were postmarked 24.2.41.)

1 Arms of Guernsey

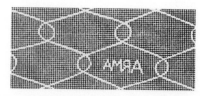

1a Loops

Stamps issued during the German Occupation

(Des E. W. Vaudin. Typo Guernsey Press Co Ltd)

1941–44. *Rouletted*

(a) *White paper. No wmk*

Cat. No.	Type No.		Unused	Used
1	**1**	½d light green (7.4.41)	6·00	3·50
		a. Emerald-green (6.41)	6·00	2·00
		b. Bluish green (11.41)	32·00	13·00
		c. Bright green (2.42)	22·00	10·00
		d. Dull green (9.42)	4·00	2·00
		e. Olive-green (2.43)	45·00	25·00
		f. Pale yellowish green (7.43 and later) (shades)	4·00	3·00
		g. Imperf (pair)	£200	
		h. Imperf between (horizontal pair)	£700	
		i. Imperf between (vertical pair)	£800	
2		1d scarlet (18.2.41)	3·25	2·00
		a. Pale vermilion (7.43) (etc) . .	5·00	2·00
		b. Carmine (1943)	3·50	2·00
		c. Imperf (pair)	£150	75·00
		d. Imperf between (horizontal pair)	£700	
		da. Imperf vert (centre stamp of horizontal strip of 3)		
		e. Imperf between (vertical pair)	£800	
		f. Ptd double (scarlet shade) . .	£100	
3		2½d ultramarine (12.4.44)	13·00	12·00
		a. Pale ultramarine (7.44)	10·00	7·00
		b. Imperf (pair)	£500	
		c. Imperf between (horizontal pair)	£1000	
1		First Day Cover		6·00
2		First Day Cover		15·00
3		First Day Cover		8·00

(b) *Bluish French bank-note paper. Wmk* **1a** (*sideways*)

4	**1**	½d bright green (11.3.42)	30·00	22·00
5		1d scarlet (9.4.42)	16·00	22·00
4		First Day Cover		90·00
5		First Day Cover		55·00

The dates for the shades of Nos. 1/3 are the months in which they were printed as indicated on the printer's imprints (see below). Others are issue dates.

Printings and imprint: The various printings can be identified from the sheet imprints as follows:

½d 1st Printing 240M/3/41
      2nd Printing 2×120M/6/41
      3rd Printing 3×120M/6/41
      4th Printing 4×120M/11/41
      5th Printing 5×120M/2/42
      6th Printing 6×240M/2/42
      7th Printing 7×120M/9/42
      8th Printing 8×120M/2/43
      9th Printing 9×120M/7/43
      10th Printing 10×120M/10/43
      11th Printing Guernsey Press Co., (stop and comma)
      12th Printing Guernsey Press Co. (stop only, margin at bottom 23 to 27 mm)
      13th Printing Guernsey Press Co. (stop only, margin at bottom 15 mm)

1d 1st Printing 120M/2/41
      2nd Printing 2×120M/2/41
      3rd Printing 3×120M/6/41
      4th Printing 4×120M/6/41
      5th Printing 5×120M/9/41
      6th Printing 6×240M/11/41
      7th Printing 7×120M/2/42
      8th Printing 8×240M/4/42
      9th Printing 9×240M/9/42
      10th Printing 10×240M/1/43
      11th Printing 11×240M/7/43
      12th Printing Guernsey Press Co.
      13th Printing PRESS TYP.
      14th Printing 'PRESS' (inverted commas unlevel)
      15th Printing 'PRESS' (inverted commas level, margin at bottom 28 mm)
      16th Printing 'PRESS' (inverted commas level, margin at bottom 12 mm)

2½d 1st Printing Guernsey Press Co.,
      2nd Printing 'PRESS' (inverted commas unlevel)
      3rd Printing 'PRESS' (inverted commas level, margin at bottom 22 mm)
      4th Printing 'PRESS' (inverted commas level, margin at bottom 15 mm)

The numbered imprints occur in the left-hand corner, bottom margin on the 1st printing of the 1d, and central, bottom margin on all other printings of all three values.

In the numbered imprints, for example, 2×120M/6/41, the '2' indicates the number of the printing; '120M' denotes the number of stamps printed in thousands, in this case 120,000; and '6/41' denotes the date of the printing, June 1941.

In the first ten printings of the ½d and the first eleven printings of the 1d the printing details are prefixed by the name of the printer, "Guernsey Press Co."

Sheets: 60 (6×10)

Quantities printed: ½d 1,772,160; 1d 2,478,000; 2½d 416,640

Withdrawn and invalidated: 13.4.46

REGIONAL ISSUES

Although specifically issued for regional use, these issues were initially valid for use throughout Great Britain. However, they ceased to be valid in Guernsey and Jersey from 1 October 1969 when these islands each established their own independent postal administration and introduced their own stamps.

DATES OF ISSUE. Conflicting dates of issue have been announced for some of the regional issues, partly explained by the stamps being released on different dates by the Philatelic Bureau in Edinburgh or the Philatelic Counter in London and in the regions. We have adopted the practice of giving the earliest known dates, since once released the stamps could have been used anywhere in the U.K.

INVALIDATION. The regional issues of Guernsey were invalidated for use in Guernsey and Jersey on 1 November 1969. The stamps continued to be valid for use in the rest of the United Kingdom until 29 February 1972. Those still current remained on sale at philatelic sales counters until 30 September 1970.

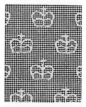

1b Multiple Crowns

2

3

(Des E. A. Piprell. Portrait by Dorothy Wilding Ltd. Photo Harrison and Sons)

1958–67. *Wmk Type* **1b.** Perf 15 × 14 (C)

6	**2**	2½d rose-red (8.6.64)	35	40
7	**3**	3d deep lilac (18.8.58)	30	30
		p. *One centre phosphor band* (24.5.67)	15	20
8		4d ultramarine (7.2.66)	25	30
		p. *Two phosphor bands* (24.10.67)	15	20
6/8p		Set of 3	70	80
6		First Day Cover		30·00
7		First Day Cover		20·00
8		First Day Cover		8·00

Cylinder Nos.: 2½d 1, 3; 3d (ord) 4, 5; 3d (phos) 5; 4d (ord) 1; 4d (phos) 1

Sheets: 240 (12×20)

Quantities sold (ordinary only): 2½d 3,485,760; 3d 25,812,360; 4d 4,415,040

Withdrawn: 31.8.66 2½d

Sold out: 6.3.68 3d and 4d (ordinary); 10.68 4d (phosphor); 11.68 3d (phosphor)

1968-69. *No wmk. Chalk-surfaced paper. One centre phosphor band (Nos. 10/11) or two phosphor bands (others). Perf 15×14 (C)*

9	**3**	4d pale ultramarine (16.4.68) . .	10	20
10		4d olive-sepia (4.9.68)	10	15
11		4d bright vermilion (26.2.69) . . .	20	25
12		5d royal blue (4.9.68)	20	30
9/12		Set of 4	50	1·00
10, 12		First Day Cover		3·00

No. 9 was not issued in Guernsey until 22 April.

Cylinder Nos. 4d (pale ultramarine) 1; 4d (olive-sepia) 1; 4d (bright vermilion) 1; 5d 1

Sold out; 3.69 4d ultramarine

Withdrawn: 30.9.69 (locally), 30.9.70 (British Philatelic Counters) 4d olive-sepia, 4d bright vermilion and 5d

INDEPENDENT POSTAL ADMINISTRATION

Guernsey established their own independent postal administration on 1 October 1969 and introduced their own stamps.

NO WATERMARK. All the following issues are on unwatermarked paper.

4 Castle Cornet and Edward the Confessor

5 Map and William I

6 Martello Tower and Henry II

7 Arms of Sark and King John

8 Arms of Alderney and Edward III

9 Guernsey Lily and Henry V

10 Arms of Guernsey and Elizabeth I

11 Arms of Alderney and Charles II

12 Arms of Sark and George III

13 Arms of Guernsey and Queen Victoria

14 Guernsey Lily and Elizabeth I

15 Martello Tower and King John

16 View of Sark

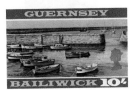

17 View of Alderney

18 View of Guernsey

Two types of 1d and 1s6d

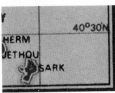

I Latitude inscr '40° 30' N'

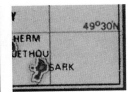

II Corrected to '49° 0' N'

(Des R. Granger Barrett. Photo Harrison (½d to 2s6d), Delrieu (others))

1969 (1 OCT)–**70**. Perf 14 (½d to 2s6d) or 12½ (others), all comb

13	**4**	½d deep magenta and black (*a*) .	10	10
		a. Thin paper	60	60
14	**5**	1d bright blue and black (I) (*a*) . .	10	10
		a. Thin paper (*b*)	50	50
14*b*		1d bright blue and black (*thin paper*) (II) (*eg*)	30	30
		c. Booklet stamp with margins (thick paper) (*c*)	40	40
15	**6**	1½d yellow-brown and black (*a*) .	10	10
16	**7**	2d gold, brt red, dp blue & blk (*a*)	10	10
		a. Thin paper (*g*)	40	40
17	**8**	3d gold, pale greenish yellow, orange-red and black (*a*) . . .	15	15
		a. Error. Wmk Block CA £1200		
		ai. Wmk inverted £900		
		b. Thin paper (*g*)	50	50
18	**9**	4d multicoloured (*a*)	20	25
		a. Booklet stamp with margins (*c*)	40	45
		ab. Yellow omitted £600		
		ac. Emerald (stem) omitted £500		
19	**10**	5d gold, bright vermilion, bluish violet and black (*a*) . . .	20	20
		a. Booklet stamp with margins (*c*)	50	50
		b. Gold (inscription etc.) omitted (booklets) £950		
20	**11**	6d gold, pale greenish yellow, light bronze-green & black (*a*)	20	30
		a. Thin paper (*g*)	45	45
21	**12**	9d gold, brt red, crimson & blk (*a*)	30	30
		a. Thin paper (*g*)	3·00	1·70
22	**13**	1s gold, brt verm, bistre & blk (*a*) .	30	30
		a. Thin paper (*g*)	1·00	75
23	**5**	1s6d turquoise-grn & blk (I) (*a*) . .	25	30
		a. Thin paper (*d*)	1·70	3·25
23*b*		1s6d turquoise-green and black (thin paper) (II) (*eg*)	2·00	1·70

24	**14**	1s9d multicoloured (a)	80	80
		a. *Emerald (stem) omitted*	£600	
		b. *Thin* paper (g)	2·20	1·90
25	**15**	2s6d brt reddish violet & black (a)	3·25	2·75
		a. *Thin* paper (g)	5·50	4·50
26	**16**	5s multicoloured (a)	2·50	2·20
27	**17**	10s multicoloured (a)	16·00	18·00
		a. *Perf* 13½×13 (f)	35·00	35·00
28	**18**	£1 multicoloured (a)	2·20	2·20
		a. *Perf* 13½ × 13 (fh)	2·20	2·20
13/28a		*Set of 16*	24·00	26·00
13/28		*First Day Cover*		28·00
13/28		*Presentation Packs (incl. both*		
		1d *and* 1s6d) (3) (9.70)	40·00	
13/25		*Set of 13 Gutter Pairs*		

Thinner paper – see note after Jersey No. 29.

There was no postal need for the ½d and 1½d values as the ½d coin had been withdrawn prior to their issue in anticipation of decimalisation. These values were only on sale at the Philatelic Bureau and at the Crown Agents as well as in the U.S.A.

Type **18** was re-issued as a booklet pane in 2001. See No. 927.

Printings: (a) 1.10.69; (b) 24.11.69; (c) 12.12.69; (d) 1.70; (e) 4.2.70; (f) 4.3.70; (g) 18.5.70; (h) 7.71

Cylinder Nos.: ½d, 1½d, 2s6d 1A–1A, 1B–1B; 1d (I) 1A–1A (a); 2A–2A, 2B–2B (b); 1d (II) 2A–2A, 2B–2B (e); 3A–3A, 3B–3B (g) 2d, 3d, 5d, 6d, 9d, 1s 1A, 1B (each ×4); 4d, 1s9d 1A, 1B (each ×5); 1s6d (I) 1A–1A, 1B–1B (a); 1A–2A, 1B–2B (d); 1s6d (II) 1B–1B, 1A–2A, 1B–2B (e); 2A–3A, 2B–3B (g) 2B–2B; 5s to £1 None

Sheets: 60 (2 panes (5×6) most sheets of the 5s, 10s and £1 were divided into two panes before issue

Imprint: Central, bottom margin (½d to 2s6d)

Quantities sold ½d 2,480,000; 1d (Nos. 14/14b) 1,560,971; 1½d 980,000; 2d 574,610; 3d 487,199; 4d 2,782,490; 5d 1,393,193; 6d 456,275; 9d 374,975; 1s 435,773; 1s6d (Nos. 23/23b) 627,003; 1s9d 255,111; 2s6d 225,732; 5s 165,047; 10s (No. 27) 114,000; 10s (No. 27a) 55,200; £1 (No. 28a) 141,802

Sold out: 8.71 10s (No. 27a)

Withdrawn: 6.10.69, ½d, 1½d, 4.2.70, 1d (No. 14), 1s6d (No. 23); others 14.2.72 (except for No. 28a which remained on sale with decimal definitives until 31.3.76)

Although officially withdrawn the ½d, 1d (No. 14), 1½d and 1s6d (No. 23) were subsequently included in Presentation Packs, whilst the ½d and 1½d remained on sale at the Philatelic Bureau until 14 February 1972.

Invalidated: 14.2.72 (except £1)

19 Isaac Brock as Colonel

20 Sir Isaac Brock as Major-General

21 Isaac Brock as Ensign

22 Arms and Flags

Birth Bicentenary of Sir Isaac Brock

(Litho Format)

1969 (1 DEC). Perf 13½×14 (2s6d) or 14×13½ (others), all comb

29	**19**	4d multicoloured	20	20
30	**20**	5d multicoloured	20	20
31	**21**	1s9d multicoloured	90	75
32	**22**	2s6d multicoloured	90	75
29/32		*Set of 4*	2·00	1·70
		First Day Cover		3·25
		Presentation Pack	3·75	
		Set of 4 Gutter Pairs	£150	

Plate Nos. 4d, 2s6d 1A, 1B, 1C, 1D (each ×6); 5d 1A, 1B, 1C, 1D (each ×7); 1s9d 1A, 1B, 1C, 1D (each ×5)

Sheets: 60 (2 panes 5×6) 2s6d; (2 panes 6×5) others

Imprint: Right-hand corner, bottom margin

Quantities sold: 4d 940,956; 5d 732,658; 1s9d 224,157; 2s6d 218,955

Withdrawn: 30.11.70

Invalidated: 14.2.72

23 H.M.S. *L103* (landing craft) entering St. Peter's Harbour

24 H.M.S. *Bulldog* and H.M.S. *Beagle* (destroyers) entering St. Peter Port

25 Brigadier Snow reading the Proclamation

25th Anniversary of Liberation

(Des and photo Courvoisier)

1970 (9 MAY). *Granite paper.* Perf 11½ (C)

33	**23**	4d blue and pale blue	20	20
34	**24**	5d brown-lake and pale grey ...	40	20
35	**25**	1s6d bistre-brown and buff	1·20	90
33/5		*Set of 3*	1·70	1·10
		First Day Cover		2·40
		Presentation Pack	4·00	

Cylinder Nos.: A1–1, B1–1 (all values)

Sheets: 25 (5×5)

Imprint: Left-hand corner, top margin (4d, 5d); bottom corner, left-hand margin (1s6d)

Quantities sold: 4d 968,873; 5d 817,958; 1s6d 248,532

Withdrawn: 8.5.71

Invalidated: 14.2.72

26 Guernsey 'Toms'

27 Guernsey Cow

28 Guernsey Bull

29 Freesias

Agriculture and Horticulture

(Des and Photo Courvoisier)

1970 (12 AUG). *Granite paper.* Perf 11½ (C)

36	**26**	4d multicoloured	55	20
37	**27**	5d multicoloured	70	20
38	**28**	9d multicoloured	2·75	1·30
39	**29**	1s6d multicoloured	2·75	2·40
36/9		*Set of 4*	6·50	4·00
		First Day Cover		5·00
		Presentation Pack	18·00	

Cylinder Nos.: A1–1–1–1, B1–1–1–1, C1–1–1–1, D1–1–1–1 (all values)

Sheets: 25 (5×5)

Imprint: Central, bottom margin

Quantities sold: 4d 1,082.608; 5d 1,000,000; 9d 237,685; 1s6d 241,816

Withdrawn: 11.8.71

Invalidated: 14.2.72

30 St. Anne's Church, Alderney

31 St. Peter's Church, Guernsey

32 St. Peter's Church, Sark

33 St. Tugual Chapel, Herm

Christmas. Guernsey Churches (1st series)

(Des and photo Courvoisier)

1970 (11 NOV). *Granite paper.* Perf 11½ (C)

40	**30**	4d multicoloured	20	10
41	**31**	5d multicoloured	20	10
42	**32**	9d multicoloured	1·20	1·00
43	**33**	1s6d multicoloured	1·50	1·20
40/3		*Set of 4*	2·50	2·00
		First Day Cover		2·10
		Presentation Pack	5·00	

See also Nos. 63/6.

Cylinder Nos.: A1–1–1–1 or B1–1–1–1 (all values)

Sheets: 50 (5×10) 4d, 5d; (10×5) others

Quantities sold: 4d 815,737; 5d 668.886; 9d 236,833; 1s6d 223,907

Withdrawn: 10.11.71

Invalidated: 14.2.72

34 Martello Tower and King John

Decimal Currency

(Photo Harrison (½p to 10p), Delrieu (others))

1971 (6 JAN)–**73**. *Designs as Type* **4** *etc., but values inscribed in decimal currency as in Type* **34**. *Chalk-surfaced paper.* Perf 14 (½p to 10p) or 13½×13) (others), all comb

44	**4**	½p deep magenta and black (*b*) .	10	15
		a. Booklet stamp with margins. Glazed, ordinary paper	15	20
		ab. Ditto. Chalk-surfaced paper (*f*)	15	20
45	**5**	1p bright blue and black (ll) (*b*) .	10	10
46	**6**	1½p yellow-brown and black (*b*) .	15	15

47	**9**	2p multicoloured (*b*)	15	15
		a. Booklet stamp with margins. Glazed, ordinary paper	20	20
		ab. Ditto. Chalk-surfaced paper (*f*)	20	20
		ac. Emerald (*stem*) omitted	£1500	
		b. Glazed, ordinary paper (*b*) ..	20	20
48	**10**	2½p gold, bright vermilion, bluish violet and black (*bf*) ..	15	10
		a. Bright vermilion omitted ...	£950	
		b. Booklet stamp with margins. Glazed, ordinary paper	20	20
		ba. Ditto. Chalk-surfaced paper (*f*)	20	20
49	**8**	3p gold, pale greenish yellow, orange-red and black (*bf*) ...	20	20
50	**14**	3½p mult (*glazed, ordinary paper*) (*b*)	20	20
51	**7**	4p multicoloured (*b*)	20	20
52	**5**	5p turquoise-green & black (ll) (*b*)	20	20
53	**11**	6p gold, pale greenish yellow, lt bronze-green and black (*b*) ..	20	20
54	**13**	7½p gold, brt verm, bistre & blk (*b*)	30	35
55	**12**	9p gold, brt red, crimson & blk (*b*)	65	65
56	**34**	10p bright reddish violet & blk (*a*)	1·70	1·70
		a. Ordinary paper. Bright reddish violet and deep black (*d*) ...	1·20	1·20
57	**16**	20p mult (*glazed, ordinary paper*) (*ag*)	70	70
		a. Shade* (*e*)	70	70
58	**17**	50p mult (*glazed, ordinary paper*) (*aeh*)	1·20	1·20
44/58		Set of 15	5·00	5·25
		First Day Covers (2)		9·00
44/58,28a		Presentation Packs (3)	12·00	
44/56		Set of 13 Gutter Pairs	18·00	

*No. 57 has the sky in a pale turquoise-blue; on No. 57*a* it is pale turquoise-green.

Printings: (*a*) 6.1.71; (*b*) 15.2.71; (*c*) 3.72; (*d*) 1.9.72; (*e*) 25.1.73; (*f*) 2.4.73; (*g*) 10.74; (*h*) 7.75

Cylinder Nos.: ½p, 1p, 1½p, 5p, 10p 1A–1A, 1B–1B; 2p, 3½p 1A, 1B (each ×5); 2½p, 3p, 4p, 6p, 7½p, 9p 1A, 1B (each ×4); 20p none; 50p 21–22–23–24. Sheets from ptg (*g*) have an additional S99 (reversed)

On the 3½p only four '1A' Nos. are shown in the margin, the black '1A' being omitted in error.

Sheets: 50 (2 panes 5×5) ½p to 10p; 30 (5×6) others

Imprint: Central, bottom margin (½p to 10p)

Quantities sold: ½p 980,959; 1p 568,509; 1½p 559,576; 2p 2,512,903; 2½p 4,469,578; 3p 2,245,564; 3½p 317,523; 4p 527,696; 5p 511,742; 6p 346,255; 7½p 322,905; 9p 349,211; 10p 538,153; 20p 630,888; 50p 258,150

Withdrawn: 1.4.75 ½p to 10p (½p, 9p 10p and Presentation Packs sold out by 5.74); 31.3.76 20p, 50p

35 Hong Kong 2c of 1862

36 Great Britain 4d of 1855–7

37 Italy 5c of 1862

38 Confederate States 5c of 1862

Thomas De La Rue Commemoration

(Des and recess De La Rue)

1971 (2 JUNE). Perf 14×13½ (C)

59	**35**	2p dull purple to brown-purple*	35	15
60	**36**	2½p carmine-red	35	15
61	**37**	4p deep bluish green	1·10	1·00
62	**38**	7½p deep blue	1·40	1·20
59/62		Set of 4	2·75	2·20
		First Day Cover		4·00
		Presentation Pack	4·50	

*These colours represent the extreme range of shades of this value. The majority of the printing, however, is an intermediate shade.

Plate Nos.: 1A, 1B each

Sheets: 25 (5×5)

Imprint: Central, bottom margin

Quantities sold: 2p 897,742; 2½p 1,404,085; 4p 210,691; 7½p 199,424

Withdrawn: 1.6.72

39 Ebenezer Church, St. Peter Port

40 Church of St. Pierre du Bois

41 St. Joseph's Church, St. Peter Port

42 Church of St. Philippe de Torteval

Christmas. Guernsey Churches (2nd series)

(Des and photo Courvoisier)

1971 (27 OCT). *Granite paper.* Perf 11½ (C)

63	**39**	2p multicoloured	10	10
64	**40**	2½p multicoloured	10	10
65	**41**	5p multicoloured	1·00	1·00
66	**42**	7½p multicoloured	1·00	1·00
63/6		Set of 4	2·00	2·00
		First Day Cover		3·00
		Presentation Pack	4·25	
		Set of 4 Gutter Pairs	21·00	

Cylinder Nos: A1–1–1–1, B1–1–1–1, C1–1–1–1, D1–1–1–1 (all values)

Sheets: 50 (2 panes 5×5)

Imprint: central, bottom margin (2p, 2½p) or left-hand corner, bottom margin (5p, 7½p)

Quantities sold: 2p 991,155; 2½p 916,004; 5p 223,412; 7½p 215,768

Withdrawn: 26.10.72

43 *Earl of Chesterfield* (1794)

44 *Dasher* (1827)

45 *Ibex* (1891)

46 *Alberta* (1900)

Mail Packet Boats (1st series)

(Des and photo Courvoisier)

1972 (10 FEB). *Granite paper.* Perf 11 (C)

67	**43**	2p multicoloured	15	10
68	**44**	2½p multicoloured	15	10
69	**45**	7½p multicoloured	40	35
70	**46**	9p multicoloured	60	50
67/70		Set of 4	1·20	95
		First Day Cover		3·00
		Presentation Pack	3·25	

See also Nos. 80/3.

Cylinder Nos.: A1–1–1–1 or B1–1–1–1 (all values)

Sheets: 25 (5×5)

Imprint: Central, bottom margin

Quantities sold: 2p 973,503; 2½p 954,263; 7½p 288,929; 9p 289,340

Withdrawn: 9.2.73

47 Guernsey Bull

World Conference of Guernsey Breeders, Guernsey

(Photo Courvoisier)

1972 (22 MAY). *Granite paper.* Perf 11½ (C)

71	**47**	5p multicoloured	30	30
		First Day Cover*		2·50
		Gutter Pair	5·50	

*Prepared by the Royal Guernsey Agricultural and Horticultural Society.

Cylinder Nos.: A1–1–1–1, B1–1–1–1

Sheets: 50 (2 panes 5×5)

48 Bermuda Buttercup

49 Heath Spotted Orchid

50 Kaffir Fig   **51** Scarlet Pimpernel

Wild Flowers

(Des and photo Courvoisier)

1972 (24 MAY). *Granite paper.* Perf 11½ (C)

72	**48**	2p multicoloured	10	10
73	**49**	2½p multicoloured	10	10
74	**50**	7½p multicoloured	50	40
75	**51**	9p multicoloured	60	50
72/5		Set of 4	1·20	90
		First Day Cover		2·50
		Presentation Pack	3·25	
		Set of 4 Gutter Pairs	5·00	

Cylinder Nos.: A1–1–1–1, B1–1–1–1, C1–1–1–1, D1–1–1–1 (all values)

Sheets: 50 (2 panes 5×5)

Imprint: 2p, 7½p Central, bottom margin, others left-hand corner, bottom margin

Quantities sold: 2p 1,006,041; 2½p 1,028,826; 7½p 249,471; 9p 244,839

Withdrawn: 23.5.73

52 Angels adoring Christ

53 The Epiphany

54 The Virgin Mary

55 Christ

Royal Silver Wedding and Christmas

(Des and photo Courvoisier)

1972 (20 NOV). *Designs show stained glass windows from Guernsey Churches. Granite paper.* Perf 11½ (C)

76	**52**	2p multicoloured	10	10
77	**53**	2½p multicoloured	15	10
78	**54**	7½p multicoloured	30	25
79	**55**	9p multicoloured	35	35
76/9		Set of 4	80	70
		First Day Cover		1·10
		Presentation Pack	1·90	
		Set of 4 Gutter Pairs	3·00	

Cylinder Nos.: A1–1–1–1, B1–1–1–1 each

Sheets: 50 (2 panes 5×5)

Imprint: Central, bottom margin of each pane

Quantities sold: 2p 878.893; 2½p 1,037,387; 7½p 314,972; 9p 313,367

Sold out: By 31.3.73

56 *St. Julien* (1925)

57 *Isle of Guernsey* (1930)

58 *St. Patrick* (1947)

59 *Sarnia* (1961)

Mail Packet Boats (2nd series)

(Des and photo Courvoisier)

1973 (9 MAR). *Granite paper.* Perf 11½ (C)

80	**56**	2½p multicoloured		10	10
81	**57**	3p multicoloured		20	20
82	**58**	7½p multicoloured		40	40
83	**59**	9p multicoloured		45	45
80/3		*Set of 4*		1·10	1·00
		First Day Cover			1·40
		Presentation Pack		2·00	
		Set of 4 Gutter Pairs		5·00	

...values A1–1–1–1, B1–1–1–1, C1–1–1–1, D1–1–1–1

...s 5×5)

...ttom margin of each pane

...947,888; 3p 1,274,699; 7½p 278,998; 9p 263,569

...3p and Presentation Pack sold out earlier)

60 Supermarine Sea Eagle

61 Westland Wessex Trimotor

62 De Havilland D.H.89 Dragon Rapide

63 Douglas DC-3

64 Vickers Viscount 800 *Anne Marie*

50th Anniversary of Air Service

(Des and photo Courvoisier)

1973 (4 JULY). *Granite paper.* Perf 11½ (C)

84	**60**	2½p multicoloured		10	10
85	**61**	3p multicoloured		10	10
86	**62**	5p multicoloured		25	25
87	**63**	7½p multicoloured		35	30
88	**64**	9p multicoloured		45	40
84/8		*Set of 5*		1·10	1·00
		First Day Cover			1·50
		Presentation Pack		2·00	
		Set of 5 Gutter Pairs		4·00	

Cylinder Nos.: A1-1-1-1, B1-1-1-1 each

Sheets: 50 (2 panes (5×5)

Imprint: Central, bottom margin of each pane

Quantities sold: 2½p 918,953; 3p 1,285,890; 5p 313,882; 7½p 294,369; 9p 288,225

Withdrawn: 3.7.74 (5p and Presentation Pack sold our earlier)

65 'The Good Shepherd'

66 Christ at the Well of Samaria

67 St. Dominic

68 Mary and the Child Jesus

Christmas

(Des and photo Courvoisier)

1973 (24 OCT). *Designs show stained glass windows from Guernsey Churches. Granite paper.* Perf 11½ (C)

89	**65**	2½p multicoloured		10	10
90	**66**	3p multicoloured		10	10

91	**67**	7½p multicoloured	....	30	30
92	**68**	20p multicoloured	....	40	40
89/92		*Set of 4*	....	75	75
		First Day Cover	....		90
		Presentation Pack	....	1·50	
		Set of 4 Gutter Pairs	......	2·75	

Cylinder Nos.: A1–1–1–1–1, B1–1–1–1–1 each

Sheets: 50 (2 panes 5×5)

Imprint: Central, bottom margin of each pane

Quantities sold: 2½p 1,284,342; 3p 1,285,851; 7½p 367,714; 20p 367,625

Withdrawn: 23.10.74

69 Princess Anne and Capt. Mark Phillips

Royal Wedding

(Des G. Anderson. Photo Courvoisier)

1973 (14 NOV). *Granite paper*. Perf 11½ (C)

93	**69**	25p multicoloured	....	45	45
		First Day Cover	....		75
		Presentation Pack	....	90	
		Gutter Pair	....	1·50	

Cylinder Nos.: A1–1–1–1, B1–1–1–1

Sheets: 50 (2 panes 5×5)

Imprint: Central, bottom margin of each pane

Quantity sold: 392,767

Withdrawn: 13.11.74

70 *John Lockett,* 1875

71 *Arthur Lionel,* 1912

72 *Euphrosyne Kendal,* 1954

73 *Arun,* 1972

150th Anniversary of Royal National Life-boat Institution

(Des and photo Courvoisier)

1974 (15 JAN). *Granite paper.* Perf 11½ (C)

94	**70**	2½p multicoloured	....	10	10
95	**71**	3p multicoloured	....	10	10
96	**72**	8p multicoloured	....	30	20
97	**73**	10p multicoloured	....	35	25
94/97		*Set of 4*	....	70	60
		First Day Cover	....		1·00
		Presentation Pack	....	1·60	
		Set of 4 Gutter Pairs	......	1·50	

Cylinder Nos.: A1–1–1–1, B1–1–1–1 each

Sheets: 50 (2 panes 5×5)

Imprint: Central, bottom margin of each pane

Quantities sold: 2½p 1,016,058; 3p 1,162,020; 8p 393,660; 10p 393,668

Withdrawn: 14.1.75 (8p, 10p and Presentation Pack sold out earlier)

74 *Private, East Regt.,* 1815

75 *Officer, 2nd North Regt.,* 1825

76 *Gunner, Guernsey Artillery,* 1787

77 *Gunner, Guernsey Artillery,* 1815

78 *Corporal, Royal Guernsey Artillery,* 1868

79 *Field Officer, Royal Guernsey Artillery,* 1895

80 *Sergeant, 3rd Regt.,* 1867

81 *Officer, East Regt.,* 1822

82 *Field Officer, Royal Guernsey Artillery,* 1895

83 Colour-Sergeant of Grenadiers, 1833

84 Officer, North Regt., 1832

85 Officer, East Regt., 1822

86 Field Officer, Rifle Company, 1868

87 Private, 4th West Regt., 1785

88 Field Officer, 4th West Regt., 1824

89 Driver, Field Battery, Royal Guernsey Artillery, 1848

90 Officer, Field Battery, Royal Guernsey Artillery, 1868

91 Cavalry Trooper, Light Dragoons, 1814

Guernsey Militia

(Photo Courvoisier (½p to 10p), Delrieu (others))

1974 (2 APR)–**78**. *Granite paper* (½p to 10p). Perf 11½ (½p to 10p), 13×13½ (20, 50p) or 13½×13 (£1), all comb

98	**74**	½p multicoloured (*ak*)		10	10
		a. Booklet strip of 8 (98×5 *and* 102×3)†		35	
		b. Booklet pane of 16 (98×4, 102×6 *and* 103×6)†		75	
99	**75**	1p multicoloured (*acj*)		10	10
		a. Booklet strip of 8 (99×4, 103, 105×2 *and* 105a) (8.2.77)† .		55	
		b. Booklet strip of 4 (99, 101×2, *and* 105a) (7.2.78)†		35	

100	**76**	1½p multicoloured (*a*)		10	10
101	**77**	2p multicoloured (*al*)		10	10
102	**78**	2½p multicoloured (*a*)		10	10
103	**79**	3p multicoloured (*a*)		10	10
104	**80**	3½p multicoloured (*a*)		10	10
105	**81**	4p multicoloured (*abc*)		10	10
105a	**82**	5p multicoloured (*f*)		15	15
106	**83**	5½p multicoloured (*a*)		10	10
107	**84**	6p multicoloured (*ae*)		10	10
107a	**85**	7p multicoloured (*f*)		25	25
108	**86**	8p multicoloured (*ah*)		15	10
109	**87**	9p multicoloured (*am*)		15	10
110	**88**	10p multicoloured (*ai*)		15	10
111	**89**	20p multicoloured (*d*)		75	40
112	**90**	50p multicoloured (*d*)		2·00	1·00
113	**91**	£1 multicoloured (*d*)		2·50	1·75
98/113		*Set of 18*		5·50	4·25
		First Day Covers (3)			5·75
		Presentation Packs (3)		5·50	
		Set of 15 Gutter Pairs (Nos. 98/110)		3·50	

†Nos. 98a/b come from a special booklet sheet of 88 (8×11), and Nos. 99a/b from booklet sheets of 80 (two panes 8×5). These sheets were put on sale in addition to the normal sheets. The strips and panes have the left-hand selvedge stuck into booklet covers, except for No. 99b which had the strip loose, and then folded and supplied in plastic wallets.

Printings: (*a*) 2.4.74; (*b*) 10.74; (*c*) 12.74; (*d*) 1.4.75; (*e*) 12.75; (*f*) 29.5.76; (*g*) 6.76; (*h*) 7.76; (*i*) 11.76; (*j*) 8.2.77; (*k*) 7.77; (*l*) 12.77; (*m*) 8.12.78

Plate Nos.: 20p to £1 none; A1–1–1–1–1, B1–1–1–1–1 1½p, 2p, 6p; A1–1–1–1, B1–1–1–1 others

Sheets: 20p to £1, 25 (5×5); others, 100 (2 panes 10×5)

Imprint: Central, bottom margin of each page

Quantities sold: ½p 1,173,560; 1p 1,367,828; 1½p 525,248; 2p 1,098,053; 2½p 1,124,091; 3p 1,953,796; 3½p 1,891,493; 4p 3,435,614; 5p 2,920,246; 5½p 634,870; 6p 2,006,983; 7p 3,103,925; 8p 811,418; 9p 717,815; 10p 1,133,141; 20p 788,840; 50p 570,505; £1 464,428

Withdrawn: 12.2.80 ½p to 20p; 4.2.81 50p, £1

92 Badge of Guernsey and U.P.U. Emblem

93 Map of Guernsey

94 U.P.U. Building, Berne, and Guernsey Flag

95 'Salles des Etats'

Centenary of Universal Postal Union

(Photo Courvoisier)

1974 (7 JUNE). *Granite paper.* Perf 11½ (C)

114	**92**	2½p multicoloured	. . . .	10	10
115	**93**	3p multicoloured	. . . .	10	10
116	**94**	8p multicoloured	. . . .	20	20
117	**95**	10p multicoloured	. . . .	20	20
114/17		*Set of 4*	. . . .	50	50
		First Day Cover	. . . .		75
		Presentation Pack	. . . .	90	
		Set of 4 Gutter Pairs	. . . . . .	1·50	

Cylinder Nos.: 2½p, 8p A1–1–1, B1–1–1; 3p A1–1–1–1, B1–1–1–1; 10p A1–1–1–1–1, B1–1–1–1–1

Sheets: 50 (2 panes 5×5)

Imprint: Central, bottom margin

Quantities sold: 2½p 1,231,657; 3p 1,839,674; 8p 345,271; 10p 356,501

Withdrawn: 6.6.75

96 'Cradle Rock'

97 'La Baie de Moulin Huet'

98 'Au Bord de la Mer'

99 Self-portrait

Renoir Paintings

(Des and photo Delrieu)

1974 (21 SEPT). Perf 13 (C)

118	**96**	3p multicoloured	. . . .	10	10
119	**97**	5½p multicoloured	. . . .	10	10
120	**98**	8p multicoloured	. . . .	25	25
121	**99**	10p multicoloured	. . . .	25	25
118/21		*Set of 4*	. . . .	60	60
		First Day Cover	. . . .		90
		Presentation Pack	. . . .	1·40	

Sheets: 25 (5×5)

Imprint: Right-hand corner, top margin (3p and 5½p), and bottom corner, right-hand margin (others)

Quantities sold: 3p 670,648; 5p 422,677; 8p 377,615; 10p 391,095

Withdrawn: 20.9.75

100 Guernsey Spleenwort

101 Guernsey Quillwort

102 Guernsey Fern

103 Least Adder's Tongue

Guernsey Ferns

(Des and photo Courvoisier)

1975 (7 JAN). *Granite paper.* Perf 11½ (C)

122	**100**	3½p multicoloured	. . . .	10	10
123	**101**	4p multicoloured	. . . .	10	10

124	**102**	8p multicoloured	25	25
125	**103**	10p multicoloured	25	25
122/5		*Set of 4*	60	60
		First Day Cover		90
		Presentation Pack	1·40	
		Set of 4 Gutter Pairs	1·40	

Cylinder Nos.: 3½p, 4p, 8p each A1–1–1–1, B1–1–1–1, C1–1–1–1, D1–1–1–1; 10p A1–1–1–1–1, B1–1–1–1–1, C1–1–1–1–1, D1–1–1–1–1

Sheets: 50 (2 panes 5×5)

Imprint: Central, bottom margin

Quantities sold: 3½p 1,089,142; 4p 1,370,743; 8p 430,672; 10p 443,636

Withdrawn: 6.1.76

104 Victor Hugo House

106 United Europe Oak, Hauteville

105 Candie Gardens

107 Tapestry Room, Hauteville

Victor Hugo's Exile in Guernsey

(Des and photo Courvoisier)

1975 (6 JUNE). *Granite paper.* Perf 11½ (C)

126	**104**	3½p multicoloured	10	10
127	**105**	4p multicoloured	10	10
128	**106**	8p multicoloured	25	25
129	**107**	10p multicoloured	25	25
126/9		*Set of 4*	60	60
		First Day Cover		80
		Presentation Pack	1·90	
MS130		114×143 mm. Nos. 126/9	65	90
		First Day Cover		6·50

Cylinder Nos.: A1–1–1–1, B1–1–1–1 each

Sheets: 50 (5×10) 3½p, 10p; (10×5) others

Imprint: Central, left-hand margin (3½p, 10p) or central, bottom margin (4p, 8p)

Quantities sold: 3½p 810,327; 4p 1,346,628; 8p 377,637; 10p 369,282; miniature sheet 269,217

Withdrawn: 5.6.76

108 Globe and Seal of Bailiwick

109 Globe and Guernsey Flag

110 Globe, Guernsey Flag and Alderney Shield

111 Globe, Guernsey Flag and Sark Shield

Christmas

(Des and photo Delrieu)

1975 (7 OCT). Perf 13 (C)

131	**108**	4p multicoloured	10	10
132	**109**	6p multicoloured	10	10
133	**110**	10p multicoloured	25	25
134	**111**	12p multicoloured	25	25
131/4		*Set of 4*	60	60
		First Day Cover		90
		Presentation Pack	1·00	

Sheets: 25 (5×5)

Imprint: Central, left-hand margin (4p, 6p); central, bottom margin (10p, 12p)

Quantities sold: 4p 678,619; 6p 667,413; 10p 392,529; 12p 361,548

Withdrawn: 6.10.76

112 Les Hanois

113 Les Casquets

114 Quesnard

115 Point Robert

Lighthouses

(Des and photo Courvoisier)

1976 (10 FEB). *Granite paper.* Perf 11½ (C)

135	**112**	4p multicoloured	10	10
136	**113**	6p multicoloured	10	10
137	**114**	11p multicoloured	20	20
138	**115**	13p multicoloured	25	25
135/8		*Set of 4*	60	60
		First Day Cover		80
		Presentation Pack	1·00	
		Set of 4 Gutter Pairs	1·50	

Cylinder Nos.: A1–1–1–1, B1–1–1–1 each

Sheets: 50 (2 panes 5×5)

Quantities sold: 4p 846,362; 6p 900,899; 11p 366,468; 13p 348,358

Withdrawn: 9.2.77

116 Milk Can

117 Christening Cup

Europa. Handicrafts

(Des and photo Courvoisier)

1976 (29 MAY). *Granite paper.* Perf 11½ (C)

139	**116**	10p brown and green	20	20
140	**117**	25p grey and blue	40	35
139/40		*Set of 2*	60	55
		First Day Cover		75
		Presentation Pack	1·20	

Sheets: 9 (3×3)

Quantities sold: 1,185,014 of each

Sold out: 4.6.76

118 Pine Forest, Guernsey

119 Herm and Jethou

120 Grand Greve
Bay, Sark

121 Trois Vaux Bay,
Alderney

Views

(Des and photo Courvoisier)

1976 (3 AUG). *Granite paper.* Perf 11½ (C)

141	**118**	5p multicoloured	10	10
142	**119**	7p multicoloured	10	10
143	**120**	11p multicoloured	25	25
144	**121**	13p multicoloured	25	25
141/4		*Set of 4*	60	60
		First Day Cover		80
		Presentation Pack	1·00	
		Set of 4 Gutter Pairs	1·50	

Cylinder Nos.: A1–1–1–1, B1–1–1–1 each

Sheets: 50 (2 panes 5×5)

Quantities sold: 5p 661,771; 7p 1,016,350; 11p 349,773; 13p 336,027

Withdrawn: 2.8.77

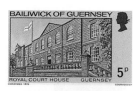

122 Royal Court House, Guernsey

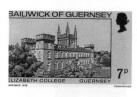

123 Elizabeth College, Guernsey

124 La Seigneurie, Sark

125 Island Hall, Alderney

Christmas. Buildings

(Des and photo Courvoisier)

1976 (14 OCT). *Granite paper.* Perf 11½ (C)

145	**122**	5p multicoloured	10	10
146	**123**	7p multicoloured	10	10
147	**124**	11p multicoloured	25	25
148	**125**	13p multicoloured	25	25
145/8		*Set of 4*	60	60
		First Day Cover		85
		Presentation Pack	1·00	
		Set of 4 Gutter Pairs ...	1·50	

Cylinder Nos.: A1–1–1–1, B1–1Ĩ–1–1–1 each

Sheets: 50 (2 panes 5 × 5)

Imprint: Central, bottom margin

Quantities sold: 5p 1,097,445; 7p 1,051,184; 11p 371,155; 13p 352,347

Withdrawn: 13.10.77

126   Queen Elizabeth II   **127**

Silver Jubilee

(Des R. Granger Barrett. Photo Courvoisier)

1977 (8 FEB). *Granite Paper.* Perf 11½ (C)

149	**126**	7p multicoloured	20	15
150	**127**	35p multicoloured	55	40
149/50		*Set of 2*	65	55
		First Day Cover		70
		Presentation Pack	90	

Cylinder Nos.: 7p A1–1–1–1–1, B1–1–1–1–1; 35p A1–1–1–1–1–1

Sheets: 25 (5×5)

Imprint: Central, bottom margin

Quantities sold: 7p 1,004,250; 35p 536,971

Withdrawn: 7.2.78

128 Woodland, Talbot's Valley

129 Pastureland, Talbot's Valley

Europa. Landscapes

(Des and photo Courvoisier)

1977 (17 MAY). *Granite paper.* Perf 11½ (C)

151	**128**	7p multicoloured	15	15
152	**129**	25p multicoloured	45	45
151/2		*Set of 2*	60	60
		First Day Cover		70
		Presentation Pack	90	
		Set of 2 Gutter Pairs ...	1·40	

Cylinder Nos.: A1–1–1–1, B1–1–1–1 each

Sheets: 50 (2 panes 5×5)

Imprint: Right-hand corner, bottom margin

Quantities sold: 7p 1,371,463; 25p 598,453

Withdrawn: 16.5.78

130 Statue-menhir, Castel

131 Megalithic Tomb, St. Saviour

132 Cist, Tourgis

133 Statue-menhir, St. Martin

Prehistoric Monuments

(Des and photo Courvoisier)

1977 (2 AUG). *Granite paper.* Perf 11½ (C)

153	**130**	5p multicoloured	10	10
154	**131**	7p multicoloured	10	10
155	**132**	11p multicoloured	25	25
156	**133**	13p multicoloured	25	25
153/6		*Set of* 4	60	60
		First Day Cover		75
		Presentation Pack	90	
		Set of 4 *Gutter Pairs*	1·40	

Cylinder Nos.: A1–1–1–1, B1–1–1–1 each

Sheets: 50 (2 panes 5×5)

Imprint: Central, right-hand margin (5p and 13p); Central, bottom margin (others)

Quantities sold: 5p 747,236; 7p 1,077,714; 11p 390,927; 13p 373,063

Withdrawn: 1.8.78

134 Mobile First Aid Unit

135 Mobile Radar Unit

136 Marine Ambulance *Flying Christine II*

137 Cliff Rescue

Christmas. St. John Ambulance Centenary

(Des P. Slade and M. Horder. Photo Courvoisier)

1977 (25 OCT). *Granite paper.* Perf 11½ (C)

157	**134**	5p multicoloured	10	10
158	**135**	7p multicoloured	10	10
159	**136**	11p multicoloured	25	25
160	**137**	13p multicoloured	25	25
157/60		*Set of* 4	60	60
		First Day Cover		75
		Presentation Pack	90	
		Set of 4 *Gutter Pairs*	1·40	

Cylinder Nos.: 5p A1–1–1–1, B1–1–1–1; others A1–1–1–1, B1–1–1–1

Sheets: 50 (2 panes 5×5)

Imprint: Right-hand corner, bottom margin (7p and 11p); top, right-hand margin (others)

Quantities sold: 5p 1,218,293; 7p 1,155,448; 11p 406,244; 13p 383,489

Withdrawn: 24.10.78

138 View from Clifton, *c* 1830

139 Market Square, St.
Peter Port, c 1838

140 Petit-Bo Bay, c 1839

141 The Quay, St. Peter
Port, c 1830

Old Guernsey Prints (1st series)

(Des, recess and litho De La Rue)

1978 (7 FEB). Perf 14×13½ (C)

161	**138**	5p black and light stone	10	10
162	**139**	7p black and cream	10	10
163	**140**	11p black and light pink	25	25
164	**141**	13p black and light azure	25	25
161/4		Set of 4	60	60
		First Day Cover		75
		Presentation Pack	90	
		Set of 4 Gutter Pairs	1·40	

See also Nos. 249/52.

Plate Nos.: All values 1A–1A, 1B–1B, 1C–1C, 1D–1D

Sheets: 50 (2 panes 5×5)

Imprint: Left-hand corner, bottom margin

Quantities sold: 5p 858,816; 7p 930,955; 11p 442,009; 13p 338,163

Withdrawn: 6.2.79

142 Prosperity Memorial

143 Victoria
Monument

Europa. Monuments

(Des R. Granger Barrett. Litho Questa)

1978 (2 MAY). Perf 14½ (C)

165	**142**	5p multicoloured	10	10
		a. Imperf between stamp and right margin		
166	**143**	7p multicoloured	25	25
165/6		Set of 2	30	30
		First Day Cover		45
		Presentation Pack	55	

Sheets: 20 (5p 5×4; 7p 4×5)

Quantities sold: 5p 2,581,345; 7p 2,370,766

Withdrawn: 1.5.79

144

Queen Elizabeth

145

25th Anniversary of Coronation

(Des R. Granger Barrett from bust by Arnold Machin. Photo Courvoisier)

1978 (2 MAY). Granite paper. Perf 11½ (C)

167	**144**	20p black, grey and bright blue . .	45	45
		First Day Cover		60
		Presentation Pack	60	
		Gutter Pair	90	

Cylinder Nos.: A1–1–1, B1–1–1

Sheets: 50 (2 panes 5×5)

Imprint: Right-hand corner, bottom margin

Quantity sold: 488,466

Withdrawn: 1.5.79

Royal Visit

(Des R. Granger Barrett from bust by Arnold Machin. Photo Courvoisier)

1978 (28 JUNE). Granite paper. Perf 11½ (C)

168	**145**	7p black, grey and bright green	20	20
		First Day Cover		45
		Presentation Pack	50	
		Gutter Pair	40	

Cylinder Nos.: A1–1–1, B1–1–1

Sheets: 50 (2 panes 5×5)

Imprint: Top corner, right-hand margin

Quantity sold: 1,149,768

Withdrawn: 27.6.79

146 Northern Gannet

147 Firecrest

148 Dartford Warbler

149 Spotted Redshank

Birds

(Des John Waddington Ltd. Photo Courvoisier)

1978 (29 AUG). *Granite paper.* Perf 11½ (C)

169	**146**	5p multicoloured	10	10
170	**147**	7p multicoloured	20	15
171	**148**	11p multicoloured	30	20
172	**149**	13p multicoloured	40	30
169/72		*Set of 4*	85	70
		First Day Cover		75
		Presentation Pack	1·20	
		Set of 4 Gutter Pairs	1·50	

Cylinder Nos.: All values A1–1–1–1, B1–1–1–1, C1–1–1–1, D1–1–1–1

Sheets: 50 (2 panes 5×5)

Imprint: Right-hand corner, bottom margin

Quantities sold: 5p 750,011; 7p 924,627; 11p 442,395; 13p 432,106

Withdrawn: 28.8.79

150 Solanum

151 Christmas Rose

152 Holly

153 Mistletoe

Christmas

(Des and photo Courvoisier)

1978 (31 OCT). *Granite paper.* Perf 11½ (C)

173	**150**	5p multicoloured	10	10
174	**151**	7p multicoloured	10	10
175	**152**	11p multicoloured	20	20
176	**153**	13p deep blue-green, grey and greenish yellow	25	25
173/6		*Set of 4*	60	60
		First Day Cover		90
		Presentation Pack	95	
		Set of 4 Gutter pairs	1·40	

Cylinder Nos.: 13p A1–1–1, B1–1–1; others A1–1–1–1, B1–1–1–1

Sheets: 50 (2 panes 5×5)

Imprint: 5, 7p central, bottom margin; others central, right-hand margin

Quantities sold: 5p 1,222,140; 7p 1,246,260; 11p 409,168; 13p 372,991

Withdrawn: 30.10.79

154 One Double, 1830

155 Two Doubles, 1899

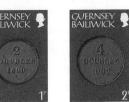

156 Four Doubles, 1902

157 Eight Doubles, 1959

158 Three Pence, 1956

159 Five New Pence, 1968

20

160 Fifty New
Pence,
1969

161 Ten New
Pence,
1970

162 Half New
Penny,
1971

163 One New
Penny, 1971

164 Two New
Pence, 1971

165 Half
Penny,
1979

166 One Penny,
1977

167 Two Pence,
1977

168 Five Pence,
1977

169 Ten Pence,
1977

170 Twenty-five
Pence,
1972

171 Ten Shillings
William I
Commem,
1966

172 Silver Jubilee
Commemorative
Crown, 1977

173 Royal Silver Wedding
Commemorative
Crown, 1972

174 Seal of the
Bailiwick

Coins

(Des R. Reed and Courvoisier (£5). Photo Courvoisier)

1979 (13 FEB)–**83**. *Granite paper.* Perf 11½ (C)

177	**154**	½p multicoloured (*a*)	10	10
		a. *Booklet pane. Nos. 177×2, 178×3, 179×2, 181, 183 and 187 (c)*	70	
		b. *Booklet pane. Nos. 177×2, 178, 179×2, 183×2, and 187×3 (c)*	90	
178	**155**	1p multicoloured (*al*)	10	10
		a. *Booklet strip of 4. Nos. 178×2, 179 and 182*	40	
179	**156**	2p multicoloured (*a*)	10	10
		a. *Booklet strip of 5. Nos. 179, 182×2 and 184×2*	90	
180	**157**	4p multicoloured (*a*)	10	10
		a. *Booklet pane of 10. Nos. 180 and 184, each ×5 (d)* . .	1·20	
		b. *Booklet pane of 15. Nos. 180, 184 and 190, each ×5 (d)*	2·50	
		c. *Booklet pane of 10. Nos. 180×2, 185×3 and 191×5 (k)*	1·90	
		d. *Booklet pane of 15. Nos. 180, 185 and 191, each ×5 (k)*	2·20	
181	**158**	5p grey-black, silver and chestnut (*a*)	10	10
		a. *Grey-black, silver and yellowish brown (f)*	30	40
		b. *Booklet pane of 10. Nos. 181a×5, 184×4 and 191 (f)*	1·70	
		c. *Booklet pane of 15. Nos. 181a, 184 and 191, each ×5 (f)*	2·20	

182	**159**	6p grey-black, silver and brown-red (a)	15	10
183	**160**	7p grey-black, silver & grn (a) .	15	15
184	**161**	8p grey-blk, silver & brn (agij) .	15	15
185	**162**	9p multicoloured (a)	15	15
186	**163**	10p mult (green background) (a)	30	25
187		10p mult (orge background) (b) .	20	15
188	**164**	11p multicoloured (a)	20	15
189	**165**	11½p multicoloured (b)	20	15
190	**166**	12p multicoloured (a)	20	15
191	**167**	13p multicoloured (ah)	25	20
192	**168**	14p grey-blk, silver & dull bl (a) .	25	20
193	**169**	15p grey-blk, silver & bistre (a) .	25	25
194	**170**	20p grey-black, silver and dull brown (a)	30	30
195	**171**	50p grey-black, orange-red and silver (b)	85	60
196	**172**	£1 grey-black, yellowish green and silver (b)	1·70	1·10
197	**173**	£2 grey-black, new blue and silver (b)	3·75	2·00
198	**174**	£5 multicoloured (e)	8·00	8·00
177/98		Set of 22	15·00	12·00
		First Day Covers (4)		14·00
		Presentation Packs (4) . . . . 18·00		
		Set of 22 Gutter Pairs . . . . . 30·00		

Nos. 177a/b, 178a, 179a, 180a/d and 181b/c come from special booklet sheets of 40 (8×5) (Nos. 177a and 178a), 30 (6×5) (Nos. 177b, 180a/b, 180d and 181b/c), 25 (5×5) (No. 179a) or 20 (4×5) (No. 180c). These were put on sale as complete sheets or separated into strips, folded and either affixed by the selvedge to booklet covers or supplied loose in plastic wallets.

The booklet sheets containing Nos. 177a/b show either four (No. 177a) or three (No. 177b) different arrangements of the same stamps.

Printings: (a) 13.2.79; (b) 5.2.80; (c) 6.5.80; (d) 24.2.81; (e) 22.5.81; (f) 2.2.82; (g) 4.82; (h) 5.82; (i) 7.82; (j) 11.82; (k) 14.3.83; (l) 6.83

Cylinder Nos.: 5, 6, 7, 8, 14, 15, 20, 50p, £1, £2 A1–1–1, B1–1–1; others A1–1–1–1, B1–1–1–1

Sheets: ½ to 20p 100 (2 panes 10×5); 50p to £5 50 (2 panes 5×5)

Imprint: 50p top corner, left-hand margin; £1, £2 right-hand corner, bottom margin; £5 bottom corner, right-hand margin; others central margin

Quantities sold: ½p 1,285,162; 1p 1,888,850; 2p 1,249,506; 4p 650,195; 5p 1,110,783; 6p 1,678,775; 7p 1,683,430; 8p 3,059,366; 9p 1,952,892; 10p (No. 186) 484,956; 10p (No. 187) 1,751,126; 11p 711,268; 11½p 351,422; 12p 957,197; 13p 1,459,086; 14p 595,744; 15p 677,289; 20p 960,124; 50p 863,760; £1 537,871; £2 375,786

Withdrawn: 4.2.81 10p (No. 186); 22.7.85 (all other values except £5); 31.12.98 £5

175 Pillar Box and Postmark, 1853, Mail Van and Postmark, 1979

176 Telephone, 1897 and Telex Machine, 1979

Europa. Communications

(Des R. Granger Barrett. Photo Courvoisier)

1979 (8 MAY). Granite paper. Perf 11½ (C)

201	**175**	6p multicoloured	10	10
202	**176**	8p multicoloured	20	20
201/2		Set of 2	30	30
		First Day Cover		45
		Presentation Pack	55	

Cylinder Nos.: Both values A1–1–1–1, B1–1–1–1

Sheets: 20 (5×4)

Quantities sold: 6p 1,863,564; 8p 2,293,379

Withdrawn: 7.5.80

177 Steam Tram, 1879

178 Electric Tram, 1896

179 Motor Bus, 1911

180 Motor Bus, 1979

History of Public Transport

(Photo Courvoisier)

1979 (7 AUG). *Granite paper.* Perf 11½ (C)

203	**177**	6p multicoloured	10	10
204	**178**	8p multicoloured	15	10
205	**179**	11p multicoloured	20	15
206	**180**	13p multicoloured	20	25
203/6		*Set of 4*	60	55
		First Day Cover		70
		Presentation Pack	1·20	
		Set of 4 Gutter Pairs	1·20	

Cylinder Nos.: 6p A1–1–1–1, B1–1–1–1; others A1–1–1–1, B1–1–1–1

Sheets: 50 (2 panes 5×5)

Imprint: Central, bottom margin

Quantities sold: 6p 676,046; 8p 981,431; 11p 384,701; 13p 371,882

Withdrawn: 6.8.80

181 Bureau and Postal Headquarters

182 'Mails and Telegrams'

183 'Parcels'

184 'Philately'

10th Anniversary of Guernsey Postal Administration

(Des R. Granger Barrett. Photo Courvoisier)

1979 (1 OCT). *Granite paper.* Perf 11½ (C)

207	**181**	6p multicoloured	10	10
208	**182**	8p multicoloured	15	10
209	**183**	13p multicoloured	20	15
210	**184**	15p multicoloured	25	25
207/10		*Set of 4*	65	55
		First Day Cover		80
		Presentation Pack	1·10	
		Set of 4 Gutter Pairs	1·40	
MS211		120×80 mm. Nos. 207/10	80	80
		First Day Cover		1·20

One copy of a pre-release sample as No. 210, but with a face value of 11p, is known. Such stamps were not sold for postal purposes.

Cylinder Nos.: All values A1–1–1–1, B1–1–1–1

Sheets: 50 (2 panes 5×5)

Imprint: Central, bottom margin

Quantities sold: 6p 1,254,914; 8p 1,376,682; 13p 389,524; 15p 386,234; miniature sheet 398,443

Withdrawn: 30.9.80

185 Major-General Le Marchant

186 Admiral Lord de Saumarez

Europa. Personalities

(Des and photo Courvoisier)

1980 (6 MAY). *Granite paper.* Perf 11½ (C)

212	**185**	10p multicoloured	15	15
213	**186**	13½p multicoloured	30	25
212/13		*Set of 2*	45	40
		First Day Cover		70
		Presentation Pack	80	

Cylinder Nos.: Both values A1–1–1–1–1, B1–1–1–1, C1–1–1–1–1, D1–1–1–1–1

Sheets: 20 (5×4)

Quantities sold: 10p 2,794,871; 13½p 1,715,880

Withdrawn: 5.5.81

187 Policewoman with Lost Child

188 Police Motorcyclist escorting Lorry

189 Police Dog-handler

60th Anniversary of Guernsey Police Force

(Litho John Waddington Ltd)

1980 (6 MAY). Perf 13½×14 (C)

214	**187**	7p multicoloured	15	15
215	**188**	15p multicoloured	25	25
216	**189**	17½p multicoloured	30	25
214/16		Set of 3	65	60
		First Day Cover		85
		Presentation Pack	1·00	
		Set of 3 Gutter Pairs	1·40	

Plate Nos: All values 1A, 1B, 1C, 1D (each ×4)

Sheets: 50 (2 panes 5×5)

Imprint: Central, bottom margin

Quantities sold: 7p 907,714; 15p 352,802; 17½p 337,551

Withdrawn: 5.5.81

190

191

192

193

T **190/3** show Golden Guernsey Goats.

Golden Guernsey Goats

(Des P. Lambert. Photo Delrieu)

1980 (5 Aug). Perf 13 (C)

217	**190**	7p multicoloured	10	10
218	**191**	10p multicoloured	20	15
219	**192**	15p multicoloured	25	20
220	**193**	17½p multicoloured	40	35
217/20		Set of 4	85	80
		First Day Cover		95
		Presentation Pack	1·20	
		Set of 4 Gutter Pairs	1·70	

Cylinder Nos.: 7p 598–599–600–601–602–603; 10p 578–580–581–583; 15p 605–606–607–608–609–610; 17½p 621–622–623–624–625–626

Sheets: 50 (2 panes 5×5)

Imprint: Bottom margin

Quantities sold: 7p 779,424; 10p 931,214; 15p 364,917; 17½p 329,133

Withdrawn: 4.4.81

194 'Sark Cottage'

195 'Moulin Huet'

196 'Boats at Sea'

197 'Cow Lane'

198 'Peter Le Lievre'

Christmas. Peter le Lievre Paintings

(Photo Courvoisier)

1980 (15 NOV). *Granite paper.* Perf 11½ (C)

221	**194**	7p multicoloured	15	10
222	**195**	10p multicoloured	20	15
223	**196**	13½p multicoloured	25	20
224	**197**	15p multicoloured	25	25
225	**198**	17½p multicoloured	40	35
221/5		*Set of 5*	1·10	95
		First Day Cover		1·40
		Presentation Pack	1·50	
		Stamp-cards (set of 5)	2·00	4·00
		Set of 5 Gutter Pairs	2·50	

Cylinder Nos.: All values A1–1–1–1, B1–1–1–1

Sheets: 50 (2 panes 5×5)

Imprint: 15, 17½p top corner, right-hand margin; others right-hand corner, bottom margin

Quantities sold: 7p 1,199,280; 10p 1,159,622; 13½p 397,812; 15p 432,182; 17½p 359,116

Withdrawn: 14.11.81

199 *Polyommatus icarus*

200 *Vanessa atalanta*

201 *Aglais urticae*

202 *Lasiommata megera*

Butterflies

(Photo Harrison)

1981 (24 FEB). Perf 14 (C)

226	**199**	8p multicoloured	15	15
227	**200**	12p multicoloured	20	20
228	**201**	22p multicoloured	35	35
229	**202**	25p multicoloured	40	40
226/9		*Set of 4*	1·00	1·00
		First Day Cover		2·20
		Presentation Pack	1·70	
		Set of 4 Gutter Pairs	2·20	

Cylinder Nos.: All values 1A, 1B (each ×5)

Sheets: 50 (2 panes 5×5)

Imprint: Right-hand corner, bottom margin

Quantities sold: 8p 986,229; 12p 971,801; 22p 438,478; 25p 438,575

Withdrawn: 23.2.82

203 Sailors paying respect to 'Le Petit Bonhomme Andriou' (rock resembling head of a man)

204 Fairies and Guernsey Lily

Europa. Folklore

(Des C. Abbott. Litho Questa)

1981 (22 MAY). Perf 14½ (C)

230	**203**	12p gold, red-brown & cinnamon	25	15
231	**204**	18p gold, indigo and azure	30	35
230/1		*Set of 2*	55	50
		First Day Cover		65
		Presentation Pack	80	
		Set of 2 Gutter Pairs	1·10	

Plate Nos.: 12p 1B, 1F, 1G, 1H (each ×3); 18p 1B, 1D, 1F, 1G, 1H (each ×3)

Sheets: 20 (2 panes 5×2)

Imprint: Central, left-hand margin

Quantities sold: 12p 2,516,514; 18p 1,937,023

Withdrawn: 21.5.82

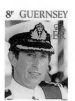

205 Prince Charles

206 Prince Charles and Lady Diana Spencer

207 Lady Diana

208 Royal Family

Royal Wedding

(Des C. Abbott. Litho Questa)

1981 (29 JULY). Perf 14½ (C)

232	**205**	8p multicoloured	15	10
		a. Strip of 3. Nos. 232/4	75	75
233	**206**	8p multicoloured	15	10
234	**207**	8p multicoloured	15	10
235	**205**	12p multicoloured	25	25
		a. Strip of 3. Nos. 235/7	1·10	1·10
236	**206**	12p multicoloured	25	25
237	**207**	12p multicoloured	25	25
238	**208**	25p multicoloured	65	60
232/8		Set of 7	2·00	1·60
		First Day Cover		3·25
		Presentation Pack	3·25	
		Stamp-cards (set of 7)	2·00	
MS239		104×127 mm. Nos. 232/8. P 14 (C)	2·50	2·50
		First Day Cover		4·00

Plate Nos.: 8p 1A, 1C (each ×6); 12p 1B (×6); 25p 1A (×6)

Sheets: 8p, 12p 60 (6×10) each value in se-tenant strips of 3 across sheet, 25p 30 (3×10)

Imprint: Bottom corner, right-hand side margin

Quantities sold: 8p 2,115,103; 12p 2,235,005; 25p 510,608; miniature sheet 432,743

Withdrawn: 28.7.82

209 Sark Launch

210 Britten Norman 'short nose' Trislander Airplane

211 Hydrofoil

212 Herm Catamaran

213 Sea Trent (coaster)

Inter-island Transport

(Des and photo Courvoisier)

1981 (25 AUG). Granite paper. Perf 11½ (C)

240	**209**	8p multicoloured	15	15
241	**210**	12p multicoloured	25	20
242	**211**	18p multicoloured	30	35
243	**212**	22p multicoloured	45	65
244	**213**	25p multicoloured	55	75
240/4		Set of 5	1·50	2·00
		First Day Cover		2·00
		Presentation Pack	2·00	
		Set of 5 Gutter Pairs	3·00	

Cylinder Nos.: All values A1–1–1–1, B1–1–1–1

Sheets: 50 (2 panes 5×5)

Imprint: Right-hand corner, bottom margin

Quantities sold: 8p 790,215; 12p 785,488; 18p 457,763; 22p 469,315; 25p 466,112

Withdrawn: 24.8.82

214 Rifle Shooting   **215** Riding

216 Swimming   **217** Circuit Construction

International Year for Disabled Persons

(Des P. le Vasseur. Litho Questa)

1981 (17 NOV). Perf 14½ (C)

245	**214**	8p multicoloured	15	10
246	**215**	12p multicoloured	25	20
247	**216**	22p multicoloured	45	35
248	**217**	25p multicoloured	55	55
245/8		Set of 4	1·20	1·10
		First Day Cover		1·10
		Presentation Pack	1·60	
		Set of 4 Gutter Pairs	2·50	

Plate Nos.: All values 1A, 1B, 1C, 1D, 1E, 1F, 1G, 1H (each ×4)

Sheets: 50 (2 panes 5×5)

Imprint: Foot of right-hand margin on each pane

Quantities sold: 8p 912,908; 12p 910,614; 22p 280,882; 25p 287,725

Withdrawn: 16.11.82

218 Jethou

219 Fermain Bay

220 The Terres

221 St. Peter Port

Old Guernsey Prints (2nd series). Sketches by T. Compton

(Des, recess and litho De La Rue)

1982 (2 FEB). Perf 14×13½ (C)

249	**218**	8p black and pale blue	15	15
250	**219**	12p black & pale turquoise-grn ..	25	20
251	**220**	22p black and pale yellow-brown	40	40
252	**221**	25p black and pale rose-lilac	50	50
249/52		Set of 4	1·10	1·10
		First Day Cover		1·40
		Presentation Pack	1·60	
		Set of 4 Gutter Pairs	2·20	

Plate Nos.: All values 1A–1A, 1B–1B, 1C–1C, 1D–1D

Sheets: 50 (2 panes 5×5)

Imprint: Left-hand corner, bottom margin

Quantities sold: 8p 350,198; 12p 346,515; 22p 346,661; 25p 244,669

Withdrawn: 1.2.83

222 Sir Edgar MacCulloch (founder-president) and Guille-Allès Library, St. Peter Port   **223** Norman Invasion Fleet crossing English Channel, 1066 ('history')'

224 H.M.S. *Crescent*, 1793 ('history')   **225** Dragonfly ('entomology')

226 Common Snipe caught for Ringing ('ornithology')   **227** Samian Bowl 160–200 A.D. ('archaeology')

Centenary of La Société Guernesiaise

(Des G. Drummond. Photo Courvoisier)

1982 (28 APR). *Granite paper. Perf 11½* (C)

253	**222**	8p multicoloured	15	15
254	**223**	13p multicoloured	30	15
255	**224**	20p multicoloured	40	25
256	**225**	24p multicoloured	50	40
257	**226**	26p multicoloured	60	50
258	**227**	29p multicoloured	65	55
253/8		Set of 6	2·30	1·70
		First Day Cover		2·00
		First Day Cover (Nos. 254/5)		2·00
		Presentation Pack	2·50	
		Presentation Pack (Nos. 254/5)		1·70
		Stamp-cards (set of 6)	2·00	4·00

The 13p and 20p (Nos. 254/5) also include the Europa C.E.P.T. emblem in the designs.

Cylinder Nos.: 24p A1–1–1–1, B1–1–1–1, C1–1–1–1, D1–1–1–1; others A1–1–1–1–, B1–1–1–1–1, C1–1–1–1–1, D1–1–1–1–1

Sheets: 20 (5×4)

Quantities sold: 8p 921,095; 13p 2,820,311; 20p 1,491,351; 24p 315,735; 26p 309,919; 29p 298,761

Withdrawn: 27.4.83

228 Sea Scouts

229 Scouts

230 Cub Scouts

231 Air Scouts

75th Anniversary of Boy Scout Movement

(Des W.L.G. Creative Services Ltd. Litho Questa)

1982 (13 JULY). *Perf 14½×14* (C)

259	**228**	8p multicoloured	15	25
260	**229**	13p multicoloured	30	25
261	**230**	26p multicoloured	55	50
262	**231**	29p multicoloured	65	1·10
259/62		Set of 4	1·50	2·10
		First Day Cover		2·20
		Presentation Pack	2·00	
		Set of 4 Gutter Pairs	3·00	

Plate Nos.: 8p 1A, 1B, 1C, 1D (each ×6); others 1A, 1B, 1C, 1D (each ×7)

Sheets: 50 (2 panes 5×5)

Imprint: Bottom corner, right-hand margin

Quantities sold: 8p 796,018; 13p 930,924; 26p 237,958; 29p 233,204

Withdrawn: 12.7.83

232 Midnight Mass

233 Exchanging Gifts

234 Christmas Meal

235 Exchanging Cards

236 Queen's Christmas Message

Christmas

(Des Lynette Hammant. Photo Harrison)

1982 (12 OCT). *Perf 14½* (C)

263	**232**	8p multicoloured	15	15
		a. Black (Queen's head, value and inscr) omitted	£2000	
264	**233**	13p multicoloured	25	15
265	**234**	24p multicoloured	50	45
266	**235**	26p multicoloured	55	50
267	**236**	29p multicoloured	65	55
263/7		Set of 5	1·90	1·60
		First Day Cover		2·00
		Presentation Pack	2·40	
		Set of 5 Gutter Pairs	4·00	

Cylinder Nos.: All values 1A, 1B (each ×5)

Sheets: 50 (2 panes 5×5)

Imprint: Right-hand corner, bottom margin

Quantities sold: 8p 944,560; 13p 927,844; 24p 227,145; 26p 249,110; 29p 232,323

Withdrawn: 11.10.83

237 Flute Player and Boats

238 Cymbal Player and Tug 'o' war

239 Trumpet Player and Bible Class

240 Drummer and Cadets marching

241 Boys' Brigade Band

Centenary of Boys' Brigade

(Des Sally Stiff. Photo Harrison)

1983 (18 JAN). Perf 14 (*C*)

268	**237**	8p multicoloured	15	10
269	**238**	13p multicoloured	25	20
270	**239**	24p multicoloured	40	40
271	**240**	26p multicoloured	55	50
272	**241**	29p multicoloured	65	55
268/72		*Set of* 5	1·70	1·60
		First Day Cover		1·90
		Presentation Pack	2·20	
		Set of 5 *Gutter Pairs*	3·50	

Cylinder Nos.: All values 1A, 1B (each ×5)

Sheets: 50 (2 panes 5×5)

Imprint: Bottom margin, right-hand corner

Quantities sold: 8p 671,921; 13p 538,257; 24p 223,069; 26p 234,482; 29p 214,723

Withdrawn: 17.1.84

242 Building Albert Pier Extension, 1850s

243 St. Peter Port Harbour, 1983

244 St. Peter Port, 1680

245 Artist's Impression of Future Development Scheme

Europa. Great Works of Human Genius. Development of St. Peter Port Harbour

(Des J. Larrivière. Artwork C. Abbott. Photo Courvoisier)

1983 (14 MAR). *Granite paper*. Perf 11½ (*C*)

273	**242**	13p multicoloured	20	15
		a. *Horiz pair. Nos.* 273/4	75	70
274	**243**	13p multicoloured	20	15
275	**244**	20p multicoloured	30	30
		a. *Horiz pair. Nos.* 275/6	1·00	1·00
276	**245**	20p multicoloured	30	30
273/6		*Set of* 4	1·60	1·50
		First Day Cover		1·60
		Presentation Pack	2·20	

Cylinder Nos.: Both values A1–1–1–1, B1–1–1–1

Sheets: 20 (4×5). The two designs of each value were printed together, *se-tenant*, in horizontal pairs throughout

Quantities sold: 13p 1,884,714; 20p 1,676,250

Withdrawn: 13.3.84

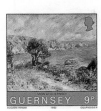

246 'View at Guernsey'

247 'Children on the Seashore'

248 'Marine, Guernesey'

249 'La Baie du Moulin Huet à travers les Arbres'

250 'Brouillard à Guernesey'

Centenary of Renoir's visit to Guernsey

(Des and photo Courvoisier)

1983 (6 SEPT). *Granite paper.* Perf 11×11½ (13p) or 11½ (others), all comb

277	**246**	9p multicoloured	20	15
278	**247**	13p multicoloured	25	25
279	**248**	26p multicoloured	55	50
280	**249**	28p multicoloured	85	80
281	**250**	31p multicoloured	1·00	90
277/81		*Set of 5*	2·50	2·40
		First Day Cover		3·00
		Presentation Pack	3·25	
		Stamp-cards (set of 5)	1·50	4·00
		Set of 5 Gutter Pairs	5·00	

Cylinder Nos.: 13p A1–1–1–1–1, B1–1–1–1–1, C1–1–1–1–1, D1–1–1–1–1; others A1–1–1–1–1, B1–1–1–1–1

Sheets: 40 (2 panes 4 × 5)

Quantities sold: 9p 547,148; 13p 757,838; 26p 185,045; 28p 219,830; 31p 305,219

Withdrawn: 5.9.84

251 Launching *Star of the West*, 1869, and Capt. J. Lenfestey

252 Leaving St. Peter Port

253 Off Rio Grande Bar

254 Off St. Lucia

255 Map of 1879–80 Voyage

Guernsey Shipping (1st series). Star of the West (brigantine)

(Des R. Granger Barrett. Litho Quensta)

1983 (15 NOV). Perf 14 (C)

282	**251**	9p multicoloured	20	20
283	**252**	13p multicoloured	25	15
284	**253**	26p multicoloured	50	50
285	**254**	28p multicoloured	85	75
286	**255**	31p multicoloured	95	80
282/6		*Set of 5*	2·50	2·10
		First Day Cover		2·40
		Presentation Pack	3·25	
		Set of 5 Gutter Pairs	4·75	

See also Nos. 415/19.

Plate Nos.: 26p, 31p 1C, 1D (each ×5); others 1A, 1B (each ×5)

Sheets: 50 (2 panes 5×5)

Imprint: Bottom corner, right-hand margin

Quantities sold: 9p 706,809; 13p 974,736; 26p 236,974; 28p 216,279; 31p 218,647

Withdrawn: 14.11.84

256 Dame of Sark as Young Woman

257 German Occupation, 1940–45

258 Royal Visit, 1957

259 Chief Pleas

260 'Dame of Sark' Rose

Birth Centenary of Sibyl Hathaway, Dame of Sark

(Des Jennifer Toombs. Litho Questa)

1984 (7 FEB). Perf 14½ (C)

287	**256**	9p multicoloured	20	20
288	**257**	13p multicoloured	30	15
289	**258**	26p multicoloured	70	55

290	**259**	28p multicoloured	75	70
291	**260**	31p multicoloured	80	75
287/91		*Set of 5*	2·50	2·10
		First Day Cover		2·50
		Presentation Pack	3·00	
		Set of 5 Gutter Pairs	5·00	

Plate Nos.: 13p 1A, 1B, 1C, 1D (each ×5); others 1A, 1B, 1C, 1D, (each ×7)

Sheets: 50 (2 panes 5×5)

Imprint: Bottom margin, right-hand corner

Quantities sold: 9p 637,566; 13p 836,270; 26p 315,561; 28p 293,716; 31p 270,742

Withdrawn: 6.2.85

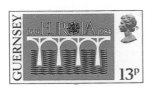

261 C.E.P.T. 25th Anniversary Logo

Europa

(Des J. Larrivière. Litho Questa)

1984 (10 APR). Perf 15×14½ (C)

292	**261**	13p cobalt, dull ultramarine & blk	25	15
293		20½p emerald, deep dull grn & blk	55	50
292/3		*Set of 2*	75	60
		First Day Cover		1·20
		Presentation Pack	1·50	

Plate Nos.: Both values 1A, 1B (each ×3)

Sheets: 20 (4×5)

Imprint: Bottom corner, right-hand margin

Quantities sold: 13p 1,680,033; 20½p 903,972

Withdrawn: 9.4.85

262 The Royal Court and St. George's Flag

263 Castle Cornet and Union Flag

Links with the Commonwealth

(Des C. Abbott. Litho Questa)

1984 (10 APR.) Perf 14×14½ (C)

294	**262**	9p multicoloured	20	15
295	**263**	31p multicoloured	85	85
294/5		*Set of 2*	1·00	95
		First Day Cover		1·20
		Presentation Pack	1·50	

Plate Nos.: Both values 1A, 1B, 1C, 1D (each ×6)

Sheets: 20 (4×5)

Imprint: Bottom corner, right-hand margin

Quantities sold: 9p 1,419,845, 31p 285,099

Withdrawn: 9.4.85

264 Little Chapel

265 Fort Grey

266 St. Apolline Chapel

267 Petit Port

268 Little Russel

269 The Harbour, Herm

270 Saints

271 St. Saviour

272 New Jetty (inscr 'Cambridge Berth')

273 Belvoir, Herm

GUERNSEY 11ᴾ

274 La Seigneurie, Sark

GUERNSEY 13ᴾ

276 St. Saviour's Reservoir

GUERNSEY 12ᴾ

275 Petit Bot

GUERNSEY 14ᴾ

277 St. Peter Port

GUERNSEY 15ᴾ

278 Havelet

GUERNSEY 16ᴾ

279 Hostel of St. John

GUERNSEY 18ᴾ

280 Le Variouf

GUERNSEY 20ᴾ

281 La Coupee, Sark

GUERNSEY 21ᴾ

282 King's Mills

GUERNSEY 26ᴾ

283 Town Church

GUERNSEY 30ᴾ

284 Grandes Rocques

GUERNSEY 40ᴾ

285 Torteval Church

GUERNSEY 50ᴾ

286 Bordeaux

GUERNSEY £1

287 Albecq

GUERNSEY £2

288 L'Ancresse

Bailiwick Views

(Des C. Abbott. Litho Questa)

1984 (18 SEPT)–**91**. Perf 14½ (C)

296	**264**	1p multicoloured (c)	10	10
297	**265**	2p multicoloured (c)	10	10
		a. *Booklet pane. Nos.* 297×2, 299×4, 300×2 *and* 305×2 (d)	1·60	
298	**266**	3p multicoloured (a)	10	10
		a. *Booklet pane. Nos.* 298, 299×2, 306×4 *and* 309×3 (f)	2·00	
299	**267**	4p multicoloured (a)	10	10
		a. *Booklet pane. Nos.* 299×2, 304×3 *and* 307×5	2·50	
		b. *Booklet pane. Nos.* 299, 304 *and* 307, *each* ×5	2·50	
		c. *Booklet pane. Nos.* 299×4, 306b×3 *and* 309c×3 (g) . . .	2·75	
		d. *Booklet pane. Nos.* 299,301, 306b×3 *and* 309d×3 (h) . . .	3·25	
		e. *Black ptg double*		
300	**268**	5p multicoloured (c)	15	10
		a. *Booklet pane. Nos.* 300×2, 301×2, 309×3 *and* 310b×3 (j)	3·75	
301	**269**	6p multicoloured (c)	15	15
		a. *Booklet pane. Nos.* 301×4, 308×4 *and* 310×2 (i)	3·25	
		b. *Uncoated paper*		
		c. *Black ptg double*		
302	**270**	7p multicoloured (c)	15	15
303	**271**	8p multicoloured (c)	20	15
304	**272**	9p multicoloured (a)	20	10
		a. *Booklet pane. Nos.* 304×4 *and* 308×6 (b)	2·50	
		b. *Booklet pane. Nos.* 304×2 *and* 308×8 (b)	2·50	
		c. *Black ptg double*		
305	**273**	10p multicoloured (a)	25	15
		a. *Booklet pane. Nos.* 305 *and* 308, *each* ×5 (e)	3·00	

306	**274**	11p multicoloured (c)	25	15
		a. Booklet pane. Nos. 306 and		
		309, each ×5 (f)	3·25	
306b	**275**	12p multicoloured (g)	35	15
		ba. Booklet pane. Nos. 306b and		
		309c, each ×5	3·00	
		bb. Booklet pane. Nos. 306b and		
		309d, each ×4 (h)	3·50	
		bc. Black ptg double		
307	**276**	13p multicoloured (a)	25	25
308	**277**	14p multicoloured (a)	25	20
		a. Booklet pane. Nos. 308 and		
		310, each ×5 (i)	3·75	
		b. Uncoated paper		
309	**278**	15p multicoloured (c)	30	30
		a. Booklet pane. Nos. 309 and		
		310b, each ×5 (j)	5·50	
		b. Imperf at sides and foot		
		(horiz pair)		
309c	**279**	16p multicoloured (g)	30	20
		ca. Black and red ptgs double ..		
309d	**280**	18p multicoloured (h)	30	20
		da. Black ptg double		
310	**281**	20p multicoloured (a)	45	25
		a. Uncoated paper		
310b	**282**	21p multicoloured (j)	45	30
310c	**283**	26p multicoloured (j)	70	50
		ca. Imperf at sides and foot		
		(horiz pair)	£900	
311	**284**	30p multicoloured (c)	65	60
312	**285**	40p multicoloured (a)	70	70
313	**286**	50p multicoloured (a)	80	75
314	**287**	£1 multicoloured (a)	1·90	1·50
315	**288**	£2 multicoloured (c)	3·75	3·50
296/315		Set of 25	12·00	10·00
		First Day Covers (5)		15·00
		Presentation Packs (3)	15·00	
		Stamp-cards (set of 25)	7·00	22·00
		Set of 25 Gutter Pairs	24·00	

For 11p, 12p, 15p and 16p stamps in a smaller size see Nos. 398/9a.

Booklet panes Nos. 297a, 298a, 299a/c, 304a/b, 305a, 306a and 306ba have margins all round and were issued, folded and loose, within the booklet covers.

Booklet panes Nos. 299d, 300a, 306bb, 308a and 309a have the outer edges imperforate on three sides and were also issued loose within the booklet covers.

Nos. 299e, 301c, 306bc and 309da come from an example of booklet pane No. 299d.

Nos. 301b, 308b and 310a come from examples of booklet panes Nos. 301a and 308a.

Unfolded booklet panes (with and without margins) were also available from the Philatelic Bureau and Head Post Office.

In addition to the presentation packs listed, there was a Tourists Definitive Pack containing the original set of 20, selling price £5.50.

Printings: (a) 18.9.84; (b) 19.3.85; (c) 23.7.85; (d) 2.12.85; (e) 1.4.86; (f) 30.3.87; (g) 28.3.88; (h) 28.2.89; (i) 27.12.89; (j) 2.4.91

Plate Nos.:All values 1A, 1B, 1C, 1D (each ×5)

Sheets: 1p, 3p, 8p, 12p, 14p, 15p, 18p, 26p, 40p, 100 (2 panes 10×5); others 100 (2 panes 5×10)

Imprint: Bottom, right-hand margin of each pane

Quantities sold: 1p 1,397,906; 2p 1,240,037; 3p 460,949; 4p 478,679; 5p 690,128; 6p 560,950; 7p 302,367; 8p 425,421; 9p 1,959,119; 10p 1,692,125; 11p 1,510,077; 12p 2,837,219; 13p 730,405; 14p 3,925,313; 15p 2,631,599; 16p 1,322,353; 18p 1,398,065; 20p 2,149,053; 21p 1,675,329; 26p 210,575; 30p 790,261; 40p 604,514; 50p 765,831; £1 647,055; £2 666,177

Withdrawn: 21.5.93

289 'A Partridge in a Pear Tree' **290** 'Two Turtle Doves' **291** 'Three French Hens'

292 'Four Colly Birds' **293** 'Five Gold Rings' **294** 'Six Geese a-laying'

295 'Seven Swans a-swimming' **296** 'Eight Maids a-milking' **297** 'Nine Drummers drumming'

298 'Ten Pipers piping' **299** 'Eleven Ladies dancing' **300** 'Twelve Lords a-leaping'

Christmas. 'The Twelve Days of Christmas'

(Des R. Downer. Litho Questa)

1984 (20 NOV). Perf 14½ (C)

316	**289**	5p multicoloured	15	15
		a. Sheetlet of 12. Nos. 316/27 .	2·00	
317	**290**	5p multicoloured	15	15
318	**291**	5p multicoloured	15	15
319	**292**	5p multicoloured	15	15
320	**293**	5p multicoloured	15	15
321	**294**	5p multicoloured	15	15
322	**295**	5p multicoloured	15	15
323	**296**	5p multicoloured	15	15
324	**297**	5p multicoloured	15	15
325	**298**	5p multicoloured	15	15
326	**299**	5p multicoloured	15	15
327	**300**	5p multicoloured	15	15
316/27		Set of 12	2·00	1·70
		First Day Cover		2·00
		Presentation Pack	2·75	

Sheets: 12 (4×3) containing Nos. 316/27 se-tenant

Imprint: Bottom, left-hand margin

Quantity sold: 271,168 sheetlets

Withdrawn: 19.11.85

301 Sir John Doyle and Coat of Arms

302 Battle of Germantown, 1777

303 Reclaiming Braye du Valle, 1806

304 Mail for Alderney, 1812

150th Death Anniversary of Lieutenant-General Sir John Doyle

(Des E. Stemp. Photo Courvoisier)

1984 (20 NOV). Granite paper. Perf 11½ (C)

328	**301**	13p multicoloured	30	25
329	**302**	29p multicoloured	65	60
330	**303**	31p multicoloured	75	70
331	**304**	34p multicoloured	90	85
328/31		Set of 4	2·40	2·10
		First Day Cover		2·50
		Presentation Pack	3·25	
		Set of 4 Gutter Pairs	4·75	

Cylinder Nos.: All values A1–1–1–1–1, B1–1–1–1–1, C1–1–1–1–1–1, D1–1–1–1–1–1

Sheets: 50 (2 panes 5×5)

Quantities sold: 13p 642,178; 29p 460,535; 31p 450,051; 34p 465,982

Withdrawn: 19.11.85

Yearbook 1984

1984 (1 DEC). *Comprises Nos. 287/95, 298/9, 304/5, 307/8, 310, 312/14, 316/31 and* A13/17

	Yearbook	35·00

Withdrawn: 29.3.86

305 Cuckoo Wrasse

306 Red Gurnard

307 Red Mullet

308 Mackerel

309 Oceanic Sunfish

Fish

(Des P. Barrett. Photo Courvoisier)

1985 (22 JAN). Granite paper. Perf 11½ (C)

332	**305**	9p multicoloured	30	25
333	**306**	13p multicoloured	40	25
334	**307**	29p multicoloured	1·00	90
335	**308**	31p multicoloured	1·00	90
336	**309**	34p multicoloured	1·10	90
332/6		Set of 5	3·50	3·00
		First Day Cover		3·25
		Presentation Pack	4·00	
		Set of 5 Gutter Pairs	7·00	

Cylinder Nos.: 13p, 29p A1–1–1–1–1, B1–1–1–1–1, C1–1–1–1–1, D1–1–1–1–1; others A1–1

1–1, B1–1–1–1, C1–1–1–1, D1–1–1–1

Sheets: 50 (2 panes 5 × 5)

Quantities sold: 9p 465,322; 13p 724,941; 29p 221,392; 31p 174,948; 34p 157,422

Withdrawn: 21.1.86

310 Dove

40th Anniversary of Peace in Europe

(Des C. Abbott. Litho Questa)

1985 (9 MAY). Perf 14×14½ (C)

337	**310**	22p multicoloured	60	60
		First Day Cover		90
		Presentation Pack	1·20	
		Gutter Pair	1·20	

Plate Nos.: 1A, 1B, 1C, 1D (each ×4)

Sheets: 50 (2 panes 5×5)

Imprint: Bottom, right-hand margin of each pane

Quantity sold: 246,024

Withdrawn: 8.5.86

311 I.Y.Y. Emblem and Young People of Different Races

312 Girl Guides cooking over Campfire

International Youth Year

(Des Suzanne Brehaut (9p), Mary Harrison (31p). Litho Questa)

1985 (14 MAY). Perf 14 (C)

338	**311**	9p multicoloured	25	15
339	**312**	31p multicoloured	75	70
338/9		Set of 2	1·00	85
		First Day Cover		1·20
		Presentation Pack (with No. 342)	3·00	

Plate Nos.: Both values 1A, 1B, 1C, 1D, 1E, 1F (each ×6)

Sheets: 20 (5×4)

Imprint: Bottom, right-hand margin

Quantities sold: 9p 1,246,421; 31p 264,938

Withdrawn: 13.5.86

313 Stave of Music enclosing Flags

314 Stave of Music and Musical Instruments

Europa. European Music Year

(Des Fiona Sloan (14p), Katie Lillington (22p). Litho Questa)

1985 (14 MAY). Perf 14×14½ (C)

340	**313**	14p multicoloured	30	25
341	**314**	22p multicoloured	60	55
340/1		Set of 2	90	80
		First Day Cover		1·40
		Presentation Pack	2·00	

Plate Nos.: Both values 1A, 1B, 1C, 1D, 1E, 1F (each ×6)

Sheets: 20 (4×5)

Imprint: Bottom, right-hand margin

Quantities sold: 14p 1,742,651; 22p 879,421

Withdrawn: 13.5.86

315 Guide Leader, Girl Guide and Brownie

75th Anniversary of Girl Guide Movement

(Des Karon Mahy. Litho Questa)

1985 (14 MAY). Perf 14 (C)

342	**315**	34p multicoloured	1·00	90
		First Day Cover		1·20

Plate Nos.: 1A, 1B, 1C, 1D (each ×6)

Sheets: 20 (5×4)

Imprint: Bottom, right-hand margin

Quantity sold: 182,426

Withdrawn: 13.5.86

316 Santa Claus

317 Lussibruden (Sweden)

318 King Balthazar

319 Saint Nicholas
(Netherlands)

320 La Befana
(Italy)

321 Julenisse
(Denmark)

322 Christkind
(Germany)

323 King Wenceslas
(Czechoslovakia)

324 Shepherd
of Les
Baux
(France)

325 King Caspar

326 Baboushka
(Russia)

327 King
Melchior

Christmas. Gift-bearers

(Des C. Abbott. Photo Courvoisier)

1985 (19 NOV). *Granite paper.* Perf 12½ (C)

343	**316**	5p multicoloured	25	15
		a. *Sheetlet of* 12. *Nos.* 343/54 .	3·50	3·50
344	**317**	5p multicoloured	25	15
345	**318**	5p multicoloured	25	15
346	**319**	5p multicoloured	25	15
347	**320**	5p multicoloured	25	15
348	**321**	5p multicoloured	25	15
349	**322**	5p multicoloured	25	15
350	**323**	5p multicoloured	25	15
351	**324**	5p multicoloured	25	15
352	**325**	5p multicoloured	25	15
353	**326**	5p multicoloured	25	15
354	**327**	5p multicoloured	25	15
343/54		*Set of* 12	3·50	3·50
		First Day Cover		3·75
		Presentation Pack	4·00	

Sheets: 12 (4×3) containing Nos. 343/54 *se-tenant*

Imprint: Central, bottom margin

Quantity sold: 236,937 sheetlets

Withdrawn: 18.11.86

328 'Vraicing'

329 'Castle Cornet'

330 'Rocquaine
Bay'

331 'Little Russel'

332 'Seaweed-
gatherers'

Paintings by Paul Jacob Naftel

(Des and photo Harrison)

1985 (19 NOV). Perf 15×14 (C)

355	**328**	9p multicoloured	20	20
356	**329**	14p multicoloured	25	25
357	**330**	22p multicoloured	65	65
358	**331**	31p multicoloured	1·00	1·00
359	**332**	34p multicoloured	1·20	1·20
355/9		*Set of* 5	3·00	3·00
		First Day Cover		3·25
		Presentation Pack	3·50	
		Set of 5 *Gutter Pairs*	6·00	

Cylinder Nos.: All values 1A, 1B (each ×5)

Sheets: 50 (2 panes 5×5)

Imprint: Left-hand margin of each pane

Quantities sold: 9p 398,472; 14p 452,728; 22p 164,922; 31p 197,422;
34p 173,428

Withdrawn: 18.11.86

Yearbook 1985

1985 (DEC). *Comprises Nos. 296/7, 300/3, 306, 309, 311, 315, 332/59 and A18/27*

Yearbook . . . . 55·00

Withdrawn: 31.12.86

333 Squadron off Nargue Island, 1809

334 Battle of the Nile, 1798

335 Battle of St. Vincent, 1797

336 H.M.S. *Crescent* off Cherbourg, 1793

337 Battle of the Saints, 1782

150th Death Anniversary of Admiral Lord De Saumarez

(Des T. Thompson. Photo Courvoisier)

1986 (4 FEB). *Granite paper.* Perf 11½ (C)

360	**333**	9p multicoloured	30	25
361	**334**	14p multicoloured	40	30
362	**335**	29p multicoloured	75	70
363	**336**	31p multicoloured	1·10	95
364	**337**	34p multicoloured	1·20	1·00
360/4		Set of 5	3·50	3·00
		First Day Cover		3·25
		Presentation Pack	3·50	
		Set of 5 Gutter Pairs	7·00	

Cylinder Nos.: All values A1–1–1–1–1, B1–1–1–1–1

Sheets: 40 (2 panes 5×4)

Quantities sold: 9p 456,518; 14p 706,727; 29p 157,693; 31p 163,612; 34p 160,724

Withdrawn: 3.2.87

338 Profile of Queen Elizabeth II (after R. Maklouf)

60th Birthday of Queen Elizabeth II

(Des C. Abbott. Litho Questa)

1986 (21 APR). Perf 14 (C)

365	**338**	60p multicoloured	1·50	1·20
		First Day Cover		2·00
		Presentation Pack	2·50	
		Gutter Pair	3·00	

Plate Nos.: 1A, 1B, 1C, 1D (each ×4)

Sheets: 40 (2 panes 5×4)

Imprint: Bottom, right-hand margin of each pane

Quantity sold: 169,661

Withdrawn: 20.4.87

339 Northern Gannet and Nylon Net ('Operation Gannet')

340 Whitsun Orchid

341 Guernsey Elm

Europa. Nature and Environmental Protection

(Des P. Newcombe. Photo Courvoisier)

1986 (22 MAY). *Granite paper.* Perf 11½ (C)

366	**339**	10p multicoloured	30	30
367	**340**	14p multicoloured	40	40
368	**341**	22p multicoloured	70	70
366/8		Set of 3	1·20	1·20
		First Day Cover		1·90
		Presentation Pack	1·90	

Cylinder Nos.: All values A1–1–1–1–1–1, B1–1–1–1–1–1, C1–1–1–1–1–1, D1–1–1–1–1–1

Sheets: 20 (4×5)

Quantities sold: 10p 977,212; 14p 995,123; 22p 662,565

Withdrawn: 21.5.87

342 Prince Andrew and Miss Sarah Ferguson **343**

Royal Wedding

(Des C. Abbott. Litho Questa)

1986 (23 JULY). Perf 14 (14p) or 13½×14 (34p), both comb

369	**342**	14p multicoloured	60	50
370	**343**	34p multicoloured	1·00	90
369/70		Set of 2	1·60	1·40
		First Day Cover		2·00
		Presentation Pack	2·40	
		Set of 2 Gutter Pairs	3·25	

Plate Nos.: Both values 1A, 1B, 1C, 1D, 1E, 1F (each ×5)

Sheets: 50 (2 panes 5×5)

Imprint: Bottom, right-hand margin of each pane

Quantities sold: 14p 292,018; 34p 199,297

Withdrawn: 22.7.87

344 Bowls   **345** Cricket

346 Squash   **347** Hockey

348 Swimming   **349** Shooting

Sport in Guernsey

(Des R. Goldsmith. Litho Questa)

1986 (24 JULY). Perf 14½ (C)

371	**344**	10p multicoloured	25	20
372	**345**	14p multicoloured	35	20
		a. Black (face value, inscr etc.) printed treble		
373	**346**	22p multicoloured	50	45
		a. Black (face value, inscr etc.) printed treble		
374	**347**	29p multicoloured	90	80
375	**348**	31p multicoloured	90	80
376	**349**	34p multicoloured	1·00	90
371/6		Set of 6	3·50	3·00
		First Day Cover		3·25
		Presentation Pack	4·00	
		Set of 4 Gutter Pairs	7·00	

Plate Nos.: All values 1A, 1B, 1C, 1D (each ×4)

Sheets: 50 (2 panes 5×5)

Imprint: Bottom, right-hand margin of each pane

Quantities sold: 10p 399,897; 14p 985,699; 22p 212,203; 29p 141,882; 31p 157,751; 34p 156,164

Withdrawn: 23.7.87

350 Guernsey Museum and Art Gallery, Candie Gardens   **351** Fort Grey Maritime Museum

352 Castle Cornet   **353** National Trust of Guernsey Folk Museum

Centenary of Guernsey Museums

(Des Sir Hugh Casson. Litho Questa)

1986 (18 NOV). Perf 14 (C)

377	**350**	14p multicoloured	30	15
378	**351**	29p multicoloured	85	80
379	**352**	31p multicoloured	85	80
380	**353**	34p multicoloured	1·00	90
377/80		Set of 4	2·75	2·40
		First Day Cover		3·00
		Presentation Pack	3·25	
		Set of 4 Gutter Pairs	5·50	

Plate Nos.: All values 1A, 1B, 1C, 1D (each ×5)

Sheets: 50 (2 panes 5×5)

Imprint: Bottom, right-hand margin of each pane

Quantities sold: 14p 796,879; 29p 141,974; 31p 159,326; 34p 144,074

Withdrawn: 17.11.87

354 'While Shepherds Watched their Flocks by Night'

355 'In the Bleak Mid-Winter'

356 'O Little Town of Bethlehem'

357 'The Holly and the Ivy'

358 'O Little Christmas Tree'

359 'Away in a Manger'

360 'Good King Wenceslas'

361 'We Three Kings of Orient Are'

362 'Hark the Herald Angels Sing'

363 'I saw Three Ships'

364 'Little Donkey'

365 'Jingle Bells'

Christmas. Carols

(Des Wendy Bramall. Photo Courvoisier)

1986 (18 NOV). *Granite paper.* Perf 12½ (C)

381	**354**	6p multicoloured	20	10
		a. Sheetlet of 12. Nos. 381/92	2·50	2·50
382	**355**	6p multicoloured	20	10
383	**356**	6p multicoloured	20	10
384	**357**	6p multicoloured	20	10
385	**358**	6p multicoloured	20	10
386	**359**	6p multicoloured	20	10
387	**360**	6p multicoloured	20	10
388	**361**	6p multicoloured	20	10
389	**362**	6p multicoloured	20	10
390	**363**	6p multicoloured	20	10
391	**364**	6p multicoloured	20	10
392	**365**	6p multicoloured	20	10
381/392		Set of 12	2·50	2·50
		First Day Cover		2·75
		Presentation Pack	3·00	

Sheets: 12 (4×3) containing Nos. 381/92 *se-tenant*

Imprint: Central, bottom margin

Quantity sold: 226,119 sheetlets

Withdrawn: 17.11.87

Yearbook 1986

1986 (DEC). *Comprises Nos. 360/92 and A28/31*

Yearbook .... 36·00

Withdrawn: 31.12.87

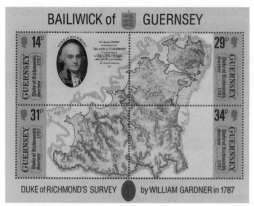

BAILIWICK of GUERNSEY

14ᵖ   29ᵖ

31ᵖ   34ᵖ

DUKE of RICHMOND'S SURVEY   by WILLIAM GARDNER in 1787

366a Duke of Richmond and Map of 1787
(*illustration reduced to half size*)

Bicentenary of Duke of Richmond's Survey of Guernsey

(Des J. Cooter. Litho Questa)

1987 (10 FEB). Perf 14½×14 (C)

MS393	134×103 mm **366a** 14p, 29p, 31p, 34p multicoloured	....	2·50	2·75
	First Day Cover	....		4·50
	Presentation Pack	....	3·75	

Quantity sold: 176,655

Withdrawn: 9.2.88

GUERNSEY 15ᵖ

367 Post Office Headquarters

GUERNSEY 15ᵖ

368 Architect's Elevation of Post Office Headquarters

GUERNSEY 22ᵖ

369 Guernsey Grammar School

GUERNSEY 22ᵖ

370 Architect's Elevation of Grammar School

Europa. Modern Architecture

(Des R. Reed. Litho Cartor)

1987 (5 MAY). Perf 13×13½ (C)

394	**367**	15p multicoloured	25	20
		a. Horiz pair. Nos. 394/5	75	75
395	**368**	15p multicoloured	25	20
396	**369**	22p multicoloured	30	35
		a. Horiz pair. Nos. 396/7	1·20	1·20
397	**370**	22p multicoloured	30	35
394/7		Set of 4	1·70	1·70
		First Day Cover		2·20
		Presentation Pack	2·50	

Plate Nos.: Both values 1A, 1B, 1C, 1D (each ×4)

Sheets: 20 (4×5), the two designs for each value printed together, *se-tenant*, in horizontal pairs throughout the sheets

Quantities sold: 15p 595,661 pairs; 22p 434,886 pairs

Withdrawn: 4.5.88

Coil Stamps

(Photo Harrison)

1987 (15 MAY)–**88**. *As Nos. 306, 306b, 309 and 309c, but smaller. 22×18 mm (11p, 16p) or 18×22 mm (12p, 15p). Perf 14×14½ (11p, 16p) or 14½×14 (12p, 15p), all comb*

398	**274**	11p multicoloured (a)	50	50
398a	**275**	12p multicoloured (b)	40	40
399	**278**	15p multicoloured (a)	60	60
399a	**279**	16p multicoloured (b)	50	50
398/9a		Set of 4	1·70	1·70
		First Day Covers (2)		12·00

Printings: (a) 15.5.87; (b) 28.3.88

Coils: Rolls of 1000 (a) or 500 (b)

Withdrawn: 26.12.89 11p, 15p; 22.5.92 12p, 16p

GUERNSEY 15ᵖ

371 Sir Edmund Andros and La Plaiderie, Guernsey

GUERNSEY 29ᵖ

372 Governor's Palace, Virginia

GUERNSEY 31ᵖ

373 Governor Andros in Boston

GUERNSEY 34ᵖ

374 Map of New Amsterdam (New York), 1661

350th Birth Anniversary of Sir Edmund Andros (colonial administrator)

(Des B. Sanders. Photo Courvoisier)

1987 (7 JULY). *Granite paper.* Perf 12 (C)

400	**371**	15p multicoloured	30	15
401	**372**	29p multicoloured	80	60
402	**373**	31p multicoloured	85	75
403	**374**	34p multicoloured	1·10	1·00
400/3		*Set of 4*	2·50	2·20
		First Day Cover		3·00
		Presentation Pack	3·25	
		Set of 4 Gutter Pairs	5·50	

Cylinder Nos.: All values A1–1–1–1–1, B1–1–1–1–1

Sheets: 40 (2 panes 5×4)

Quantites sold: 15p 707,843; 29p 129,462; 31p 136,308; 34p 129,527

Withdrawn: 6.7.88

375 The Jester's Warning to Young William

376 Hastings Battlefield

377 Norman Soldier with Pennant

378 William the Conqueror

379 Queen Matilda and Abbaye aux Dames, Caen

380 William's Coronation Regalia and Halley's Comet

900th Death Anniversary of William the Conqueror

(Des P. le Vasseur. Litho Cartor)

1987 (9 SEPT). Perf 13½×14 (C)

404	**375**	11p multicoloured	20	15
405	**376**	15p multicoloured	30	25
		a. Horiz pair. Nos. 405/6	60	60
406	**377**	15p multicoloured	30	25
407	**378**	22p multicoloured	60	60
		a. Horiz pair. Nos. 407/8	1·20	1·20
408	**379**	22p multicoloured	60	60
409	**380**	34p multicoloured	1·00	1·10
404/9		*Set of 6*	2·75	2·75
		First Day Cover		3·00
		Presentation Pack	3·75	
		Set of 4 Gutter Pairs	5·50	

Plate Nos.: All values 1A, 1B, 1C, 1D (each ×4)

Sheets: 40 (2 panes 4×5), the two designs for the 15p and 22p values were printed together, *se-tenant*, in horizontal pairs throughout the sheets

Imprint: Bottom, left-hand margin

Quantities sold: 11p 639,904; 15p 241,572 pairs; 22p 142,718 pairs; 34p 131,655

Withdrawn: 8.9.88

381 John Wesley preaching on the Quay, Alderney

382 Preaching at Mon Plaisir, St. Peter Port

383 Preaching at Assembly Rooms

384 Wesley and La Ville Baudu (early Methodist meeting place)

385 Wesley and first Methodist Chapel, St. Peter Port

Bicentenary of John Wesley's Visit to Guernsey

(Des R. Geary. Litho Questa)

1987 (17 NOV). Perf 14½ (C)

410	**381**	7p multicoloured	20	15
411	**382**	15p multicoloured	25	25
412	**383**	29p multicoloured	80	75
413	**384**	31p multicoloured	90	85
414	**385**	34p multicoloured	90	85
410/14		*Set of 5*	2·75	2·50
		First Day Cover		3·00
		Presentation Pack	3·75	
		Set of 5 Gutter Pairs	5·50	

Plate Nos.: All values 1A, 1B, 1C, 1D (each ×4)

Sheets: 50 (2 panes 5×5)

Imprint: Bottom, right-hand margin of each pane

Quantities sold: 7p 762,772; 15p 887,797; 29p 122,322; 31p 126,591; 34p 125,863

Withdrawn: 16.11.88

Yearbook 1987

1987 (DEC). *Comprises Nos.* **MS**393/7, 400/14 *and* A32/6
Yearbook . . . . 37·00

Withdrawn: 31.12.88

386 *Golden Spur* off St. Sampson's Harbour

387 Entering Hong Kong Harbour

388 Anchored off Macao

389 In China Tea Race

390 *Golden Spur* and Map showing Voyage of 1872–74

Guernsey Shipping (2nd series). **Golden Spur** *(full-rigged ship)*

(Des R. Granger Barrett. Litho B.D.T.)

1988 (9 FEB). Perf 13½ (C)

415	**386**	11p multicoloured	25	25
416	**387**	15p multicoloured	35	35
417	**388**	29p multicoloured	1·00	1·00
418	**389**	31p multicoloured	1·00	1·00
419	**390**	34p multicoloured	1·20	1·20
415/19		Set of 5	3·50	3·50
		First Day Cover		3·50
		Presentation Pack	3·50	
		Set of 5 Gutter Pairs	7·20	

Plate Nos.: All values 1A, 1B, 1C, 1D (each ×4)

Sheets: 50 (2 panes 5×5)

Imprint: Central, side margins of each pane

Quantities sold: 11p 213,291; 15p 214,048; 29p 136,246; 31p 143,815; 34p 141,177

Withdrawn: 8.2.89

391 Rowing Boat and Bedford 'Rascal' Mail Van

392 Rowing Boat and Vickers Viscount 800 Mail Plane

393 Postman on Bicycle and Horse-drawn Carriages, Sark

394 Postmen on Bicycles and Carriage

Europa. Transport and Communications

(Des C. Abbott. Litho Questa)

1988 (10 MAY). Perf 14½ (C)

420	**391**	16p multicoloured	35	35
		a. Horiz pair. Nos. 420/1	80	70
421	**392**	16p multicoloured	35	35
422	**393**	22p multicoloured	70	70
		a. Horiz pair. Nos. 422/3	1·40	1·40
423	**394**	22p multicoloured	70	70
420/3		Set of 4	2·00	1·90
		First Day Cover		2·20
		Presentation Pack	2·50	

Plate Nos.: Both values 1A, 1B, 1C, 1D (each ×5)

Sheets: 20 (4×5), the two designs for each value printed together, *se-tenant,* in horizontal pairs throughout the sheets

Imprint: Top, right-hand margin

Quantities sold: 16p 387,699 pairs; 22p 359,634 pairs

Withdrawn: 9.5.89

395 Frederick Corbin Lukis and Lukis House, St. Peter Port

396 Natural History Books and Reconstructed Pot

397 Lukis directing Excavation of Le Creux ès Faies and Prehistoric Beaker

398 Lukis House Observatory and Garden

399 Prehistoric Artifacts

Birth Bicentenary of Frederick Corbin Lukis (archaeologist)

(Des Wendy Bramall, Photo Courvoisier)

1988 (12 JULY). *Granite paper.* Perf 12½ (C)

424	**395**	12p multicoloured	25	25
425	**396**	16p multicoloured	30	25
426	**397**	29p multicoloured	90	85
427	**398**	31p multicoloured	90	85
428	**399**	34p multicoloured	90	90
424/8		Set of 5	3·00	2·75
		First Day Cover		3·00
		Presentation Pack	3·75	
		Set of 5 Gutter Pairs	6·00	

Cylinder Nos.: 29p, 34p A1–1–1–1, B1–1–1–1, C1–1–1–1, D1–1–1–1; others A1–1–1–1–1, B1–1–1–1–1, C1–1–1–1, D1–1–1–1–1

Sheets: 40 (2 panes 5×4)

Quantities sold: 12p 634,056; 16p 510,713; 29p 120,538; 31p 114,192; 34p 134,358

Withdrawn: 11.7.89

400 *Cougar, Rocky* and *Annabella* (power-boats) and Westland Wessex Rescue Helicopter off Jethou

401 *Paul Picot* and other Powerboats in Gouliot Passage

402 Start of Race at St. Peter Port

403 Admiralty Chart showing Course

World Offshore Powerboat Championships

(Des and photo Courvoisier)

1988 (6 SEPT). *Granite paper.* Perf 12 (C)

429	**400**	16p multicoloured	35	25
430	**401**	30p multicoloured	85	85
431	**402**	32p multicoloured	1·00	90
432	**403**	35p multicoloured	1·10	1·00
429/32		Set of 4	3·00	2·75
		First Day Cover		3·00
		Presentation Pack	3·75	
		Set of 4 Gutter Pairs	6·00	

Cylinder Nos.: 16p, 32p A1–1–1–1, B1–1–1–1; 30p, 35p C1–1–1–1, D1–1–1–1

Sheets: 40 (2 panes 5×4) 16p, 30p or (2 panes 4×5) others

Quantities sold: 16p 582,190; 30p 127,183; 32p 166,804; 35p 128,552

Withdrawn: 5.9.89

404 Joshua Gosselin and Herbarium

405 Hares-tail Grass

406 Dried Hares-tail Grass

407 Variegated Catchfly

408 Dried Variegated
Catchfly

409 Rock Sea
Lavender

Bicentenary of Joshua Gosselin's Flora Sarniensis

(Des M. Oxenham. Litho Cartor)

1988 (15 NOV). Perf 13½×14 (C)

433	**404**	12p multicoloured	25	25
434	**405**	16p multicoloured	40	35
		a. Horiz pair. Nos. 434/5	80	70
435	**406**	16p multicoloured	40	35
436	**407**	23p multicoloured	55	50
		a. Horiz pair. Nos. 436/7	1·10	1·00
437	**408**	23p multicoloured	55	50
438	**409**	35p multicoloured	1·00	1·00
433/8		Set of 6	2·75	2·50
		First Day Cover		3·25
		Presentation Pack	3·50	
		Set of 4 Gutter Pairs	5·50	

Plate Nos.: All values 1A, 1B, 1C, 1D (each ×4)

Sheets: 40 (2 panes 4×5), the two designs for the 16p and 23p
values printed together, se-tenant, in horizontal pairs throughout
the sheets

Imprint: Bottom, left-hand margin

Quantities sold: 12p 562,702; 16p 378,679 pairs; 23p 141,152 pairs;
35p 133,205

Withdrawn: 14.11.89

410 Coutances
Cathedral,
France

411 Interior of
Notre Dame
du Rosaire
Church,
Guernsey

412 Stained
Glass, St.
Sampson's
Church,
Guernsey

413 Dol-de-
Bretagne
Cathedral,
France

414 Bishop's
Throne, Town
Church,
Guernsey

415 Winchester
Cathedral

416 St. John's
Cathedral,
Portsmouth

417 High Altar,
St. Joseph's
Church,
Guernsey

418 Mont Saint-
Michel,
France

419 Chancel,
Vale Church,
Guernsey

420 Lychgate,
Forest
Church,
Guernsey

421 Marmoutier
Abbey,
France

Christmas. Ecclesiastical Links

(Des R. Downer. Litho Questa)

1988 (15 NOV). Perf 14½ (C)

439	**410**	8p multicoloured	20	10
		a. Sheetlet of 12. Nos. 439/50 .	2·20	2·20
440	**411**	8p multicoloured	20	10
441	**412**	8p multicoloured	20	10
442	**413**	8p multicoloured	20	10
443	**414**	8p multicoloured	20	10
444	**415**	8p multicoloured	20	10
445	**416**	8p multicoloured	20	10
446	**417**	8p multicoloured	20	10
447	**418**	8p multicoloured	20	10
448	**419**	8p multicoloured	20	10
449	**420**	8p multicoloured	20	10
450	**421**	8p multicoloured	20	10
439/50		Set of 12	2·20	2·20
		First Day Cover		2·75
		Presentation Pack	3·25	

Sheets: 12 (4×3) containing Nos. 439/50 *se-tenant*

Imprint: Bottom, left-hand margin

Quantity sold: 185,939 sheetlets

Withdrawn: 14.11.89

Yearbook 1988

1988 (DEC). *Comprises Nos. 306b, 309c and 415/50*

Yearbook . . . . 37·00

Withdrawn: 31.12.89

422 Lé Cat (Tip Cat)

423 Girl with Cobo Alice Doll

424 Lé Colimachaön (hopscotch)

Europa. Children's Toys and Games

(Des P. le Vasseur. Litho Cartor)

1989 (28 FEB). Perf 13½ (C)

451	**422**	12p multicoloured	25	20
452	**423**	16p multicoloured	40	40
453	**424**	23p multicoloured	80	85
451/3		*Set of 3*	1·20	1·20
		First Day Cover		1·60
		Presentation Pack	1·90	

Plate Nos.: All values 1A, 1B, 1C (each ×4)

Sheets: 20 (4 × 5)

Imprint: Top, right-hand margin

Quantities sold: 12p 839,111; 16p 829,156; 23p 448,761

Withdrawn: 27.2.90

425 Outline Map of Guernsey

Coil Stamps

(Photo Harrison)

1989 (3 APR–27 DEC). *No value expressed.* Perf 14½×14 (C)

454	**425**	(–) ultramarine (*b*)	60	60
455		(–) emerald (*a*)	65	70
454/5		*Set of 2*	1·20	1·20
		First Day Covers (2)		18·00

No. 454 is inscribed 'MINIMUM BAILIWICK POSTAGE PAID' and No. 455 'MINIMUM FIRST CLASS POSTAGE TO UK PAID'. They were originally sold at 14p and 18p, but this was changed in line with postage rate rises.

Printings: (*a*) 3.4.89; (*b*) 27.12.89

Coils: Rolls of 500, numbered on the reverse of every fifth stamp

Withdrawn: 30.6.96

426 Guernsey Airways De Havilland D.H.86 Dragon Express and Mail Van

427 Supermarine Southampton II Flying Boat at Mooring

428 B.E.A. De Havilland D.H.89 Dragon Rapide

429 Short S.25 Sunderland Mk V Flying Boat taking off

430 Air U.K. British Aerospace BAe 146

431 Avro Shackleton M.R.3

50th Anniversaries of Guernsey Airport (Nos. 456, 458 and 460) and 201 Squadron's Affiliation with Guernsey (Nos. 457, 459 and 461)

(Des N. Foggo. Litho B.D.T.)

1989 (5 MAY). Perf 13½ (C)

456	**426**	12p multicoloured	35	30
		a. Booklet pane. No. 456×6 . .	2·00	
457	**427**	12p multicoloured	35	30
458	**428**	18p multicoloured	50	50
		a. Booklet pane. No. 458×6 . .	3·00	
459	**429**	18p multicoloured	50	50

460	**430**	35p multicoloured	1·00	90
		a. Booklet pane. No. 460×6 ..	6·00	
461	**431**	35p multicoloured	1·00	1·00
456/61		Set of 6	3·25	3·25
		First Day Cover		4·75
		Presentation Pack	4·50	
		Set of 4 Gutter Pairs	6·50	

Each booklet pane has margins all round with text printed at the foot.

Plate Nos.: All values 1A, 1B (each ×4)

Sheets: 50 (2 panes 5×5)

Imprint: Central, side margins of each pane

Quantities sold: No. 456, 461,080; No. 457, 362,154; No. 458, 436,134; No. 459, 388,274; No. 460, 172,574; No. 461, 149,134

Withdrawn: 4.5.90

432 'Queen Elizabeth II' (June Mendoza)

Royal Visit

(Des A. Theobald. Lithi B.D.T.)

1989 (23 MAY). Perf 15×14

462	**432**	30p multicoloured	75	80
		First Day Cover		1·70
		Presentation Pack	2·00	

Plate Nos.: 1A (×5)

Sheets: 20 (5×4)

Imprint: Top, right-hand margin

Quantity sold: 180,900

Withdrawn: 22.5.90

433 *Ibex* at G.W.R. Terminal, St. Peter Port

434 *Great Western* (paddle-steamer) in Little Russel

435 *St. Julien* passing Casquets Light

436 *Roebuck* off Portland

437 *Antelope* and Boat Train on Weymouth Quay

Centenary of Great Western Railway Steamer Service to Channel Islands

(Des C. Jaques. Litho B.D.T.)

1989 (5 SEPT). Perf 13½ (C)

463	**433**	12p multicoloured	20	20
464	**434**	18p multicoloured	45	45
465	**435**	29p multicoloured	70	75
466	**436**	34p multicoloured	1·00	95
467	**437**	37p multicoloured	1·20	1·10
463/7		Set of 5	3·25	3·00
		First Day Cover		4·00
		Presentation Pack	5·00	
		Set of 5 Gutter Pairs	6·00	
MS468		115×117 mm. Nos. 463/7	3·00	3·25
		First Day Cover		7·00

Plate Nos.: All values 1A, 1B (each ×4)

Sheets: 50 (2 panes (5×5)

Imprint: Central, side margins of each pane

Quantities sold: 12p 741,870; 18p 666,520; 29p 223,570; 34p 202,570; 37p 209,020; miniature sheet 74,127

Withdrawn: 4.9.90

438 Two-toed Sloth

439 Capuchin Monkey

440 White-lipped Tamarin

441 Common Squirrel-Monkey

442 Common Gibbon

10th Anniversary of Guernsey Zoological Trust. Animals of the Rainforest

(Des Anne Farncombe. Litho Cartor)

1989 (17 NOV). Perf 13½×14) (C)

469	**438**	18p multicoloured	70	70
		a. Strip of 5. Nos. 469/73	3·50	3·50
470	**439**	29p multicoloured	70	70
471	**440**	32p multicoloured	70	70
472	**441**	34p multicoloured	70	70
473	**442**	37p multicoloured	70	70
469/73		Set of 5	3·50	3·50
		First Day Cover		3·75
		Presentation Pack	4·25	
		Stamp-cards (set of 5)	2·00	7·00

Plate Nos.: 1B (×4)

Sheets: 20 (5×4). Nos. 469/73 were printed in *se-tenant* strips of 5 across the sheet

Imprint: Top, right-hand margin

Quantities sold: 148,505 of each value

Withdrawn: 16.11.90

Christmas. Christmas Tree Decorations

(Des Wendy Bramall. Litho B.D.T.)

1989 (17 NOV). Perf 13 (C)

474	**443**	10p multicoloured	25	15
		a. Sheetlet of 12. Nos. 474/85 .	2·50	2·50
475	**444**	10p multicoloured	25	15
476	**445**	10p multicoloured	25	15
477	**446**	10p multicoloured	25	15
478	**447**	10p multicoloured	25	15
479	**448**	10p multicoloured	25	15
480	**449**	10p multicoloured	25	15
481	**450**	10p multicoloured	25	15
482	**451**	10p multicoloured	25	15
483	**452**	10p multicoloured	25	15
484	**453**	10p multicoloured	25	15
485	**454**	10p multicoloured	25	15
474/85		Set of 12	2·50	2·50
		First Day Cover		3·00
		Presentation Pack	3·50	

Sheets: 12 (3×4) containing Nos. 474/85 *se-tenant*

Imprint: Central, left-hand margin

Quantity sold: 229,000 sheetlets

Withdrawn: 16.11.90

Yearbook 1989

1989 (17 NOV). *Comprises Nos.* 309d, 451/3, 456/62, **MS**468/85 *and* A37/41

Yearbook .... 35·00

Withdrawn: 31.12.90

443 Star

444 Fairy

445 Candles

446 Bird

447 Present

448 Carol-singer

449 Christmas Cracker

450 Bauble

451 Christmas Stocking

452 Bell

453 Fawn

454 Church

455 Sark Post Office, c 1890

456 Sark Post Office, 1990

457 Arcade Post Office Counter, St. Peter Port, c 1840

47

458 Arcade Post Office Counter, St. Peter Port, 1990

GUERNSEY 1990-ARCADE POST OFFICE 24p

Europa. Post Office Buildings

(Des C. Abbott. Litho Enschedé)

1990 (27 FEB). Perf 13½ × 14 (C)

486	**455**	20p blackish brown, sepia and pale cinnamon	45	45
487	**456**	20p multicoloured	45	45
488	**457**	24p blackish brown, sepia and pale cinnamon	60	65
489	**458**	24p multicoloured	60	65
486/9		Set of 4	1·90	2·00
		First Day Cover		2·40
		Presentation Pack	2·40	

Plate Nos.: Nos. 486 and 488 1A, 1B (each ×3); Nos. 487 and 489 1A, 1B (each ×4)

Sheets: 20 (4×5)

Imprint: Central, side margins

Quantities sold: No. 486, 498,819; No. 487, 398,759; 488, 495,039; No. 489, 397,759

Withdrawn: 26.2.91

459 Penny Black and Mail Steamer off St. Peter Port, 1840

460 Penny Red, 1841, and Pillar Box of 1853

461 Bisected 2d., 1940, and German Army Band

462 Regional 3d., 1958, and Guernsey Emblems

463 Independent Postal Administration 1½d., 1969, and Queue at Main Post Office

150th Anniversary of the Penny Black

(Des Jennifer Toombs. Litho Questa)

1990 (3 MAY). Perf 14 (C)

490	**459**	14p multicoloured	35	35
491	**460**	20p multicoloured	45	45
492	**461**	32p multicoloured	80	80
493	**462**	34p multicoloured	1·00	1·00
494	**463**	37p multicoloured	1·00	1·00
490/4		Set of 5	3·25	3·25
		First Day Cover		4·00
		Presentation Pack	5·50	
		Set of 5 Gutter Pairs	6·50	
MS495		151×116 mm. Nos. 490/4	3·25	3·50
		First Day Cover		15·00

No. **MS**495 also commemorates 'Stamp World London 90' International Stamp Exhibition. It was reissued on 24 August 1990 overprinted for 'NEW ZEALAND 1990' and sold at this international stamp exhibition in Auckland. (*Price £4 unused, £4·50 used, £18 on first day cover.*)

Plate Nos.: 14p, 32p 1A, 1B (each ×4); 20p, 34p 1C, 1D (each ×4); 37p 1A, 1B, 1C, 1D (each ×4)

Sheets: 50 (2 panes 5×5)

Imprint: Bottom corner, right-hand margin of each pane

Quantities sold: 14p 687,850; 20p 662,800; 32p 155,960; 34p 143,850; 37p 174,830; miniature sheet 92,701

Withdrawn: 2.5.91

464 Lt. Philip Saumarez writing Log Book

465 Anson's Squadron leaving Portsmouth, 1740

466 Ships at St. Catherine's Island, Brazil

467 H.M.S. *Tryal* (sloop) dismasted, Cape Horn, 1741

468 Crew of H.M.S. *Centurion* on Juan Fernandez

250th Anniversary of Anson's Circumnavigation

(Des R. Granger Barrett. Litho Enschedé)

1990 (26 JULY). Perf 13½×14 (C)

496	**464**	14p multicoloured	30	30
497	**465**	20p multicoloured	40	40
498	**466**	29p multicoloured	80	80
499	**467**	34p multicoloured	1·00	90
500	**468**	37p multicoloured	1·10	95
496/500		Set of 5	3·25	3·00
		First Day Cover		3·75
		Presentation Pack	3·75	
		Stamp-cards (set of 5)	2·00	6·00
		Set of 5 Gutter Pairs	6·50	

Plate Nos.: 14p, 20p, 29p 1A, 1B, 1C, 1D (each ×4); 34p, 37p 1A, 1B (each ×4)

Sheets: 50 (2 panes 5×5)

Imprint: Central, side margins of each pane

Quantities sold: 14p 985,850; 20p 481,400; 29p 162,800; 34p 143,500; 37p 138,450

Withdrawn: 25.7.91

469 Grey Seal and Pup

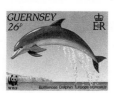

470 Bottle-nosed Dolphin

471 Basking Shark

472 Common Porpoise

Marine Life

(Des Jennifer Toombs. Litho Questa)

1990 (16 OCT). Perf 14½ (C)

501	**469**	20p multicoloured	45	45
502	**470**	26p multicoloured	95	95
503	**471**	31p multicoloured	1·00	1·00
504	**472**	37p multicoloured	1·20	1·20
501/4		Set of 4	3·25	3·25
		First Day Cover		4·25
		Presentation Pack	3·50	
		Set of 4 Gutter Pairs	6·50	

Plate Nos.: 20p, 31p 1A, 1B (each ×4); 26p, 37p 1C, 1D (each ×4)

Sheets: 50 (2 panes 5×5)

Imprint: Top, right-hand margin of each pane

Quantities sold: 20p 973,900; 26p 478,200; 31p 328,650; 37p 303,600

Withdrawn: 15.10.91

473 Blue Tit and Great Tit

474 Snow Bunting

475 Common Kestrel

476 Common Starling

477 Western Greenfinch

478 European Robin

479 Winter Wren

480 Barn Owl

481 Mistle Thrush

482 Grey Heron

483 Chaffinch

484 Common Kingfisher

Christmas. Winter Birds

(Des Wendy Bramall. Litho B.D.T.)

1990 (16 OCT). Perf 13 (C)

505	**473**	10p multicoloured	35	15
		a. Sheetlet of 12. Nos. 505/16 .	3·50	3·25
506	**474**	10p multicoloured	35	15
507	**475**	10p multicoloured	35	15
508	**476**	10p multicoloured	35	15
509	**477**	10p multicoloured	35	15
510	**478**	10p multicoloured	35	15
511	**479**	10p multicoloured	35	15
512	**480**	10p multicoloured	35	15
513	**481**	10p multicoloured	35	15
514	**482**	10p multicoloured	35	15
515	**483**	10p multicoloured	35	15
516	**484**	10p multicoloured	35	15
505/16		Set of 12	3·50	3·25
		First Day Cover		3·50
		Presentation Pack	3·75	

Sheets: 12 (3×4) containing Nos. 505/16 se-tenant

Imprint: Central, left-hand margin

Quantity sold: 237,602 sheetlets

Withdrawn: 15.10.91

Yearbook 1990

1990 (1 NOV). Comprises Nos. 486/9, **MS**495, 496/516, A12a and A42/6

Yearbook . . . . 35·00

Withdrawn: 31.12.91

485 Air Raid and 1941 ½d. Stamp

486 1941 1d. Stamp

487 1944 2½d. Stamp

50th Anniversary of First Guernsey Stamps

(Des C. Abbott. Litho B.D.T.)

1991 (18 FEB). Perf 13½ (C)

517	**485**	37p multicoloured	1·00	1·10
		a. Booklet pane. Nos. 517/19 .	4·00	
518	**486**	53p multicoloured	1·30	1·50
519	**487**	57p multicoloured	1·30	1·50
517/19		Set of 3	3·25	3·75
		First Day Cover		4·00
		Presentation Pack	4·25	
		Set of 3 Gutter Pairs	7·50	

Booklet pane No. 517a exists in three versions, which differ in the order of the stamps from left to right and in the information printed on the pane margins.

Plate Nos.: 37p, 53p 1A, 1B (each ×4); 57p 1A, 1B, 1C, 1D (each ×4)

Sheets: 40 (2 panes 5×4)

Imprint: Central, side margins

Quantities sold: 37p 260,015; 53p 250,536; 57p 250,219

Withdrawn: 17.2.92

488 Visit of Queen Victoria to Guernsey, and Discovery of Neptune, 1846

489 Visit of Queen Elizabeth II and Prince Philip to Sark, and Flight of 'Sputnik' (1st artificial satellite, 1957)

490 Maiden Voyage of Sarnia (ferry), and 'Vostok 1' (first manned space flight), 1961

491 Cancelling Guernsey Stamps, and First Manned Landing on Moon, 1969

Europa. Europe in Space

(Des Jennifer Toombs. Litho Enschedé)

1991 (30 APR). Perf 13½×14 (C)

520	**488**	21p multicoloured	55	50
521	**489**	21p multicoloured	55	50
522	**490**	26p multicoloured	65	60
523	**491**	26p multicoloured	65	60
520/3		Set of 4	1·90	1·90
		First Day Cover		2·20
		Presentation Pack	2·75	

Plate Nos.: Both values 1A, 1B (each ×5)

Sheets: 20 (4×5)

Imprint: Central, side margins

Quantities sold: No. 520, 390,924; No. 521, 390,834; No. 522, 369,404; No. 523, 370,244

Withdrawn: 29.4.92

492 Children in Guernsey Sailing Trust 'GP14' Dinghy

493 Guernsey Regatta

494 Lombard Channel Islands' Challenge Race

495 Rolex Swan Regatta

496 Old Gaffers' Association Gaff-rigged Yacht

Centenary of Guernsey Yacht Club

(Des C. Abbott. Litho B.D.T.)

1991 (2 JULY). Perf 14 (C)

524	**492**	15p multicoloured	45	15
525	**493**	21p multicoloured	70	25
526	**494**	26p multicoloured	80	80
527	**495**	31p multicoloured	90	1·10
528	**496**	37p multicoloured	1·00	1·40
524/8		Set of 5	3·50	3·25
		First Day Cover		3·75
		Presentation Pack	5·00	
		Set of 5 Gutter Pairs	7·00	
MS529	163×75 mm. Nos. 524/8		3·50	4·00
		First Day Cover		10·00

Stamps from No. **MS**529 show 'GUERNSEY' and the face value in yellow.

Plate Nos.: 37p 1C, 1D (each ×5); others 1A, 1B (each ×5)

Sheets: 50 (2 panes 5×5)

Imprint: Top corner, right-hand margin of each pane

Quantities sold: 15p 711,043; 21p 708,743; 26p 188,894; 31p 158,938; 37p 138.543; miniature sheet 81,012

Withdrawn: 1.7.92

497 Pair of Oystercatchers

498 Three Ruddy Turnstones

499 Dunlins and Ruddy Turnstones

500 Curlew and Ruddy Turnstones

501 Ringed Plover with Chicks

502 Black-headed Gull, Sea Campion and Sea Radish

503 Yellow Horned Poppy

504 Pair of Common Stonechats, Hare's Foot Clover and Fennel

505 Hare's Foot Clover, Fennel and Slender Oat

506 Ruddy Turnstone and Sea Kale on Shore

Nature Conservation. L'Eree Shingle Bank Reserve

(Des Wendy Bramall. Litho Questa)

1991 (15 OCT). Perf 14½ (C)

530	**497**	15p multicoloured	35	20
		a. Horiz strip of 5. Nos. 530/4 .	2·75	2·50
531	**498**	15p multicoloured	35	20
532	**499**	15p multicoloured	35	20
533	**500**	15p multicoloured	35	20
534	**501**	15p multicoloured	35	20
535	**502**	21p multicoloured	45	25
		a. Horiz strip of 5. Nos. 535/9 .	2·75	2·50
536	**503**	21p multicoloured	45	25
537	**504**	21p multicoloured	45	25
538	**505**	21p multicoloured	45	25
539	**506**	21p multicoloured	45	25
530/9		Set of 10	4·50	4·00
		First Day Cover		5·00
		Presentation Pack	5·00	
		Stamp-cards (set of 10)	4·00	10·00

Plate Nos.: Both values 1A, 1B, 1C, 1D (each ×4)

Sheets: 20 (5×4), the five designs for each value printed together, se-tenant, in horizontal strips throughout the sheets.

Imprint: Bottom, left-hand margin

Quantities sold: 15p 270,830 strips; 21p 272,198 strips

Withdrawn: 14.10.92

507 'Rudolph the Red-nosed Reindeer' (Melanie Sharpe)

508 'Christmas Pudding' (James Quinn)

509 'Snowman' (Lisa Guille)

510 'Snowman in Top Hat' (Jessica Ede-Golightly)

511 'Robins and Christmas Tree' (Sharon Le Page)

512 'Shepherds and Angels' (Anna Coquelin)

513 'Nativity' (Claudine Lithou)

514 'Three Wise Men' (Jonathan Le Noury)

515 'Star of Bethlehem and Angels' (Marcia Mahy)

516 'Christmas Tree' (Laurel Garfield)

517 'Santa Claus' (Rebecca Driscoll)

518 'Snowman and Star' (Ian Lowe)

Christmas. Children's Paintings

(Litho B.D.T.)

1991 (15 OCT). Perf 13½×13 (C)

540	**507**	12p multicoloured	30	15
		a. Sheetlet of 12. Nos. 540/51 .	3·25	3·25
541	**508**	12p multicoloured	30	15
542	**509**	12p multicoloured	30	15
543	**510**	12p multicoloured	30	15
544	**511**	12p multicoloured	30	15
545	**512**	12p multicoloured	30	15
546	**513**	12p multicoloured	30	15
547	**514**	12p multicoloured	30	15
548	**515**	12p multicoloured	30	15
549	**516**	12p multicoloured	30	15
550	**517**	12p multicoloured	30	15
551	**518**	12p multicoloured	30	15
540/51		Set of 12	3·25	3·25
		First Day Cover		3·50
		Presentation Pack	3·75	

Sheets: 12 (3×4) containing Nos. 540/51 se-tenant

Imprint: Central, left-hand margin

Quantity sold: 192,203 sheetlets

Withdrawn: 14.10.92

1991 (1 NOV). *Comprises Nos.* 310*b*/*c*, 517/51, A12*b and* A47/51

     Yearbook . . . . 35·00

Withdrawn: 31.12.92

519 Queen Elizabeth 'II in 1952

520 In 1977

521 In 1986

522 In 1991

40th Anniversary of Accession

   (Des C. Abbott. Litho Questa)

1992 (6 FEB). Perf 14 (C)

552	**519**	23p multicoloured	50	50
553	**520**	28p multicoloured	65	65
554	**521**	33p multicoloured	90	90
555	**522**	39p multicoloured	1·10	1·10
552/5		*Set of 4*	2·75	2·75
		First Day Cover		3·25
		Presentation Pack	3·25	
		Set of 4 Gutter Pairs	5·50	

Plate Nos.: All values 1A, 1B (each ×6)

Sheets: 50 (2 panes 5×5)

Quantities sold: 23p 773,200; 28p 479,095; 33p 212,446; 39p 219,900

Withdrawn: 5.2.93

523 Christopher Columbus

524 Examples of Columbus's Signature

525 *Santa Maria*

526 Map of First Voyage

Europa. 500th Anniversary of Discovery of America by Columbus

   (Des R. Ollington. Litho Walsall)

1992 (6 FEB). Perf 13½×14 (C)

556	**523**	23p multicoloured	65	60
557	**524**	23p multicoloured	65	60
558	**525**	28p multicoloured	1·20	1·20
559	**526**	28p multicoloured	1·20	1·20
556/9		*Set of 4*	3·25	3·25
		First Day Cover		3·75
		Presentation Pack	3·75	
MS560		157×77 mm. Nos. 556/9	4·50	5·00
		First Day Cover		7·00

No. **MS**560 was reissued on 22 May 1992 overprinted for 'WORLD COLUMBIAN STAMP EXPO 92' and sold at this international stamp exhibition in Chicago. (*Price* 5·00 *unused*, 6·00 *used*, 9·00 *on first day cover*).

Plate Nos.: All values 1A, 1B, 1C (each ×4)

Sheets: 20 (4×5)

Imprint: Bottom, right-hand margin

Quantities sold: No. 556, 543,672; No. 557, 575,663; No. 558, 363,124; No. 559, 364,684; miniature sheet 157,166

Withdrawn: 5.2.93

527a Guernsey Calves

150th Anniversary of Royal Guernsey Agricultural and Horticultural Society

(Des R. Goldsmith. Litho Questa)

1992 (22 MAY). *Sheet* 93×71 *mm.* Perf 14 (C)
MS561 **527a** 75p multicoloured .... 2·10   2·00
        First Day Cover ....   3·25
        Presentation Pack .... 2·75

Quantity sold: 142,549

Withdrawn: 21.5.93

528 *Stephanotis floribunda*

529 Potted Hydrangea

530 Stock

531 Anemones

532 Gladiolus

533 *Asparagus plumosus, Gypsophila paniculata*

534 Guernsey Lily

535 Enchantment Lily

536 Clematis 'Freckles'

537 Alstroemeria

538 Standard Carnation

539 Standard Rose

540 Spray Rose

541 Mixed Freesia

542 Standard Rose

543 Iris 'Ideal'

544 Freesia 'Pink Glow'

545 Lisianthus

546 Spray Chrysanthemum

547 Spray Carnation

548 Single Freesia

549 Floral Arrangement

550 Chelsea Flower Show Exhibit

551 'Floral Fantasia' (exhibit)

54

Guernsey Flowers

(Des R. Gorringe. Litho Walsall (Nos. 572a, 572ba, 574a, 575a, 576b and 577a), Questa (No. 576a), Cartor (No. 582a) or B.D.T. (others))

1992 (22 MAY)–**97**. Perf 14 (£1, £2) or 13 (others), all comb

562	**528**	1p multicoloured (b)	....	10	10
563	**529**	2p multicoloured (b)	....	10	10
564	**530**	3p multicoloured (a)	....	10	10
565	**531**	4p multicoloured (a)	....	15	15
566	**532**	5p multicoloured (a)	....	15	15
567	**533**	6p multicoloured (b)	....	15	15
568	**534**	7p multicoloured (b)	....	20	20
569	**535**	8p multicoloured (b)	....	20	20
570	**536**	9p multicoloured (b)	....	20	25
571	**537**	10p multicoloured (a)	....	25	25
572	**538**	16p multicoloured (a)	....	50	35
		a. Perf 14 (ab)	....	60	50
		ab. Lavender ptg double	......		
		ac. Booklet pane. Nos. 572a×5 and 574a×3 (a)	....	4·00	
		ad. Booklet pane of 8 (b)	......	3·25	
572b	**539**	18p multicoloured (e)	....	55	45
		ba. Perf 14	....	55	45
		bb. Booklet pane of 8	....	4·00	
573	**540**	20p multicoloured (a)	....	60	50
574	**541**	23p multicoloured (a)	....	60	55
		a. Perf 14	....	80	60
		ab. Brownish grey ptg double	..		
		ac. Booklet pane of 8	....	6·00	
575	**542**	24p multicoloured (b)	....	70	60
		a. Perf 14	....	80	60
		ab. Booklet pane of 8	....	6·00	
576	**543**	25p multicoloured (c)	....	70	60
		a. Perf 14½×15	....	80	60
		ab. Booklet pane of 4	....	3·75	
576b	**544**	26p multicoloured (e)	....	70	60
		ba. Perf 14	....	80	60
		bb. Booklet pane of 4	....	3·75	
577	**545**	28p multicoloured (b)	....	80	65
		a. Perf 14	....	1·10	65
		ab. Booklet pane of 4	....	3·50	
578	**546**	30p multicoloured (b)	....	80	70
579	**547**	40p multicoloured (a)	....	1·00	75
580	**548**	50p multicoloured (a)	....	1·20	90
581	**549**	£1 multicoloured (a)	....	2·00	1·50
582	**550**	£2 multicoloured (b)	....	4·00	3·00
582a	**551**	£3 multicoloured (d)	....	6·00	5·00
562/82a		Set of 24	....	18·00	16·00
		First Day Covers (5)	....		25·00
		Presentation Packs (3)	.....	25·00	
		Stamp-cards (set of 24)	....	5·00	27·00
		Set of 24 Gutter Pairs	.....	40·00	

Nos. 572a, 572ba, 574a, 575a, 576a, 576ba and 577a were only issued in booklets with the upper and lower edges of the panes imperforate and in unfolded booklet panes, available from the Philatelic Bureau and Head Post Office.

For No. 581 in miniature sheets see Nos. **MS**644 (with imprint date '1994') and **MS**681 (with imprint date '1995').

Printings: (a) 22.5.92; (b) 2.3.93; (c) 18.2.94; (d) 24.1.96; (e) 2.1.97, each with appropriate imprint date

Plate Nos.: £1 1A, 1B (each ×8); £3 1A, 1B, 1C, 1D (each ×5); others 1A, 1B, 1C, 1D (each ×6)

Sheets: 1p, 2p, 3p, 4p, 5p, 6p, 7p, 8p, 9p, 10p, 18p, 20p, 40p 100 (2 panes 10×5); 16p, 23p, 24p, 25p, 26p, 28p, 30p, 50p (2 panes 5×10); £1, £2, £3 50 (2 panes 5×5)

Imprints: 1p, 2p, 3p, 4p, 5p, 6p, 7p, 8p, 9p, 10p, 18p, 20p, 40p, £1, £2 left-hand corner, top and bottom margin; £3 central, side margins; others top of side margin

Withdrawn: 31.8.99 1p to £2; 31.8.2003 £3

552 Building the Ship

553 Loading the Cargo

554 Ship at Sea

555 Ship under Attack

556 Crew swimming Ashore

'Operation Asterix' (excavation of Roman ship)

(Des Studio Legrain. Litho Cartor)

1992 (18 SEPT). Perf 13 (C)

583	**552**	16p multicoloured	....	45	35
		a. Booklet pane. Nos. 583/7 plus label	....	3·50	
584	**553**	23p multicoloured	....	60	45
585	**554**	28p multicoloured	....	80	70
586	**555**	33p multicoloured	....	95	90
587	**556**	39p multicoloured	....	1·10	1·00
583/7		Set of 5	....	3·50	3·00
		First Day Cover	....		4·25
		Presentation Pack	.....	4·25	
		Set of 5 Gutter Pairs	......	7·00	

Booklet pane No. 583a has margins all round and exists with marginal inscriptions in either English, French, Italian or German.

Plate Nos.: All values 1A, 1B, 1C, 1D (each ×4)

Sheets: 50 (2 panes 5×5)

Imprint: Central, side margins

Quantities sold: 16p 904,428; 23p 743,228; 28p 308,091; 33p 281,941; 39p 291,841

Withdrawn: 17.9.93

557 Tram No. 10 decorated for Battle of Flowers

558 Tram No. 10 passing Hougue a la Perre

559 Tram No. 1 at St. Sampsons

560 First Steam Tram at St. Peter Port, 1879

561 Last Electric Tram, 1934

Guernsey Trams

(Des A. Peck. Litho Enschedé)

1992 (17 NOV). Perf 13½ (C)

588	**557**	16p multicoloured	45	30
589	**558**	23p multicoloured	60	35
590	**559**	28p multicoloured	75	80
591	**560**	33p multicoloured	90	1·00
592	**561**	39p multicoloured	1·10	1·10
588/92		Set of 5	3·50	3·25
		First Day Cover		4·25
		Presentation Pack	4·75	
		Set of 5 Gutter Pairs	7·50	

Plate Nos.: 39p, 1A, 1B, 1C, 1D (each ×6); others 1A, 1B (each ×6)

Sheets: 50 (2 panes 5×5)

Imprint: Central, side margins of each pane

Quantities sold: 16p 366,400; 23p 282,520; 28p 181,670; 33p 130,920; 39p 156,170

Withdrawn: 16.11.93

562 Man in Party Hat

563 Girl and Christmas Tree

564 Woman and Balloons

565 Mince Pies and Champagne

566 Roast Turkey

567 Christmas Pudding

568 Christmas Cake

569 Fancy Cakes

570 Cheese

571 Nuts

572 Ham

573 Chocolate Log

Christmas. Seasonal Fayre

(Des Wendy Bramall. Litho B.D.T.)

1992 (17 NOV). Perf 13 (C)

593	**562**	13p multicoloured	30	15
		a. Sheetlet of 12. Nos. 593/604	3·50	3·25
		ab. Gold ptg double		
594	**563**	13p multicoloured	30	15
595	**564**	13p multicoloured	30	15
596	**565**	13p multicoloured	30	15
597	**566**	13p multicoloured	30	15
598	**567**	13p multicoloured	30	15
599	**568**	13p multicoloured	30	15
600	**569**	13p multicoloured	30	15
601	**570**	13p multicoloured	30	15
602	**571**	13p multicoloured	30	15
603	**572**	13p multicoloured	30	15
604	**573**	13p multicoloured	30	15
593/604		Set of 12	3·50	3·25
		First Day Cover		4·00
		Presentation Pack	4·50	

Sheets: 12 (3×4) containing Nos. 593/604 se-tenant, forming a composite design showing family during Christmas meal

Imprint: Central, left-hand margin

Quantity sold: 183,550 sheetlets

Withdrawn: 16.11.93

Yearbook 1992

1992 (18 NOV). Comprises Nos. 552/61, 564/6, 571/4, 579/81, 583/604, A12c and A52/5

	Yearbook	35·00

Withdrawn: 31.12.93

24 GUERNSEY **574** Rupert Bear, Bingo and Dog

574a Rupert and Friends
(*illustration reduced. Actual size 116×97 mm*)

Rupert Bear and Friends (cartoon characters created by Mary and Herbert Tourtel)

(Des J. Harold. Litho Walsall)

1993 (2 FEB). Perf 13½×13 (C)
605 **574** 24p multicoloured 50 75
First Day Cover . . . . 2·00
Gutter Pair . . . . 1·50
MS606 116×97 mm. **574a** 16p Airplane and castle; 16p Professor's servant and Autumn Elf; 16p Algy Pug; 16p Baby Badger on sledge; 24p Bill Badger, Willie Mouse, Reggie Rabbit and Podgy playing in snow; 24p Type **574**; 24p The Balloonist avoiding Gregory on toboggan; 24p Tiger Lily and Edward Trunk . . . . 4·50 4·00
a. Black ptg double . . . . 4·50
First Day Cover . . . . 4·50
Presentation Pack (Nos. 605/6) . . . . 6·00

The 24p values in No. **MS**606 are as Type **574**; the 16p designs are smaller, each 25½×26 mm.

Plate Nos.: 24p 1A, 1B (each ×4)
Sheets: 50 (2 panes 5×5)
Imprint: Top left-hand margin of each pane
Quantities sold: 24p 523,690; miniature sheet 107,258
Withdrawn: 1.2.94

575 Tapestry by Kelly Fletcher

576 'Le Marchi a Paisson' (etching and aquatint, Sally Reed)

577 'Red Abstract' (painting, Molly Harris)

578 'Dress Shop, King's Road' (painting, Damon Bell)

Europa. Contemporary Art

(Des B. Bell. Litho Enschedé)

1993 (7 MAY). Perf 13½×14 (C)
607 **575** 24p multicoloured 70 70
608 **576** 24p multicoloured 70 70
609 **577** 28p multicoloured 80 80
610 **578** 28p multicoloured 80 80
607/10 Set of 4 . . . . 2·75 2·75
First Day Cover . . . . 3·00
Presentation Pack . . . . 3·00

Plate Nos.: 24p (No. 607) 1A, 1B, 1C, 1D (each ×5); others 1A, 1B (each ×5)
Sheets: 20 (4×5)
Imprint: Central, side margins
Quantities sold: No. 607, 289,838; No. 608, 292,450; No. 609, 283,627; No. 610, 280,150
Withdrawn: 6.5.94

579 Arrest of Guernsey Parliamentarians, Fermain Bay

580 Parliamentary Ships attacking Castle Cornet

581 Parliamentary Captives escaping

582 Castle Cannon firing at St. Peter Port

583 Surrender of Castle Cornet, 19 December 1651

350th Anniversary of Siege of Castle Cornet

(Des C. Abbott. Litho Questa)

1993 (7 MAY). Perf 14½×14 (C)

611	**579**	16p multicoloured	35	35
612	**580**	24p multicoloured	60	60
613	**581**	28p multicoloured	75	75
614	**582**	33p multicoloured	85	85
615	**583**	39p multicoloured	90	90
611/15		Set of 5	3·00	3·00
		First Day Cover		3·75
		Presentation Pack	3·75	
		Set of 5 Gutter Pairs	6·00	
MS616		203×75 mm. Nos. 611/15	3·25	4·00
		First Day Cover		10·00

Plate Nos.: All values 1A, 1B (each ×5)

Sheets: 40 (2 panes 4×5)

Imprint: Central, right-hand margin

Quantities sold: 16p 253,310; 24p 289,408; 28p 125,877; 33p 124,981; 39p 125,761; miniature sheet 184,308

Withdrawn: 6.5.94

584 Playing Cards

585 Fountain Pens

586 Envelope-folding Machine

587 Great Britain 1855 4d Stamp

588 Thomas de la Rue and Mauritius £1 Banknote

Birth Bicentenary of Thomas de la Rue (printer)

(Des J. Stephenson. Litho (16, 24, 28p) or recess (33, 39p) Enschedé)

1993 (27 JULY). Perf 13½ (C)

617	**584**	16p multicoloured	40	45
		a. Booklet pane of 4 with margins all round	1·50	
618	**585**	24p multicoloured	65	65
		a. Booklet pane of 4 with margins all round	2·20	
619	**586**	28p multicoloured	80	80
		a. Booklet pane of 4 with margins all round	3·00	
620	**587**	33p carmine-lake	95	95
		a. Booklet pane of 4 with margins all round	3·25	
621	**588**	39p blackish green	1·10	1·10
		a. Booklet pane of 4 with margins all round	3·75	
617/21		Set of 5	3·50	3·50
		First Day Cover		3·75
		Presentation Pack	4·00	
		Set of 5 Gutter Pairs	7·25	

Plate Nos.: 16p, 24p 1A×4; 28p 1A, 1B (each ×4); 33p, 39p 1A

Sheets: 50 (2 panes 5×5)

Imprint: Central, side margins of each pane

Quantities sold: 16p 465,736; 24p 452,982; 28p 111,030; 33p 113,299; 39p 119,548

Withdrawn: 26.7.94

589 'The
Twelve
Pearls'

590 'Healing
Rays'

591 'Hand of
God over
the Holy
City'

592 'Wing and
Seabirds'
(facing left)

593 'Christ the
Healer'

594 'Wing and
Seabirds'
(facing right)

595 'The Young
Jesus in
the Temple'

596 'The Raising
of Jarius'
Daughter'

597 'Suffer Little
Children to
come unto
Me'

598 'Pilgrim's
Progress'

599 'The Light of
the World'

600 'Raphael,
Archangel
of Healing,
with Tobias'

**Christmas. Stained Glass Windows by Mary-Eily de
Putron from Chapel of Christ the Healer**

(Des Jennifer Toombs. Litho B.D.T.)

1993 (2 NOV.) Perf 13 (C)

622	**589**	13p multicoloured	. . . .	30	15
		a. Sheetlet. Nos. 622/33	. . . . .	3·50	3·25
623	**590**	13p multicoloured	. . . .	30	15
624	**591**	13p multicoloured	. . . .	30	15
625	**592**	13p multicoloured	. . . .	30	15
626	**593**	13p multicoloured	. . . .	30	15

627	**594**	13p multicoloured	. . . .	30	15
628	**595**	13p multicoloured	. . . .	30	15
629	**596**	13p multicoloured	. . . .	30	15
630	**597**	13p multicoloured	. . . .	30	15
631	**598**	13p multicoloured	. . . .	30	15
632	**599**	13p multicoloured	. . . .	30	15
633	**600**	13p multicoloured	. . . .	30	15
622/33		*Set of* 12	. . . .	3·50	3·25
		First Day Cover	. . . .		4·00
		Presentation Pack	. . . .	4·00	

Sheets: 12 (3×4) containing Nos. 622/33 *se-tenant*

Imprint: Central, left-hand margin

Quantity sold: 150,594 sheetlets

Withdrawn: 1.11.94

Yearbook 1993

1993 (2 NOV). *Comprises Nos.* 562/3, 567/70, 575, 577/8,
582, 605/33, A12*d/e and* A56/9

Yearbook . . . . 35·00

Withdrawn: 30.12.94

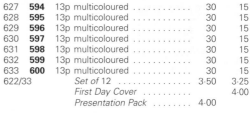

601 Les Fouaillages
(ancient burial ground)

602 Mounted Celtic Warrior

603 Jars, Arrow Heads
and Stone Axe from
Les Fouaillages

604 Sword, Spear Head and Torque from King's Road Burial

Europa. Archaeological Discoveries

(Des Miranda Schofield. Litho Cartor)

1994 (18 FEB). Perf 13½ (C)

634	**601**	24p multicoloured	55	55
635	**602**	24p multicoloured	55	55
636	**603**	30p multicoloured	80	75
637	**604**	30p multicoloured	80	75
634/7		*Set of 4*	2·40	2·20
		First Day Cover		2·75
		Presentation Pack	2·75	

Some sheets of No. 635 were overprinted with the 'Hong Kong '94' emblem on the left margin for sale at this philatelic exhibition.

Plate Nos.: All values 1A

Sheets: 10 (2×5) with large inscribed margin at left

Quantities sold: No. 634, 241,910; No. 635, 241,943; No. 636, 237,126; No. 637, 232,797; 'Hong Kong '94' margin opt 31,124 sheets.

Withdrawn: 17.2.95

605a Canadian Supermarine Spitfires Mk V over Normandy Beaches

50th Anniversary of D-Day

(Des N. Trudgian. Litho B.D.T.)

1994 (6 JUNE). *Sheet* 93×71 *mm*. Perf 14 (C)

MS638	**605a**	£2 multicoloured	4·00	4·25
		First Day Cover		6·50
		Presentation Pack	5·00	

Quantity sold: 156,793

Withdrawn: 5.6.95

606 Peugeot 'Type 3', 1894   **607** Mercedes 'Simplex', 1903

608 Humber Tourer, 1906   **609** Bentley Sports Tourer, 1936

610 MG TC Midget, 1948

Centenary of First Car in Guernsey

(Des R. Ollington. Litho B.D.T.)

1994 (19 JULY). Perf 14½×14 (C)

639	**606**	16p multicoloured	40	40
		a. Booklet pane of 4 with margins all round	1·70	
640	**607**	24p multicoloured	60	45
		a. Booklet pane of 4 with margins all round	2·75	
641	**608**	35p multicoloured	90	1·00
		a. Booklet pane of 4 with margins all round	4·00	
642	**609**	41p multicoloured	1·00	1·00
		a. Booklet pane of 4 with margins all round	4·25	
643	**610**	60p multicoloured	1·50	1·40
		a. Booklet pane of 4 with margins all round	6·50	
639/43		*Set of 5*	4·00	3·75
		First Day Cover		4·25
		Presentation Pack	4·75	
		Set of 5 Gutter Pairs	9·00	

Plate Nos.: 60p 1A, 1B, 1C, 1D (each ×5); others 1A, 1B (each ×5)

Sheets: 50 (2 panes 5×5)

Imprint: Central, side margins of each pane

Quantities sold: 16p 279,325; 24p 238,478; 35p 114,668; 41p 116,567; 60p 117,435

Withdrawn: 18.7.95

610a Floral Arrangement
(*illustration reduced. Actual size* 110×90 *mm*)

'Philakorea '94' International Stamp Exhibition, Seoul

(Des R. Gorringe and M. Whyte. Litho Cartor)

1994 (16 AUG). *Sheet* 110×90 *mm containing stamp as No.* 581 *with changed imprint date.* Perf 13 (C)
MS644	**610a**	£1 multicoloured	3·25	3·00
		First Day Cover		5·50
		Presentation Pack	4·50	

Quantity sold: 78,679

Withdrawn: 15.8.95

611 *Trident* (Herm Ferry)

612 Handley Page HPR-7 Super Dart Herald of Channel Express

613 Britten Norman Trislander G-JOEY of Aurigny Air Services

614 *Bon Marin de Serk* (Sark Ferry)

615 Map of Bailiwick

25th Anniversary of Guernsey Postal Administration

(Des A. Copp. Litho Questa)

1994 (1 OCT). Perf 14 (C)
645	**611**	16p multicoloured	35	30
646	**612**	24p multicoloured	55	50
647	**613**	35p multicoloured	85	75
648	**614**	41p multicoloured	1·00	85
649	**615**	60p multicoloured	1·40	1·20
645/9		Set of 5	3·75	3·25
		First Day Cover		3·75
		Presentation Pack	4·50	
		Stamp-cards (set of 5)	1·60	5·50
MS650		150×100 mm. Nos. 645/9	4·00	4·25
		First Day Cover		5·50

Plate Nos.: All values 1A (×5)

Sheets: 20 (5×4)

Imprint: Central, left-hand margin

Quantities sold: 16p 218,779; 24p 188,946; 35p 129,318; 41p 139,622; 60p 140,855; miniature sheet 63,283

Withdrawn: 30.9.95

616 Dolls' House

617 Doll

618 Teddy in Bassinette

619 Sweets in Pillar Box and Playing Cards

620 Spinning Top

621 Building Blocks

622 Rocking Horse

623 Teddy Bear

624 Tricycle

625 Wooden Duck

626 Hornby Toy Locomotive

627 Ludo Game

The welcoming face of
GUERNSEY 24

The welcoming face of
GUERNSEY 24

630 Flowers 'Face'

631 Fruit and Vegetables 'Face'

Christmas. Bygone Toys

(Des A. Peck. Litho B.D.T.)

1994 (1 OCT). Perf 13 (C)

651	**616**	13p multicoloured	40	15
		a. Sheetlet. Nos. 651/6	2·00	2·20
652	**617**	13p multicoloured	40	15
653	**618**	13p multicoloured	40	15
654	**619**	13p multicoloured	40	15
655	**620**	13p multicoloured	40	15
656	**621**	13p multicoloured	40	15
657	**622**	24p multicoloured	75	30
		a. Sheetlet. Nos. 657/62	3·50	4·00
658	**623**	24p multicoloured	75	30
659	**624**	24p multicoloured	75	30
660	**625**	24p multicoloured	75	30
661	**626**	24p multicoloured	75	30
662	**627**	24p multicoloured	75	30
651/62		*Set of 12*	5·00	5·50
		First Day Covers (2)		6·50
		Presentation Pack	5·75	

Sheets: 6 (3×2) containing Nos. 650/5 or 656/61 *se-tenant*

Imprint: Bottom, left-hand margin

Quantities sold: 13p 192,937 sheetlets; 24p 133,416 sheetlets

Withdrawn: 30.9.95

The welcoming face of
GUERNSEY 24

The welcoming face of
GUERNSEY 24

632 Sea Shells and Seaweed 'Face'

633 Anchor and Life Belts 'Face'

Yearbook 1994

1994 (1 OCT). *Comprises Nos. 576, 634/62 and A60/76*

Yearbook (*softback*) . . . . 40·00

Yearbook (*hardback*) . . . . 65·00

Withdrawn: 29.12.95

The welcoming face of
GUERNSEY 24

The welcoming face of
GUERNSEY 24

634 Glasses, Cork and Cutlery 'Face'

635 Butterflies and Caterpillars 'Face'

Greetings Stamps. 'The Welcoming Face of Guernsey'

(Des R. Ollington. Litho Questa)

1995 (28 FEB). Perf 14 (C)

663	**628**	24p multicoloured	60	55
664	**629**	24p multicoloured	60	55
665	**630**	24p multicoloured	60	55
666	**631**	24p multicoloured	60	55
667	**632**	24p multicoloured	60	55
668	**633**	24p multicoloured	60	55
669	**634**	24p multicoloured	60	55
670	**635**	24p multicoloured	60	55
663/70		*Set of 8*	4·25	4·00
		First Day Cover		5·00
		Presentation Pack	5·00	
		Stamp-cards (set of 8)	1·70	6·00
		Set of 8 Gutter Pairs	8·50	
MS671		137×109 mm. Nos. 663/70	4·25	4·25
		First Day Cover		8·00

MS671 was used for the make up of stamp booklet SB54.

The welcoming face of
GUERNSEY 24

628 Seafood 'Face'

The welcoming face of
GUERNSEY 24

629 Buckets and Spade 'Face'

Plate Nos.: All values 1A, 1B (each x5)

Sheets: 50 (2 panes 5×5)

Imprint: Central, left-hand margin

Quantities sold: No. 663, 138,328; No. 664, 113,568; No. 665, 138,555; No. 666, 138,474; No. 667, 113,520; No. 668, 113,568; No. 669, 113,573; No. 670, 113,580; miniature sheet 128,702

Withdrawn: 27.2.96

636 Winston Churchill and Wireless

637 Union Jack and Royal Navy Ships off St. Peter Port

638 Royal Arms and Military Band

639 *Vega* (Red Cross supply ship)

640 Rejoicing Crowd

50th Anniversary of Liberation

(Des M. Whyte. Litho Enschedé)

1995 (9 MAY). Perf 13½×14 (C)

672	**636**	16p multicoloured	45	30
673	**637**	24p multicoloured	60	50
674	**638**	35p multicoloured	90	90
675	**639**	41p multicoloured	90	90
676	**640**	60p multicoloured	1·50	1·20
672/6		*Set of 5*	4·00	3·50
		First Day Cover		4·50
		Presentation Pack	5·50	
		Set of 5 Gutter Pairs	8·00	
MS677	189×75 mm. Nos. 672/6		4·50	4·75
		First Day Cover		6·00

Plate Nos.: 60p 1A, 1B, 1C, 1D (each ×4); others 1A, 1B (each ×4)

Sheets: 50 (2 panes 5×5)

Imprint: Central, side margins

Quantities sold: 16p 558,373; 24p 410,244; 35p 130,472; 41p 158,351; 60p 159,394; miniature sheet 86,502

Withdrawn: 8.5.96

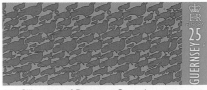

641 Silhouette of Doves on Ground

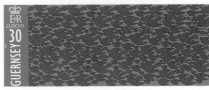

642 Silhouette of Doves in Flight

Europa. Peace and Freedom

(Des K. Bassford. Litho Walsall)

1995 (9 MAY). Perf 14 (C)

678	**641**	25p multicoloured	55	65
679	**642**	30p multicoloured	75	85
678/9		*Set of 2*	1·20	1·50
		First Day Cover		2·00
		Presentation Pack	2·10	

The designs of Nos. 678/9 each provide a stereogram or hidden three-dimensional image of a single dove designed by D. Burder.

Plate Nos.: Both values 1A, 1B, 1C (each ×4)

Sheets: 10 (2×5)

Imprint: Central, bottom margin

Quantities sold: 25p 219,750; 30p 171,902

Withdrawn: 8.5.96

643 Prince Charles, Castle Cornet and Bailiwick Arms

Royal Visit

(Des C. Abbott. Litho Questa)

1995 (9 MAY). Perf 14 (C)

680	**643**	£1.50 multicoloured	3·00	3·25
		First Day Cover		4·00
		Presentation Pack	4·00	
		Gutter Pair	7·00	

Plate Nos.: 1A, 1B, 1C, 1D (each ×5)

Sheets: 40 (2 panes 5×4)

Imprint: Central, left-hand margin

Quantity sold: 140,954

Withdrawn: 8.5.96

643a (*illustration reduced. Actual size 110×90 mm*)

'Singapore '95' International Stamp Exhibition

(Des R. Gorringe and M. Whyte. Litho Cartor)

1995 (1 SEPT). *Sheet 110×90 mm containing stamp as No. 581 with changed imprint date. Perf 13 (C)*

MS681	643a	£1 multicoloured	3·00	2·75
		First Day Cover		4·50
		Presentation Pack	3·75	

Quantity sold: 64,768

Withdrawn: 31.8.96

644

645

646

647

50th Anniversary of United Nations

(Des K. Bassford. Litho and embossed Enschedé)

1995 (24 OCT). Perf 14×13½ (C)

682	644	50p pale new blue and gold	1·10	1·10
		a. Block of 4. Nos. 682/5	4·25	4·25
683	645	50p pale new blue and gold	1·10	1·10
684	646	50p pale new blue and gold	1·10	1·10
685	647	50p pale new blue and gold	1·10	1·10
682/5		Set of 4	4·00	4·25
		First Day Cover		5·00
		Presentation Pack	5·00	

Plate Nos.: 1A–1A

Sheets: 36 (6×6). Nos. 682/5 were printed together, *se-tenant*, throughout the sheet with each block of 4 showing the complete United Nations emblem

Imprint: Central, side margins

Quantity sold: 448,348

Withdrawn: 23.10.96

648 'Christmas Trees for Sale in Bern' **649**
(Cornelia Nussbrum-Weibel)

650 'Evening Snowfall' **651**
(Katerina Mertikas)

652 'It came upon a Midnight Clear' **653**
(Georgia Guback)

654 'Children of the World' **655**

Christmas. 50th Anniversary of U.N.I.C.E.F.

(Adapted M. Whyte from U.N.I.C.E.F. Christmas Cards. Litho
B.D.T.)

1995 (16 NOV). Perf 13 (C)

686	**648**	13p multicoloured	40	15
		a. *Horiz pair. Nos.* 686/7	80	70
687	**649**	13p multicoloured	40	15
688	**650**	13p + 1p multicoloured	40	20
		a. *Horiz pair. Nos.* 688/9	80	90
689	**651**	13p + 1p multicoloured	40	20
690	**652**	24p multicoloured	70	30
		a. *Horiz pair. Nos.* 690/1	1·40	1·40
691	**653**	24p multicoloured	70	30
692	**654**	24p + 2p multicoloured	70	30
		a. *Horiz pair. Nos.* 692/3	1·40	1·40
693	**655**	24p + 2p multicoloured	70	30
686/93		*Set of* 8	4·00	4·00
		First Day Cover		5·00
		Presentation Pack	5·00	

Sheets: 12 (4×3), the two designs for each value printed together, *se-tenant*, in horizontal pairs throughout the sheets, each pair forming a composite design

Quantities sold: Nos. 686/7, 540,858; Nos. 688/9, 352,684; Nos. 690/1, 365,098; Nos. 692/3, 365,740

Withdrawn: 15.11.96

Yearbook 1995

1995 (1 DEC). *Comprises Nos.* 663/93 *and* A77/84
Yearbook .... 50·00

Withdrawn: 31.12.97

656 Princess Anne (President, Save the Children Fund) and Children

657 Queen Elizabeth II and people of the Commonwealth

Europa. Famous Women

(Des D. Miller. Litho B.D.T.)

1996 (21 APR). Perf 14 (C)

694	**656**	25p multicoloured	55	50
695	**657**	30p multicoloured	70	75
694/5		*Set of* 2	1·20	1·20
		First Day Cover		2·00
		Presentation Pack	2·00	

The background designs of Nos. 694/5 continue on to the vertical sheet margins.

Plate Nos.: Both values 1A, 1B (each ×4)

Sheets: 10 (2×5)

Quantities sold: 25p 224,821; 30p 268,410

Withdrawn: 20.4.97

658 England v U.S.S.R., 1968   **659**

660 Italy v Belgium, 1972   **661**

662 Ireland v Netherlands, 1988   **663**

664 Denmark v Germany, 1992 Final   **665**

European Football Championship, England

(Des M. Whyte. Litho Questa)

1996 (25 APR). Perf 14½×14 (C)

696	**658**	16p multicoloured	55	20
		a. *Horiz pair. Nos.* 696/7	1·20	1·10
697	**659**	16p multicoloured	55	20
698	**660**	24p multicoloured	75	25
		a. *Horiz pair. Nos.* 698/9	1·50	1·50
699	**661**	24p multicoloured	75	25
700	**662**	35p multicoloured	80	40
		a. *Horiz pair. Nos.* 700/1	1·60	1·60
701	**663**	35p multicoloured	80	40
702	**664**	41p multicoloured	95	45
		a. *Horiz pair. Nos.* 702/3	2·00	1·90
703	**665**	41p multicoloured	95	45
696/703		*Set of* 8	6·00	5·50
		First Day Cover		6·00
		Presentation Pack	6·00	
		Souvenir Folder (complete sheets)	24·00	

Plate Nos.: All values 1A (×4)

Sheets: 8 (2×4), the two designs for each value printed together, *se-tenant*, in horizontal pairs throughout sheets with illustrated margins, each pair forming a composite design

Quantities sold: 16p 386,746; 24p 369,805; 35p 360,860; 41p 364,757

Withdrawn: 24.4.97

666a Maj-Gen. Brock meeting Tecumseh (Indian Chief) (24p); Maj-Gen. Isaac Brock on Horseback, 1812 (£1) (*illustration reduced. Actual size* 110×90 *mm*)

'CAPEX '96' International Stamp Exhibition, Toronto

(Des A. Peck. Litho Enschedé)

1996 (8 JUNE). *Sheet* 110×90 *mm. Perf* 13½ (C)
MS704	**666a**	24p, £1 multicoloured	3·00	2·75
		First Day Cover		4·00
		Presentation Pack	3·75	

Quantity sold: 93,054

Withdrawn: 7.6.97

667 Runner

668 Throwing the Javelin

669 Throwing the Discus

670 Wrestling

671 Jumping

Centenary of Modern Olympic Games. Ancient Greek Athletes

(Des K. Bassford. Litho Questa)

1996 (19 JULY). Perf 14 (C)

705	**667**	16p black, orange-yellow & orge	50	40
706	**668**	24p black, orange-yellow & orge	95	90
707	**669**	41p black, orange-yellow & orge	1·10	1·20
708	**670**	55p black, orange-yellow & orge	1·40	1·50
709	**671**	60p black, orange-yellow & orge	1·60	1·70
705/9		Set of 5	5·00	5·25
		First Day Cover		5·50
		Presentation Pack	6·00	
		Set of 5 Gutter Pairs	10·00	
MS710		192×75 mm. Nos. 705/9	5·25	5·25
		First Day Cover		5·75

No. 708 also includes the 'OLYMPHILEX '96' International Stamp Exhibition, Atlanta, logo.

Plate Nos.: All values 1A, 1B (each ×3)

Sheets: 55p 50 (2 panes 5×5); others 100 (2 panes 10×5)

Imprint: Central, right-hand margin of top pane

Quantities sold: 16p 337,288; 24p 305,309; 41p 132,730; 55p 122,263; 60p 141,372; miniature sheet 87,045

Withdrawn: 18.7.97

672 Humphrey Bogart as Philip Marlowe

673 Peter Sellers as Inspector Clouseau

674 Basil Rathbone as Sherlock Holmes

675 Margaret Rutherford as Miss Marple

676 Warner Oland as Charlie Chan

Centenary of Cinema. Screen Detectives

(Des R. Ollington. Litho Enschedé)

1996 (6 NOV). Perf 15×14 (C)

711	**672**	16p multicoloured	40	40
		a. Booklet pane. No. 711×3 with margins all round	1·40	
		b. Booklet pane. Nos. 711/15 with margins all round	4·50	
712	**673**	24p multicoloured	60	60
		a. Booklet pane. No. 712×3 with margins all round	2·30	
713	**674**	35p multicoloured	85	85
		a. Booklet pane. No. 713×3 with margins all round	2·75	
714	**675**	41p multicoloured	90	90
		a. Booklet pane. No. 714×3 with margins all round	3·00	
715	**676**	60p multicoloured	1·40	1·40
		a. Booklet pane. No. 715×3 with margins all round	4·50	
711/15		Set of 5	3·75	3·75
		First Day Cover		4·75
		Presentation Pack	4·75	
		Set of 5 Gutter Pairs	7·50	

Plate Nos.: All values 1A, 1B (each ×4)

Sheets: 50 (2 panes 5×5)

Imprint: Central, side margins

Quantities sold: 16p 140,740; 24p 141,567; 35p 141,953; 41p 139,648; 60p 138,363

Withdrawn: 5.11.97

☒ GUERNSEY 13 | ☒ GUERNSEY 13 | ☒ GUERNSEY 13

677 The Annunciation | **678** Journey to Bethlehem | **679** Arrival at the Inn

☒ GUERNSEY 13 | ☒ GUERNSEY 13 | ☒ GUERNSEY 13

680 Angel and Shepherds | **681** Mary, Joseph and Jesus in Stable | **682** Shepherds worshipping Jesus

☒ GUERNSEY 13 | ☒ GUERNSEY 13 | ☒ GUERNSEY 13

683 Three Kings following Star | **684** Three Kings with Gifts | **685** The Presentation in the Temple

☒ GUERNSEY 13 | ☒ GUERNSEY 13 | ☒ GUERNSEY 13

686 Mary and Jesus | **687** Joseph warned by Angel | **688** The Flight into Egypt

☒ GUERNSEY 24 | ☒ GUERNSEY 25

689 Mary cradling Jesus | **690** The Nativity

Christmas

(Des P. le Vasseur. Litho B.D.T.)

1996 (6 NOV). Perf 13 (C)

716	**677**	13p multicoloured	30	15
		a. Sheetlet. Nos. 716/27	3·50	4·50
717	**678**	13p multicoloured	30	15
718	**679**	13p multicoloured	30	15
719	**680**	13p multicoloured	30	15
720	**681**	13p multicoloured	30	15
721	**682**	13p multicoloured	30	15
722	**683**	13p multicoloured	30	15
723	**684**	13p multicoloured	30	15
724	**685**	13p multicoloured	30	15
725	**686**	13p multicoloured	30	15
726	**687**	13p multicoloured	30	15
727	**688**	13p multicoloured	30	15
728	**689**	24p multicoloured	60	40
729	**690**	25p multicoloured	60	60
716/29		Set of 14	4·25	4·50
		First Day Cover		5·00
		Presentation Pack	5·00	
		Set of 2 Gutter Pairs (24, 25p)		2·40

Plate Nos.: 24p, 25p 1A, 1B (each ×4)

Sheets: 13p 12 (4×3) containing Nos. 716/27 *se-tenant*; 24p, 25p 100 (2 panes 5×10)

Imprint: 13p bottom, left-hand margin; 24p, 25p central, side margins

Quantities sold: 13p 1,212,144 sheetlets; 24p 416,811; 25p 121,820

Withdrawn: 5.11.97

Yearbook 1996

1996 (1 DEC). Comprises Nos. 582a, 694/729 and A85/95
Yearbook . . . . 60·00

Sold out: 6.99

691 Holly Blue (*Celastrina argiolus*)

692 Hummingbird Hawk-moth (*Macroglossum stellatarum*)

693 Emperor Moth (*Saturnia pavonia*)

694 Brimstone (*Gonepteryx rhamni*)

695a Painted Lady (*Cynthia cardui*)

Endangered Species. Butterflies and Moths

(Des A. Peck. Litho B.D.T.)

1997 (12 FEB). Perf 14 (C)

730	**691**	18p multicoloured	. . . .	55	50
731	**692**	25p multicoloured	. . . .	65	60
732	**693**	26p multicoloured	. . . .	85	85
733	**694**	37p multicoloured	. . . .	1·10	1·10
730/3		Set of 4	. . . .	2·75	2·75
		First Day Cover	. . . .		3·25
		Presentation Pack	. . . .	3·25	
		Souvenir Folder (complete sheets)	. . . .	25·00	

MS734   92×68 mm. **695a** £1 multicoloured.
Perf 13½ (C) . . . . 3·00   2·50
First Day Cover . . . .   3·75
Presentation Pack . . . .   3·50

No. **MS**734 includes the 'HONG KONG '97' International Stamp Exhibition logo on the sheet margin.

Plate Nos.: All values 1A, 1B (each ×4)

Sheets: 10 (2×5) with designs extending into side margins

Quantities sold: 18p 244,917; 25p 244,899; 26p 168,917; 37p 169,909; miniature sheet 147,990

Withdrawn: 11.2.98

696 Gilliatt fighting Octopus

697 Gilliatt grieving on Rock

Europa. Tales and Legends. Scenes from Les Travailleurs de la Mer by Victor Hugo

(Des M. Wilkinson. Litho Cartor)

1997 (24 APR.) Perf 13½ (C)

735	**696**	26p multicoloured	. . . .	55	60
736	**697**	31p multicoloured	. . . .	75	65
735/6		Set of 2	. . . .	1·20	1·20
		First Day Cover	. . . .		2·10
		Presentation Pack	. . . .	2·10	

Plate Nos.: Both values 1A, 1B (each ×4)

Sheets: 10 (2×5) with enlarged inscribed margins at left

Quantities sold: 26p 246,098; 31p 246,080

Withdrawn: 23.4.98

698 Shell Beach, Herm

699 La Seigneurie, Sark

700 Castle Cornet, Guernsey

Guernsey Scenes (1st series)

(Litho B.D.T.)

1997 (24 APR). *Self-adhesive.* Perf 9½ (diecut)

737	**698**	18p multicoloured	60	30
		a. Booklet pane of 8	5·00	
738	**699**	25p multicoloured	70	60
		a. Booklet pane of 8	6·00	
739	**700**	26p multicoloured	80	75
		a. Booklet pane of 4	4·75	
737/9		*Set of 3*	1·90	1·50
		First Day Cover		3·00
		Presentation Pack	3·00	

Nos. 737/9 were issued in stamp booklets or as rolls of 100 (18p and 25p).
See also Nos. 770/3.

Quantities sold: 18p 2,789,925; 25p 2,788,039; 26p 415,882
Withdrawn: 31.3.98

701a 19th-century Shipyard, St. Peter Port (30p);
Costa Rica Packet (barque) (£1)
(*illustration reduced. Actual size* 110×90 *mm*)

'PACIFIC '97' World Philatelic Exhibition, San Francisco

(Des C. Abbott. Litho Questa)

1997 (29 MAY). *Sheet* 110×90 *mm.* Perf 14 (C)

MS740	**701a**	30p brn-olive & gold; £1 mult	5·00	4·00
		First Day Cover		4·50
		Presentation Pack	5·50	

Quantity sold: 86,711
Withdrawn: 28.5.98

702 Transistor Radio, Microphone and Radio Logos

703 Television, Video Camera and Satellite Dish

704 Fax Machine, Telephones and Mobile Phone

705 Printing Press, Newspaper and Type

706 Stamp, Coding Machine and Postbox

707 C.D., Computer and Disk

Methods of Communication

(Des Miranda Schofield. Litho Cartor)

1997 (21 AUG). Perf 13½×13 (C)

741	**702**	18p multicoloured	40	40
742	**703**	25p multicoloured	60	60
743	**704**	26p multicoloured	60	60
744	**705**	37p multicoloured	90	85
745	**706**	43p multicoloured	1·20	1·20
746	**707**	63p multicoloured	1·50	1·70
741/6		*Set of 6*	5·00	5·00
		First Day Cover		5·50
		Presentation Pack	5·25	
		Set of 6 Gutter Pairs	9·00	

Plate Nos.: All values 1A, 1B (each ×4)

Sheets: 50 (2 panes 5×5)

Imprint: Central, side margins

Quantities sold: 18p 193,539; 25p 144,558; 26p 143,542; 37p 140,565; 43p 143,565; 63p 193,524

Withdrawn: 20.8.98

708 Teddy Bear making Cake

709 Teddy Bears decorating Christmas Tree

710 Two Teddy Bears in Armchair

711 Teddy Bear as Father Christmas

712 Teddy Bears unwrapping Presents

713 Teddy Bears eating Christmas Dinner

Christmas. Teddy Bears

(Des Sally Diamond. Litho Walsall)

1997 (6 NOV). Perf 14½×14 (C)

747	**708**	15p multicoloured	45	45
748	**709**	25p multicoloured	70	70
749	**710**	26p multicoloured	70	70
750	**711**	37p multicoloured	1·00	1·00
751	**712**	43p multicoloured	1·10	1·10
752	**713**	63p multicoloured	1·60	1·60
747/52		Set of 6	5·00	5·00
		First Day Cover		5·50
		Presentation Pack	5·25	
		Set of 6 Gutter Pairs	10·00	
MS753		123×107 mm. Nos. 747/52	6·00	6·00
		First Day Cover		5·75

Plate Nos.: All values 1A, 1B (each ×4)

Sheets: 50 (2 panes 5×5)

Imprint: Central, right-hand margin

Quantities sold: 15p 1,793,893; 25p 443,027; 26p 143,322; 37p 118,980; 43p 119,090; 63p 118,894; miniature sheet 86,125

Withdrawn: 5.11.98

714 Visiting Guernsey, 1957

715 Coronation Day, 1953 (inscr '1947')

716 Royal Family, 1957

717 On Royal Yacht, 1972

718 Queen Elizabeth and Prince Philip at Trooping the Colour, 1987

719 Queen Elizabeth and Prince Philip, 1997

Golden Wedding of Queen Elizabeth and Prince Philip

(Des M. Whyte. Litho Questa)

1997 (20 NOV). Perf 14½ (C)

754	**714**	18p multicoloured	40	40
		a. Booklet pane. Nos. 754/5, each ×3	3·25	
		b. Booklet pane. Nos. 754/9 ..	5·50	
755	**715**	25p multicoloured	60	60
756	**716**	26p multicoloured	60	60
		a. Booklet pane. Nos. 756/7, each ×3	5·00	
757	**717**	37p multicoloured	90	90
758	**718**	43p multicoloured	1·00	1·00
		a. Booklet pane. Nos. 758/9, each ×3	8·75	
759	**719**	63p multicoloured	1·40	1·40
754/9		Set of 6	4·50	4·50
		First Day Cover		5·50
		Presentation Pack	5·25	
		Set of 6 Gutter Pairs	9·00	

Plate Nos.: All values 1A, 1B (each ×6)
Sheets: 50 (2 panes 5×5)
Imprint: Central, right-hand margin
Quantities sold: 18p 220,866; 25p 218,707; 26p 218,240; 37p 216,772; 43p 217,837; 63p 216,874
Withdrawn: 19.11.98

Yearbook 1997

1997 (1 DEC). Comprises Nos. 572b, 576b, 730/59, A70b, A72b/c and A96/109

Yearbook .... 55·00

Sold out: 9.99

720 11th-century
(St. Martin)

721 12th-century
(St. Saviour)

722 13th-century
(Vale)

723 14th-century
(St. Sampson)

724 15th-century
(Torteval)

725 16th-century
(Castel)

726 17th-century
(St. Andrew)

727 18th-century
(Forest)

728 19th-century (St.
Pierre du Bois)

729 20th-century
(St. Peter Port)

The Millennium Tapestries Project

(Des Sally Diamond. Litho Questa)

1998 (10 FEB). Perf 15×14½ (C)

760	**720**	25p multicoloured	60	30
		a. Horiz strip of 10 or two strips of 5. Nos. 760/9	5·50	5·50
		b. Booklet pane. Nos. 760/1, each ×2, and 762/3 with margins all round	3·50	
		c. Booklet pane. Nos. 760/1 and 768/9, each ×2 with margins all round	3·50	
761	**721**	25p multicoloured	60	30
762	**722**	25p multicoloured	60	30
		a. Booklet pane. Nos. 762/3, each ×2, and 764/5 with margins all round	3·50	

763	**723**	25p multicoloured	. . . .	60	30
764	**724**	25p multicoloured	. . . .	60	30
		a. Booklet pane. Nos. 764/5, each ×2, and 766/7 with margins all round	. . . .	3·50	
765	**725**	25p multicoloured	. . . .	60	30
766	**726**	25p multicoloured	. . . .	60	30
		a. Booklet pane. Nos. 766/7, each ×2, and 768/9 with margins all round	. . . .	3·50	
767	**727**	25p multicoloured	. . . .	60	30
768	**728**	25p multicoloured	. . . .	60	30
769	**729**	25p multicoloured	. . . .	60	30
760/9		Set of 10	. . . .	5·50	5·50
		First Day Cover	. . . .		6·25
		Presentation Pack	. . . .	6·00	

Plate Nos.: 1A, 1B (each ×4)

Sheets: 50 (10×5); the ten designs printed together, *se-tenant*, in horizontal strips throughout the sheet

Imprint: Central, side margins

Withdrawn: 9.2.99

730 Fort Grey

731 Grand Havre

732 Little Chapel

733 Guernsey Cow

Guernsey Scenes (2nd series)

(Des Joanna Brehaut. Litho B.D.T.)

1998 (25 MAR). *Self-adhesive.* Perf 9½ (diecut)
770	**730**	(20p) multicoloured	. . . .	45	55
		a. Horiz pair. Nos. 770/1	. . . . .	90	1·10
		b. Booklet pane. Nos. 770/1, each ×4 with margins all round	. . . .	6·00	
771	**731**	(20p) multicoloured	. . . .	45	55
772	**732**	(25p) multicoloured	. . . .	55	65
		a. Horiz pair. Nos. 772/3	. . . . . .	1·20	1·20
		b. Booklet pane. Nos. 772/3, each ×4 with margins all round	. . . .	6·00	
773	**733**	(25p) multicoloured	. . . .	55	65
770/3		Set of 4	. . . .	2·00	2·10
		First Day Cover	. . . .		3·00
		Presentation Pack	. . . .	3·00	

Nos. 770/1 are inscribed 'Bailiwick Minimum Postage Paid' and were initially sold at 20p. Nos. 772/3 are inscribed 'UK Minimum Postage Paid' and were initially sold at 25p.

Nos. 770/3 were issued in stamp booklets or as rolls of 100, each roll containing two designs.

Sold out: 6.2001

734 Fairey IIIC, Balloon, Sopwith Camel and Avro 504

735 Fairey Swordfish, Tiger Moth, Supermarine Walrus and Gloster Gladiator

736 Hawker Hurricane, Supermarine Spitfire, Vickers Wellington, Short Sunderland (flying boat), Westland Lysander and Bristol Blenheim

737 De Havilland Mosquito, Avro Lancaster, Auster III, Gloster Meteor and Horsa Glider

738 Canberra, Hawker Sea Fury, Bristol Sycamore, Hawker Hunter, Handley Page Victor and BAe Lightning

739 Panavia Tornado GR1, BAe Hawk, BAe Sea Harrier, Westland Lynx (helicopter) and Hawker Siddeley Nimrod

80th Anniversary of the Royal Air Force

(Des C. Abbott. Litho Cartor)

1998 (7 MAY). Perf 13½×13 (C)

774	**734**	20p multicoloured	50	50
775	**735**	25p multicoloured	60	60
776	**736**	30p multicoloured	70	70
777	**737**	37p multicoloured	90	85
778	**738**	43p multicoloured	1·00	1·20
779	**739**	63p multicoloured	1·40	1·50
774/9		Set of 6	5·00	5·00
		First Day Cover		5·75
		Presentation Pack	5·25	

Plate Nos.: All values 1A (×5)

Sheets: 50 (5×10)

Imprint: Central, side margins

Withdrawn: 6.5.99

740a Jules Rimet (first President of FIFA) (30p); Bobby Moore and Queen Elizabeth II, 1966 (£1.75) (*illustration reduced. Actual size 110×90 mm*)

150th Anniversary of the Cambridge Rules for Football

(Des A. Peck. Litho Enschedé)

1998 (7 MAY). *Sheet* 110×90 *mm.* Perf 13½×14 (C)

MS780	**740a**	30p, £1.75 multicoloured ...	4·00	4·00
		First Day Cover		5·50
		Presentation Pack	5·25	

Withdrawn: 6.5.99

741 Girls in Traditional Costume watching Sheep Display, West Show

742 Marching Band and 'Battle of Flowers' Exhibit, North Show

743 Prince Charles, Monument and Tank, Liberation Day

744 Goat, Dahlias and Show-jumping, South Show

Europa. National Festivals

(Des Sally Diamond. Litho Enschedé)

1998 (11 AUG). Perf 13½ (C)

781	**741**	20p multicoloured	45	45
782	**742**	25p multicoloured	55	55
783	**743**	30p multicoloured	65	65
784	**744**	37p multicoloured	85	85
781/4		Set of 4	2·20	2·20
		First Day Cover		3·75
		Presentation Pack	3·50	

Plate Nos.: All values 1A, 1B, 1C (each ×4)

Sheets: 10 (2×5) with enlarged inscribed margin at left

Imprint: Central, right-hand margin

Withdrawn: 10.8.99

745 Outboard Motorboat

746 St. John Ambulance Inshore Rescue Dinghy

747 Pilot Boat, St. Peter Port

748 *Flying Christine III* (St. John Ambulance launch)

749 Crab-fishing Boat

750 Herm Island Ferry

751 *Sarnia* (St. Peter Port Harbour Authority launch)

752 *Leopardess* (States' fisheries protection launch)

753 Trawler

754 Powerboat

755 Dart 18 Racing Catamaran

756 30ft Bermuda-rigged Sloop

757 Motor Cruiser

758 Ocean-going Sailing Yacht

759 Motor Yacht, Beaucette Marina

760 *Queen Elizabeth 2* (liner)

761 *Oriana* (liner)

762 *Queen Mary 2* (liner)

763 Royal Yacht *Britannia*

Maritime Heritage

(Des M. Wilkinson. Litho Walsall (1p to 75p), litho and embossed Walsall (£1, £3) BDT (£4) or Questa (£5))

1998 (11 AUG)–**2005**. Perf 14 (1p to 9p), 14½×14 (10p to 75p), 14×14½ (£1, £3), 13½ (£4) or 15×14½ (£5), all comb

785	**745**	1p multicoloured (*b*)	. . . .	10	10
786	**746**	2p multicoloured (*b*)	. . . .	10	10
787	**747**	3p multicoloured (*b*)	. . . .	10	10
788	**748**	4p multicoloured (*b*)	. . . .	10	10
789	**749**	5p multicoloured (*b*)	. . . .	10	10
790	**750**	6p multicoloured (*b*)	. . . .	10	10
791	**751**	7p multicoloured (*b*)	. . . .	15	20
792	**752**	8p multicoloured (*b*)	. . . .	15	20
793	**753**	9p multicoloured (*b*)	. . . .	20	25
794	**754**	10p multicoloured (*b*)	. . . .	20	25
795	**755**	20p multicoloured (*c*)	. . . .	40	45
796	**756**	30p multicoloured (*c*)	. . . .	60	65
797	**757**	40p multicoloured (*b*)	. . . .	80	85
798	**758**	50p multicoloured (*b*)	. . . .	1·00	1·10
799	**759**	75p multicoloured (*b*)	. . . .	1·50	1·30
800	**760**	£1 multicoloured (*b*)	. . . .	2·00	1·80
801	**761**	£3 multicoloured (*c*)	. . . .	6·00	5·50
802	**762**	£4 multicoloured (*d*)	. . . .	8·00	8·25
803	**763**	£5 multicoloured (*a*)	. . . .	13·00	10·00
785/803		Set of 19	. . . .	31·00	28·00
		First Day Covers (4)	. . . .		35·00
		Presentation Packs (4)	. . . . .	34·00	
		Set of 17 Gutter Pairs (1p to £3)	. . . .	25·00	

Printings: (*a*) 11.8.98; (*b*) 27.7.99; (*c*) 4.8.2000; (*d*) 9.5.2005

Plate Nos.: £5 1A, 1B, 1C, 1D (each ×5); £4 1A (×4); others 1A, 1B (each ×4)

Sheets: 1p to £3 50 (2 panes 5×5); £4 10 (2×5); £5 10 (5×2)

Imprint: Side margins (£5) or centre, left-hand margin (others)

Sold out: 11.2002 (£5)

Withdrawn: 8.2007 (except 20p, 30p, £3 and £4)

74

769 Modern Tree, Teletubby Po and Playstation

770 1960s Tinsel Tree, Toy Bus and Doll

771 1930s Gold Foil Tree, Panda and Toy Tank

772 1920s Tree, Model of *Bluebird* and Doll

773 1900s Tree, Teddy Bear and Toy Train

774 1850s Tree, Wooden Doll and Spinning Top

150th Anniversary of the Introduction of the Christmas Tree

(Des R. Ollington. Litho B.D.T.)

1998 (10 NOV). Perf 13½ (C)

810	**769**	17p multicoloured	40	40
811	**770**	25p multicoloured	60	60
812	**771**	30p multicoloured	70	70
813	**772**	37p multicoloured	90	90
814	**773**	43p multicoloured	90	90
815	**774**	63p multicoloured	1·50	1·50
810/15		*Set of* 6	4·50	4·50
		First Day Cover		5·50
		Presentation Pack	5·50	
MS816		160×94 mm. Nos. 810/15	5·00	6·00
		First Day Cover		6·00

Plate Nos.: 17p, 25p 1A, 1B (each ×4); others 1A (×4)

Sheets: 50 (5×10)

Imprint: Central, side margins

Withdrawn: 9.11.99

Yearbook 1998

1998 (1 DEC). *Comprises Nos.* 760/84, 802, 810/16 *and* A110/23

Yearbook . . . . 55·00

Sold out: 4.2001

775 Elizabeth Bowes-Lyon, 1907

776 On Wedding Day, 1923

777 Holding Princess Elizabeth, 1926

778 At Coronation, 1937

779 Visiting Bombed Areas of London, 1940

780 Fishing near Auckland, New Zealand, 1966

781 At Guernsey Function, 1963

782 Receiving Flowers on Birthday, 1992

783 Presenting Trophy, Sandown Park Races, 1989

784 Opening Royal Norfolk Regimental Museum, Norwich, 1990

Life and Times of Queen Elizabeth the Queen Mother

(Des R. Ollington. Litho Cartor)

1999 (4 FEB). Perf 13 (C)

817	**775**	25p multicoloured	70	30
		a. Horiz strip of 10 or two strips of 5. Nos. 817/26	6·50	6·50
		b. Booklet pane. Nos. 817/18, each ×2, and 819/20, with margins all round	4·00	
		c. Booklet pane. Nos. 817/18 and 825/6, each ×2, with margins all round	4·00	
818	**776**	25p multicoloured	70	30
819	**777**	25p multicoloured	70	30
		b. Booklet pane. Nos. 819/20, each ×2, and 821/2, with margins all round	4·00	
820	**778**	25p multicoloured	70	30
821	**779**	25p multicoloured	70	30
		b. Booklet pane. Nos. 821/2, each ×2, and 823/4, with margins all round	4·00	
822	**780**	25p multicoloured	70	30
823	**781**	25p multicoloured	70	30
		b. Booklet pane. Nos. 823/4, each ×2, and 825/6, with margins all round	4·00	
824	**782**	25p multicoloured	70	30
825	**783**	25p multicoloured	70	30
826	**784**	25p multicoloured	70	30
817/26		*Set of 10*	6·50	6·50
		First Day Cover		6·75
		Presentation Pack	6·75	

Plate Nos.: 1A, 1B (each ×5)

Sheets: 50 (10×5), the ten designs printed together, *se-tenant*, as horizontal strips throughout the sheets

Imprint: Central, side margins

Withdrawn: 3.2.2000

785 *Spirit of Guernsey,* 1995

786 *Sir William Arnold,* 1973

787 *Euphrosyne Kendal,* 1954

788 *Queen Victoria,* 1929

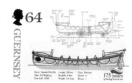

789 *Arthur Lionel,* 1912

790 *Vincent Kirk Ella,* 1888

175th Anniversary of Royal National Lifeboat Institution

(Des K. Wisdom. Litho Cartor)

1999 (27 APR). Perf 13½×13 (C)

827	**785**	20p multicoloured	50	50
828	**786**	25p multicoloured	60	60
829	**787**	30p multicoloured	70	70
830	**788**	38p multicoloured	90	90
831	**789**	44p multicoloured	1·10	1·10
832	**790**	64p multicoloured	1·50	1·50
827/32		*Set of 6*	5·00	4·75
		First Day Cover		6·00
		Presentation Pack	5·75	

Plate Nos.: All values 1A (×5)

Sheets: 50 (5×10)

Imprint: Central, side margins

Withdrawn: 26.4.2000

791 Burnet Rose and Local Carriage Label

792 Atlantic Puffin

793 Small Heath
Butterfly

794 Shells on Shell
Beach

796 Major-General
Le Marchant
(founder) and
Cadet at Sword
Drill

797 Duke of York
(official sponsor)
and Cadet on
Horseback

Europa. Parks and Gardens. Herm Island

(Des Colleen Corlett. Litho Walsall)

1999 (27 APR). Perf 13½×13 (C)

833	**791**	20p multicoloured	50	45
834	**792**	25p multicoloured	60	55
835	**793**	30p multicoloured	70	65
836	**794**	38p multicoloured	90	80
833/6		Set of 4	2·50	2·40
		First Day Cover		4·00
		Presentation Pack	3·50	

Plate Nos.: All values 1A, 1B (each ×4)

Sheets: 10 (2×5) with enlarged illustrated margin at left (20, 30p) or
right (25, 38p)

Imprint: Central right (20, 30p) or left (25, 38p) margin

Withdrawn: 26.4.2000

798 Field-Marshal
Earl Haig and
Cadets on
Parade

799 Field-Marshal
Viscount
Montgomery
and Bridging
Exerxcise

The Marriage of HRH Prince Edward and Sophie Rhys-Jones, 19th June 1999.

795 Prince Edward and Miss Sophie Rhys-Jones
(*illustration reduced. Actual size* 93×70 *mm*)

800 David Niven
(actor) and
Rifle Practice

801 Sir Winston
Churchill and
Tank

Royal Wedding

(Des Sally Diamond. Litho B.D.T.)

1999 (19 JUNE). *Sheet* 93×70 *mm.* Perf 13 (C)

MS837	**795**	£1 multicoloured	2·50	2·50
		First Day Cover		4·00
		Presentation Pack	3·50	

Withdrawn: 18.6.2000

Bicentenary of The Royal Military Academy, Sandhurst

(Des R. Ollington. Litho B.D.T.)

1999 (27 JULY). Perf 14 (C)

838	**796**	20p multicoloured	50	45
839	**797**	25p multicoloured	60	55
840	**798**	30p multicoloured	75	70
841	**799**	38p multicoloured	90	85
842	**800**	44p multicoloured	1·10	1·00
843	**801**	64p multicoloured	1·50	1·50
838/43		Set of 6	4·75	4·50
		First Day Cover		5·50
		Presentation Pack	6·00	

Plate Nos.: All values 1A (×4)

Sheets: 50 (5×10)

Imprint: Lower side margins

Withdrawn: 26.7.2000

802 The Nativity

803 Virgin Mary and Child

804 Holy Family

805 Cattle around Manger

806 Adoration of the Shepherds

807 Adoration of the Magi

Christmas. Wood Carvings by Denis Brehaut from Notre Dame Church

(Des Sally Diamond. Litho Questa)

1999 (19 OCT). Perf 14×14½ (C)

844	**802**	17p multicoloured	45	40
845	**803**	25p multicoloured	60	55
846	**804**	30p multicoloured	75	70
847	**805**	38p multicoloured	90	85
848	**806**	44p multicoloured	1·10	1·20
849	**807**	64p multicoloured	1·50	1·70
844/9		Set of 6	4·75	5·00
		First Day Cover		6·00
		Presentation Pack	5·75	
MS850		159×86 mm. Nos. 844/9	5·50	5·50
		First Day Cover		6·00

Plate Nos.: All values 1A, 1B, 1C (each ×4)

Sheets: 50 (5×10)

Imprint: Bottom, right-hand margin

Withdrawn: 18.10.2000

Yearbook 1999

1999 (1 DEC). Comprises Nos. 785/94, 797/800, 817/50 and **MS**A124/39

	Yearbook	55·00

Sold out: By 12.2002

808 'Space Bus' (Fallon Ephgrave)

809 'Children holding Hands' (Abigail Downing)

810 'No Captivity' (Laura Martin)

811 'Post Office of the Future' (Sarah Haddow)

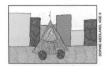

812 'Solar-powered Car' (Sophie Medland)

813 'Woman flying' (Danielle McIver)

New Millennium. 'Stampin' the Future' (children's stamp design competition)

(Litho Questa)

2000 (1 JAN). Perf 14×14½ (C)

851	**808**	20p multicoloured	60	45
852	**809**	25p multicoloured	60	55
853	**810**	30p multicoloured	70	65
854	**811**	38p multicoloured	90	80
855	**812**	44p multicoloured	1·00	95
856	**813**	64p multicoloured	1·40	1·40
851/6		Set of 6	4·75	4·75
		First Day Cover		5·50
		Presentation Pack	5·50	

Plate Nos.: All values 1A, 1B (each ×5)

Sheets: 50 (5×10)

Imprint: Lower right-hand margin

Withdrawn: 31.12.2000

814 Bristol Blenheim

815 Hawker Hurricane

816 Boulton Paul Defiant II

817 Gloster Gladiator

818 Bristol Beaufighter IF

819 Supermarine Spitfire IIc

820 Guernsey
Flag on Kite
and '2000'

821 Stylized
Sails bearing
National
Flowers

822 'Building
Europe'

823 Rainbow
and Three
Doves

Europa

(Des J.-P. Cousin (36p), KWL (others). Litho B.D.T.)

2000 (9 MAY). Perf 13 (C)

863	**820**	21p multicoloured	50	45
864	**821**	26p multicoloured	60	55
865	**822**	36p multicoloured	1·00	90
866	**823**	65p multicoloured	1·60	1·60
863/6		Set of 4	3·50	3·40
		First Day Cover		4·00
		Presentation Pack	4·00	

Plate Nos.: All values 1A (×4)

Sheets: 10 (2×5) with enlarged inscribed margin at left

Imprint: Centre, right-hand margin

Withdrawn: 8.5.2001

60th Anniversary of Battle of Britain. R.A.F. Aircraft

(Des R. Ollington. Litho Cartor)

2000 (28 APR). Perf 13½×13 (C)

857	**814**	21p multicoloured	50	50
		a. Booklet pane. Nos. 857 and 859/61	3·50	
		b. Booklet pane. Nos. 857/8, 860 and 862	3·50	
		c. Booklet pane. Nos. 857/9 and 861	3·00	
858	**815**	26p multicoloured	60	55
		a. Booklet pane. Nos. 858/61 .	3·50	
859	**816**	36p multicoloured	95	85
860	**817**	40p multicoloured	1·00	95
861	**818**	45p multicoloured	1·10	1·20
862	**819**	65p multicoloured	1·50	1·50
		a. Booklet pane. No. 862×2 . .	3·00	
857/62		Set of 6	5·50	5·50
		First Day Cover		5·50
		Presentation Pack	5·75	

Plate Nos.: All values 1A (×5)

Sheets: 50 (5×10)

Imprint: Central, side margins

Withdrawn: 27.4.2001

GUERNSEY 26

824 *Iris Stylosa*

GUERNSEY 26

825 *Watsonia*

GUERNSEY 26

826 *Richardia maculata*

GUERNSEY 26

827 *Narcissus bulbocodium*

GUERNSEY 26

828 *Triteleia laxa*

GUERNSEY 26

829 *Tigridia pavonia*

GUERNSEY 26

830 *Agapanthus umbellatus*

GUERNSEY 26

831 *Sparaxis*

GUERNSEY 26

832 *Pancratium maritimum*

GUERNSEY 26

833 *Nerine sarniensis*

'A Botanist's Sketchbook'. Restoration of Candie Gardens, St. Peter Port

(Des Petula Stone. Litho Enschedé)

2000 (4 AUG). Perf 13½×13 (C)

867	**824**	26p multicoloured	45	30
		a. *Horiz strip of 10 or two strips of 5. Nos.* 867/76	5·50	5·50

868	**825**	26p multicoloured	45	30
869	**826**	26p multicoloured	45	30
870	**827**	26p multicoloured	45	30
871	**828**	26p multicoloured	45	30
872	**829**	26p multicoloured	45	30
873	**830**	26p multicoloured	45	30
874	**831**	26p multicoloured	45	30
875	**832**	26p multicoloured	45	30
876	**833**	26p multicoloured	45	30
867/76		*Set of 10*	5·50	5·50
		First Day Cover		6·25
		Presentation Pack	6·50	

Plate Nos.: All values 1A, 1B (each ×5)

Sheets: 50 (10×5). Nos. 867/76 were printed together, *se-tenant*, in horizontal strips of 10 throughout the sheet

Imprint: Upper side margins

Withdrawn: 3.8.2001

834 Town Church, St. Peter Port

835 Children leaving St. Sampson's Church

836 Flying Kite by Vale Church

837 Carol singing outside St. Pierre du Bois Church

838 Building Snowman near St. Martin's Church

839 Street Scene including St. John's Church, St. Peter Port

Christmas. Guernsey Churches

(Des Gill Brown. Litho Questa)

2000 (19 OCT). Perf 14½×14 (C)

877	**834**	18p multicoloured	....	40	40
878	**835**	26p multicoloured	....	60	55
879	**836**	36p multicoloured	....	90	85
880	**837**	40p multicoloured	....	95	95
881	**838**	45p multicoloured	....	1·10	1·10
882	**839**	65p multicoloured	....	1·50	1·50
877/82		Set of 6	....	5·00	4·75
		First Day Cover	....		7·00
		Presentation Pack	....	6·00	
MS883		160×86 mm. Nos. 877/82	....	5·50	6·00
		First Day Cover	....		8·00

Plate Nos.: All values 1A (×5)

Sheets: 50 (5×10)

Imprint: Bottom, right-hand margin

Withdrawn: 18.10.2001

Yearbook 2000

2000 (1 DEC). *Comprises Nos. 795/6, 801, 851/83 and A140/61*

	Yearbook	.... 65·00

Sold out: By 12.2002

840 Queen Victoria and Diamond Jubilee Statue

841 Letter of Thanks to Guernsey, 1846

842 Statues of Queen Victoria and Prince Albert

843 Stone commemorating 1846 Visit

844 Statue of Prince Albert

845 Victoria Tower, 1848

Death Centenary of Queen Victoria

(Des A. Fothergill. Litho Questa)

2001 (22 JAN). Perf 15×14½ (C)

884	**840**	21p multicoloured	....	50	50
885	**841**	26p multicoloured	....	60	55
886	**842**	36p multicoloured	....	90	85
887	**843**	40p multicoloured	....	95	95
888	**844**	45p multicoloured	....	1·10	1·10
889	**845**	65p multicoloured	....	1·50	1·50
884/9		Set of 6	....	5·00	5·00
		First Day Cover	....		6·00
		Presentation Pack	....	5·75	
MS890		165×80 mm. Nos. 884/9. Perf 14½ (C)		6·00	7·00
		a. Imperf	....	£750	
		First Day Cover	....		7·50

No. **MS**890 includes the logo of the 'Hong Kong 2001' Stamp Exhibition on the sheet margin.

Plate Nos.: All values 1A (×4)

Sheets: 50 (10×5)

Imprint: Central, left-hand margin

Withdrawn: 21.1.2002

846 River Kingfisher

847 Garganey

848 Little Egret

849 Little Ringed Plover

Europa. Water, a Natural Treasure. Water Birds

(Des Wendy Bramall. Litho B.D.T.)

2001 (1 FEB). Perf 14×15 (C)

891	**846**	21p multicoloured	60	40
892	**847**	26p multicoloured	90	75
893	**848**	36p multicoloured	1·20	1·50
894	**849**	65p multicoloured	1·70	1·90
891/4		Set of 4	4·00	4·00
		First Day Cover		4·50
		Presentation Pack	4·50	

Plate Nos.: All values 1A (×4)

Sheets: 10 (2×5) with enlarged inscribed margins at left

Imprint: Central, right-hand margin

Withdrawn: 31.1.2002

850 Cavalier King
Charles Spaniel

851 Miniature Schnauzer

852 German
Shepherd Dog

853 Cocker Spaniel

854 West Highland
White Terrier

855 Dachshund

Centenary of Guernsey Dog Club

(Des A. Peck. Litho B.D.T.)

2001 (26 APR). Perf 13 (C)

895	**850**	22p multicoloured	55	50
896	**851**	27p multicoloured	65	60
897	**852**	36p multicoloured	90	85
898	**853**	40p multicoloured	95	95
899	**854**	45p multicoloured	1·10	1·10
900	**855**	65p multicoloured	1·50	1·50
895/900		Set of 6	5·00	5·00
		First Day Cover		6·00
		Presentation Pack	6·00	

Plate Nos.: All values 1A (×4)

Sheets: 50 (10×5)

Imprint: Upper right-hand margin

Withdrawn: 25.4.2002

856 La Corbière
Sunset

857 Rue des
Hougues

858 St. Saviour's
Reservoir

859 Shell Beach,
Herm

860 Telegraph Bay,
Alderney

861 Alderney Railway

862 Vazon Bay

863 La Coupée,
Sark

864 Les Hanois
Lighthouse

865 Albecq Beach

866 Droplets of Water on
Leaf ('Vision')

867 Ruby-throated
Hummingbird
('Understanding')

Island Scenes

(Des Sally Diamond)

2001 (26 APR). *Self-adhesive. Perf 14 (die-cut). (a) Litho
Enschedé (from sheetlets of 10 and booklets)*

901	**856**	(22p) multicoloured	....	45	50
		a. Sheetlet of 10. Nos. 901/10		8·00	8·50
		b. Booklet pane. Nos. 901/5,			
		each ×2	....	4·50	
902	**857**	(22p) multicoloured	....	45	50
903	**858**	(22p) multicoloured	....	45	50
904	**859**	(22p) multicoloured	....	45	50
905	**860**	(22p) multicoloured	....	45	50
906	**861**	(27p) multicoloured	....	55	60
		b. Booklet pane. Nos. 906/10,			
		each ×2	....	5·50	
907	**862**	(27p) multicoloured	....	55	60
908	**863**	(27p) multicoloured	....	55	60
909	**864**	(27p) multicoloured	....	55	60
910	**865**	(27p) multicoloured	....	55	60
901/10		Set of 10	....	8·00	8·50
		First Day Cover	....		8·00
		Presentation Pack	....	9·00	

(b) Photo Enschedé (from rolls of 100)

911	**856**	(22p) multicoloured	....	45	50
		a. Strip of 5. Nos. 911/15	...	4·00	
912	**857**	(22p) multicoloured	....	45	50
913	**858**	(22p) multicoloured	....	45	50
914	**859**	(22p) multicoloured	....	45	50
915	**860**	(22p) multicoloured	....	45	50
916	**861**	(27p) multicoloured	....	55	60
		a. Strip of 5. Nos. 916/20	...	4·00	
917	**862**	(27p) multicoloured	....	55	60
918	**863**	(27p) multicoloured	....	55	60
919	**864**	(27p) multicoloured	....	55	60
920	**865**	(27p) multicoloured	....	55	60
911/20		Set of 10	....	8·00	8·50

Nos. 901/5 and 911/15 were intended for postage within
the Bailiwick and are inscribed 'GY'. They were each initially
sold at 22p. Nos. 906/10 and 916/20 were intended for
postage to Great Britain and are inscribed 'UK'. They were
each initially sold at 27p.

Sheets: Nos. 901/10 were printed in sheetlets of 10 (2×5) or in
booklets with the surplus self-adhesive paper around each stamp
retained. Nos. 911/20 were printed in rolls of 100, one for each
rate, and have the surplus self-adhesive paper removed. The
photogravure printing can be identified by the lack of outlines
around the inscriptions.

Sold out: By 7.2004 booklets and rolls of 100; by 5.2007 sheetlets

868 Butterfly's Wing
('Individuality')

869 Sea Shell
('Strength')

870 Honeycomb
('Community')

871 Dandelion
('Maturity')

Incorporation of Guernsey Post Ltd

(Des Charlotte Barnes. Litho Walsall)

2001 (1 AUG). *(a) Perf 13½×13 (C)*

921	**866**	22p multicoloured	....	45	50
		a. Booklet pane of 3	....	1·20	
922	**867**	27p multicoloured	....	55	60
		a. Booklet pane of 3	....	1·60	
923	**868**	36p multicoloured	....	70	75
		a. Booklet pane of 3	....	2·10	
924	**869**	40p multicoloured	....	80	85
		a. Booklet pane of 3	....	2·40	
925	**870**	45p multicoloured	....	90	95
		a. Booklet pane of 3	....	2·50	
926	**871**	65p multicoloured	....	1·20	1·40
		a. Booklet pane of 3	....	3·75	
921/6		Set of 6	....	4·50	5·00
		First Day Cover	....		5·75
		Presentation Pack	....	5·75	

*(b) Design as No. 28 (1969 £1), but redrawn and printed in
litho. Perf 14×14½ (C)*

927	**18**	£1 multicoloured	....	5·00	5·50
		a. Booklet pane of 1	....	5·00	

No. 927 was only sold as part of a £8.05 stamp booklet but loose panes (without stitch holes) were provided free to regular Guernsey Philatelic Bureau customers. In addition to the change of printing process, No. 927 differs from the original 1969 stamp by showing the Queen's portrait without a tiara and by having 'GUERNSEY BAILIWICK' in white instead of grey.

Plate Nos.: All values 1A (×4)

Sheets: 50 (5×10)

Imprint: Upper right-hand margin

Withdrawn: 31.7.2002

872 'Tree of Joy', St. Peter Port

873 Cross, Les Cotils Christian Centre

874 Les Ruettes Cottage, St. Saviour's

875 Farmhouse, Le Preel, Castel

876 Sark Post Office

877 High Street, St. Peter Port

Christmas. Festive Lights

(Des Sally Diamond. Litho Questa)

2001 (16 OCT). Perf 14×14½ (C)

928	**872**	19p multicoloured	40	45
929	**873**	27p multicoloured	55	60
930	**874**	36p multicoloured	75	80
931	**875**	40p multicoloured	1·00	1·10
932	**876**	45p multicoloured	1·10	1·20
933	**877**	65p multicoloured	1·50	1·60
928/33		Set of 6	5·00	5·50
		First Day Cover		5·75
		Presentation Pack	5·75	
MS934	150×100 mm. Nos. 928/33		6·00	6·50
		First Day Cover		5·75

No. **MS**934 includes the 'Hafnia 01' International Stamp Exhibition logo on the sheet margin.

Plate Nos.: 19p, 27p 1A, 1B, 1C, 1D (each ×4); others 1A (×4)

Sheets: 50 (5×10)

Imprint: Upper right-hand margin

Withdrawn: 15.10.2002

Yearbook 2001

2001 (1 DEC). *Comprises Nos. 884/910, 921/6, 928/34 and A162/83*

Yearbook .... 65·00

Sold out: By 4.2003

878 Victor Hugo and St. Peter Port

879 Cosette

880 Valjean

881 Inspector Javert

882 Cosette and Marius

883 Novel and score for *Les Misérables* (musical by Alain Boublil and Claude-Michel Schönberg)

Birth Bicentenary of Victor Hugo (French author). Les Misérables *(novel)*

(Des R. Ollington. Litho Cartor)

2002 (6 FEB). Perf 13½×13 (C)

935	**878**	22p multicoloured	45	50
936	**879**	27p multicoloured	55	60
937	**880**	36p multicoloured	75	80
938	**881**	40p multicoloured	90	95
939	**882**	45p multicoloured	1·10	1·10
940	**883**	65p multicoloured	1·50	1·60
935/40		Set of 6	5·00	5·25
		First Day Cover		5·75
		Presentation Pack	5·75	
MS941	150×100 mm. Nos. 935/40		5·25	6·00
		First Day Cover		7·00

The 27p value reproduces the main image from promotional material for Cameron Mackintosh's musical production.

Plate Nos.: All values 1A (×4)

Sheets: 50 (5×10)

Imprint: Central, side margins

Withdrawn: 5.2.2003

884 Juggling

885 Clowns

886 Trapeze Artists

887 Knife Thrower

888 Acrobat

889 High-wire Cyclist

890 Queen Elizabeth and Crowd

891 Queen Elizabeth at St. Peter Port

892 Queen Elizabeth and Prince Philip at St. Anne's School, Alderney

893 Queen Elizabeth and La Seigneurie, Sark

894 At Millennium Stone, L'Ancresse

895 In Evening Dress, and Floodlit Castle Cornet

Golden Jubilee

(Des Sarah Thomas. Litho B.D.T.)

2002 (30 APR). Perf 13½ (C)

948	**890**	22p multicoloured	45	50
		a. *Booklet pane. Nos. 948 and 951/3 with margins all round*	4·50	
		b. *Booklet pane. Nos. 948/50 and 953 with margins all round*	3·00	
		c. *Booklet pane. Nos. 948/53 with margins all round*	4·50	
949	**891**	27p multicoloured	55	60
		a. *Booklet pane. Nos. 949/52 with margins all round*	3·00	
950	**892**	36p multicoloured	70	75
951	**893**	40p multicoloured	80	85
952	**894**	45p multicoloured	90	95
953	**895**	65p multicoloured	1·20	1·40
948/53		*Set of 6*	4·50	5·00
		First Day Cover		5·75
		Presentation Pack	5·75	

Plate Nos.: All values 1A (×4)

Sheets: 50 (10×5)

Imprint: Upper right-hand margin

Withdrawn: 29.4.2003

Europa. The Circus

(Des R. Carter. Litho Questa)

2002 (6 FEB). Perf 14½ (C)

942	**884**	22p multicoloured	45	50
943	**885**	27p multicoloured	55	60
944	**886**	36p multicoloured	70	75
945	**887**	40p multicoloured	80	90
946	**888**	45p multicoloured	90	95
947	**889**	65p multicoloured	1·20	1·40
942/7		*Set of 6*	4·50	5·00
		First Day Cover		6·50
		Presentation Pack	5·75	

Plate Nos.: All values 1A (×4)

Sheets: 10 (2×5) with enlarged illustrated margins at right

Imprint: Central, left-hand margin

Withdrawn 5.2.2003

896a Original Pillar Box, Union Street

150th Anniversary of First Pillar Box

(Des Sally Diamond. Litho Questa)

2002 (30 APR). *Sheet* 55×90 *mm.* Perf 14½×14 (C)

MS954 896a £1.75, multicoloured . . . . 4·00 4·50
First Day Cover . . . . 6·00
Presentation Pack . . . . 4·50

Withdrawn: 29.4.2003

897 Family and Ferry,
La Maseline

898 Passenger Tractors

899 Campsite

900 Cyclists at La
Coupée

901 Swimming in
Venus Pool

902 La Seigneurie
Gardens

903 Posting Cards

904 Carriage Ride

905 Tea at a Café

906 On the Beach at
Creux Harbour

Holidays on Sark

(Des M. Remphry. Litho B.D.T.)

2002 (30 JULY). Perf 13 (C)

955	**897**	27p multicoloured	45	30
		a. *Block of* 10 *of two horiz*		
		strips of 5. *Nos.* 955/64 . . .	6·00	6·00
956	**898**	27p multicoloured	45	30
957	**899**	27p multicoloured	45	30
958	**900**	27p multicoloured	45	30
959	**901**	27p multicoloured	45	30
960	**902**	27p multicoloured	45	30
961	**903**	27p multicoloured	45	30
962	**904**	27p multicoloured	45	30
963	**905**	27p multicoloured	45	30
964	**906**	27p multicoloured	45	30
955/64		*Set of* 10	6·00	6·00
		First Day Cover		6·50
		Presentation Pack	6·50	

Plate Nos.: 1A (×4)

Sheets: 50 (5×10). Nos. 955/64 were printed together, *se-tenant*, in blocks of 10 throughout the sheet

Imprint: Upper side margins

Withdrawn: 29.7.2003

907 Elizabeth College and
Cadet Corps Parade,
1934

908 Captain Le Patourel in
Action, Tunisia, 1942,
and V.C.

909 Captain Le Patourel and Nurse, 1943

910 Award Ceremony, Cairo, 1943

911 Major Le Patourel welcomed Home to Guernsey, 1948

912 Herbert Le Patourel carrying the King's Colour, 1968

60th Anniversary of Herbert Le Patourel's Victoria Cross

(Des A. Theobald. Litho Cartor)

2002 (30 JULY). Perf 13½×13 (C)

965	**907**	22p multicoloured	. . . .	45	50
966	**908**	27p multicoloured	. . . .	55	60
967	**909**	36p multicoloured	. . . .	70	75
968	**910**	40p multicoloured	. . . .	80	85
969	**911**	45p multicoloured	. . . .	90	95
970	**912**	65p multicoloured	. . . .	1·20	1·40
965/70		Set of 6	. . . .	4·50	5·00
		First Day Cover	. . . .		5·75
		Presentation Pack	. . . .	5·75	

Plate Nos.: All values 1A (×4)

Sheets: 50 (5×10)

Imprint: Central, side margins

Withdrawn: 29.7.2003

913a Queen Elizabeth the Queen Mother and Bouquet
(illustration reduced. Actual size 140×98 mm)

Queen Elizabeth the Queen Mother Commemoration

(Des M. Whyte. Litho and die-stamped Enschedé)

2002 (4 AUG). *Sheet* 140×98 *mm.* Perf 13½ (C)

MS971	**913a**	£2 multicoloured	. . . .	4·50	4·25
		First Day Cover	. . . .		5·00
		Presentation Pack	. . . .	5·00	

Withdrawn: 3.8.2003

914 Mary and Jesus

915 Mary, Joseph and Jesus in the Stable

916 Angel appearing to Shepherds

917 Shepherds with Mary and Jesus

918 Three Wise Men

919 Stable with Star Overhead

Christmas

(Des Petula Stone. Litho Cartor)

2002 (17 OCT). Perf 13 (C)

972	**914**	22p multicoloured	. . . .	45	50
973	**915**	27p multicoloured	. . . .	55	60
974	**916**	36p multicoloured	. . . .	70	75
975	**917**	40p multicoloured	. . . .	80	85
976	**918**	45p multicoloured	. . . .	90	95
977	**919**	65p multicoloured	. . . .	1·20	1·40
972/7		Set of 6	. . . .	4·00	4·50
		First Day Cover	. . . .		5·75
		Presentation Pack	. . . .	5·75	
MS978		130×102 mm. Nos. 972/7		4·50	5·00
		First Day Cover	. . . .		5·75

Plate Nos.: All values 1A (×5)

Sheets: 50 (5×10)

Imprint: Central, side margins

Withdrawn: 16.10.2003

Yearbook 2002

2002 (1 DEC). *Comprises Nos.* 935/78 *and* **MS**A184/202
Yearbook . . . . 65·00

Sold out: 6.2005

920 Lancaster Bomber
and Crew

921 Flight of Lancaster
bombers crossing
English coast

922 Lancaster
bombers in
enemy
searchlights

923 Dropping
bouncing
bombs

924 H.M.S. *Charybdis*
(cruiser) and H.M.S.
Limbourne (destroyer)

**Memories of the Second World War (1st issue). 60th
Anniversary of Operation Tunnel (£1.50) and
Dambusters Raid (others).**

(Des N. Watton. Litho Questa)

2003 (30 JAN). Perf 14½ (£1.50) or 14 (others) (both comb)

979	**920**	22p multicoloured	45	50
980	**921**	27p multicoloured	55	60
981	**922**	36p multicoloured	70	75
982	**923**	40p multicoloured	80	85
983	**924**	£1.50 multicoloured	3·00	3·25
979/83		Set of 5	5·50	5·75
		First Day Cover		6·50
		Presentation Pack	6·50	

See also Nos. 1027/31.

Plate Nos.: All values 1A (×5)

Sheets: 50 (5×10)

Imprint: Upper right-hand margin

Withdrawn: 29.1.2004

925 Hurdling

926 Cycling

927 Gymnastics

928 Sailing

929 Golf

930 Running

Island Games, Guernsey

(Des Charlotte Barnes. Litho Cartor)

2003 (30 JAN). Perf 12½ (C)

984	**925**	22p multicoloured	45	50
985	**926**	27p multicoloured	55	60
986	**927**	36p multicoloured	75	80
987	**928**	40p multicoloured	80	85
988	**929**	45p multicoloured	90	95
989	**930**	65p multicoloured	1·20	1·40
984/9		Set of 6	4·50	5·00
		First Day Cover		5·75
		Presentation Pack	5·75	
MS990		140×75 mm. Nos. 984/9	4·50	5·00
		First Day Cover		5·75

Plate Nos.: All values 1A (×4)

Sheets: 50 (5×10)

Imprint: Central, side margins

Withdrawn: 29.1.2004

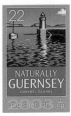

931 St. Peter Port
Harbour
('Naturally
Guernsey',
2003)

932 Motor-cruiser
off Guernsey
('The islands
of Guernsey',
1995)

933 'Children on
the Seashore'
(Renoir)
('Holiday
Guernsey',
1988)

934 St. Peter Port
Harbour
('Bailiwick of
Guernsey',
1978)

935 St. Peter Port
and Cliffs
('Guernsey —
The Charming
Channel
Island', 1968)

936 Secluded
Bay
('Guernsey',
1956)

Europa. Poster Art

(Des M. Quéru. Litho De La Rue)

2003 (10 APR). Perf 14½ (C)

991	**931**	22p multicoloured	45	50
992	**932**	27p multicoloured	55	60
993	**933**	36p multicoloured	75	80
994	**934**	40p multicoloured	80	85
995	**935**	45p multicoloured	90	95
996	**936**	65p multicoloured	1·20	1·40

991/6	Set of 6	4·50	5·00
	First Day Cover		5·75
	Presentation Pack	5·75	

Sheets: 10 (2×5) with enlarged illustrated margin at right

Imprint: Central, left-hand margin

Withdrawn: 9.4.2004

937a H.M.S. *Guernsey*
(*illustration reduced. Actual size* 117×84 *mm*)

Decommissioning of H.M.S. Guernsey *(fishery protection patrol vessel)*

(Des K. Taylor. Litho De La Rue)

2003 (10 APR). *Sheet* 117×84 *mm. Perf* 13½×14 (C)

MS997	**937a**	£1.50 multicoloured	4·50	4·00
		First Day Cover		4·50
		Presentation Pack	4·75	

Withdrawn: 9.4.2004

938 Princess Diana
and Baby Prince
William

939 Prince William,
aged 3, with
Prince Charles
and Prince Harry
at Kensington
Palace

940 Aged 4, in Parachute Regiment Uniform

941 Aged 7, with Prince Harry on his First Day at Wetherby School

942 Aged 8, with Prince Charles at Guards Polo

943 Aged 9, on Ski Slopes with Princess Diana

944 On First Day at Eton, 1995

945 With Prince Charles and Prince Harry at Balmoral, 1997

946 Wearing Hard Hat during Community Project in Chile, 2000

947 Playing Polo, 2002

21st Birthday of Prince William of Wales

(Des Sally Diamond. Litho Enschedé)

2003 (21 JUNE). Perf 13½×13 (C)

998	**938**	27p multicoloured	55	30
		a. Horiz strip of 10. Nos. 998/1007	6·50	7·00
		b. Perf 13½×14	55	60
		ba. Booklet pane. Nos. 998b, 1000b, 1003b/4b and 1006b/7b with margins all round	3·25	
		bb. Booklet pane. Nos. 998b, 1001b, 1003b/5b and 1007b with margins all round	3·25	
		bc. Booklet pane. Nos. 998b/1000b, 1002b, 1005b and 1007b with margins all round	3·25	
999	**939**	27p multicoloured	55	30
		b. Perf 13½×14	55	60
		ba. Booklet pane. Nos. 999b/1002b and 1005b/6b with margins all round	3·25	
		bb. Booklet pane. Nos. 999b, 1001b/1004b and 1006b with margins all round	3·25	
1000	**940**	27p multicoloured	55	30
		b. Perf 13½×14	55	60
1001	**941**	27p multicoloured	55	30
		b. Perf 13½×14	55	60
1002	**942**	27p multicoloured	55	30
		b. Perf 13½×14	55	60
1003	**943**	27p multicoloured	55	30
		b. Perf 13½×14	55	60
1004	**944**	27p multicoloured	55	30
		b. Perf 13½×14	55	60
1005	**945**	27p multicoloured	55	30
		b. Perf 13½×14	55	60
1006	**946**	27p multicoloured	55	30
		b. Perf 13½×14	55	60
1007	**947**	27p multicoloured	55	30
		b. Perf 13½×14	55	60
998/1007		Set of 10	6·50	7·00
		First Day Cover		6·50
		Presentation Pack	6·50	

Nos. 998b/1007b were only issued in £8.10 booklets, No. SB72.

Plate Nos.: 1A (×4)

Sheets: 50 (10×5). Nos. 998/1007 were printed together, se-tenant, in horizontal strips of ten throughout the sheet

Imprint: Upper side margins

Withdrawn: 20.6.2004

GUERNSEY £5 948 Letters of Alphabet

(Des A. Fothergill. Litho and die-stamped Enschedé)

2003 (3 JULY). Perf 13½ (C)

1008	**948**	£5 pale orange, royal blue and silver	10·00	10·50
		First Day Cover		11·00
		Presentation Pack		11·00

The alphabet letters are printed in thermochromic ink which fades from pale orange to white when exposed to heat. No. 1008 was retained in use as a definitive stamp.

Sheets: 4 (4×1)

949 Sleeping Boy and Christmas Tree

950 Boy opening Shutter to see Santa's Sleigh

951 Santa on Roof with Reindeer

952 Santa with Presents

953 Santa leaving Presents under Christmas Tree

954 Santa in Sleigh

Christmas. Scenes from Poem 'Twas the Night before Christmas' by Clement Clarke Moore

(Des Petula Stone. Litho DLR)

2003 (16 OCT). Perf 14×14½ (C)

1009	**949**	10p multicoloured	20	25
1010	**950**	27p multicoloured	55	60
1011	**951**	36p multicoloured	70	75
1012	**952**	40p multicoloured	80	85
1013	**953**	45p multicoloured	1·20	1·30
1014	**954**	65p multicoloured	1·50	1·70
1009/14		*Set of 6*	4·75	5·00
		First Day Cover		5·75
		Presentation Pack		5·75
MS1015		130×104 mm. Nos. 1009/14	4·75	4·75
		First Day Cover		5·75

Plate Nos.: All values 1A (×4)

Sheets: 50 (5×10)

Imprint: Upper right-hand margin

Withdrawn: 15.10.2004

Yearbook 2003

2003 (1 DEC). *Comprises Nos.* 979/**MS**1015 *and* **MS**A203/22

	Yearbook	70·00

Sold out: By 3.2007

955a Golden Snub-nosed Monkey
(*illustration reduced. Actual size* 120×85 *mm*)

Endangered Species (1st series). Golden Snub-nosed Monkey

(Des J. Kirk. Litho De La Rue)

2004 (29 JAN). *Sheet* 120×85 *mm.* Perf 14 (C)

MS1016	**955a**	£2 multicoloured	6·50	6·50
		First Day Cover		8·50
		Presentation Pack		8·50

Withdrawn: 28.1.2005

956 'Rosemoor'

957 'Arctic Queen'

958 'Harlow Carr'

959 'Guernsey Cream'

960 'Josephine'

961 'Blue Moon'

962 'Wisley'

963 'Liberation'

964 'Royal Velvet'

965 'Hyde Hall'

Raymond Evison's Guernsey Clematis
(Des R. Evison. Litho Cartor)

2004 (29 JAN). *Self-adhesive.* Perf 12½ (die-cut)

1017	**956**	(22p) multicoloured		75	75
		a. *Sheetlet. Nos.* 1017/26 . . .	8·00		
		b. *Booklet pane. Nos.* 1017/21, *each* ×2	7·00		
		c. *Booklet pane. Nos.* 1017/21, *each* ×2	7·00		
1018	**957**	(22p) multicoloured		75	75
1019	**958**	(22p) multicoloured		75	75
1020	**959**	(22p) multicoloured		75	75
1021	**960**	(22p) multicoloured		75	75
1022	**961**	(27p) multicoloured		85	85
		a. *Booklet pane. Nos.* 1022/6, *each* ×2	8·75		
		b. *Booklet pane. Nos.* 1022/6, *each* ×2	8·75		
1023	**962**	(27p) multicoloured		85	85
1024	**963**	(27p) multicoloured		85	85
1025	**964**	(27p) multicoloured		85	85
1026	**965**	(27p) multicoloured		85	85
1017/26		*Set of* 10		8·00	8·00
		First Day Cover			9·00
		Presentation Pack	9·00		

Nos. 1017/21 were intended for postage within the Bailiwick and are inscribed "GY". They were each initially sold at 22p. Nos. 1022/6 were intended for postage to Great Britain and are inscribed "UK". They were each initially sold at 27p.

Sheets: 10 (5×2). Nos. 1017/26 were printed in sheetlets of ten containing Nos. 1017/26 and in booklets of ten or 100, all with the surplus self-adhesive paper around each stamp retained. The booklets of ten contain either Nos. 1017/21×2 (pane No. 1017*b*) or Nos. 1022/6×2 (pane No. 1022*a*), and the stamps are peeled directly from the cover in two blocks 3×2 and 2×2, the blocks separated by a gutter containing text. The booklets of 100 contain ten panes of either Nos. 1017/21×2 (pane No. 1017*c*) or Nos. 1022/6×2 (pane No. 1022*b*). These panes have the stamps in one block 5×2, on plain white backing paper, the panes being separated from the booklet by a line of rouletting.

966 Supermarine Spitfire

967 Landing Craft and Ship

968 Troops going Ashore at Gold Beach

969 Troops in Water

970 *Vega* (Red Cross supply ship)

Memories of the Second World War (2nd issue). 60th Anniv of D-Day Landings

(Des N. Watton. Litho BDT)

2004 (12 MAY). Perf 15×14 (£1.50) or 14 (others) (both comb)

1027	**966**	26p multicoloured	85	85
1028	**967**	32p multicoloured	1·00	1·00
1029	**968**	36p multicoloured	1·20	1·20
1030	**969**	40p multicoloured	1·30	1·30
1031	**970**	£1.50 multicoloured	5·00	5·00
1027/31		*Set of 5*	9·25	9·25
		First Day Cover		11·50
		Presentation Pack . . . . . . 11·50		

Plate Nos.: All values 1A (×4)

Sheets: 50 (5×10)

Imprint: Upper side margins

Withdrawn: 11.5.2005

971 Sandcastle, Rider, Bucket and Spade, Deckchair and Canoeist

972 Pathway Sign, Walking Trails, Bench and Guernsey Landscapes

973 Lighthouse and Yachts in Marina, St. Peter Port

974 Glasses of Red Wine and Meals on Table

975 Statue-menhir at Castel and Loop Holed Tower, Le Gran'mere Statue-menhir, Little Chapel and Victor Hugo Statue

976 Guernsey Lily, Wildflowers and Robin

Europa. Holidays

(Des P. Furness. Litho BDT)

2004 (12 MAY). Perf 13½ (C)

1032	**971**	26p multicoloured	85	85
1033	**972**	32p multicoloured	1·10	1·10
1034	**973**	36p multicoloured	1·20	1·20
1035	**974**	40p multicoloured	1·30	1·30
1036	**975**	45p multicoloured	1·50	1·50
1037	**976**	65p multicoloured	2·10	2·10
1032/7		*Set of 6*	8·00	8·00
		First Day Cover		10·00
		Presentation Pack . . . . 10·00		

Sheets: 10 (2×5) with enlarged illustrated margins at right

Imprint: Central, left-hand margin

Withdrawn: 11.5.2005

977 Three Crowns (Loyalty)

978 Three Ships (Trade)

979 Knotted Rope (Unity)

980 Three Castle Turrets (Protection)

981 Three Scrolls (Justice)

982 Three Leaping Fish (Industry)

800th Anniv of Allegiance to England

(Des Charlotte Barnes. Litho Enschedé)

2004 (24 JUNE). Perf 13½×14 (C)

1038	**977**	26p multicoloured	85	85
1039	**978**	32p multicoloured	1·10	1·10
1040	**979**	36p multicoloured	1·20	1·20
1041	**980**	40p multicoloured	1·30	1·30
1042	**981**	45p multicoloured	1·50	1·50
1043	**982**	65p multicoloured	2·10	2·10
1038/43		Set of 6	8·00	8·00
		First Day Cover		10·00
		Presentation Pack . . . . 10·00		
MS1044		140×80 mm. Nos. 1038/43.		
P 14×13½		. . . .	8·00	8·00
		First Day Cover		10·00

Plate Nos.: All values 1A (×5)

Sheets: 50 (10×5)

Imprint: Upper side margins

Withdrawn: 23.6.2005

983 Discus Thrower

984 Javelin Thrower

985 Runners

986 Wrestlers

987a Olympic Sports
(*illustration reduced. Actual size 152×85 mm*)

Olympic Games, Athens, Greece

(Des A. Fothergill. Litho BDT)

2004 (29 JULY). Perf 13½ (C)

1045	**983**	32p multicoloured	1·00	1·00
		a. Booklet pane. No. 1045×2 and Nos. 1046/7 with margins all round	4·75	
		b. Booklet pane. No. 1045, No. 1047×2 and No. 1048 with margins all round	6·00	
		c. Booklet pane. Nos. 1045/6 and 1048×2 with margins all round	6·50	
		d. Booklet pane. Nos. 1045/8 with margins all round	5·75	
1046	**984**	36p multicoloured	1·20	1·20
		a. Booklet pane. No. 1046×2 and Nos. 1047/8 with margins all round	6·00	
1047	**985**	45p multicoloured	1·50	1·50
1048	**986**	65p multicoloured	2·10	2·10
1045/8		Set of 4	5·75	5·75
		First Day Cover		7·75
		Presentation Pack	7·75	
MS1049		152×98 mm. **987a** £1 multicoloured. Perf 15×14 (C)	3·25	3·25
		a. Booklet pane. As No. **MS**1049, but with line of roulettes at left	3·25	
		First Day Cover		5·25
		Presentation Pack	5·25	

Plate Nos.: All values 1A (×4)

Sheets: 50 (10×5)

Imprint: Upper side margins

Withdrawn: 28.7.2005

988 'Little Donkey'

989 'While Shepherds Watched'

990 'Away in a Manger'

991 'Unto Us a Child is Born'

992 'We Three Kings'

993 Angels Wings

994 Bauble

995 Holly

996 Detail of Snowman

997 Star atop Tree

'The Innocence of Christmas'
(Des J. Almer. Litho Cartor)

2004 (28 OCT). Perf 13 (C)

1050	**988**	20p multicoloured	65	25
		a. Horiz strip of 5. Nos. 1050/4	3·25	3·50
1051	**989**	20p multicoloured	65	25
1052	**990**	20p multicoloured	65	25
1053	**991**	20p multicoloured	65	25
1054	**992**	20p multicoloured	65	25
1055	**993**	32p multicoloured	1·10	1·10
1056	**994**	36p multicoloured	1·20	1·20
1057	**995**	40p multicoloured	1·30	1·30
1058	**996**	45p multicoloured	1·50	1·50
1059	**997**	65p multicoloured	2·20	2·20
1050/9		Set of 10	10·50	10·50
		First Day Covers (2)		14·50
		Presentation Pack	13·50	

Plate Nos.: All values 1A (×4)

Sheets: 50 (5×10) The 20p values were printed together, *se-tenant*, in horizontal strips of 5 with the backgrounds forming a composite design

Imprint: Upper and lower side margins

Withdrawn: 27.10.2005

Yearbook 2004
2004 (1 DEC). *Comprises Nos.* **MS**1016/59 *and* A223/47

Yearbook . . . . 65·00

998 British Soldiers in Landrover and welcoming Crowd

999 Guernsey Woman waving and Liberty Sign and Flags on Building

1000 Parents and Children reunited

1001 Return of Local Men from Hampshire Regiment

1002 Winston Churchill

Memories of the Second World War (3rd issue). 60th Anniv of Liberation
(Des N. Watton. Litho BDT)

2005 (3 FEB). Perf 15×14½ (£1.50) or 14½ (others) (both comb)

1060	**998**	26p multicoloured	50	55
1061	**999**	32p multicoloured	65	70
1062	**1000**	36p multicoloured	70	75
1063	**1001**	40p multicoloured	80	85
1064	**1002**	£1.50 multicoloured	3·00	3·25
1060/4		Set of 5	5·50	6·00
		First Day Cover		7·00
		Presentation Pack	7·00	

Plate Nos.: All values 1A (×4)

Sheets: 50 (5×10)

Imprint: Upper left-hand margin

Withdrawn: 2.2.2006

1003 Iris 'Dorothea' and 'Royal'

1004 Nerine Fothergilli 'Major'

1005 Iris 'Garnet'

1006 Narcissus 'Sir Watkin'

1007 Narcissus 'Rip van Winkle'

1008 Narcissus 'Sulphur Phoenix'

Birth Centenary of William J. Caparne (artist and iris breeder). Watercolour Paintings of Flowers

(Litho Enschedé)

2005 (3 FEB). Perf 13½ (C)				
1065	**1003**	26p multicoloured	50	55
1066	**1004**	32p multicoloured	65	70
1067	**1005**	36p multicoloured	70	75
1068	**1006**	40p multicoloured	85	85
1069	**1007**	45p multicoloured	1·00	95
1070	**1008**	65p multicoloured	1·50	1·40
1065/70		Set of 6	5·00	5·00
		First Day Cover		6·00
		Presentation Pack	6·00	
MS1071	140×85 mm. Nos. 1065/70		5·00	5·00
		First Day Cover		6·00

Plate Nos.: All values 1A (×4)

Sheets: 50 (10×5)

Imprint: Upper left-hand margin

Withdrawn: 2.2.2006

1009 Spider Crab

1010 Seared Red Mullet and Crab Cake

1011 Lobster Salad

1012 Brill on Spinach with Local Moules

1013 Prawn Salad

1014 Salmon Wrapped in Spinach with Local Moules

Europa. Gastronomy. Seafood and Coastal Scenes

(Des P. Furness. Litho Enschedé)

2005 (9 MAY) Perf 14×13½ (C)				
1072	**1009**	26p multicoloured	50	55
1073	**1010**	32p multicoloured	65	70
1074	**1011**	36p multicoloured	70	75
1075	**1012**	40p multicoloured	80	85
1076	**1013**	45p multicoloured	90	95
1077	**1014**	65p multicoloured	1·30	1·40
1072/7		Set of 6	4·75	5·00
		First Day Cover		6·00
		Presentation Pack	6·25	

Plate Nos.: All values 1A (×4)

Sheets: 10 (2×5) with enlarged illustrated right-hand margins

Imprint: Lower left-hand margin

Withdrawn: 8.5.2006

1015 King George VI   **1016** Queen Elizabeth II

60th Anniv of Liberation of Guernsey

(Des Keren Le Patourel. Litho and embossed BDT)

2005 (9 MAY). Perf 15×14½ (C)

1078	**1015**	£1 multicoloured	1·80	1·30
		a. Horiz pair. Nos. 1078/9 . . .	3·50	4·00
1079	**1016**	£1 multicoloured	1·80	1·30
1078/9		Set of 2	3·50	4·00
		First Day Cover		5·50
		Presentation Pack	5·50	

Nos. 1078/9 were retained in use as definitive stamps.

Plate Nos.: 1A (×5)

Sheets: 20 (4×5); the two designs printed together, *se-tenant*, in horizontal pairs throughout the sheet, each pair forming a composite background design.

Imprint: Central, side margins

1017 Fishing Boat

1018 Yacht off Herm Harbour

1019 Windsurfer

1020 Sea Angler on Rocks at Albecq

1021 Horse and Rider on Beach, Vazon Bay

'Sea Guernsey 2005'

(Des Sally Diamond. Litho Enschedé)

2005 (21 JULY). Perf 13½×14 (C)

1080	**1017**	26p multicoloured	50	55
		a. Booklet pane. Nos. 1080/1, each ×2, with margins all round	2·30	
		b. Booklet pane. Nos. 1080 and 1084, each ×2, with margins all round	3·50	
1081	**1018**	32p multicoloured	65	70
		a. Booklet pane. Nos. 1081/2, each ×2, with margins all round	2·75	
		b. Booklet pane. Nos. 1081/4 with margins all round . . .	3·50	
1082	**1019**	36p multicoloured	70	75
		a. Booklet pane. Nos. 1082/3, each ×2, with margins all round	3·00	
1083	**1020**	40p multicoloured	80	85
		a. Booklet pane. Nos. 1083/4, each ×2, with margins all round	4·00	
1084	**1021**	65p multicoloured	1·30	1·40
1080/4		Set of 5	3·75	4·00
		First Day Cover		5·25
		Presentation Pack	5·25	

Plate Nos.: All values 1A (×4)

Sheets: 10 (2×5)

Imprint: Lower right-hand margin

Withdrawn: 20.7.2006

1022 Basking Shark
(*illustration reduced. Actual size 185×65 mm*)

Endangered Species (2nd issue). Basking Shark

(Des J. Kirk. Litho BDT)

2005 (21 JULY). *Sheet* 185×65 *mm. Perf* 13½ (C)

MS1085	**1022**	£2 multicoloured	5·00	5·00
		First Day Cover		6·00
		Presentation Pack	6·00	

Withdrawn: 20.7.2006

1023 Christ holding Guernsey Flag, St. Pierre du Bois

1024 Madonna and Child, St. Saviour

1025 John baptising Christ, St. Martin

1026 Christ the Light of the World, Torteval

1027 Madonna and Child, St. Sampson

1028 Madonna and Child, Vale

1029 Three Kings, Castel

1030 St. Nicholas, Alderney

1031 Madonna and Child, St. Andrew

1032 St. Marguerite, Forest

Christmas. Stained-glass Windows from Guernsey and Alderney Parish Churches

(Des K. Taylor. Litho Austrian State Ptg Wks, Vienna)

2005 (27 OCT). Perf 14×14½ (C)

1086	**1023**	20p multicoloured	....	40	45
		a. Horiz strip of 5. Nos. 1086/90	....	2·00	2·20
1087	**1024**	20p multicoloured	....	40	45
1088	**1025**	20p multicoloured	....	40	45
1089	**1026**	20p multicoloured	....	40	45
1090	**1027**	20p multicoloured	....	40	45
1091	**1028**	32p multicoloured	....	65	70
1092	**1029**	36p multicoloured	....	70	75
1093	**1030**	40p multicoloured	....	80	85
1094	**1031**	45p multicoloured	....	90	95
1095	**1032**	65p multicoloured	....	1·30	1·40
1086/95		Set of 10	....	6·25	6·75
		First Day Covers (2)	.....		9·00
		Presentation Pack	....	7·75	

Plate Nos.: All values 1A (×4)

Sheets: 50 (10×5) The 20p values were printed together, *se-tenant*, in horizontal strips of 5 with the backgrounds forming a composite design

Imprint: Lower side margins

Withdrawn: 26.10.2006

Yearbook 2005

2005 (1 DEC). *Comprises Nos*. 802, 1060/95 *and* A248/ **MS**A266

Yearbook .... 65·00

1033 Atlantic Leatherback Turtle; American Wood Ibis (*illustration reduced. Actual size 110×90 mm*)

Endangered Species of the Florida Everglades

(Des J. Kirk. Litho BDT)

2006 (16 FEB). *Sheet 110×90 mm.* Perf 14×15 (C)

MS1096	£1, £1.50 multicoloured	....	6·00	6·00
	First Day Cover	....		7·00
	Presentation Pack	.....	7·00	

Withdrawn: 15.2.2007

1034 Iraq Conflict, 2004

1035 Falklands War, 1982

1036 Battle of El Alamein, 1942

1037 Gallipoli Campaign, 1915

1038 Battle of Rorke's Drift, 1879

1039 Charge of the Light Brigade, 1854

150th Anniversary of the Victoria Cross

(Des M. Hargreaves. Litho Austrian State Ptg Wks, Vienna)

2006 (16 FEB). Perf 14×13½ (C)

1097	**1034**	29p multicoloured	60	65
1098	**1035**	34p multicoloured	70	75
1099	**1036**	38p multicoloured	75	80
1100	**1037**	42p multicoloured	85	90
1101	**1038**	47p multicoloured	95	1·00
1102	**1039**	68p multicoloured	1·40	1·50
1097/102		*Set of 6*	5·25	5·50
		First Day Cover		6·50
		Presentation Pack	6·50	

Plate Nos.: All values 1A (×4)

Sheets: 50 (5×10)

Imprint: Upper left-hand margin

Withdrawn: 15.2.2007

1040 Pilbeam MP58, British Speed Hill Climb Championship, 1995

1041 Renault Spider Cup, 1999

1042 British Formula 3, 2001

1043 FIA European Touring Car Championship, 2004

1044 Nürburgring, Germany, 2005

1045 FIA World Touring Car Championship, 2005

Andy Priaulx's Motor Racing Victories

(Des P. Furness. Litho BDT)

2006 (20 MAY). Perf 13½ (C)

1103	**1040**	29p multicoloured	60	65
1104	**1041**	34p multicoloured	70	75
1105	**1042**	42p multicoloured	85	90
1106	**1043**	45p multicoloured	90	95
1107	**1044**	47p multicoloured	1·20	1·20
1108	**1045**	68p multicoloured	1·70	1·70
1103/8		*Set of 6*	5·75	6·00
		First Day Cover		7·00
		Presentation Pack	6·50	
MS1109	160×100 mm. Nos. 1103/8		6·00	6·00
		First Day Cover		7·00

Plate Nos.: All values 1A (×4)

Sheets: 10 (2×5) with enlarged illustrated right margins

Imprint: Central, left-hand margin

Withdrawn: 19.5.2007

1046 Brunel and Mailbags at Paddington Station

1047 Duke Class Locomotive No. 3258 *King Arthur* at Paddington Station

1048 *King Arthur* on Wharncliffe Viaduct

1049 Loading Mail from Train onto *Ibex* at Weymouth Harbour

1050 Weymouth & Channel Island Steam Packet *Ibex*

1051 Unloading Mail from *Ibex* at St. Peter Port Harbour

1052 Student working as Waiter in Paris

1053 Sphinx, Egypt

1054 Great Wall of China

1055 Student and Aborigines at Ayers Rock, Australia

1056 Head of Statue of Liberty, New York

1057 Students at Taj Mahal, India

Birth Bicentenary of Isambard Kingdom Brunel (engineer)

(Des N. Watton. Litho Cartor)

2006 (20 MAY). Perf 13½×13 (C)

1110	**1046**	29p multicoloured	60	65
		a. Booklet pane. Nos. 1110/13	3·00	
		b. Booklet pane. Nos. 1110 and 1113/15	3·75	
		c. Booklet pane. Nos. 1110/11 and 1114/15	5·00	
		d. Booklet pane. Nos. 1110/12 and 1115	4·00	
1111	**1047**	34p multicoloured	70	75
		a. Booklet pane. Nos. 1111/14	4·00	
1112	**1048**	42p multicoloured	85	90
		a. Booklet pane. Nos. 1112/15	5·00	
1113	**1049**	45p multicoloured	90	95
1114	**1050**	47p multicoloured	1·20	1·20
1115	**1051**	68p multicoloured	1·70	1·70
1110/15		*Set of 6*	5·75	6·00
		First Day Cover		7·00
		Presentation Pack	7·00	

Plate Nos.: All values 1A (×4)

Sheets: 50 (5×10)

Imprint: Upper and lower left-hand margins

Withdrawn: 19.5.2007

Europa. Integration. Student's Gap Year Travels

(Des R. Carter. Litho Cartor)

2006 (20 MAY). Perf 13½×14 (C)

1116	**1052**	29p multicoloured	60	65
1117	**1053**	34p multicoloured	70	75
1118	**1054**	42p multicoloured	85	90
1119	**1055**	45p multicoloured	1·00	95
1120	**1056**	47p multicoloured	1·20	1·00
1121	**1057**	68p multicoloured	1·50	1·50
1116/21		*Set of 6*	5·50	5·75
		First Day Cover		6·50
		Presentation Pack	6·50	

Plate Nos.: All values 1A (×4)

Sheets: 10 (2×5) with enlarged illustrated margins at right and foot

Imprint: Lower left-hand margin

Withdrawn: 19.5.2007

1058 Queen Elizabeth II

80th Birthday of Queen Elizabeth II

(Des P. Furness. Litho and embossed Cartor)

2006 (17 JUNE). Perf 14½ (C)

1122	**1058**	£10 multicoloured ....22·00	22·00	
		First Day Cover	24·00	
		Presentation Pack ....24·00		
		Souvenir Folder (No. 1122 & complete sheets of Nos. A274/81) ....65·00		

Sheets: 5 (5×1)

Imprint: Top, right-hand margin

No. 1122 was retained in use as a definitive stamp

1059 Grey Seal

1060 Ormer

1061 Common Blenny

1062 Le Creux ès Faies (Neolithic grave)

1063 Yellow Horned Poppy

1064 Oystercatcher

Designation of L'Erée Wetland as Ramsar Site

(Des Wendy Bramall. Litho Enschedé)

2006 (27 JULY). Perf 14×13½ (C)

1123	**1059**	29p multicoloured	60	65
1124	**1060**	34p multicoloured	70	75
1125	**1061**	42p multicoloured	85	90
1126	**1062**	45p multicoloured	1·00	95
1127	**1063**	47p multicoloured	1·20	1·00
1128	**1064**	68p multicoloured	1·50	1·50
1123/8		Set of 6	5·50	5·75
		First Day Cover		6·50
		Presentation Pack	6·50	
MS1129		140×95 mm. Nos. 1123/8	6·50	5·75
		First Day Cover		6·50

Plate Nos.: All values 1A (×4)

Sheets: 10 (2×5) with enlarged illustrated margins at right and foot

Imprint: Central, left-hand margin

Withdrawn: 26.7.2007

1065 A Partridge in a Pear Tree

1066 Two Turtle Doves

1067 Three French Hens

1068 Four Calling Birds

1069 Five Gold Rings

1070 Six Geese a-laying

1071 Seven Swans a-swimming

1072 Eight Maids a-milking

1073 Nine Ladies Dancing

1074 Ten Lords a-leaping

1075 Eleven Pipers Piping

1076 Twelve Drummers Drumming

Christmas. 'The Twelve Days of Christmas' (carol)

(Des M. Wilkinson. Litho Austrian State Ptg Wks, Vienna)

2006 (2 NOV). Perf 15 (C)

1130	**1065**	22p multicoloured	45	50
		a. Horiz strip of 6. Nos. 1130/5	2·50	
1131	**1066**	22p multicoloured	45	50
1132	**1067**	22p multicoloured	45	50
1133	**1068**	22p multicoloured	45	50
1134	**1069**	22p multicoloured	45	50

1135	**1070**	22p multicoloured	45	50
1136	**1071**	29p multicoloured	60	65
1137	**1072**	34p multicoloured	70	75
1138	**1073**	42p multicoloured	85	90
1139	**1074**	45p multicoloured	90	95
1140	**1075**	47p multicoloured	95	1·00
1141	**1076**	68p multicoloured	1·40	1·50
1130/41		*Set of 12*	8·00	8·75
		First Day Covers (2)		11·00
		Presentation Pack	9·25	

Plate Nos.: All values 1A (×4)

Sheets: 22p 60 (6×10); 29p to 68p 50 (10×5) The 22p values were printed together, *se-tenant*, in horizontal strips of 6

Imprint: Upper side margins

Withdrawn: 1.11.2007

Yearbook 2006

2006 (1 DEC). *Comprises Nos.* **MS**1096/141, *A267/97 and* A306/7

Yearbook £100

1077 Departure of Troops on *Queen Elizabeth 2*, Southampton

1078 Troops landing at San Carlos Bay

1079 Sea Harriers flying over SS *Canberra*

1080 Lt. Col. H. Jones firing Machine Gun

1081 Helicopter and H.M.S. *Invincible*

1082 Troops marching with Union Jack towards Port Stanley

25th Anniversary of the Battle for the Falklands

(Des R. Carter. Litho BDT)

2007 (8 MAR). Perf 13½ (C)

1142	**1077**	32p multicoloured	75	75
1143	**1078**	37p multicoloured	90	90

1144	**1079**	45p multicoloured	1·10	1·10
1145	**1080**	48p multicoloured	1·10	1·10
1146	**1081**	50p multicoloured	1·20	1·20
1147	**1082**	71p multicoloured	1·70	1·70
1142/7		*Set of 6*	6·75	6·75
		First Day Cover		8·50
		Presentation Pack	8·50	
MS1148		150×100 mm. Nos. 1142/7	6·75	6·75
		First Day Cover		8·50

Plate Nos.: All values 1A (×4)

Sheets: 10 (2×5) with enlarged illustrated margins at right and foot

Imprint: Central, left-hand margin

Withdrawn: 7.3.2008

1083 Rocks at Albecq

1084 Ivy Bee

1085 Vale Church

1086 Common Frog

1087 Parasol Mushroom

1088 Southern Marsh Orchid

1089 Shore Crab

1090 Alderney Blonde Hedgehog

1091 Barn Owl

1092 Le Trépied Dolmen

125th Anniversary of La Société Guernesiaise

(Des A. Wallace. Litho Cartor)

2007 (8 MAR). *Self-adhesive.* Perf 12½ (die-cut)

1149	**1083**	(32p) multicoloured	80	80
		a. Sheetlet. Nos. 1149/58 ..	8·00	
		b. Booklet pane. Nos. 1149/53, each ×2	7·50	
		c. Booklet pane. Nos. 1149/53, each ×2	7·50	
1150	**1084**	(32p) multicoloured	80	80
1151	**1085**	(32p) multicoloured	80	80
1152	**1086**	(32p) multicoloured	80	80
1153	**1087**	(32p) multicoloured	80	80
1154	**1088**	(37p) multicoloured	80	80
		a. Booklet pane. Nos. 1154/8, each ×2	8·75	
		b. Booklet pane. Nos. 1154/8, each ×2	8·75	
1155	**1089**	(37p) multicoloured	80	80
1156	**1090**	(37p) multicoloured	80	80
1157	**1091**	(37p) multicoloured	80	80
1158	**1092**	(37p) multicoloured	80	80
1149/58		Set of 10	8·00	8·00
		First Day Cover		9·00
		Presentation Pack	9·00	

Nos. 1149/53 were intended for postage within the Bailiwick, are inscribed "GY" and sold for 32p. each. Nos. 1154/8 were intended for postage to Great Britain, are inscribed "UK" and sold for 37p. each.

Sheets: 10 (5×2). Nos. 1149/58 were printed in sheetlets of ten containing Nos. 1149/58 and in booklets of ten or 100, all with the surplus self-adhesive paper around each stamp retained. The booklets of ten contain either Nos. 1149/53×2 (pane No. 1149b) or Nos. 1154/8×2 (pane No. 1154a), and the stamps are peeled directly from the cover in two blocks 3×2 and 2×2, the blocks separated by a gutter containing text. The booklets of 100 contain ten panes of either Nos. 1149/53×2 (pane No. 1149c) or Nos. 1154/8×2 (pane No. 1154b). These panes have the stamps in one block 5×2, on plain white backing paper.

1093 Scouts camping, 1907

1094 Scout sailing, 1924

1095 Two Scouts fishing from Rocks, 1947

1096 Scouts making and flying Model Aircraft, 1968

1097 Scouts on Caving Expedition, 1990

1098 Scouts rollerblading, Cambridge Park, St. Peter Port, 2007

Europa. Centenary of Scouting

(Des Björn Von Schlippe. Litho Cartor)

2007 (24 MAY). Perf 13½ (C)

1159	**1093**	32p multicoloured	75	75
1160	**1094**	37p multicoloured	90	90
1161	**1095**	45p multicoloured	1·10	1·10
1162	**1096**	48p multicoloured	1·10	1·10
1163	**1097**	50p multicoloured	1·50	1·20
1164	**1098**	71p multicoloured	2·00	1·70
1159/64		Set of 6	7·00	6·75
		First Day Cover		8·50
		Presentation Pack	8·50	

Sheets: 10 (2×5) with enlarged illustrated margins at right and foot

Imprint: Central, left-hand margin

Withdrawn: 23.5.2008

1099 Mike Hawthorn, 1958

1100 Jackie Stewart, 1971

1101 Graham Hill, 1962

1102 James Hunt, 1976

1103 Jim Clark, 1963

1104 Nigel Mansell, 1992

1105 John Surtees, 1964

1106 Damon Hill, 1996

British Formula One World Champions

(Des Chris Griffiths. Litho Austrian State Ptg Wks, Vienna)

2007 (24 MAY). Perf 14 (C)

1165	**1099**	32p multicoloured	75	75
1166	**1100**	32p multicoloured	75	75
1167	**1101**	37p multicoloured	85	85
1168	**1102**	37p multicoloured	85	85
1169	**1103**	45p multicoloured	1·20	1·10
1170	**1104**	48p multicoloured	1·50	1·10
1171	**1105**	50p multicoloured	1·70	1·20
1172	**1106**	71p multicoloured	2·50	1·70
1165/72		Set of 8	9·00	8·25
		First Day Cover		10·00
		Presentation Pack	10·50	

Plate Nos.: All values 1A (×4)

Sheets: 10 (2×5) with enlarged illustrated margins at left and foot

Imprint: Lower right-hand margin

Withdrawn: 23.5.2008

1107 Mountain Gorillas
(*illustration reduced. Actual size* 118×84 *mm*)

Endangered Species (4th series). Mountain Gorilla (Gorilla beringei beringei)

(Des Joel Kirk. Litho Austrian State Ptg Wks, Vienna)

2007 (2 AUG). *Sheet* 118×84 mm. Perf 14 (C)

MS1173	**1107**	£2.50 multicoloured	7·00	6·00
		First Day Cover		7·75
		Presentation Pack	7·75	

Withdrawn: 1.8.2008

1108 Engagement, 1947

1109 With Baby Princess Anne

1110 Off-duty

1111 On Tour

1112 With Princes William and Harry

1113 In Recent Years

Diamond Wedding of Queen Elizabeth II and Duke of Edinburgh

(Des Mark Whyte. Litho Enschedé)

2007 (2 AUG). Perf 13½×14 (C)

1174	**1108**	32p multicoloured	75	75
		a. Booklet pane. Nos. 1174/5, each ×2, with margins all round	3·25	
		b. Booklet pane. Nos. 1174 and 1179, each ×2, with margins all round	5·00	
1175	**1109**	37p multicoloured	90	90
		a. Booklet pane. Nos. 1175/6, each ×2, with margins all round	4·00	
1176	**1110**	45p multicoloured	1·10	1·10
		a. Booklet pane. Nos. 1176/7, each ×2, with margins all round	4·50	
1177	**1111**	48p multicoloured	1·10	1·10
		a. Booklet pane. Nos. 1177/8, each ×2, with margins all round	4·50	
1178	**1112**	50p multicoloured	1·20	1·20
		a. Booklet pane. Nos. 1178/9, each ×2, with margins all round	5·75	
1179	**1113**	71p multicoloured	1·70	1·70
1174/9		Set of 6	6·75	6·75
		First Day Cover		8·50
		Presentation Pack	8·50	

Plate Nos.: All values 1A (×4)

Sheets: 10 (2×5) with enlarged illustrated margins at right and foot

Imprint: Central, left-hand margin

Withdrawn: 1.8.2008

1114 St. Peter Port Harbour

1115 Fort Grey, Rocquaine Bay

1116 Point Robert Lighthouse, Sark

1117 Brecqhou seen from Sark

1118 Vazon Bay

1119 Fontenelle Bay

Sea Guernsey

(Litho Austrian State Ptg Wks, Vienna)

2007 (1 OCT). Perf 14×13½ (C)

1180	**1114**	32p multicoloured	75	75
1181	**1115**	37p multicoloured	90	90
1182	**1116**	45p multicoloured	1·10	1·10
1183	**1117**	48p multicoloured	1·10	1·10
1184	**1118**	50p multicoloured	1·50	1·20
1185	**1119**	71p multicoloured	2·00	1·70
1180/5		Set of 6	7·00	6·75
		First Day Cover		8·50
		Presentation Pack	8·50	

The 45p value includes the 'sepac' emblem. This value was also available in a souvenir folder with ten other 'sepac' logo stamps issued by othr participating administrations.

Plate Nos.: All values 1A (×4)

Sheets: 50 (5×10)

Imprint: Upper side margins

Withdrawn: 30.9.2008

1120 Crystal Angel

1121 Crystal Decoration

1122 Pine Cone

1123 Bauble

1124 Snowflake

1125 Decoration with Star

1126 Gold Bauble

1127 Candles

1128 Gold Bell

1129 Wrapped Present

1130 Spiky Star

1131 Fairy

Christmas. Decorations

(Litho Austrian State Ptg Wks, Vienna)

2007 (25 OCT). Perf 14½×15 (C)

1186	**1120**	27p multicoloured	60	60
1187	**1121**	27p multicoloured	60	60
1188	**1122**	27p multicoloured	60	60
1189	**1123**	27p multicoloured	60	60
1190	**1124**	27p multicoloured	60	60
1191	**1125**	27p multicoloured	60	60
1192	**1126**	32p multicoloured	75	75
1193	**1127**	37p multicoloured	90	90
1194	**1128**	45p multicoloured	1·10	1·10
1195	**1129**	48p multicoloured	1·10	1·10
1196	**1130**	50p multicoloured	1·20	1·20
1197	**1131**	71p multicoloured	1·70	1·70
1186/97		Set of 12	10·00	10·00
		First Day Cover		11·50
		Presentation Pack	11·50	

Plate Nos.: All values 1A (×4)

Sheets: 50 (10×5)

Imprint: Upper side margins

Withdrawn: 24.10.2008

Yearbook 2007

2007 (1 DEC). *Comprises Nos.* 1142/97 *and* A298, A301, A304, A308 *and* A309/28.

Yearbook . . . . 85·00

1132 World Touring Car Championship, 2005; 2006; 2007 (*illustration reduced. Actual size* 140×95 *mm*)

Andy Priaulx Triple World Touring Car Champion 2005–2007

(Des Chris Griffiths. Litho Walsall)

2008 (18 JAN). *Sheet* 140×95 *mm.* Perf 14×14½ (C)

MS1198	**1132**	£1×3 multicoloured	7·00	7·00
		First Day Cover		8·75
		Presentation Pack	8·75	

Withdrawn: 17.1.2009

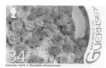
1133 Beadlet Anemones

1134 Sand Crocus

1135 Fulmar

1136 Sheep's-bit

1137 Thick-lipped Grey Mullet

1138 Light Bulb Sea-Squirt

Designation of Gouliot Headland and Caves, Sark as RAMSAR Site

(Des Wendy Bramall. Litho BDT)

2008 (28 FEB). Perf 13½ (C)

1199	**1133**	34p multicoloured	80	80
1200	**1134**	40p multicoloured	95	95
1201	**1135**	48p multicoloured	1·10	1·10
1202	**1136**	51p multicoloured	1·20	1·20
1203	**1137**	53p multicoloured	1·30	1·30
1204	**1138**	74p multicoloured	1·70	1·70
1199/204		*Set of 6*	7·00	7·00
		First Day Cover		8·75
		Presentation Pack	8·75	
MS1205		140×95 mm. Nos. 1199/204	7·00	7·00
		First Day Cover		8·75

Plate Nos.: All values 1A (×4)

Sheets: 10 (2×5) with enlarged illustrated margins at right and foot

Imprint: Central, left-hand margin

Withdrawn: 27.2.2009

1139 Red Campion

1140 Great Bindweed

1141 Spear Thistle

1142 Greater Bird's-foot Trefoil

1143 Sheep's-bit

1144 Marguerite

1145 Sea Campion

Wild Flowers

(Litho (£1, £2 also embossed) Austrian State Ptg Wks)

2008 (28 FEB). Perf 14 (C)

1211	**1139**	10p multicoloured	25	25
1212	**1140**	20p multicoloured	45	45
1213	**1141**	30p multicoloured	70	70
1214	**1142**	40p multicoloured	95	95
1215	**1143**	50p multicoloured	1·20	1·20
1216	**1144**	£1 multicoloured	2·30	2·30
1217	**1145**	£2 multicoloured	4·75	4·75
1211/17		*Set of 7*	10·50	10·50
		First Day Cover		14·00
		Presentation Pack	12·50	
		Set of 7 Gutter Pairs	21·00	

Nos. 1206/10 and 1218/19 are left for possible additions to this definitive series.

Plate Nos.: All values 1A (×4)

Sheets: 50 (2 panes 5×5)

Imprint: Upper side margins

1153 'À la perchôine' ('Till the next time')

1154 'Banjour' ('Hello')

1155 'Oh! Té v'là' ('Oh! There you are')

1156 'Mais oy-ous!' ('Good gracious!')

1157 'Cor chapin!' ('Gor blimey!')

1158 'L'affaire va-t-alle?' ('How are things?')

Europa. The Letter. Quotations in Guernsiasis (Guernsey French) and their English Translations

(Des Chris Griffiths. Litho Cartor)

2008 (15 MAY). Perf 13½×13 (C)

1220	**1153**	34p multicoloured	80	80
1221	**1154**	40p multicoloured	95	95
1222	**1155**	48p multicoloured	1·10	1·10
1223	**1156**	51p multicoloured	1·20	1·20
1224	**1157**	53p multicoloured	1·30	1·30
1225	**1158**	74p multicoloured	1·70	1·70
1220/5		Set of 6	7·00	7·00
		First Day Cover		8·75
		Presentation Pack	8·75	

The new blue plate number/colour dab on the sheet margin of the 40p value is invisible because of the matching background colour.

Plate Nos.: All values 1A (×4)

Sheets: 10 (2×5) with enlarged illustrated left margins

Imprint: Upper right-hand margin

1159 Mr. Happy

1160 Mr. Bump

1161 Little Miss Naughty

1162 Mr. Greedy

1163 Mr. Strong

1164 Mr. Tickle

Mr. Men and Little Miss Series of Children's Books by Roger Hargreaves

(Des Andrew Fothergill. Litho Enschedé)

2008 (15 MAY). Perf 14×13½ (C)

1226	**1159**	34p Type 242	80	80
1227	**1160**	40p Mr. Bump	95	95
1228	**1161**	48p Little Miss Naughty	1·10	1·10
1229	**1162**	51p Mr. Greedy	1·20	1·20
1230	**1163**	53p Mr. Strong	1·30	1·30
1231	**1164**	74p Mr. Tickle	1·70	1·70
1226/31		Set of 6	7·00	7·00
		First Day Cover		8·75
		Presentation Pack	8·75	

Plate Nos.: All values 1A (×4)

Sheets: 10 (2×5) with enlarged illustrated margins at left and foot

Imprint: Lower right-hand margin

1165 Pleimont Point

1166 Saint's Harbour

1167 Rocks at Albecq

1168 Groynes at Vazon Bay

1169 La Bette Bay

1170 Bordeaux Harbour

1171 St. Saviour's Reservoir

1172 Vazon Bay

1173 St. Peter Port Lighthouse

1174 Petit Port

'Abstract Guernsey'. Photographs of Guernsey Coastline

(Litho Walsall)

2008 (9 JUNE). *Self-adhesive.* Perf 12½ (die-cut)

1232	**1165**	(34p) multicoloured	80	80
		a. *Sheetlet. Nos.* 1232/41 . .	8·75	
		b. *Booklet pane. Nos.* 1232/6, *each* ×2	8·00	
		c. *Booklet pane. Nos.* 1232/6, *each* ×2	8·00	
1233	**1166**	(34p) multicoloured	80	80
1234	**1167**	(34p) multicoloured	80	80
1235	**1168**	(34p) multicoloured	80	80
1236	**1169**	(34p) multicoloured	80	80
1237	**1170**	(40p) multicoloured	95	95
		a. *Booklet pane. Nos.* 1237/41, *each* ×2	9·50	
		b. *Booklet pane. Nos.* 1237/41, *each* ×2	9·50	
1238	**1171**	(40p) multicoloured	95	95
1239	**1172**	(40p) multicoloured	95	95
1240	**1173**	(40p) multicoloured	95	95
1241	**1174**	(40p) multicoloured	95	95
1232/41		*Set of* 10	8·75	8·75
		First Day Cover		10·50
		Presentation Pack	10·50	

Nos. 1232/6 were intended for postage within the Bailiwick and are inscribed 'GY'. They were each initially sold at 34p. Nos. 1237/41 were intended for postage to Great Britain and are inscribed 'UK'. They were each initially sold at 40p.

Stamps from the sheetlet 1232*a* measure 12.4 all round, but stamps from booklet panes have a slightly different perforation, 12.4×12.7.

Sheets: (5×2). Nos. 1232/41 were printed in sheetlets of ten containing Nos. 1232/41 (available only from the Philatelic Bureau) and also in booklets of ten or 100, all with the surplus self-adhesive paper around each stamp retained. The booklets of ten contain either Nos. 1232/6×2 (pane no. 1232*b*) or Nos. 1237/41×2 (pane No. 1237*a*), and the stamps are peeled directly from the cover in two blocks 3×2 and 2×2, the blocks separated by a gutter containing text. The

booklets of 100 contain ten panes of either Nos. 1232/6×2 (pane No. 1232*c*) or 1237/41×2 (pane No. 1237*b*). These panes have the stamps in one block 5×2, with plain white backing paper and are stitched at left.

1175 Ford Model T Touring Car, 1913

1176 Delivery Van, 1912

1177 Pick-up, 1925

1178 Couplet, 1917

1179 First World War Army Ambulance

1180 Roadster, 1912

Centenary of the Ford Model T

(Des Robin Carter. Litho BDT)

2008 (31 JULY). Perf 13½ (C)

1242	**1175**	34p multicoloured	80	80
		a. *Booklet pane. Nos.* 1242/5 *with margins all round* . . .	4·00	
		b. *Booklet pane. Nos.* 1242/3 *and* 1246/7 *with margins all round*	4·75	
		c. *Booklet pane. Nos.* 1242, 1244/6 *and* 1247 *with margins all round*	4·75	
		d. *Booklet pane. Nos.* 1242/3 *and* 1245/6 *with margins all round*	4·25	

1243	**1176**	40p multicoloured	95	95
		a. Booklet pane. Nos. 1243/4 and 1246/7 with margins all round	5·00	
1244	**1177**	48p multicoloured	1·10	1·10
		a. Booklet pane. Nos. 1244/7 with margins all round . . .	5·25	
1245	**1178**	51p multicoloured	1·20	1·20
1246	**1179**	53p multicoloured	1·30	1·30
1247	**1180**	74p multicoloured	1·70	1·70
1242/7		Set of 6	7·00	7·00
		First Day Cover		8·75
		Presentation Pack	8·75	

Plate Nos.: All values 1A (×4)

Sheets: 10 (2×5) with enlarged illustrated margins at right and foot

Imprint: Central, left-hand margin

1181 Early Drawing of St. Paul's Cathedral

1182 Cathedral and River Thames, 1860s

1183 Cathedral during World War II Blitz

1184 Cathedral illuminated at Night

1185 Close-up of St. Paul's Cathedral

1186 Cathedral seen from Millennium Bridge

Guernsey Granite at St. Paul's Cathedral, London

(Des Mark Whyte. Litho Cartor)

2008 (31 OCT). Perf 13½ (C)

1248	**1181**	34p multicoloured	80	80
1249	**1182**	40p multicoloured	95	95
1250	**1183**	48p multicoloured	1·10	1·10
1251	**1184**	51p multicoloured	1·20	1·20
1252	**1185**	53p multicoloured	1·30	1·30
1253	**1186**	74p multicoloured	1·70	1·70
1248/53		Set of 6	7·00	7·00
		First Day Cover		8·75
		Presentation Pack	8·75	

Nos. 1248/53 commemorate the 300th anniversary of St. Paul's Cathedral.

They all have powdered Guernsey granite applied to the value tablets.

Plate Nos.: All values 1A (×4)

Sheets: 25 (5×5)

Imprint: Upper left margin

1187 Spruce

1188 Christmas Cactus

1189 Ivy

1190 Cyclamen

1191 Mistletoe

1192 Butchers Broom

1193 Holly

1194 Poinsettia

1195 Bracken

1196 Hawthorn **1197** Clematis **1198** Pyracantha
'Peppermint'

Christmas. Festive Foliage

(Des Andrew Fothergill. Litho Enschedé)

2008 (31 OCT). Perf 14×13½ (C)

1254	**1187**	29p multicoloured	70	70
1255	**1188**	29p multicoloured	70	70
1256	**1189**	29p multicoloured	70	70
1257	**1190**	29p multicoloured	70	70
1258	**1191**	29p multicoloured	70	70
1259	**1192**	29p multicoloured	70	70
1260	**1193**	34p multicoloured	80	80
1261	**1194**	40p multicoloured	95	95
1262	**1195**	48p multicoloured	1·10	1·10
1263	**1196**	51p multicoloured	1·20	1·20
1264	**1197**	53p multicoloured	1·20	1·20
1265	**1198**	74p multicoloured	1·70	1·70
1254/65		*Set of* 12	11·00	11·00
		First Day Cover		14·50
		Presentation Pack	12·50	

Plate Nos.: All value 1A (×4)

Sheets: 50 (10×5)

Imprint: Upper side margins

Yearbook 2008

2008 (1 DEC). *Comprises Nos.* 1199/265 *and* A329/55

Yearbook £110

POSTAGE DUE STAMPS

D **1** Castle Cornet   D **2** Castle Cornet

(Des R. Barrett. Photo Delrieu)

1969 (1 OCT). *Face value in black; background colour given.*
No wmk. Perf 12½×12 (C)

D1	D **1**	1d plum	2·00	1·20
D2		2d bright green	2·00	1·20
D3		3d vermilion	3·00	4·00
D4		4d ultramarine	4·00	5·00
D5		5d yellow-ochre	6·00	4·00
D6		6d turquoise-blue	6·00	4·50
D7		1s lake-brown	10·00	8·00
D1/7		*Set of 7*	30·00	25·00

Sheets: 60 (10×6)

Quantities sold: 1d 82,802; 2d 75,340; 3d 74,532; 4d 74,659; 5d 71,129; 6d 72,912; 1s 71,659

Withdrawn and Invalidated: 14.2.72

Decimal Currency

(Des R. Granger Barrett. Photo Delrieu)

1971 (15 FEB)–**76**. *No wmk. Perf 12½×12 (C)*

D8	D **2**	½p plum (*a*)	10	10
D9		1p bright green (*a*)	10	10
D10		2p vermilion (*a*)	10	10
D11		3p ultramarine (*a*)	10	10
D12		4p yellow-ochre (*a*)	10	10
D13		5p turquoise-blue (*a*)	10	10
D14		6p violet (*c*)	10	10
D15		8p yellow-orange (*b*)	20	40
D16		10p lake-brown (*a*)	20	20
D17		15p grey (*c*)	30	50
D8/17		*Set of 10*	1·20	1·50
D1/13, 16		*Presentation Pack* (*a*)	75·00	
D8/17		*Presentation Pack* (*c*)	2·00	

Printings: (*a*) 15.2.71; (*b*) 7.10.75; (*c*) 10.2.76

Sheets: 60 (10×6)

Withdrawn: 14.2.72 Presentation Pack (Nos. D1/13 and D16); 1.8.78 ½p to 15p (½p and 1p sold out by 6.78)

D **3** St. Peter Port

(Photo Delrieu)

1977 (2 AUG)–**80**. *Face value in black; background colour given. Perf 13 (C)*

D18	D **3**	½p lake-brown (*a*)	10	10
D19		1p bright purple (*a*)	10	10
D20		2p bright orange (*a*)	10	10
D21		3p vermilion (*a*)	10	10
D22		4p turquoise-blue (*a*)	10	10
D23		5p yellow-green (*a*)	10	10
D24		6p turquoise-green (*a*)	10	10
D25		8p brown-ochre (*a*)	10	10
D26		10p ultramarine (*a*)	10	10
D27		14p green (*b*)	20	20
D28		15p bright violet (*a*)	20	20
D29		16p rose-red (*b*)	30	30
D18/29		*Set of 12*	1·50	1·50
D18/26, 28		*Presentation Pack*	2·00	

Printings: (*a*) 2.8.77; (*b*) 5.2.80

Sheets: 50 (5×10)

Withdrawn: 12.7.83 (Presentation Pack sold out earlier)

D **4** Milking Cow

D **5** Vale Mill

D **6** Sark Cottage   D **7** Quay-side, St. Peter Port

D **8** Well, Water Lane, Moulin Huet

D **9** Seaweed Gathering

D **10** Upper Walk, White Rock   D **11** Cobo Bay

112

D **12** Saint's Bay

D**13** La Coupée, Sark

D **14** Old Harbour, St. Peter Port

D **15** Greenhouse, Doyle Road, St. Peter Port

Guernsey Scenes, c. 1900

(Des C. Abbott. Litho Questa)

1982 (13 JULY). Perf 14½ (C)

D30	D **4**	1p indigo, blue-black & brt grn .	10	10
D31	D **5**	2p yellow-brown, sepia & azure	10	10
D32	D **6**	3p blackish green, black & lilac .	10	10
D33	D **7**	4p bottle green, blk & dull orge	10	10
D34	D **8**	5p deep violet-blue, blue-black and turquoise-green	10	10
D35	D **9**	16p dp grey-blue, dp bl & cobalt .	30	35
D36	D **10**	18p steel bl, indigo & apple grn .	35	40
D37	D **11**	20p brown-olive, agate & pale bl	40	45
D38	D **12**	25p Prussian blue, blue-black and rose-pink	50	55
D39	D **13**	30p deep bluish green, blackish olive and bistre-yellow	60	65
D40	D **14**	50p olive-brown, sepia and dull violet-blue	1·00	1·10
D41	D **15**	£1 lt brown, brown & pale brn .	2·00	2·10
D30/41		*Set of 12*	5·25	5·75
		Presentation Pack	6·00	

Sheets: 50 (5×10)

Imprint: Bottom corner, right-hand margin

Withdrawn: 30.9.2001

STAMP BOOKLETS

Prices given are for complete booklets. Booklets Nos. SB1/12 are stitched.

B **1** Military Uniforms

1969 (12 DEC). *White covers as Type B* **1**, *printed in black*

SB1   2s. booklet containing 3×4d (No. 18*a*), 2×5d (No. 19*a*) and 2×1d (No. 14*c*) (*cover showing Trooper, Royal Guernsey Cavalry (Light Dragoons*), 1814)   50

SB2   4s booklet containing 6×4d (No. 18*a*), 4×5d (No. 19*a*) and 4×1d (No. 14*c*) (*cover showing Officer, St. Martin's Company (La Milice Bleue*), *Guernsey*, 1720) . . . .   1·50

SB3   6s booklet containing 9×4d (No. 18*a*), 6×5d (No. 19*a*) and 6×1d (No. 14*c*) (*cover showing Colour Sergeant of Grenadiers and Rifleman, East (Town*) *Regiment, Guernsey*, 1833) . . . .   1·50

Withdrawn: 14.2.72

1970 (29 JUNE). *White covers as Type B* **1**. *Printed in black (SB4), green (SB5) or red (SB6). Same composition as Nos. SB1/3*

SB4   2s booklet (*cover showing Officer, Royal Guernsey Horse Artillery*, 1793) . . . .   2·00

SB5   4s booklet (*cover showing Gunner, Royal Guernsey Artillery*, 1743) . . . .   12·00

SB6   6s booklet (*cover showing Sergeant, Royal Guernsey Light Infantry*, 1832) . . . .   12·00

Quantities sold: 2s (SB1, SB4), 81,928; 4s (SB2, SB5), 23,817; 6s (SB3, SB6), 25,123

Withdrawn: 14.2.72

Decimal Currency

1971 (15 FEB). *White covers as Type B* **1**. *Printed in black (SB7), green (SB8) or red (SB9)*

SB7   10p booklet containing 2×½p (No. 44*a*), 2×2p (No. 47*a*) and 2×2½p (No. 48*b*) (*cover showing Officer, Royal Guernsey Horse Artillery*, 1850)   85

SB8   20p booklet containing 4×½p (No. 44*a*), 4×2p (No. 47*a*) and 4×2½p (No. 48*b*) (*cover showing Sergeant, Guernsey Light Infantry (Grenadiers*), 1826)   70

SB9   30p booklet containing 6×½p (No. 44*a*), 6×2p (No. 47*a*) and 6×2½p (No 48*b*) (*cover showing Sergeant and Bandsman, Royal Guernsey Light Infantry (North Regiment*), 1866) . . . . .   1·00

Withdrawn: 27.6.73 (SB7); 12.3.75 (SB8); 15.1.75 (SB9)

1973 (2 APR). *White covers as Type B* **1**. *Printed in black* (SB10), *green* (SB11) *or red* (SB12)

SB10　10p booklet containing 2×½p (No. 44*ab*), 2×2p (No. 47*ab*) and 2×2½p (No. 48*ba*) (*cover showing Officer, Guernsey Horse Artillery, 1828*) 40

SB11　20p booklet containing 4×½p (No. 44*ab*), 4×2p (No. 47*ab*) and 4×2½p (No. 48*ba*) (*cover showing Grenadier, Guernsey Light Infantry, 1792*) 45

SB12　30p booklet containing 6×½p (No. 44ab), 6×2p (No. 47*ab*) and 6×2½p (No. 48*ba*) (*cover showing Insignia, Royal Guernsey Light Infantry*) 70

Nos. SB10/12 are inscribed 'January 1973' on back cover.

Withdrawn: 1.4.75

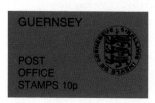

B **2** Arms of Guernsey

1974 (2 APR). *Silver* (SB13) *or gold cover* (SB140 *as Type* B **2**

SB13　10p booklet containing five ½p stamps and three 2½p in *se-tenant* strip (No. 98*a*) 35

SB14　35p booklet containing four ½p stamps, six 2½p and six 3p in *se-tenant* pane (No. 98*b*) 75

The strips and panes have the left-hand selvedge stuck into booklet covers and then folded and supplied in plastic wallets.

Withdrawn: 6.2.79

1977 (8 FEB). *Green cover as Type* B **2**

SB15　20p booklet containing No. 99*a* 55

The note beneath No. SB14 also applies here.

Withdrawn: 12.2.80

BOOKLET PANES from Nos. SB16/18 are loose within card covers supplied in plastic sachets.

1978 (7 FEB). *Blue cover as Type* B **2**

SB16　10p booklet containing No. 99*b* 35

Withdrawn: 12.2.80

1979 (13 FEB). *Covers as Type* B **2**

SB17　10p booklet containing No. 178*a* (*black and green cover*) 40

SB18　30p booklet containing No. 179*a* (*black and red cover*) 90

Withdrawn: 23.2.82

B **3** Castle Cornet

1980 (6 MAY). *Horiz covers as Type B* **3**. *Folded*

SB19　30p booklet containing No. 177*a* (*blue printed cover, Type C*) 60

SB20　50p booklet containing No. 177*b* (*brown printed cover showing view from the sea*) .. 90

Withdrawn: 4.5.83

1981 (24 FEB). *Covers similar to Type B* **3**, *but vert. Folded*

SB21　60p booklet containing No. 180*a* (*red printed cover showing Fort Grey*) .... 1·20

SB22　£1.20 booklet containing No. 180*b* (*green printed cover showing Rokaine Castle*) ..... 2·50

Withdrawn 23.2.84

1982 (2 FEB). *Covers similar to Type B* **3** *showing Fort George. Folded*

SB23　70p booklet containing No. 181*b* (*orange printed cover showing main entrance*) ...... 1·50

SB24　£1.30 booklet containing No. 181*c* (*magenta printed cover showing aerial view of Citadel*) 2·20

Withdrawn: 22.7.85

1983 (14 MAR). *Covers similar to Type B* **3**. *Folded*

SB25　£1 booklet containing No. 180*c* (*new blue printed cover showing States Office, St. Peter Port*) .... 1·90

SB26　£1.30 booklet containing No. 180*d* (*sepia printed cover showing Constable's Office, St. Peter Port*) .... 2·50

Withdrawn: 22.7.85

BOOKLET PANES from Nos. SB27/38 are loose within card covers.

B **4** View of Post Office Headquarters, St. Peter Port

1984 (18 SEPT). *Multicoloured covers as Type* B **4**
SB27 £1 booklet containing No. 299*a* . . . . 2·00
SB28 £1.30 booklet containing No. 299*b* (*cover
    showing Head Post Office, St. Peter Port*) . . 2·50

Quantities sold: SB27 50,393; SB28 25,372
Withdrawn: 1.87

1985 (19 MAR). *Multicoloured covers as Type* B **4**
SB29 £1.20 booklet containing No. 304*a* (*cover
    showing French Halles, St. Peter Port*) . . . . 2·50
SB30 £1.30 booklet containing No. 304*b* (*cover
    showing Market Halls, St. Peter Port*) . . . . . . 2·50

Quantities sold: SB29 49,248; SB30 45,463
Withdrawn: 8.87

1985 (2 DEC). *Multicoloured cover as Type* B **4**, *but vert*
SB31 50p booklet containing No. 297*a* (*cover
    showing Victoria Tower, St. Peter Port*) . . . . . 1·60

Quantity sold: 55,768
Withdrawn: 8.87

1986 (1 APR). *Multicoloured cover as Type* B **4**, *but vert*
SB32 £1.20 booklet containing No. 305*a* (*cover
    showing St. James-the-Less, St. Peter Port*) . 3·00

Quantity sold: 32,627
Withdrawn: 2.89

1987 (30 MAR). *Multicoloured covers as Type* B **4**, *but vert*
SB33 £1 booklet containing No. 298*a* (*cover
    showing Lukis Observatory, St. Peter Port*) . . 2·50
SB34 £1.30 booklet containing No. 306*a* (*cover
    showing Weighbridge, St. Peter Port*) . . . . . . 3·00

Quantities sold: SB33 42,478; SB34 36,369
Withdrawn: 2.89

1988 (28 MAR). *Multicoloured covers as Type* B **4**, *but vert*
SB35 £1 booklet containing No. 299*c* (*cover
    showing North Pier Light, St. Peter Port*) . . . 2·75
SB36 £1·40 booklet containing No. 306*ba* (*cover
    showing Castle Light, St. Peter Port*) . . . . 3·00

Quantities sold: SB35 41,092; SB36 39,478
Withdrawn: 2.90

1989 (28 Feb). *Multicoloured covers as Type* B **4**, *but vert*
SB37 £1 booklet containing No. 299*d* (*cover
    showing Town Church, St. Peter Port*) . . . . . . 3·00
SB38 £1·20 booklet containing No. 306*bb* (*cover
    showing St. Barnabas Church, St. Peter Port*) 3·50

Quantities sold: SB37 47,175; SB38 41,235
Withdrawn: 12.90

B **5** Opening Ceremony, 1939
    (*illustration reduced. Actual size* 163×97 *mm*)

50th Anniversary of Guernsey Airport
1989 (5 MAY). *Multicoloured cover, Type* B **5**. *Booklet
    contains text and illustrations on panes and interleaving
    pages. Stitched*
SB39 £3.90 booklet containing Nos. 456*a*, 458*a* and
    460*a* . . . . 11·00

Quantity sold: 38,025
Sold out: By 11.89

1989 (27 DEC). *Multicoloured covers as Type* B **4**, *but vert*
SB40 £1.20 booklet containing No. 301*a* (*cover
    showing Fish Market, St. Peter Port*) . . . . 3·00
SB41 £1.70 booklet containing No. 308*a* (*cover
    showing Lloyds Bank, St. Peter Port*) . . . . . . 3·75

Quantities sold: SB40 31,736; SB41 31,743
Withdrawn: 21.5.92

B **6** Crown Hotel
    (*illustration reduced. Actual size* 163×97 *mm*)

50th Anniversary of First Guernsey Stamps
1991 (18 FEB). *Multicoloured cover, Type* B **6**. *Booklet
    contains text on panes and text and illustrations on
    interleaving pages. Stitched*
SB42 £4.41 booklet containing No. 517*a*×3 . . . . . . 12·00

Quantity sold: 31,955
Withdrawn: 17.2.92

1991 (2 APR). *Multicoloured covers as Type B* **4**, *but vert*
SB43 £1.30 booklet containing No. 300*a* (*cover showing Golden Lion Inn, St. Peter Port*) ... 3·75
SB44 £1.80 booklet containing No. 309*a* (*cover showing National Trust Building, St. Peter Port* 5·50

Quantities sold: SB43 36,066; SB44 26,029

Withdrawn: 21.5.92

B **7** Carnations

1992 (22 MAY). *Multicoloured covers as Type B* **7**. *Without barcode on the reverse*. *Panes attached by selvedge*
SB45 £1.45 booklet containing pane No. 572*ac* (*cover Type B* **7**) .... 4·00
SB46 £1.80 booklet containing pane No. 574*ac* (*cover showing mixed freesias*) .... 6·00

Withdrawn: 31.8.99

B **8** Bow of Ship and Relics
  (*illustration reduced. Actual size* 163×97 *mm*)

'Operation Asterix'

1992 (18 SEPT). *Multicoloured cover, Type B* **8**. *Booklet contains text and illustrations on interleaving pages. Stitched*
SB47 £5.60 booklet containing No. 583*a*×4 ...... 15·00

Quantity sold: 24,211

Withdrawn: 17.9.93

1993 (2 MAR)–**95**. *Multicoloured covers as Type B* **7**, *but different Guernsey Post Office logo*. *Without barcode on the reverse*. *Panes attached by selvedge*
SB48 £1.12 booklet containing pane No. 577*ab* (*cover showing Lisianthus*) .... 3·50

SB49 £1.28 booklet containing pane No. 572*ad* (*cover Type B* **7**) .... 3·25
  a. With barcode sticker on reverse (6.95) ... 7·00
  b. Barcode printed on reverse (10.95) ...... 4·00
SB50 £1.92 booklet containing pane No. 575*ab* (*cover showing standard roses*) .... 5·50
  a. With barcode sticker on reverse (3.95) ... 9·00
  b. Barcode printed on reverse (6.95) .... 5·25

Withdrawn: 31.8.99

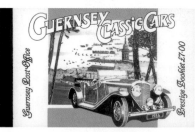

B **9** Thomas de la Rue
  (*illustration reduced. Actual size* 163×97 *mm*)

Birth Bicentenary of Thomas de la Rue (printer)

1993 (27 JULY). *Multicoloured cover as Type B* **9**. *Booklet contains text and illustrations on interleaving pages. Stapled*
SB51 £5.60 booklet containing panes Nos. 617*a*/21*a* .... 13·00

Withdrawn: 26.7.94

1994 (18 FEB). *Multicoloured cover as Type B* **7**, *but different Guernsey Post Office logo. With barcode on reverse. Pane attached by selvedge*
SB52 £1 booklet containing pane No. 576*ab* (*cover showing Iris 'Ideal'*) .... 3·00

Withdrawn: 31.8.99

B **10** Guernsey View and 1936 Bentley
  (*illustration reduced. Actual size* 162×97 *mm*)

Centenary of First Car in Guernsey

1994 (19 JULY). *Black and grey cover as Type B* **10**. *Booklet contains text and illustrations on labels attached to panes and on interleaving pages. Stitched*
SB53 £7 booklet containing panes Nos. 639*a*/43*a* . 19·00

Withdrawn 18.7.95

B **11** Coins, Postbox and Stamps 'Face'

Greetings Stamps. 'The Welcoming Face of Guernsey'
1995 (28 FEB). *Multicoloured cover as Type B* **11**. *Miniature sheet folded and attached by selvedge*
SB54   £1.92 booklet containing No. **MS**671 . . . . . .   4·50

Withdrawn: 27.2.96

B **12** Stamps and Magnifying Glass
(*illustration reduced. Actual size* 97×163 *mm*)

Centenary of Cinema. Screen Detectives
1996 (6 NOV). *Multicoloured cover as Type B* **12**. *Booklet contains text and illustrations on margins of panes and interleaving pages. Stitched*
SB55   £7.04 booklet containing panes Nos. 711a/15a . . . .   19·00

Quantity sold: 18,370
Withdrawn: 5.11.97

B **13** Freesia 'Pink Glow'

1997 (2 JAN). *Multicoloured covers as Type B* **13**. *With barcode on reverse. Panes attached by selvedge*
SB56   £1.04 booklet containing pane No. 576bb (*cover Type B* **13**) . . . .   4·50
SB57   £1.44 booklet containing pane No. 572bb (*cover showing Standard Rose*) . . . .   4·75
SB58   £2 booklet containing No. 576ab×2 (*cover showing Iris 'Ideal'*) . . . .   10·00

Withdrawn: 31.8.99

B **14** Castle Cornet, Guernsey

Guernsey Scenes (1st series)
1997 (24 APR). *Multicoloured covers as Type B* **14**. *Self-adhesive*
SB59   £1.04 booklet containing pane No. 739a (*cover as Type B* **14**) . . . .   6·00
SB60   £1.44 booklet containing pane No. 737a (*cover showing Shell Beach, Herm*) . . . .   7·50
SB61   £2 booklet containing pane No. 738a (*cover showing La Seigneurie, Sark*) . . . .   8·50

Withdrawn: 31.3.98

B **15** Queen Elizabeth and Prince Philip
(*illustration reduced. Actual size 162×95 mm*)

Golden Wedding

1997 (20 NOV). *Multicoloured cover as Type* B **15**. *Booklet contains text and illustrations on panes and interleaving pages. Stitched*
SB62 £8.48 booklet containing Nos. 754a/b, 756a
and 758a . . . . 22·00

Withdrawn: 19.11.98

B **16** Millennium Tapestry
(*illustration reduced. Actual size 162×97 mm*)

The Millennium Tapestries Project

1998 (10 FEB). *Multicoloured cover as Type* B **16**. *Booklet contains text and illustrations on pane margins and interleaving pages. Stitched*
SB63 £7.50 booklet containing Nos. 760b/c, 762a,
764a and 766a . . . . 18·00

Withdrawn: 9.2.99

B **17** Fort Grey

Guernsey Scenes (2nd series)

1998 (25 MAR). *Multicoloured covers as Type* B **17**. *Self-adhesive*
SB64 £1.60 booklet containing pane No. 770b
(*cover as Type* B **17**) . . . . 7·00
SB65 £2 booklet containing pane No. 772b (*cover
showing Guernsey cow*) . . . . 8·00

Sold out: 6.2001

B **18** Queen Elizabeth the Queen Mother
(*illustration reduced. Actual size 160×100 mm*)

Life and Times of Queen Elizabeth the Queen Mother

1999 (4 FEB). *Multicoloured cover as Type* B **18**. *Booklet contains text and illustrations on pane margins and interleaving pages. Stitched*
SB66 £7.50 booklet containing panes Nos. 817b/c,
819b, 821b and 923b . . . . 20·00

Withdrawn: 3.2.2000

B **19** Supermarine Spitfire over St. Peter Port
(*illustration reduced. Actual size* 163×97 *mm*)

60th Anniversary of Battle of Britain

2000 (28 APR). *Multicoloured cover as Type B* **19**. *Booklet contains text and illustrations on interleaving pages. Stitched*
SB67 £6.99 booklet containing pages Nos. 857a/c, 858a and 862a . . . . 18·00

Withdrawn: 27.4.2001

B **20** Albecq Beach
(*illustration reduced. Actual size* 100×60 *mm*)

Island Scenes

2001 (26 APR). *Multicoloured covers as Type B* **20**. *Self-adhesive.*
SB68 (£2.20) booklet containing pane No. 901b
(*cover as Type B* **20**) . . . . 5·00
SB69 (£2.70) booklet containing pane No. 906b
(*cover showing Telegraph Bay, Alderney*) . . . 7·50

Sold out: By 7.2004

B **21** Droplet of Water on Leaf
(*illustration reduced. Actual size* 160×95 *mm*)

Incorporation of Guernsey Post Ltd

2001 (1 AUG). *Multicoloured cover as Type B* **21**. *Booklet contains text on panes and transparent interleaves. Stitched*
SB70 £8.05 booklet containing panes Nos. 921a/7a 18·00

Withdrawn: 31.7.02

B **22** Queen Elizabeth carrying Bouquet
(*illustration reduced. Actual size* 165×98 *mm*)

Golden Jubilee

2002 (30 APR). *Multicoloured cover as Type B* **22**. *Booklet contains text and photographs on interleaving panes. Stitched*
SB71 £9.05 booklet containing panes Nos. 948a/c and 949a with Alderney No. **MS**A184 . . . . . . 21·00

Withdrawn: 29.4.2003

B **23** Prince William and His Coat of Arms
(*illustration reduced. Actual size* 162×98 *mm*)

21st Birthday of Prince William of Wales

2003 (21 JUNE). *Multicoloured cover as Type B* **23**. *Booklet contains text and photographs on panes and interleaving pages. Stitched.*
SB72 £8.10 booklet containing panes Nos. 998ba/bc and 999ba/bb . . . . 18·00

Withdrawn: 20.6.2004

B **24** Clematis 'Pistachio'
(*illustration reduced. Actual size 100×60 mm*)

Raymond Evison's Guernsey Clematis

2004 (29 JAN). *Multicoloured covers as Type B* **24**. *Self-adhesive (Nos. SB73/4) or stitched (Nos. SB75/6).*

SB73	(£2.20) booklet containing pane No. 1017*b* (*cover Type B* **24**)	7·00
SB74	(£2.70) booklet containing pane No. 1022*a*) (*cover showing Clematis 'Anna Louise'*)	8·75
SB75	(£22) booklet containing ten panes of No. 1017*c* (*cover as Type B* **24**, *but* 181×59 *mm*)	50·00
SB76	(£27) booklet containing ten panes of No. 1022*b*) (*cover showing Clematis 'Anna Louise'*, 181×59 *mm*)	60·00

Sold out: By 10.2007

B **25** Ruins of Ancient Greece
(*illustration reduced. Actual size 163×98 mm*)

Olympic Games, Athens, Greece

2004 (29 JULY). *Multicoloured cover as Type B* **25**. *Booklet contains text and illustrations on panes and interleaving pages. Stitched.*

SB77	£9.90 booklet containing panes Nos. 1045*a*/*d*, 1046*a* and **MS**1049*a*	29·00

Withdrawn: 28.7.2005

B **26** St. Peter Port Harbour and Castle Cornet at Dawn
(*illustration reduced. Actual size 164×98 mm*)

'Sea Guernsey 2005'

2005 (21 JULY). *Multicoloured cover as Type B* **26**. *Booklet contains text and illustrations on panes and interleaving pages. Stitched.*

SB78	£9.69 booklet containing panes Nos. 1080*a*/*b*, 1081*a*/*b*, 1082*a* and 1083*a*	19·00

Withdrawn: 20.7.2006

B **27** Isambard Kingdom Brunel
(*illustration reduced. Actual size 163×98 mm*)

Birth Bicentenary of Isambard Kingdom Brunel (engineer)

2006 (20 MAY). *Multicoloured cover as Type B* **27**. *Booklet contains text and illustrations on panes and interleaving pages. Stitched.*

SB79	£10.60 booklet containing panes Nos. 1110*a*/*d*, 1111*a* and 1112*a*	25·00

Withdrawn: 19.5.2007

B **28** Seashore
(*illustration reduced. Actual size 101×59 mm*)

125th Anniversary of La Société Guernesiaise

2007 (8 MAR). *Multicoloured covers as Type* B **28**. *Self-adhesive* (*Nos.* SB80/1) *or stitched* (*Nos.* SB82/3).

SB80   (£3.20) booklet containing pane No. 1149*b*
     (*cover Type* B **28**) . . . .   7·50
SB81   (£3.70) booklet containing pane No. 1154*a*
     (*cover showing lighthouse*) . . . .   8·75
SB82   (£32) booklet containing ten panes of No.
     1149*c* (*cover as Type* B **28**, *but* 180×59 *mm*)   65·00
SB83   (£37) booklet containing ten panes of No.
     1154*b* (*cover showing lighthouse*, 180×59
     mm) . . . .   75·00

B **29** Queen Elizabeth II and Duke of Edinburgh
     (*illustration reduced. Actual size* 161×98 *mm*)

Diamond Wedding of Queen Elizabeth II and Duke of Edinburgh

2007 (2 AUG). *Cover as Type* B **29** *showing black/white photograph. Booklet contains text and illustrations on panes and interleaving pages. Stitched.*

SB84   £11.32 booklet containing panes Nos.
     1174*a/b* and 1175*a/8a* . . . .   27·00

Withdrawn: 1.8.2008

B **30** Coastal Rocks
     (*illustration reduced. Actual size* 101×59 *mm*)

'Abstract Guernsey'

2008 (8 JUNE). *Multicoloured covers as Type* B **30**. *Self-adhesive* (*Nos.* SB85/6) *or stitched* (*Nos.* SB87/8).

SB85   (£3.40) booklet containing pane No. 1232*c*
     (*cover Type* B **30**) . . . .   8·00
SB86   (£4) booklet containing pane No. 1237*b* (*cover
     showing coastal rocks at sunset*) . . . .   9·50

SB87   (£34) booklet containing ten panes of No.
     1232*d* (*cover as Type* B **30**, *but* 182×58 *mm*)   65·00
SB88   (£40) booklet containing ten panes of No.
     1237*c* (*cover showing coastal rocks at
     sunset*, 182×58 *mm*) . . . .   75·00

B **31** Ford Model T Production Line
     (*illustration reduced. Actual size* 162×98 *mm*)

Centenary of the Ford Model T

2008 (31 JULY). *Multicoloured cover as Type* B **31**. *Booklet contains text and illustrations on panes and interleaving pages. Stitched.*

SB89   £12 booklet containing panes Nos. 1242*a/d*,
     1243*a* and 1244*a* . . . .   28·00

ALDERNEY

The following issues are provided by the Guernsey Post Office for use on Alderney. They are also valid for postal purposes throughout the rest of the Bailiwick of Guernsey.

A **1** Island Map

A **2** Hanging Rock

A **3** States' Building, St. Anne

A **4** St. Anne's Church

A **5** Yachts in Braye Bay

A **6** Victoria St, St. Anne

A **7** Map of Channel

A **8** Fort Clonque

A **9** Corblets Bay and Fort

A **10** Old Tower, St. Anne

A **11** Golf Course and Essex Castle

A **12** Old Harbour

A **12a** Quesnard Lighthouse

A **12b** Braye Harbour

A **12c** The Island Hall

A **12d** *J. T. Daly* (steam locomotive)

A **12e** *Louis Marchesi of Round Table* (lifeboat)

Island Scenes

(Des G. Drummond. Litho B.D.T. (20p to 28p) or photo Courvoisier (others))

1983 (14 JUNE)–**93**. *Granite paper* (1p to 18p). Perf 15×14 (20p to 28p) or 11½ (others), both comb

A1	A **1**	1p multicoloured (*a*)	10	10
A2	A **2**	4p multicoloured (*a*)	10	10
A3	A **3**	9p multicoloured (*a*)	15	15
A4	A **4**	10p multicoloured (*a*)	20	15
A5	A **5**	11p multicoloured (*a*)	20	20
A6	A **6**	12p multicoloured (*a*)	25	20
A7	A **7**	13p multicoloured (*a*)	25	20
A8	A **8**	14p multicoloured (*a*)	30	20
A9	A **9**	15p multicoloured (*a*)	35	20
A10	A **10**	16p multicoloured (*a*)	35	25
A11	A **11**	17p multicoloured (*a*)	40	30
A12	A **12**	18p multicoloured (*a*)	40	30

A12a	A **12a**	20p multicoloured (b)	. . . .	1·00	90
A12b	A **12b**	21p multicoloured (c)	. . . .	1·00	90
A12c	A **12c**	23p multicoloured (d)	. . . .	95	85
A12d	A **12d**	24p multicoloured (e)	. . . .	1·70	1·70
A12e	A **12e**	28p multicoloured (e)	. . . .	2·20	2·20
A1/12e		Set of 17	. . . .	9·00	8·00
		First Day Covers (6)	. . . . . .		22·00
		Presentation Pack (2)	. . . .	10·00	
		Set of 17 Gutter Pairs	. . . .	18·00	

Printings: (a) 14.6.83; (b) 27.12.89; (c) 2.4.91; (d) 6.2.92; (e) 2.3.93

Plate and Cylinder Nos.: 1p, 12p, 13p, 17p, 20p to 28p 1A, 1B, 1C, 1D (each ×4); others 1A, 1B, 1C, 1D (each ×5)

Sheets: 40 (2 panes 5×4)

Imprint: Central, bottom margin

Quantities sold: 1p 1,337,865; 4p 465,887; 9p 680,896; 10p 709,197; 11p 778,483; 12p 573,124; 13p 671,772; 14p 1,027,248; 15p 740,519; 16p 542,970; 17p 404,323; 18p 491,877; 20p 248,694; 21p 233,975; 23p 237,345; 24p 311,144; 28p 134,765

Withdrawn: 4.6.94

A **13** Oystercatcher

A **14** Ruddy Turnstone

A **15** Ringed Plover

A **16** Dunlin

A **17** Curlew

Birds

(Des and photo Harrison)

1984 (12 JUNE). Perf 14½ (C)

A13	A **13**	9p multicoloured	. . . .	1·10	60
A14	A **14**	13p multicoloured	. . . .	1·10	75
A15	A **15**	26p multicoloured	. . . .	2·50	2·75
A16	A **16**	28p multicoloured	. . . .	2·50	2·75
A17	A **17**	31p multicoloured	. . . .	2·50	1·70
A13/17		Set of 5	. . . .	8·75	7·75
		First Day Cover	. . . .		9·00
		Presentation Pack	. . . .	10·00	
		Set of 5 Gutter Pairs	. . . . . .	18·00	

Cylinder Nos.: All values 1A, 1B (each ×5)

Sheets: 50 (2 panes 5×5)

Imprint: Bottom margin, right-hand corner

Quantities sold: 9p 285,931; 13p 360,619; 26p 246,916; 28p 261,370; 31p 334,484

Withdrawn: 11.6.85

A **18** Westland Wessex HCC.4 Helicopter of the Queen's Flight

A **19** Britten Norman 'long-nose' Trislander

A **20** De Havilland D.H.114 Heron 1B

A **21** De Havilland D.H.89A Dragon Rapide Sir Henry Lawrence

A **22** Saro A.21 Windhover Amphibian City of Portsmouth

50th Anniversary of Alderney Airport

(Des A. Theobald. Photo Courvoisier)

1985 (19 MAR). Granite paper. Perf 11½ (C)

A18	A **18**	9p multicoloured	. . . .	1·40	70
A19	A **19**	13p multicoloured	. . . .	1·70	1·00
A20	A **20**	29p multicoloured	. . . .	3·00	2·75
A21	A **21**	31p multicoloured	. . . .	3·50	3·50
A22	A **22**	34p multicoloured	. . . .	3·50	3·50
A18/22		Set of 5	. . . .	12·00	11·00
		First Day Cover	. . . .		14·00
		Presentation Pack	. . . . . .	14·00	

Cylinder Nos.: All values A1–1–1–1–1, B1–1–1–1–1

Sheets: 25 (5×5)

Quantities sold: 9p 294,437; 13p 321,276; 29p 231,422; 31p 171,528; 34p 162,429

Withdrawn: 18.3.86

A **23** Royal Engineers, 1890

A **24** Duke of Albany's Own Highlanders (72nd Highland Regt), 1856

A **25** Royal Artillery, 1855

A **26** South Hampshire Regiment, 1810

A **27** Royal Irish Regiment, 1782

Regiments of the Alderney Garrison

(Des E. Stemp. Litho Harrison)

1985 (24 SEPT). Perf 14½ (C)

A23	A **23**	9p multicoloured	25	20
A24	A **24**	14p multicoloured	80	40
A25	A **25**	29p multicoloured	80	70
A26	A **26**	31p multicoloured	1·10	1·10
A27	A **27**	34p multicoloured	1·40	1·50
A23/7		Set of 5	4·00	3·75
		First Day Cover		6·00
		Presentation Pack	6·00	
		Set of 5 Gutter Pairs	8·00	

No. A24 shows the tartan and insignia of the 78th Highland Regiment in error.

Plate Nos.: All values 1A, 1B, 1C, 1D (each ×5)
Sheets: 50 (2 panes 5×5)
Imprint: Central, left-hand margin of each pane
Quantities sold: 9p 286,572; 14p 283,493; 29p 224,196; 31p 151,948; 34p 145,422
Withdrawn: 23.9.86

A **28** Fort Grosnez

A **29** Fort Tourgis

A **30** Fort Clonque

A **31** Fort Albert

Alderney Forts

(Des R. Reed. Litho Cartor)

1986 (23 SEPT). Perf 13×13½ (C)

A28	A **28**	10p multicoloured	80	20
A29	A **29**	14p multicoloured	90	80
A30	A **30**	31p multicoloured	2·50	3·00
A31	A **31**	34p multicoloured	2·50	3·00
A28/31		Set of 4	6·00	6·25
		First Day Cover		8·00
		Presentation Pack	7·00	
		Set of 4 Gutter Pairs	12·00	

Plate Nos.: All values 1A, 1B, 1C, 1D (each ×5)
Sheets: 50 (2 panes 5×5)
Imprint: Left-hand margin of left-hand pane
Quantities sold: 10p 325,706; 14p 231,891; 31p 143,423; 34p 138,556
Withdrawn: 22.9.87

A **32** Liverpool (full-rigged ship), 1902

A **33** Petit Raymond (schooner), 1906

A **34** *Maina* (yacht), 1910

A **35** *Burton* (steamer), 1911

A **36** *Point Law* (oil tanker), 1975

A **39** Goodwin's Map of 1831

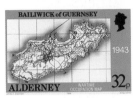

A **40** General Staff Map of 1943

A **41** Ordnance Survey Map of 1988

Alderney Shipwrecks

(Des C. Jacques. Litho Questa)

1987 (5 MAY). Perf 14×14½ (C)

A32	A **32**	11p multicoloured		1·60	50
A33	A **33**	15p multicoloured		1·70	60
A34	A **34**	29p multicoloured		3·00	3·50
A35	A **35**	31p multicoloured		3·75	3·50
A36	A **36**	34p multicoloured		4·00	4·25
A32/6		*Set of* 5		12·00	11·00
		First Day Cover			11·00
		Presentation Pack		15·00	
		Set of 5 *Gutter Pairs*		24·00	

Plate Nos.: All values 1A, 1B, 1C, 1D (each ×4)

Sheets: 50 (2 panes 5×5)

Imprint: Bottom, right-hand margin of each pane

Quantities sold: 11p 228,998; 15p 233,861; 29p 139,453; 31p 148,572; 34p 145,641

Withdrawn: 4.5.88

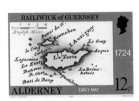

A **37** Moll's Map of 1724

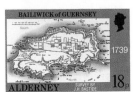

A **38** Bastide's Survey of 1739

250th Anniversary of Bastide's Survey of Alderney

(Des J. Cooter. Litho Enschedé)

1989 (7 JULY). Perf 13½×14 (C)

A37	A **37**	12p multicoloured	25	25
A38	A **38**	18p blk, greenish blue & orge-brn	45	30
A39	A **39**	27p black, greenish blue and dull yellow-green	95	1·10
A40	A **40**	32p black, greenish blue & brt rose-red	1·10	1·10
A41	A **41**	35p multicoloured	1·50	1·40
A37/41		*Set of* 5	3·75	3·75
		First Day Cover		4·75
		Presentation Pack	5·00	
		Set of 5 *Gutter Pairs*	7·50	

Plate Nos.: 12p 1–1–1–1; 18p, 27p, 32p 1–1–1; 35p 1–1–1–1–1

Sheets: 50 (2 panes 5×5)

Imprint: Central, both margins of each pane

Quantities sold: 12p 169,993; 18p 194,667; 27p 148,621; 32p 158,600; 35p 153,544

Withdrawn: 6.7.90

A **42** H.M.S. *Alderney* (bomb ketch), 1738

A **43** H.M.S. *Alderney* (frigate), 1742

A **44** H.M.S. *Alderney* (sloop), 1755

A **45** H.M.S. *Alderney* (submarine), 1945

A **46** H.M.S. *Alderney* (patrol vessel), 1979

A **51** Trinity House Vessel *Patricia* and Arms

Royal Navy Ships named after Alderney

(Des A. Theobald. Litho B.D.T.)

1990 (3 MAY). Perf 13½ (C)

A42	A **42**	14p black and olive-bistre	25	20
A43	A **43**	20p black and orange-brown	45	35
A44	A **44**	29p black and cinnamon	1·00	1·00
A45	A **45**	34p black & pale turquoise-blue	1·10	1·50
A46	A **46**	37p black and cobalt	1·40	1·50
A42/6		*Set of 5*	3·75	4·00
		First Day Cover		5·50
		Presentation Pack	4·50	
		Set of 5 Gutter Pairs	7·50	

Plate Nos.: 14p, 20p, 29p, 34p 1A–1A, 1B–1B, 37p 1A–1A, 1B–1B, 1C–1C, 1D–1D

Sheets: 50 (2 panes 5×5)

Imprint: Central, side margins of each pane

Quantities sold: 14p 290,801; 20p 291,996; 29p 142,011; 34p 146,711; 37p 151,711

Withdrawn: 4.5.91

Automation of the Casquets Lighthouse

(Des A. Theobald. Litho Cartor)

1991 (30 APR). Perf 14×13½ (C)

A47	A **47**	21p multicoloured	80	50
A48	A **48**	26p multicoloured	1·90	1·70
A49	A **49**	31p multicoloured	2·00	2·20
A50	A **50**	37p multicoloured	2·75	3·25
A51	A **51**	50p multicoloured	3·75	3·50
A47/51		*Set of 5*	10·00	9·00
		First Day Cover		9·00
		Presentation Pack	10·50	
		Set of 5 Gutter Pairs	20·00	

Plate Nos.: All values 1A, 1B, 1C, 1D (each ×4)

Sheets: 50 (2 panes 5×5)

Imprint: Central, side margins

Quantities sold: 21p 280,555; 26p 164,155; 31p 158,465; 37p 158,375; 50p 238,825

Withdrawn: 29.4.92

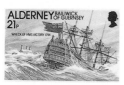

A **47** Wreck of H.M.S. *Victory*, 1744

A **48** Lighthouse Keeper's Daughter rowing back to the Casquets

A **49** MBB-Bolkow Bo105D Helicopter leaving pad on St. Thomas Tower

A **50** Migrating Birds over Lighthouse

A **52** Two French Warships on Fire

A **53** Crews leaving burning Ships

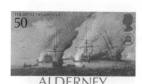

A **54** French Warship sinking

A **55** 'The Battle of La Hogue'

126

300th Anniversary of Battle of La Hogue

(Des C. Abbott. Litho B.D.T.)

1992 (18 SEPT). Perf 14×15 (50p) or 13½ (others), both comb

A52	A **52**	23p multicoloured	1·10	1·00
A53	A **53**	28p multicoloured	2·40	2·50
A54	A **54**	33p multicoloured	2·75	3·00
A55	A **55**	50p multicoloured	3·00	3·50
A52/5		Set of 4	8·00	9·00
		First Day Cover		8·50
		Presentation Pack	9·00	
		Set of 4 Gutter Pairs	16·00	

Nos. A52/4 show details of the painting on the 50p value.

Plate Nos.: All values 1A, 1B (each ×5)

Sheets: 50 (2 panes 5×5)

Imprint: Central, right-hand margin (50p) or central, side margins (others)

Quantities sold: 23p 238,820; 28p 188,685; 33p 172,565; 50p 186,096

Withdrawn: 17.9.93

A **56** Spiny Lobster

A **57** Plumrose Anemone

A **58** Starfish

A **59** Sea Urchin

Endangered Species. Marine Life

(Des A. Peck. Litho Questa)

1993 (2 NOV). Perf 14½ (C)

A56	A **56**	24p multicoloured	60	30
		a. Horiz strip of 4. Nos. A56/9 .	5·50	6·00
A57	A **57**	28p multicoloured	60	35
A58	A **58**	33p multicoloured	70	40
A59	A **59**	39p multicoloured	90	60
A56/9		Set of 4	5·50	6·00
		First Day Cover		6·00
		Presentation Pack	6·50	

Plate Nos.: All values 1A, 1B (each ×5)

Sheets: 16 (4×4), Nos. A56/9 were printed together, *se-tenant*, in horizontal strips of 4 throughout the sheet

Imprint: Central, right-hand margin

Quantity sold: 216.788 strips

Withdrawn: 1.11.94

A **60** Blue-tailed Damselfly, Dark Hair Water Crowfoot and Branched Bur-reed

A **61** White-toothed Shrew and Flax-leaved St. John's Wort

A **62** Fulmar and Kaffir Fig

A **63** Clouded Yellow (butterfly) and Red Clover

A **64** Bumble Bee, Prostrate Broom and Giant Broomrape

A **65** Dartford Warbler and Lesser Dodder

A **66** Peacock (butterfly) and Stemless Thistle

A **67** Mole and Bluebell

A **68** Great Green
Grasshopper and
Common Gorse

A **69** Six-spot Burnet
(moth) and
Viper's Bugloss

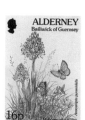

A **70** Common Blue
(butterfly) and
Pyramidal Orchid

A **70a** Small Tortoiseshell
(butterfly) and
Buddleia

A **71** Common Rabbit
and Creeping
Buttercup

A **72** Greater Black-
backed Gull and
Sand Crocus

A **72a** Rock Pipit and
Sea Stock

A **72b** Sand Digger Wasp
and Sea Bindweed

A **73** Atlantic Puffin
and English
Stonecrop

A **74** Emperor (moth)
and Bramble

A **75** Pale-spined
Hedgehog and
Pink Oxalis

A **76** Common Tern and
Bermuda Grass

A **77** Northern Gannet and
Fucus vesiculosus
(seaweed)

Flora and Fauna

(Des Wendy Bramall. Litho B.D.T. (No. A71a) or Questa
(others))

1994 (5 MAY)–**98**. Perf 14½ (C)

A60	A **60**	1p multicoloured (a)	10	10
A61	A **61**	2p multicoloured (a)	10	10
A62	A **62**	3p multicoloured (a)	10	10
A63	A **63**	4p multicoloured (a)	10	10
A64	A **64**	5p multicoloured (a)	10	10
A65	A **65**	6p multicoloured (a)	15	20
A66	A **66**	7p multicoloured (a)	15	20
A67	A **67**	8p multicoloured (a)	15	20
A68	A **68**	9p multicoloured (a)	20	25
A69	A **69**	10p multicoloured (a)	20	25
A70	A **70**	16p multicoloured (a)	55	40
		a. Perf 14×15	55	50
		ab. Booklet pane of 8	4·00	
A70b	A **70a**	18p multicoloured (c)	35	40
		ba. Perf 14×15	35	40
		bb. Booklet pane of 8	3·00	
A71	A **71**	20p multicoloured (a)	40	45
		a. Perf 14×15 (d)	40	45
		ab. Booklet pane of 8	3·75	

128

A72	A **72**	24p multicoloured (*a*)	50	55
		a. Perf 14×15	50	55
		ab. Booklet pane of 8	4·25	
A72*b*	A **72a**	25p multicoloured (*c*)	50	55
		ba. Perf 14×15	50	55
		bb. Booklet pane of 8	4·00	
A72*c*	A **72b**	26p multicoloured (*c*)	50	55
A73	A **73**	30p multicoloured (*a*)	60	65
A74	A **74**	40p multicoloured (*a*)	80	85
A75	A **75**	50p multicoloured (*a*)	1·50	1·20
A76	A **76**	£1 multicoloured (*a*)	2·50	2·20
A77	A **77**	£2 multicoloured (*b*)	5·00	4·50
A60/77		Set of 21	12·50	13·00
		First Day Covers (5)		17·00
		Presentation Packs (3)	16·00	
		Stamp-cards (set of 21)	4·50	18·00
		Set of 21 Gutter Pairs	25·00	

Nos. A70*a*, A70*ba*, A71*a*, A72*a* and A72*ba* were issued in booklets with the upper and lower edges of the panes imperforate. Unfolded booklet panes were also available from the Philatelic Bureau and Head Post Office.

Printings: (*a*) 5.5.94; (*b*) 28.2.95; (*c*) 2.1.97; (*d*) 25.3.98

Plate Nos.: 1p, 3p, 5p, 7p, 9p, 16p, 18p, 20p, 25p, 26p, 40p 1A, 1B (each ×4); 2p, 4p, 6p, 8p, 10p, 24p, 30p, 50p 1C, 1D (each ×4); £1, £2 1A, 1B, 1C, 1D (each ×4)

Sheets: 50 (2 panes 5 × 5)

Imprint: £1, £2 Central left margin of each pane; others central left or right margin of each pane

Sold out: 4.2001 (1p to 16p, 20p, 24p, 30p to £1); by 10.2006 (18p, 25p, 26p and £2)

A **78** Royal Aircraft Factory SE5A

A **79** Miles Master II and other Miles Aircraft

A **80** Miles Aerovan and Miles Monitor

A **81** Miles Falcon Six winning King's Cup Air Race, 1935

A **82** Miles Hawk Speed Six winning Manx Air Derby, 1947

A **83** Miles Falcon Six breaking U.K.–Cape Record, 1936

Birth Centenary of Tommy Rose (aviator)

(Des C. Abbott. Litho B.D.T.)

1995 (1 SEPT). Perf 14×15 (C)

A78	A **78**	35p multicoloured	95	95
		a. Horiz strip of 3. Nos. A78/80	2·75	2·75
A79	A **79**	35p multicoloured	95	95
A80	A **80**	35p multicoloured	95	95
A81	A **81**	41p multicoloured	1·10	1·10
		a. Horiz strip of 3. Nos. A81/3	3·25	3·25
A82	A **82**	41p multicoloured	1·10	1·10
A83	A **83**	41p multicoloured	1·10	1·10
A78/83		Set of 6	6·00	6·00
		First Day Cover		6·75
		Presentation Pack	7·50	
		Gutter strips of 6 (2)	12·00	

Plate Nos.: Both values 1A, 1B, 1C (each ×5)

Sheets: 12 (2 panes 3×2). Nos. A78/80 and A81/3 were printed together, *se-tenant*, as horizontal strips of 3 throughout the sheet

Imprint: Central, bottom margin

Quantities sold: 35p 361,895 strips; 41p 362,801 strips

Withdrawn: 31.8.96

RETURN OF THE ISLANDERS 15 DECEMBER 1945

A **84a** Returning Islanders
(*illustration reduced. Actual size* 93×70 *mm*)

50th Anniversary of Return of Islanders to Alderney

(Des C. Abbott. Litho B.D.T.)

1995 (16 NOV). *Sheet* 93×70 *mm. Perf* 13½ (C)
MSA84 A **84a** £1.65 multicoloured . . . . . . 5·00 5·00
   First Day Cover . . . .   5·50
   Presentation Pack . . . .   5·50

Quantity sold: 139,665

Withdrawn: 15.11.96

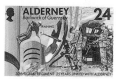

A **85** Signallers training on Alderney

A **86** Communications Station, Falkland Islands

A **87** Dish Aerial and Land Rover, Gulf War

A **88** Service with United Nations

25th Anniversary of Adoption of 30th Signal Regiment by Alderney

(Des A. Theobald. Litho Walsall)

1996 (24 JAN). *Perf* 14 (C)
A85 A **85** 24p multicoloured 45 35
   a. Horiz strip of 4. Nos. A85/8 . 5·50 5·50
A86 A **86** 41p multicoloured 75 55
A87 A **87** 60p multicoloured . . . . 1·10 80

A88 A **88** 75p multicoloured . . . . 1·10 1·10
A85/8   *Set of 4* . . . . 5·50 5·50
   First Day Cover . . . .   6·00
   Presentation Pack . . . .   6·75
   Gutter Strip of 8 . . . . 11·00

Plate Nos.: All values 1A, 1B, 1C, 1D, 1E, 1F (each x4)

Sheets: 16 (2 panes 4×2). Nos. A85/8 were printed in *se-tenant* strips of 4 across the sheet, each strip forming a composite design

Imprint: Central, bottom margin

Quantities sold: 24p 141,697; 41p 141,631; 60p 141,679; 75p 141,680

Withdrawn: 28.1.97

A **89** Cat with Butterfly

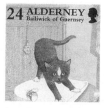

A **90** Blue and White on Table

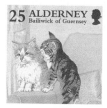

A **91** Tabby Kitten grooming Blue and White Persian Kitten

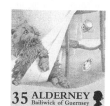

A **92** Red Persian under Table

A **93** White Cat with Tortoiseshell in Toy Cart

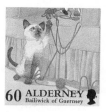

A **94** Siamese playing with Wool

Cats

(Des P. le Vasseur. Litho B.D.T.)

1996 (19 JULY). *Perf* 13½ (C)
A89 A **89** 16p multicoloured 45 35
A90 A **90** 24p multicoloured 65 40
A91 A **91** 25p multicoloured 65 65
A92 A **92** 35p multicoloured . . . . 1·20 1·20

A93	A **93**	41p multicoloured	1·50	1·70
A94	A **94**	60p multicoloured	2·00	2·00
A89/94		Set of 6	6·00	6·00
		First Day Cover		8·00
		Presentation Pack	7·00	
		Set of 6 Gutter Pairs	12·00	
MSA95		144×97 mm. Nos. A89/94	6·50	6·50
		First Day Cover		10·00

Plate Nos.: All values 1A, 1B (each ×4)

Sheets: 50 (2 panes 5×5)

Imprint: Central, right-hand margin of top pane

Quantities sold: 16p 243,841; 24p 243,457; 25p 193,625; 35p 193,393; 41p 192,612; 60p 191,587; miniature sheet 83,144

Withdrawn: 18.7.97

A **95** Harold Larwood

A **96** John Arlott

A **97** Pelham J. Warner

A **98** W. G. Grace

A **99** John Wisden

150th Anniversary of Cricket on Alderney

(Des R. Ollington. Litho Walsall)

1997 (21 AUG). Perf 13½ (C)

A96	A **95**	18p multicoloured	50	30
A97	A **96**	25p multicoloured	65	35
A98	A **97**	37p multicoloured	1·00	1·20
A99	A **98**	43p multicoloured	1·20	1·50
A100	A **99**	63p multicoloured	1·60	1·70
A96/100		Set of 5	4·50	4·50
		First Day Cover		5·50
		Presentation Pack	8·00	
		Set of 5 Gutter Pairs	9·00	
MSA101		190×75 mm. Nos. A96/100 and label	9·00	9·00
		First Day Cover		12·00

Plate Nos.: All values 1A, 1B (each ×5)

Sheets: 50 (2 panes 5×5)

Imprint: Central, top and bottom margins

Quantities sold: 18p 246,846; 25p 246,765; 37p 146,969; 43p 146,886; 63p 148,816; miniature sheet 87,220

Withdrawn: 20.8.98

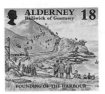

A **100** Railway under Construction

A **101** *Ariadne* (paddle steamer) at Anchor

A **102** Quarrying Stone

A **103** Quarry Railway

A **104** Queen Victoria and Prince Albert on Alderney

A **105** Royal Yacht *Victoria and Albert* and Guard of Honour

A **106** Railway Workers greet Queen Victoria

A **107** Royal Party in Railway Wagons

Garrison Island (1st series). 150th Anniversary of Harbour

(Des R. Carter. Litho Questa)

1997 (20 NOV)–98. Perf 14½×14 (C)

A102	A **100**	18p multicoloured	45	20
		a. Horiz pair. Nos. A102/3 ..	1·10	1·10
		b. Booklet pane. Nos. A102/5 with margins all round (10.11.98)	2·50	
		c. Booklet pane. Nos. A102/3 and A106/7 with margin round (10.11.98) .	2·75	
A103	A **101**	18p multicoloured	45	20
A104	A **102**	25p multicoloured	65	30
		a. Horiz pair. Nos. A104/5 ..	1·50	1·50
		b. Booklet pane. Nos. A104/5 and A108/9 with margins all round (10.11.98)	3·50	
A105	A **103**	25p multicoloured	65	30
A106	A **104**	26p multicoloured	70	30
		a. Horiz pair. Nos. A106/7 ..	1·70	1·70
		b. Booklet pane. Nos. A106/9 with margins all round (10.11.98)	3·75	
A107	A **105**	26p multicoloured	70	30
A108	A **106**	31p multicoloured	80	35
		a. Horiz pair. Nos. A108/9 ..	2·00	2·00
A109	A **107**	31p multicoloured	80	35
A102/9		Set of 8	6·00	6·00
		First Day Cover		6·50
		Presentation Pack	8·00	

See also Nos. A116/23, A132/9, A154/61 and A176/83.

Plate Nos.: All values 1A, 1B (each ×4)

Sheets: 20 (4×5), the two designs for each value printed together, *se-tenant*, in horizontal pairs throughout the sheets, each pair forming a composite design

Imprint: Central, side margins

Quantities sold: 18p 145,264; 25p 145,364; 26p 145,464; 31p 115,164

Withdrawn: 19.11.98

A **108** Modern Superlite Helmet and Wreck of *Point Law* (oil tanker)

A **109** Cousteau-Gagnan Demand Valve and Wreck of *Stella* (steamer)

A **110** Heinke Closed Helmet and *Liverpool* (full-rigged ship)

A **111** Siebe Closed Hemet

A **112** Deane Open Helmet

21st Anniversary of Alderney Diving Club

(Des Victoria Kinnersly. Litho B.D.T.)

1998 (10 FEB). Perf 13 (C)

A110	A **108**	20p multicoloured	60	40
A111	A **109**	30p multicoloured	85	85
A112	A **110**	37p multicoloured	1·20	1·20
A113	A **111**	43p multicoloured	1·70	1·70
A114	A **112**	63p multicoloured	2·20	2·30
A110/14		Set of 5	6·00	6·00
		First Day Cover		6·50
		Presentation Pack	8·00	
		Set of 5 Gutter Pairs	12·00	
MSA115		190×75 mm. Nos. A110/14 and label	8·00	8·00
		First Day Cover		10·00

Plate Nos.: All values 1A, 1B (each ×5)

Sheets: 50 (2 panes 5×5)

Imprint: Central, side margins

Withdrawn: 9.2.99

A **113** Alderney Post Office

A **114** Traders in Victoria Street

A **115** Court House

A **116** Police Station and Fire Engine

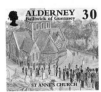

A **117** St. Anne's Church

A **118** Wedding Party at Albert Gate

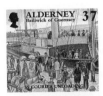

A **119** *Courier* (ferry) at Braye Bay

A **120** Fishermen at Quay

Garrison Island (2nd series)

(Des R. Carter. Litho Questa)

1998 (10 NOV). Perf 14½×14 (C)

A116	A **113**	20p multicoloured		50	25
		a. Horiz pair. Nos. A116/17		1·10	1·10
		b. Booklet pane. Nos. A116/19 with margins all round		2·50	
		c. Booklet pane. Nos. A116/17 and A120/1 with margins all round		2·75	
A117	A **114**	20p multicoloured		50	25
A118	A **115**	25p multicoloured		60	30
		a. Horiz pair. Nos. A118/19		1·50	1·50
		b. Booklet pane. Nos. A118/19 and A122/3 with margins all round		3·50	
A119	A **116**	25p multicoloured		60	30
A120	A **117**	30p multicoloured		70	35
		a. Horiz pair. Nos. A120/1		1·70	1·70
		b. Booklet pane. Nos. A120/3 with margins all round		3·75	
A121	A **118**	30p multicoloured		70	35

A122	A **119**	37p multicoloured		85	40
		a. Horiz pair. Nos. A122/3		2·00	2·00
A123	A **120**	37p multicoloured		85	40
A116/23		*Set of 8*		6·00	6·00
		First Day Cover			5·50
		Presentation Pack		6·00	

Plate Nos.: 20p, 30p 1A (×4); 25p, 37p 1B (×4)

Sheets: 20 (4×5), the two designs for each value were printed together, *se-tenant*, in horizontal pairs throughout the sheets, each pair forming a composite design

Imprint: Central, side margins

Withdrawn: 9.11.99

A **121a** Stained Glass Window commemorating Mary Rogers (Chief Stewardess) (25p); *Stella* leaving Southampton (£1.75)
(*illustration reduced. Actual size* 110×90 *mm*)

Centenary of the Wreck of Stella (mail steamer)

(Des Joanna Brehaut. Litho B.D.T.)

1999 (5 FEB). *Sheet* 110×90 *mm*. Perf 14 (C)

MSA124	A **121a**	25p, £1.75, multicoloured	6·00	6·00
		First Day Cover		8·00
		Presentation Pack	8·00	

Withdrawn: 3.2.2000

A **122** Solar Eclipse at 10.15 am

A **123** At 10.51 am

A **124** At 11.14 am

A **125** At 11.16 am   A **126** At 11.17 am   A **127** At 11.36 am

Total Eclipse of the Sun on 11 August

(Des Victoria Kinnersly. Litho Enschedé)

1999 (27 APR). Perf 13½×13 (C)

A125	A **122**	20p multicoloured	50	50
A126	A **123**	25p multicoloured	60	60
A127	A **124**	30p multicoloured	70	70
A128	A **125**	38p multicoloured	1·00	1·00
A129	A **126**	44p multicoloured	1·50	1·50
A130	A **127**	64p multicoloured	1·70	1·90
A125/30		Set of 6	6·00	6·00
		First Day Cover	8·00	
		Presentation Pack	8·00	
		Set of 6 Gutter Pairs	12·00	
MSA131		191×80 mm. Nos. A125/30 and label	6·50	6·50
		First Day Cover		10·00
		Postcard	1·00	

No. **MS**A131 also includes the 'PHILEXFRANCE '99', Paris, and the 'iBRA '99', Nuremberg, emblems on the sheet margin.

Plate Nos.: All values 1A, 1B (each ×4)
Sheets: 50 (2 panes 5×5)
Imprint: Central, side margins
Withdrawn: 26.4.2000

A **128** Field Gun and Crew, Fort Grosnez, c 1855

A **129** Parade of 9th Bn, Royal Garrison Artillery

A **130** The Arsenal, Fort Albert, c 1862

A **131** Royal Engineers loading Wagons

A **132** 2nd Bn, Royal Scots on Parade

A **133** Garrison at Work, Fort Tourgis, c 1865

A **134** Gun Emplacement, Fort Houmet Herbé, c 1870

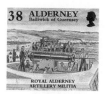

A **135** Royal Alderney Artillery Militia loading Cannon

Garrison Island (3rd series). Forts

(Des R. Carter. Litho Questa)

1999 (19 OCT). Perf 14½×14 (C)

A132	A **128**	20p multicoloured	45	25
		a. Horiz pair. Nos. A132/3 . .	1·10	1·10
		b. Booklet pane. Nos. A132/5, with margins all round	2·50	
		c. Booklet pane. Nos. A132/3 and A136/7, with margins all round	3·00	
		d. Booklet pane. Nos. A132/3 and A138/9, with margins all round	2·75	
A133	A **129**	20p multicoloured	45	25
A134	A **130**	25p multicoloured	55	30
		a. Horiz pair. Nos. A134/5 . .	1·50	1·50
		b. Booklet pane. Nos. A134/7, with margins all round	3·25	
		c. Booklet pane. Nos. A134/5 and A138/9, with margins all round	3·50	
A135	A **131**	25p multicoloured	55	30
A136	A **132**	30p multicoloured	65	35
		a. Horiz pair. Nos. A136/7 . .	1·70	1·70
		b. Booklet pane. Nos. A136/9, with margins all round	3·75	
A137	A **133**	30p multicoloured	65	35
A138	A **134**	38p multicoloured	80	40
		a. Horiz pair. Nos. A138/9 . .	2·00	2·00
A139	A **135**	38p multicoloured	80	40
A132/9		Set of 8	6·00	6·00
		First Day Cover		8·00
		Presentation Pack	8·50	

Plate Nos.: All values 1A, 1B (each ×4)

Sheets: 20 (4×5), the two designs for each value were printed together, *se-tenant*, in horizontal pairs throughout the sheets, each pair forming a composite design

Imprint: Central, right-hand margin

Withdrawn: 18.10.2000

A **136** Peregrine Falcon attacking Ruddy Turnstone

A **137** Two Falcons and Prey

A **138** Falcon guarding Eggs

A **139** Falcon feeding Young

A **140** Falcon and Prey

A **141** Two Young Falcons

Endangered Species. Peregrine Falcon

(Des R. Gorringe. Litho Questa)

2000 (4 FEB). Perf 14½×14 (C)

A140	A **136**	21p multicoloured	50	45
		a. Booklet pane of 10	5·00	
A141	A **137**	26p multicoloured	55	55
		a. Booklet pane of 10	5·75	
A142	A **138**	34p multicoloured	95	95
A143	A **139**	38p multicoloured	1·00	1·00
A144	A **140**	44p multicoloured	1·50	1·50
A145	A **141**	64p multicoloured	2·00	2·00
A140/5		Set of 6	6·00	6·00
		First Day Cover		6·50
		Presentation Pack	6·50	

Nos. A142/5 include the W.W.F. emblem.

Booklet panes Nos. A140*a* and A141*a* show the upper and lower edges of the panes imperforate and have margins at left and right.

Plate Nos.: All values 1A (×6)

Sheets: 10 (2×5) with enlarged illustrated margin at left

Imprint: Central, right-hand margin

Withdrawn: 3.2.2001

A **142** Wombles around Map of Alderney

A **143** Alderney and Shansi on Beach

A **144** Wellington by Lighthouse

A **145** Madame Cholet and Bungo having Picnic

A **146** Tomsk playing Golf

A **147** Orinoco at Airport

'A Wombling Holiday' (characters from children's television programme)

(Des Sally Diamond. Litho Questa)

2000 (28 APR). Perf 14½×14 (C)

A146	A **142**	21p multicoloured	45	45
A147	A **143**	26p multicoloured	55	55
A148	A **144**	36p multicoloured	95	95
A149	A **145**	40p multicoloured	1·10	1·10
A150	A **146**	45p multicoloured	1·50	1·50
A151	A **147**	65p multicoloured	2·00	2·00
A146/51		Set of 6	6·00	6·00
		First Day Cover		6·50
		Presentation Pack	6·50	
		Set of 6 Gutter Pairs	12·00	
MSA152	160×86 mm. Nos. A146/51		6·50	6·50
		First Day Cover		10·00

No. **MS**A152 also includes the logo for 'The Stamp Show 2000', International Stamp Exhibition, London, on the sheet margin.

Plate Nos.: All values 1A (×4)

Sheets: 50 (2 panes 5×5)

Imprint: Lower right-hand margin

Withdrawn: 27.4.2001

A **148a** Queen Elizabeth the Queen Mother on Alderney, 1984
(*illustration reduced. Actual size 93×70 mm*)

Queen Elizabeth the Queen Mother's 100th Birthday

(Des M. Whyte. Litho Walsall)

2000 (4 AUG). *Sheet 93×70 mm. Perf 13½ (C)*

MSA153	A **148a**	£1.50, multicoloured . . .	4·00	4·50
		First Day Cover		6·00
		Presentation Pack	6·00	

Withdrawn: 3.8.2001

A **149** Regimental Boxing Tournament

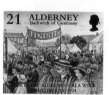

A **150** Sports Day, Alderney Gala Week, 1924

A **151** Regimental Orchestra playing at Ball

A **152** Garrison Ball in Fort Albert Mess, 1873

A **153** Royal Engineers' Colour Party, 1859

A **154** Royal Artillery on Parade, Queen's 40th Birthday, 1859

A **155** Royal Artillery Guard of Honour

A **156** Arrival of Maj.-Gen. Marcus Slade, 1863

Garrison Island (4th series). Events

(Des R. Carter. Litho Cartor)

2000 (19 OCT). Perf 13 (C)

A154	A **149**	21p multicoloured	45	25
		a. *Horiz pair. Nos.* A154/5. . .	90	85
		b. *Booklet pane. Nos.* A154/7 *with margins all round* . . .	2·40	
		c. *Booklet pane. Nos.* A154/5 *and* A160/1 *with margins all round*	3·00	
A155	A **150**	21p multicoloured	45	25
A156	A **151**	26p multicoloured	55	30
		a. *Horiz pair. Nos.* A156/7 . .	1·10	1·10
		b. *Booklet pane. Nos.* A156/9 *with margins all round* . . .	3·00	
A157	A **152**	26p multicoloured	55	30
A158	A **153**	36p multicoloured	75	40
		a. *Horiz pair. Nos.* 158/9 . . .	2·00	2·00
		b. *Booklet pane. Nos.* A158/61 *with margins all round*	4·50	
A159	A **154**	36p multicoloured	75	40
A160	A **155**	40p multicoloured	90	45
		a. *Horiz pair. Nos.* A160/1 . .	2·50	2·50
A161	A **156**	40p multicoloured	90	45
A154/61		*Set of 8*	6·00	6·00
		First Day Cover		6·25
		Presentation Pack	6·25	

Plate Nos.: All values 1A (×4)

Sheets: 20 (4×5), the two designs for each value were printed together, *se-tenant*, in horizontal pairs throughout the sheets, each pair forming a composite design

Imprint: Central, right-hand margin

Withdrawn: 18.10.2001

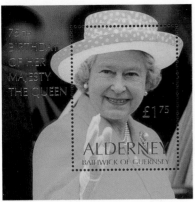

A **157a** Queen Elizabeth II

75th Birthday of Queen Elizabeth II

(Des C. Abbott. Litho and die-stamped. B.D.T.)

2001 (1 FEB). *Sheet* 70×70 *mm.* Perf 14 (C)

MSA162	A **157a**	£1.75, multicoloured . . .	4·50	4·50
		First Day Cover		6·00
		Presentation Pack	5·50	

Withdrawn: 31.1.2002

A **158** Nurse with Clipboard and Patient in X-Ray

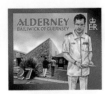

A **159** Nurse with Tray and Mignot Memorial Hospital

A **160** Doctor and Princess Anne visiting Hospital, 1972

A **161** Nurse from 1960s and Maternity Unit

A **162** Nurse from 1957 and Queen Elizabeth II laying Hospital Foundation Stone

A **163** Nurse of 1926 with Baby and opening of Original Hospital

Community Services (1st series). Healthcare

(Des Sally Diamond. Litho Walsall)

2001 (26 APR)–**02**. Perf 14×14½ (C)

A163	A **158**	22p multicoloured (*a*)	45	50
		a. Perf 13½×13 (*b*)	60	80
		ab. Booklet pane. Nos. A163a/6a with margins all round	3·75	
		ac. Booklet pane. Nos. A163a/4a and A167a/8a with margins all round . . .	4·50	
A164	A **159**	27p multicoloured (*a*)	55	60
		a. Perf 13½×13 (*b*)	55	60
A165	A **160**	36p multicoloured (*a*)	70	75
		a. Perf 13½×13 (*b*)	70	75
		ab. Booklet pane. Nos. A165a/8a with margins all round	4·50	
A166	A **161**	40p multicoloured (*a*)	80	85
		a. Perf 13½×13 (*b*)	1·00	1·20
A167	A **162**	45p multicoloured (*a*)	90	95
		a. Perf 13½×13 (*b*)	1·30	1·50
A168	A **163**	65p multicoloured (*a*)	1·20	1·40
		a. Perf 13½×13 (*b*)	1·50	2·00
A163/8		*Set of 6*	4·50	5·00
		First Day Cover		6·00
		Presentation Pack	7·50	

Nos. A63*a*/8*a* were only issued in £9.40 stamp booklets. See also Nos. A197/202.

Printings: (*a*) 26.4.01; (*b*) 17.10.02

Plate Nos.: All values 1A (×4)

Sheets: 10 (2×5) with enlarged illustrated margin at left (22, 27, 36p) or right (40, 45, 65p)

Imprint: Central, right-hand margin (22, 27, 36p) or central, left-hand margin (40, 45, 65p)

Withdrawn: 25.4.2002 (sheets)

A **164** 'Feathery'
Golf Ball,
1901

A **165** Golfing
Fashions of
the 1920s

A **166** Alderney
Golf Course
in 1970s

A **167** Modern
Putter

A **168** Modern
Golf Gloves
and Shoes

A **169** Modern
'lofted
wood'

30th Anniversary of Alderney Golf Club

(Des Colleen Corlett. Litho Questa)

2001 (1 AUG). Perf 14½ (C)

A169	A **164**	22p multicoloured	. . . .	45	50
A170	A **165**	27p multicoloured	. . . .	55	60
A171	A **166**	36p multicoloured	. . . .	80	75
A172	A **167**	40p multicoloured	. . . .	1·10	1·10
A173	A **168**	45p multicoloured	. . . .	1·50	1·50
A174	A **169**	65p multicoloured	. . . .	1·70	1·70
A169/74			Set of 6	6·00	6·00
			First Day Cover		8·00
			Presentation Pack	7·50	
			Set of 6 Gutter Pairs	12·00	
MSA175		190×75 mm. Nos. A169/74		6·50	6·50
			First Day Cover		9·00

No. **MS**A175 shows the 'Philanippon '01' logo on the margin.

Plate Nos.: All values 1A (×5)

Sheets: 50 (2 panes 5×5)

Imprint: Upper right-hand margin

Withdrawn: 31.7.2002

A **170** Construction of
New Breakwater,
1853

A **171** Official Party
inspecting Harbour,
1853

A **172** H.M.S. *Emerald*
(steam frigate)
aground, 1860

A **173** Disembarking
Troops from
H.M.S. *Emerald*,
1860

A **174** Moored Torpedo
Boats, 1890

A **175** Quick-firing Gun
on Railway
Wagon, 1890

A **176** H.M.S. *Majestic*
(battleship) at
Anchor, 1901

A **177** Torpedo Boats
outside Harbour,
1901

Garrison Island (5th series). The Royal Navy

(Des R. Carter. Litho Cartor)

2001 (16 OCT). Perf 13 (C)

A176	A **170**	22p multicoloured	45	25
		a. *Horiz pair. Nos.* A176/7	1·00	1·00
		b. *Booklet pane. Nos.* A176/9 *with margins all round*	2·50	
		c. *Booklet pane. Nos.* A176/7 *and* A182/3 *with margins all round*	3·00	
A177	A **171**	22p multicoloured	45	25
A178	A **172**	27p multicoloured	55	30
		a. *Horiz pair. Nos.* A178/9	1·20	1·20
		b. *Booklet pane. Nos.* A178/81 *with margins all round*	3·00	
		c. *Booklet pane. Nos.* A178/9 *and* A182/3 *with margins all round*	3·75	
A179	A **173**	27p multicoloured	55	30
A180	A **174**	36p multicoloured	70	40
		a. *Horiz pair. Nos.* A180/1	1·60	1·60
		b. *Booklet pane. Nos.* A180/3 *with margins all round*	3·50	
A181	A **175**	36p multicoloured	70	40
A182	A **176**	40p multicoloured	80	45
		a. *Horiz pair. Nos.* A182/3	2·00	2·00
A183	A **177**	40p multicoloured	80	45
A176/83		*Set of 8*	6·00	6·00
		First Day Cover		8·00
		Presentation Pack	8·00	

Plate Nos: All values 1A (×4)

Sheets: 20 (4 × 5), the two designs for each value were printed together, *se-tenant*, in horizontal pairs throughout the sheets, each pair forming a composite design

Imprint: Central, right-hand margin

Withdrawn: 15.10.2002.

A **178a** Queen Elizabeth and Prince Philip arriving at London Airport, Feb 1952
(*illustration reduced. Actual size* 159×98 *mm*)

Golden Jubilee

(Des A. Fothergill. Litho B.D.T.)

2002 (6 FEB). *Sheet* 159×98 *mm*. Perf 13½ (C)

MSA184	A **178a**	£2 blackish purple and gold	4·00	4·25
		a. *Black omitted*	£950	
		b. *Booklet pane. No.* **MS**A184	4·00	
		First Day Cover		5·50
		Presentation Pack	5·50	

Withdrawn: 5.2.2003

A **179** Northern Hobby

A **180** Black Kite

A **181** Merlin

A **182** Honey Buzzard

A **183** Osprey

A **184** Marsh Harrier

Migrating Birds (1st series). Raptors

(Des G. Austin. Litho Questa)

2002 (30 APR). Perf 14 (C)

A185	A **179**	22p multicoloured	45	50
A186	A **180**	27p multicoloured	55	60
A187	A **181**	36p multicoloured	85	85
A188	A **182**	40p multicoloured	1·00	1·00
A189	A **183**	45p multicoloured	1·20	1·20
A190	A **184**	65p multicoloured	1·70	1·70
A185/90		*Set of 6*	6·00	6·00
		First Day Cover		6·50
		Presentation Pack	7·50	
MSA191		170×80 mm. Nos. A185/90	6·50	6·50
		First Day Cover		7·50

Plate Nos.: All values 1A (×4)

Sheets: 10 (2×5)

Imprint: Central, left-hand margin

Withdrawn: 29.4.2003

A **185** Coal Fire
Beacon,
1725

A **186** Oil
Lantern,
1779

A **187** Argand
Lamp,
1790

A **188** Revolving
Light,
1818

A **189** Electric Light, 1952

A **190** Ambulance
Technician, and
Ambulance
Station

A **191** Ambulance
Technician
using Radio,
and Ambulance

A **192** Doctor, and
loading Patient
onto Aircraft

A **193** Pilot, and
Trislander over
Alderney

A **194** Emergency
Operator, and
Patient on
Stretcher

A **195** Lifeboatman,
and *Roy
Barker One*
(lifeboat)

**50th Anniversary of Electrification of Les Casquets
Lighthouse**

(Des N. Watton. Litho Enschedé)

2002 (30 JULY). Perf 13×13½ (C)

A192	A **185**	22p multicoloured	50	50
A193	A **186**	27p multicoloured	60	60
A194	A **187**	36p multicoloured	75	75
A195	A **188**	45p multicoloured	95	95
A196	A **189**	65p multicoloured	1·40	1·40
A192/6		*Set of 5*	4·00	4·00
		First Day Cover		7·50
		Presentation Pack	7·50	
		Set of 5 Gutter Pairs	8·00	

No. A196 is inscribed 'Elictrification' in error.

Plate Nos.: All values 1A (×4)

Sheets: 50 (2 panes 5×5)

Imprint: Lower left-hand margin

Withdrawn: 29.7.2003

**Community Services (2nd series). Emergency Medical
Aid**

(Des Sally Diamond. Litho Walsall)

2002 (17 OCT). Perf 14×14½ (C)

A197	A **190**	22p multicoloured	45	50
		a. Perf 13½×13	90	90
		ab. Booklet pane. Nos. A197a/200a, with margins all round	5·75	
		ac. Booklet pane. Nos. A197a/8a and A200a/2a, with margins all round . . .	11·00	
A198	A **191**	27p multicoloured	55	60
		a. Perf 13½×13	1·00	1·00
A199	A **192**	36p multicoloured	95	95
		a. Perf 13½×13	1·70	1·70
		ab. Booklet pane. Nos. A199a/202a, with margins all round	11·00	
A200	A **193**	40p multicoloured	1·10	1·10
		a. Perf 13½×13	2·00	2·00

```
A201   A 194   45p multicoloured . . . . . . . . .   1·70    1·70
               a. Perf 13½×13 . . . . . . . . . .   3·00    3·00
A202   A 195   65p multicoloured . . . . . . . . .   2·00    2·00
               a. Perf 13½×13 . . . . . . . . . .   4·00    4·00
A197/202       Set of 6 . . . . . . . . . . . . .   6·00    6·00
               First Day Cover . . . . . . .               7·50
               Presentation Pack . . . . . .   7·50
```

Nos. A197a/202a were only issued in £9.40 stamp booklets.

Plate Nos.: All values 1A (×4)

Sheets: 10 (2×5) with enlarged illustrated margin at left

Imprint: Central, right-hand margin

Withdrawn: 16.10.2003

A **196** St. Edward's Crown
(*illustration reduced. Actual size* 128×90 *mm*)

50th Anniversary of Coronation

(Des A. Fothergill. Litho and embossed Enschedé)

2003 (30 JAN). *Sheet* 128×90 *mm.* Perf 13½ (C)
MSA203   A 196   £2 multicoloured . . . .   4·00   4·25
                   First Day Cover . . . .   7·50
                   Presentation Pack . . . .   6·50

Withdrawn: 29.1.2004

A **197** Wright Brothers' *Flyer I*, 1903

A **198** Alcock and Brown's Vickers FB-27 Vimy, 1919

A **199** Douglas DC-3, 1936

A **200** De Havilland DH106 Comet 4, 1946

A **201** British Aerospace/ Aerospatiale Concorde, 1969

A **202** Projected Airbus Industrie A380

Centenary of Powered Flight

(Des M.Wilkinson. Litho B.D.T.)

2003 (10 APR). Perf 13½ (C)
```
A204   A 197   22p multicoloured . . . . . . . . .   50      50
A205   A 198   27p multicoloured . . . . . . . . .   75      75
A206   A 199   36p multicoloured . . . . . . . . .   85      85
A207   A 200   40p multicoloured . . . . . . . . .   1·00    1·00
A208   A 201   45p multicoloured . . . . . . . . .   1·20    1·20
A209   A 202   65p multicoloured . . . . . . . . .   1·50    1·50
A204/9         Set of 6 . . . . . . . . . . . . .   6·00    6·00
               First Day Cover . . . . . . .               7·50
               Presentation Pack . . . . . .   7·50
               Set of 6 Gutter Pairs . . . . 12·00
```

Plate Nos.: All values 1A (×4)

Sheets: 50 (2 panes 5×5)

Imprint: Central, left-hand margin

Withdrawn: 9.4.2004

A **203** Arctic Tern

A **204** Great Skua

A **205** Sandwich Tern

A **206** Sooty
Shearwater

A **207** Arctic Skua

A **208** Manx
Shearwater

A **209** Policeman with
Clipboard and
Constables on Beat

A **210** Policeman and
Land Rover

A **211** Forensic Team

A **212** Police Constable
and Policeman
with Child Cyclist

A **213** Policeman directing
Traffic and Police at
Scene of Accident

A **214** Policewoman and
Policeman with
Customs Officer

Migrating Birds (2nd series). Seabirds.

(Des G. Austin. Litho Questa)

2003 (3 JULY). Perf 14 (C)

A210	A **203**	22p multicoloured	45	50
A211	A **204**	27p multicoloured	55	60
A212	A **205**	36p multicoloured	75	75
A213	A **206**	40p multicoloured	1·00	1·00
A214	A **207**	45p multicoloured	1·50	1·50
A215	A **208**	65p multicoloured	2·00	2·00
A210/15		*Set of 6*	6·00	6·00
		First Day Cover		7·50
		Presentation Pack	7·50	
MSA216		80×170 mm. Nos. A210/15	6·00	6·00
		First Day Cover		7·50

Plate Nos.: All values 1A (×4)

Sheets: 10 (2×5) with enlarged illustrated margin at right

Imprint: Central, left-hand margin

Withdrawn: 2.7.2004

Community Services (3rd series). Alderney Police

(Des Sally Diamond. Litho Walsall)

2003 (16 OCT). Perf 13½×13 (C)

A217	A **209**	22p multicoloured	50	50
		a. Booklet pane. Nos. A217/20	4·00	
		b. Booklet pane. Nos. A217/18 and A221/2	4·75	
		c. Booklet pane. Nos. A217/19 and A221	4·00	
		d. Booklet pane. Nos. A217/18, A220 and A222	4·50	
A218	A **210**	27p multicoloured	60	60
A219	A **211**	36p multicoloured	80	80
		a. Booklet pane. Nos. A219/22	5·50	
A220	A **212**	40p multicoloured	1·00	1·00
A221	A **213**	45p multicoloured	1·50	1·50
A222	A **214**	65p multicoloured	2·00	2·00
A217/22		*Set of 6*	6·00	6·00
		First Day Cover		7·50
		Presentation Pack	7·50	

Plate Nos.: All values 1A (×4)

Sheets: 10 (2×5) with enlarged illustrated margin at left

Imprint: Central, right-hand margin

Withdrawn: 15.10.2004

A **215** *Hypholoma fasciculare*

A **216** *Aleuria aurantia*

A **217** *Coprinus micaceus*

A **218** *Langermannia gigantea*

A **219** *Macrolepiota procera*

A **220** *Xylaria hypoxylon*

A **221** Boys playing Football, Tourgis Close

A **222** Three Children playing Football, Braye Beach

A **223** Two Boys playing Football in Playground

A **224** Teenagers playing Football, Arch Bay

A **225** Football Match

A **226** Father and Two Children playing Football, Arch Bay

Fungi

(Des Petula Stone. Litho Enschedé)

2004 (29 JAN). Perf 13½ (C)

A223	A **215**	22p multicoloured	70	70
A224	A **216**	27p multicoloured	85	85
A225	A **217**	36p multicoloured	1·20	1·20
A226	A **218**	40p multicoloured	1·30	1·30
A227	A **219**	45p multicoloured	1·40	1·40
A228	A **220**	65p multicoloured	2·10	2·10
A223/8		Set of 6	7·50	7·50
		First Day Cover		9·75
		Presentation Pack	9·75	
		Set of 6 Gutter Pairs	12·00	

Plate Nos.: All values 1A (×4)

Sheets: 50 (2 panes 5×5)

Imprint: Upper side margins

Withdrawn: 28.1.2005

Centenary of FIFA (Fédération Internationale de Football Association)

(Des A. Robinson. Litho Cartor)

2004 (12 MAY). Perf 13½ (C)

A229	A **221**	26p multicoloured	85	85
A230	A **222**	32p multicoloured	1·10	1·10
A231	A **223**	36p multicoloured	1·20	1·20
A232	A **224**	40p multicoloured	1·30	1·30
A233	A **225**	45p multicoloured	1·50	1·50
A234	A **226**	65p multicoloured	2·10	2·10
A229/34		Set of 6	8·00	8·00
		First Day Cover		10·00
		Presentation Pack	10·00	

Nos. A229/34 were each perforated in a circle contained within an outer perforated square which continued the design.

Plate Nos.: All values 1A (×4)

Sheets: 50 (5×10)

Imprint: Upper and lower side margins

Withdrawn: 11.5.2005

A **227** Northern
Wheatear

A **228** Common
Redstart

A **233** Fire Engine

A **234** Fireman up
Ladder and Fire
Engine at Fort
Tourgis

A **229** Yellow Wagtail

A **230** Hoopoe

A **235** Airport Service
Fire Truck

A **236** Alderney Fire
Station

A **231** Ring Ousel
('Ouzel')

A **232** Sand Martin

A **237** Airport Training
Ground

A **238** Road Accident
Training Exercise

Migrating Birds (3rd series). Passerines

(Des A. Robinson. Litho Enschedé)

2004 (29 JULY). Perf 13½ (C)

A235	A **227**	26p multicoloured	85	85
A236	A **228**	32p multicoloured	1·10	1·10
A237	A **229**	36p multicoloured	1·20	1·20
A238	A **230**	40p multicoloured	1·30	1·30
A239	A **231**	45p multicoloured	1·50	1·50
A240	A **232**	65p multicoloured	2·10	2·10
A235/40		*Set of* 6	8·00	8·00
		First Day Cover		10·00
		Presentation Pack	10·00	
MSA241		170×80 mm. Nos. A235/40	8·00	8·00
		First Day Cover		10·00

Plate Nos.: All values 1A, 1B, 1C, 1D (each ×4)

Sheets: 10 (2×5) with enlarged illustrated right-hand margin

Imprint: Central, left-hand margin

Withdrawn: 28.7.2005

Community Services (4th series). Fire Service

(Des M. Legg. Litho Walsall)

2004 (28 OCT). Perf 13½ ×13 (C)

A242	A **233**	26p multicoloured	85	85
		a. Booklet pane. Nos. A242/5		
		with margins all round . . .	4·50	
		b. Booklet pane. Nos. A242/3		
		and A246/7 with margins		
		all round	5·50	
		c. Booklet pane. Nos. A242/4		
		and A246 with margins all		
		round	4·50	
		d. Booklet pane. Nos.		
		A242/3, A245 and A247		
		with margins all round . . .	5·50	
A243	A **234**	32p multicoloured	1·10	1·10
A244	A **235**	36p multicoloured	1·20	1·20
		a. Booklet pane. Nos. A244/7		
		with margins all round . . .	6·00	

A245 A **236** 40p multicoloured . . . . 1·30 1·30
A246 A **237** 45p multicoloured . . . . 1·50 1·50
A247 A **238** 65p multicoloured . . . . 2·10 2·10
A242/7 *Set of 6* . . . . 8·00 8·00
First Day Cover . . . . 10·00
Presentation Pack . . . . . . 10·00

Plate Nos.: All values 1A×4
Sheets: 10 (2×5) with enlarged illustrated left-hand margin
Imprint: Central, right-hand margin
Withdrawn: 27.10.2005

A **239** Mermaid at her Undersea Home

A **240** Mermaid rescuing drowning Prince

A **241** Mermaid with Sea Witch bargaining her Voice for a Human Life

A **242** Mermaids waving to Prince and his Lover on Seashore

A **243** Mermaid carried away by Angels

Birth Bicentenary of Hans Christian Andersen. Scenes from The Little Mermaid

(Des N. Watton. Litho Enschedé)

2005 (3 FEB). Perf 13½×14 (C)
A248 A **239** 26p multicoloured 50 55
A249 A **240** 32p multicoloured 65 70
A250 A **241** 36p multicoloured 70 75
A251 A **242** 40p multicoloured . . . . 1·70 1·50

A252 A **243** 65p multicoloured . . . . 2·75 2·50
A248/52 *Set of 5* . . . . 5·00 5·00
First Day Cover . . . . 6·00
Presentation Pack . . . . . . 6·00

Plate Nos.: All values 1A (×4)
Sheets: 50 (5×10)
Imprint: Upper left-hand margin
Withdrawn: 2.2.2006

A **244** Admiral Horatio Nelson

A **245** H.M.S. *Victory*

A **246** Marine firing musket

A **247** Wounded Nelson with Captain Hardy

A **248** H.M.S. *Victory* in battle with *Redoutable*

A **249** Admiral James Lord de Saumarez

Bicentenary of the Battle of Trafalgar

(Des S. Shackleton. Litho Enschedé)

2005 (9 MAY). Perf 14×13½ (C)
A253 A **244** 26p multicoloured 50 55
a. Booklet pane. Nos. A253/6 with margins all round . . . 2·50
b. Booklet pane. Nos. A253/4 and A257/8 with margins all round . . . . 4·75
c. Booklet pane. Nos. A253 and A256/8 with margins all round . . . . 5·00
A254 A **245** 32p multicoloured 65 70
a. Booklet pane. Nos. A254/5 and A257/8 . . . . 5·00

A255	A **246**	36p multicoloured	70	75
		a. Booklet pane. Nos. A255/8		
		with margins all round . . .	5·00	
A256	A **247**	40p multicoloured	80	85
A257	A **248**	45p multicoloured	1·50	1·70
A258	A **249**	65p multicoloured	2·00	2·50
A253/8		Set of 6	6·00	6·50
		First Day Cover		7·50
		Presentation Pack	7·50	

Plate Nos.: All values 1A (×4)

Sheets: 10 (2×5) with enlarged illustrated left margins

Imprint: Central right-hand margins

Withdrawn: 8.5.2006

A **250** Little Stint

A **251** Common Greenshank

A **252** Golden Plover

A **253** Bar-tailed Godwit

A **254** Green Sandpiper

A **255** Sanderling

Migrating Birds (4th series). Waders

(Des A. Robinson. Litho Enschedé)

2005 (21 JULY). Perf 13½ (C)

A259	A **250**	26p multicoloured	50	55
A260	A **251**	32p multicoloured	65	70
A261	A **252**	36p multicoloured	70	75
A262	A **253**	40p multicoloured	1·00	85
A263	A **254**	45p multicoloured	2·00	2·00
A264	A **255**	65p multicoloured	3·00	3·00
A259/64		Set of 6	7·50	7·50
		First Day Cover		8·50
		Presentation Pack	8·50	

MSA265	170×80 mm. Nos. A259/64	8·00	8·00
	First Day Cover	9·00	

Plate Nos.: All values 1A (×4)

Sheets: 10 (2×5) with enlarged illustrated right margins.

Imprint: Lower left-hand margins

Withdrawn: 20.7.2006

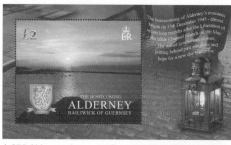

A **256** Alderney Arms and Sunset
(*illustration reduced. Actual size 140×80 mm*)

60th Anniversary of Return of War Evacuees

(Des P. Furness. Litho BDT)

2005 (27 OCT). Sheet 140×80 mm. Perf 14 (C)

MSA266	A **256**	£2 multicoloured	6·00	7·50
		First Day Cover		8·50
		Presentation Pack	8·50	

Withdrawn: 26.10.2006

A **257** Young King Arthur

A **258** Merlyn

A **259** Morgause

A **260** Queen Guenever

A **261** Lancelot

A **262** Mordred

'The Once and Future King'

(Des N. Watton. Litho Enschedé)

2006 (16 FEB). **Perf** 13½×14 (C)

A267	A **257**	29p multicoloured	. . . .	60	65
A268	A **258**	34p multicoloured	. . . .	70	75
A269	A **259**	38p multicoloured	. . . .	1·00	1·00
A270	A **260**	42p multicoloured	. . . .	1·50	1·50
A271	A **261**	47p multicoloured	. . . .	1·90	1·90
A272	A **262**	68p multicoloured	. . . .	2·20	2·20
A267/72		*Set of 6*	. . . .	8·00	8·00
		First Day Cover	. . . .		9·00
		Presentation Pack	. . . . . .	9·00	
MSA273		120×90 mm. Nos. A267/72	. . . . .	8·50	8·50
		First Day Cover	. . . .		9·50

Nos. A267/**MS**A273 commemorate the birth centenary of Terence Hanbury White, author of 'The Once and Future King'.

Plate Nos.: All values 1A (×4)

Sheets: 10 (2×5) with enlarged illustrated right margins

Imprint: Lower left-hand margin

Withdrawn: 15.2.2007

A **263** Princess Elizabeth

A **264** Princess Elizabeth

A **265** Queen Elizabeth II, *c.* 1955

A **266** Wearing Brown Coat and Hat

A **267** Wearing Tiara

A **268** Wearing Red Jacket and Red and White Hat

A **269** Wearing Pale Pink Hat

A **270** Wearing Mauve Dress and Hat

80th Birthday of Queen Elizabeth II

(Des P. Furness. Litho Austrian State Ptg Wks, Vienna)

2006 (21 APR). **Perf** 14 (C)

A274	A **263**	29p multicoloured	. . . .	30	30
		a. Horiz pair. Nos. A274/5	. .	1·30	1·30
A275	A **264**	29p multicoloured	. . . .	30	30
A276	A **265**	34p multicoloured	. . . .	50	50
		a. Horiz pair. Nos. A276/7	. .	1·50	1·50
A277	A **266**	34p multicoloured	. . . .	50	50
A278	A **267**	42p multicoloured	. . . .	85	90
		a. Horiz pair. Nos. A278/9	. .	2·50	2·50
A279	A **268**	42p multicoloured	. . . .	85	90
A280	A **269**	45p multicoloured	. . . .	90	95
		a. Horiz pair. Nos. A280/1	. .	3·00	3·00
A281	A **270**	45p multicoloured	. . . .	90	95
A274/81		*Set of 8*	. . . .	8·00	8·00
		First Day Cover	. . . .		9·50
		Presentation Pack	. . . . . .	9·50	

Nos. A274/81 in sheets of ten were included in a souvenir folder, together with the £10 stamp issued by Guernsey to celebrate The Queen's birthday (see Guernsey No. 1122).

Plate Nos.: All values 1A (×4)

Sheets: 10 (2×5) with enlarged illustrated left margins. Nos. A274/5, A276/7, A278/9 and A280/1 were each printed together, *se-tenant*, in horizontal pairs throughout the sheets

Imprint: Lower right-hand margin

Withdrawn: 20.4.2007

A **271** Fulmar

A **272** Gannet

A **273** Lesser Black-backed Gull

A **274** Storm Petrel

A 275 Kittiwake

A 276 Puffin

Resident Birds (1st series). Seabirds

(Des A. Robinson. Litho BDT)

2006 (27 JULY). Perf 14 (C)

A282	A **271**	29p multicoloured	65	65
		a. Booklet pane. No. A282×4 with margins all round	2·50	
A283	A **272**	34p multicoloured	75	75
		a. Booklet pane. No. A283×4 with margins all round	3·00	
A284	A **273**	42p multicoloured	1·00	1·00
		a. Booklet pane. No. A284×4 with margins all round	4·00	
A285	A **274**	45p multicoloured	1·50	1·50
		a. Booklet pane. No. A285×4 with margins all round	6·00	
A286	A **275**	47p multicoloured	2·00	2·00
		a. Booklet pane. No. A286×4 with margins all round	8·00	
A287	A **276**	68p multicoloured	3·00	3·00
		a. Booklet pane. No. A287×4 with margins all round	12·00	
A282/7		Set of 6	8·00	8·00
		First Day Cover		9·50
		Presentation Pack	9·50	

Plate Nos.: All values 1A (×4)

Sheets: 10 (2×5) with enlarged illustrated margins at right and foot

Imprint: Upper left-hand margin

Withdrawn: 26.7.2007

A 277 Cerianthus lloydii (burrowing anemone)

A 278 Parazoanthus axinellae (colonial anemone)

A 279 Corynactis viridis (jewel anemone colony)

A 280 Sagartia elegans (elegant anemone)

A 281 Alcyonium glomeratum (red fingers)

A 282 Metridium senile (plumose anemone)

A 283 Eunicella verrucosa (fan coral)

A 284 Corynactis viridis (jewel anemone)

A 285 Actinothoe sphyrodeta (sandalled anemone)

A 286 Anemonia viridis (snakelocks anemone)

A 287 Caryophyllia smithii (Devonshire cup coral)

A 290 Actinothoe sphyrodeta (fried egg anemone)

A 293 Calliactis parasitica (parasitic anemone)

A 295 Actinia equina (beadlet anemone)

A 296 Leptopsammia pruvoti (sunset cup coral)

A 297 Actinia fragacea (strawberry anemone)

148

Corals and Anemones

(Des Sue Daly. Litho (£4 also embossed) Austrian State Ptg Wks, Vienna (20p to 50p, £4) or Enschedé (others))

2006 (2 NOV)–**2007**. Perf 14 (20p to 50p, £4) or 13×13½ (others), both comb

A288	A **277**	1p multicoloured	10	10
A289	A **278**	2p multicoloured	10	10
A290	A **279**	3p multicoloured	10	10
A291	A **280**	4p multicoloured	10	15
A292	A **281**	5p multicoloured	10	15
A293	A **282**	6p multicoloured	10	15
A294	A **283**	7p multicoloured	15	20
A295	A **284**	8p multicoloured	15	20
A296	A **285**	9p multicoloured	20	25
A297	A **286**	10p multicoloured	20	25
A298	A **287**	20p multicoloured (b)	45	45
A301	A **290**	40p multicoloured (b)	95	95
A304	A **293**	50p multicoloured (b)	1·20	1·20
A306	A **295**	£1 multicoloured	2·00	2·10
A307	A **296**	£2 multicoloured	4·00	4·25
A308	A **297**	£4 multicoloured (b)	9·50	9·50
A288/308		Set of 16	19·00	20·00
		First Day Covers (4)		23·00
		Presentation Packs (2) . . .	22·00	
		Set of 16 Gutter Pairs . . .	38·00	

Nos. A299/300, A302/3 and A305 are left for additions to these definitive stamps.

Printings: (a) 2.11.2006; (b) 2.8.2007

Plate Nos.: All values 1A (×4)

Sheets: 50 (2 panes 5×5)

Imprint: Central, side margins

A **298** Cushion Starfish   A **299** Gannet Colony at Les Etacs

A **300** Spiny Squat Lobster   A **301** Grey Seal

A **302** Golden Samphire near Fort Clonque   A **303** Little Egret and Oystercatchers

Designation of Alderney West Coast and the Burhou Islands as Ramsar Site

(Des Wendy Bramall. Litho BDT)

2007 (8 MAR). Perf 13½ (C)

A309	A **298**	32p multicoloured	75	75
A310	A **299**	37p multicoloured	90	90
A311	A **300**	45p multicoloured	1·10	1·10
A312	A **301**	48p multicoloured	1·10	1·10
A313	A **302**	50p multicoloured	1·20	1·20
A314	A **303**	71p multicoloured	1·70	1·70
A309/14		Set of 6	6·75	6·75
		First Day Cover		8·50
		Presentation Pack	8·50	
MSA315		140×95 mm. Nos. A309/14	6·75	6·75
		First Day Cover		8·50

Plate Nos.: All values 1A (×4)

Sheets: 10 (2×5) with enlarged illustrated margins at right and foot

Imprint: Central, left-hand margin

Withdrawn: 7.3.2007

A **304** Blackbird   A **305** Dartford Warbler

A **306** Blue Tit   A **307** Wren

A **308** House Sparrow   A **309** Jackdaw

Resident Birds (2nd series). Passerines

(Des Andrew Robinson. Litho BDT)

2007 (24 MAY). Perf 14 (C)

A316	A **304**	32p multicoloured	75	75
		a. Booklet pane. No. A316×4 with margins all round	3·00	

A317	A **305**	37p multicoloured	90	90
		a. *Booklet pane. No.* A317×4 *with margins all round*	3·50	
A318	A **306**	45p multicoloured	1·10	1·10
		a. *Booklet pane. No.* A318×4 *with margins all round*	4·50	
A319	A **307**	48p multicoloured	1·10	1·10
		a. *Booklet pane. No.* A319×4 *with margins all round*	4·50	
A320	A **308**	50p multicoloured	1·20	1·20
		a. *Booklet pane. No.* A320×4 *with margins all round*	4·75	
A321	A **309**	71p multicoloured	1·70	1·70
		a. *Booklet pane. No.* A321×4 *with margins all round*	6·75	
A316/21		*Set of 6*	6·75	6·75
		First Day Cover		8·50
		Presentation Pack	8·50	

Plate Nos.: All values 1A (×4)

Sheets: 10 (2×5) with enlarged illustrated margins at right and foot

Imprint: Central, left margin

Withdrawn: 23.5.2008

A **310** 'How the Camel got his Hump'

A **311** 'How the Whale got his Throat'

A **312** 'The Elephant's Child'

A **313** 'How the Leopard got his Spots'

A **314** 'The Cat that walked by Himself'

A **315** 'How the Rhinoceros got his Skin'

Rudyard Kipling's Just So Stories

(Des Nick Watton. Litho BDT)

2007 (25 OCT). Rudyard Kipling's Just So Stories. Perf 13½ (C)

A322	A **310**	32p multicoloured	75	75
A323	A **311**	37p multicoloured	90	90
A324	A **312**	45p multicoloured	1·10	1·10
A325	A **313**	48p multicoloured	1·10	1·10
A326	A **314**	50p multicoloured	1·20	1·20
A327	A **315**	71p multicoloured	1·70	1·70
A322/7		*Set of 6*	6·75	6·75
		First Day Cover		8·50
		Presentation Pack	8·50	
MSA328		140×95 mm. Nos. A322/7	6·75	6·75
		First Day Cover		8·50

Sheets: 10 (2×5) with enlarged illustrated margins at right and foot

Imprint: Central, left-hand margin

Withdrawn: 24.10.2008

A **316** *Vanessa cardui* (painted lady)

A **317** *Hipparchia semele* (grayling)

A **318** *Callophrys rubi* (green hairstreak)

A **319** *Pararge aegeria* (speckled wood)

A **320** *Polyommatus icarus* (common blue)

A **321** *Melitaea cinxia* (Glanville fritillary)

Butterflies

(Des Petula Stone. Litho BDT)

2008 (28 FEB). Perf 14 (C)

A329	A **316**	34p multicoloured	80	80
A330	A **317**	40p multicoloured	95	95
A331	A **318**	48p multicoloured	1·10	1·10
A332	A **319**	51p multicoloured	1·20	1·20

A333	A **320**	53p multicoloured	1·30	1·30
A334	A **321**	74p multicoloured	1·70	1·70
A329/34		Set of 6	7·00	7·00
		First Day Cover		8·75
		Presentation Pack	8·75	
MSA335	140×100 mm. Nos. A329/34		7·00	7·00
		First Day Cover		8·75

Plate Nos.: All values 1A (×4)

Sheets: 10 (2×5) with enlarged illustrated margins at right and foot

Imprint: Central, left-hand margin

Withdrawn: 27.2.2009

A **322** Common Buzzard

A **323** Peregrine Falcon

A **324** Kestrel

A **325** Barn Owl

A **326** Long-eared Owl

A **327** Sparrowhawk

Resident Birds (3rd series). Raptors

(Des Andrew Robinson. Litho BDT)

2008 (15 MAY). Perf 14 (C)

A336	A **322**	34p multicoloured	80	80
		a. Booklet pane. No. A336		
		×4 with margins all round	3·25	
A337	A **323**	40p multicoloured	95	95
		a. Booklet pane. No. A337		
		×4 with margins all round	3·75	
A338	A **324**	48p multicoloured	1·10	1·10
		a. Booklet pane. No. A338		
		×4 with margins all round		4·50
A339	A **325**	51p multicoloured	1·20	1·20
		a. Booklet pane. No. A339		
		×4 with margins all round	4·75	

A340	A **326**	53p multicoloured	1·30	1·30
		a. Booklet pane. No. A340		
		×4 with margins all round	5·00	
A341	A **327**	74p multicoloured	1·70	1·70
		a. Booklet pane. No. A341		
		×4 with margins all round	7·00	
A336/41		Set of 6	7·00	7·00
		First Day Cover		8·75
		Presentation Pack	8·75	

Plate Nos.: All values 1A (×4)

Sheets: 10 (2×5) with enlarged illustrated margins at right and foot

Imprint: Central, left-hand margin

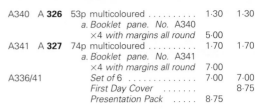

A **328** Old Harbour

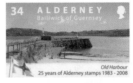

A **329** The Breakwater

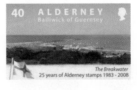

A **330** Fort Clonque Causeway

A **331** Golf Course

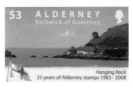

A **332** Hanging Rock

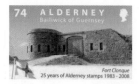
A **333** Fort Clonque

25th Anniversary of Alderney Stamps

(Des Andrew Fothergill. Litho Austrian State Ptg Wks, Vienna)

2008 (14 JUNE). Perf 14 (C)

A342	A **328**	34p multicoloured	80	80
A343	A **329**	40p multicoloured	95	95
A344	A **330**	48p multicoloured	1·10	1·10
A345	A **331**	51p multicoloured	1·20	1·20
A346	A **332**	53p multicoloured	1·30	1·30
A347	A **333**	74p multicoloured	1·70	1·70
A342/7		Set of 6	7·00	7·00
		First Day Cover		8·75
		Presentation Pack	8·75	
		Souvenir Folder (Nos.		
		A342/8)	55·00	

Plate Nos.: All values 1A (×4)

Sheets: 10 (2×5) with enlarged illustrated margins at left and foot

Imprint: Lower right-hand margin

A **334** Lion Rampant from Alderney Flag

(Des Andrew Fothergill. Litho and embossed Austrian State Ptg Wks, Vienna)

2008 (14 JUNE). Perf 14½ ×13½ (C)

A348	A **334**	£5 multicoloured	12·00	12·00
		First Day Cover		13·50
		Presentation Pack	13·50	

Sheets: 5 (5×1) with enlarged illustrated margins

Imprint: Top margin

A **335** Britten-Norman Islander

A **336** Britten-Norman Trislander

A **337** DHC-6 Twin Otter

A **338** Short 360

A **339** Saab 340   A **340** ATR 72

40th Anniv of Aurigny Air Services

(Des Mark Wilkinson. Litho BDT)

2008 (31 OCT). Perf 13½ (C)

A349	A **335**	34p multicoloured	80	80
A350	A **336**	40p multicoloured	95	95
A351	A **337**	48p multicoloured	1·10	1·10
A352	A **338**	51p multicoloured	1·20	1·20
A353	A **339**	53p multicoloured	1·30	1·30
A354	A **340**	74p multicoloured	1·70	1·70
A349/54		Set of 6	7·00	7·00
		First Day Cover		8·75
		Presentation Pack	8·75	
MS355		140×95 mm. Nos. A349/54	7·00	7·00
		First Day Cover		8·75

Plate Nos.: All values 1A (×4)

Sheets: 10 (2×5) with enlarged illustrated margins at right and foot

Imprint: Central, left-hand margin

STAMP BOOKLETS

PRICES given are for complete booklets.

AB **1** Common Blue and Pyramidal Orchid
 (*illustration reduced. Actual size 99×60 mm*)

1994 (5 MAY)–**95**. *Multicoloured covers as Type* AB **1**.
*Without barcode on the reverse. Panes attached by
selvedge*
ASB1   £1.28 booklet containing pane No. A70*ab*
 (*cover Type* AB **1**) . . . .   4·00
 a. With barcode sticker on reverse (1995) . . .   8·50
ASB2   £1.92 booklet containing pane No. A72*ab*
 (*cover showing Great Black-backed Gull and
 Sand Crocus*) . . . .   4·50

  Withdrawn: By 10.2006

1997 (2 JAN). *Multicoloured covers as Type* AB **1**. *Without
barcode on the reverse. Panes attached by selvedge*
ASB3   £1.44 booklet containing pane No. A70*bb*
 (*cover showing Small Tortoiseshell (butterfly)
 and Buddleia*) . . . .   3·00
ASB4   £2 booklet containing pane No. A72*bb* (*cover
 showing Rock Pipit and Sea Stock*) . . . .   4·00

  Sold out: 9.99 (No. ASB3); Withdrawn by 10.2006 (No. ASB4)

1998 (25 MAR). *Multicoloured cover as Type* AB **1**. *With
barcode on the reverse. Pane attached by selvedge*
ASB5   £1.60 booklet containing pane No. A71*ab*
 (*cover showing Common Rabbit and Creeping
 Buttercup*) . . . .   4·00

  Sold out: By 11.2006

AB **2** Map of Alderney
 (*illustration reduced. Actual size 164×98 mm*)

1998 (10 NOV). *Multicoloured cover as Type* AB **2** *containing
text and illustrations on panes and interleaving pages.
Stitched*
ASB6   £8.48 booklet containing panes Nos. A102*b/c*,
 A104*b*, A106*b*, A116*b/c*, A118*b* and 120*b* . . .   20·00

  Withdrawn: 9.11.99

Garrison Island (3rd series). Forts

1999 (19 OCT). *Multicoloured cover as Type* AB **2** *containing
text and illustrations on panes and interleaving pages.
Stitched*
ASB7   £6.78 booklet containing panes Nos. A132*b/d*,
 A134*b/c*. and A136*b* (*cover showing view of
 fortified coastline*) . . . .   17·00

  Withdrawn: 18.10.2000

AB **3** Peregrine Falcon
 (*illustration reduced*). *Actual size* 105×60 *mm*)

Endangered Species. Peregrine Falcon

2000 (4 FEB). *Multicoloured covers as Type* AB **3**. *Panes
attached by selvedge*
ASB8   £2.10 booklet containing pane No. A140*a*
 (*cover Type* AB **3**) . . . .   5·00
ASB9   £2.60 booklet containing pane No. A141*a*
 (*cover showing falcon with prey*) . . . .   5·75

  Withdrawn: 3.2.2001

Garrison Island (4th series). Events

2000 (19 OCT). *Multicoloured cover as Type* AB **2** *containing
text and illustrations on panes and interleaving pages.
Stitched.*
ASB10   £7.38 booklet containing panes Nos. A154*b*,
 A154*c*×2, A156*b*×2 and A158*b* (*cover
 showing Braye Road with Fort Albert in the
 distance*) . . . .   18·00

  Withdrawn: 18.10.2001

Garrison Island (5th series). The Royal Navy

2001 (16 OCT). *Multicoloured cover as Type* AB **2** *containing
text and illustrations on panes and interleaving pages.
Stitched.*
ASB11   £7.50 booklet containing panes Nos. A176*b*,
 A176*c*×2, A178*b/c*, and A180*b* (*cover
 showing Alderney Harbour*) . . . .   18·00

  Withdrawn: 15.10.2002

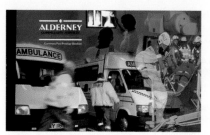

AB **4** Medical and Rescue Services
(*illustration reduced. Actual size* 162×98 *mm*)

Community Services (1st and 2nd series)

2002 (17 OCT). *Multicoloured cover as Type* AB **4** *containing text and illustrations on panes and interleaving pages. Stitched.*
ASB12 £9.40 booklet containing panes Nos. A163*ab/ac*, A165*ab*, A197*ab/ac* and A199*ab* . 35·00

Withdrawn: 16.10.2003

Community Services (3rd series)

(Des M. Legg)

2003 (16 OCT). *Multicoloured cover as Type* AB **4** *containing text and illustrations on panes and interleaving pages. Stitched.*
ASB13 £9.40 booklet containing panes Nos. A217*a/d* and A219*a* . . . . 25·00

Withdrawn: 15.10.2004

Community Services (4th series)

(Des M. Legg)

2004 (28 OCT). *Multicoloured cover as Type* AB **4** *containing text and illustrations on panes and interleaving pages. Stitched.*
ASB14 £9.76 booklet containing panes Nos. A242*a/d* and A244*a*×2 . . . . 35·00

Withdrawn: 27.10.2005

AB **5** Gun Carriage
(*illustration reduced. Actual size* 162×98 *mm*)

Bicentenary of the Battle of Trafalgar

2005 (9 MAY). *Multicoloured cover as Type* AB **5**. *Booklet contains text and illustrations on panes and interleaving pages. Stitched.*
ASB15 £9.76 booklet containing panes Nos. A253*a*×2, A253*b/c*, A254*a* and A255*a* . . . . . 25·00

Withdrawn: 8.5.2006

AB **6** Gannet
(*illustration reduced. Actual size* 164×98 *mm*)

Resident Birds (1st series). Seabirds

2006 (27 JULY). *Multicoloured cover as Type* AB **6**. *Booklet contains text and illustrations on panes and interleaving pages. Stitched.*
ASB16 £10.60 booklet containing panes Nos. A282*a/7a* . . . . 36·00

Withdrawn: 26.7.2007

Resident Birds (2nd series). Passerines

2007 (24 MAY). *Multicoloured cover as Type* AB **6**. *Booklet contains text and illustrations on panes and interleaving pages. Stitched.*
ASB17 £11.32 booklet containing panes Nos. A316*a/21a* . . . . 27·00

Withdrawn: 23.5.2008

Resident Birds (3rd series). Raptors

2008 (15 MAY). *Multicoloured cover as Type* AB **6**. *Booklet contains text and illustrations on panes and interleaving pages. Stitched.*
ASB18 £12 booklet containing panes Nos. A337*a/41a* . . . . 28·00

Isle of Man

REGIONAL ISSUES

Although specifically issued for regional use, these issues were initially valid for use throughout the U.K. Regional issues ceased to be valid in the Isle of Man from 5 July 1973 when the island established its own independent postal administration and introduced its own stamps.

DATES OF ISSUE. Conflicting dates of issue have been announced for some of the regional issues, partly explained by the stamps being released on different dates by the Philatelic Bureau in Edinburgh or the Philatelic Counter in London and in the regions. We have adopted the practice of giving the earliest known dates, since once released the stamps could have been used anywhere in the U.K.

INVALIDATION. Nos. 1/7 were invalidated as from 1 March 1972 in common with other British '£sd' stamps. Nos. 8/11 were invalidated for use in the Isle of Man on 5 July 1973 but, together with other British stamps, were accepted for the prepayment of postage on letters from the island until 5 August 1973. The Manx Regionals remained valid for use in the rest of the United Kingdom and were withdrawn from sale at the British Post Office Philatelic Sales counters on 4 July 1974.

1 Multiple Crowns   **2**   **3**

(Des J. Nicholson. Portrait by Dorothy Wilding Ltd. Photo Harrison)

1958–68. *Wmk Type* **1**. *Perf* 15×14 (C)

1	**2**	2½d carmine-red (8.6.64)	50	1·20
2	**3**	3d deep lilac (18.8.58)	50	20
		a. Chalk-surfaced paper (17.5.63)	12·00	12·00
		p. One centre phosphor band (27.6.68)	20	50
3		4d ultramarine (7.2.66)	1·50	1·50
		p. Two phosphor bands (5.7.67) .	20	30
1/3p		Set of 3	80	1·60
1		First Day Cover		45·00
2		First Day Cover		32·00
3		First Day Cover		15·00

Cylinder Nos.: 2½d 1; 3d (ord and phos) 1; 4d (ord and phos) 1

Sheets: 240 (12×20)

Quantities sold (ordinary only): 2½d 4,298,160; 3d 35,959,420 (up to 31.3.68 and including 1,080,000 on chalky paper); 4d 4,353,840

Withdrawn: 31.8.66 2½d

Sold out: 11.67 4d ordinary; 12.68 3d ordinary, 4d phosphor; 4.69 3d phosphor

1968–69. *No wmk. Chalk-surfaced paper. One centre phosphor band* (*Nos. 5/6*) *or two phosphor bands* (*others*). Perf 15×14 (C)

4	**3**	4d blue (24.6.68)	25	30
5		4d olive-sepia (4.9.68)	25	30
6		4d bright vermilion (26.2.69)	45	75
7		5d royal blue (4.9.68)	45	75
4/7		Set of 4	1·20	2·00
5, 7		First Day Cover		4·00

Cylinder Nos.: 4d (blue) 1; 4d (olive-sepia) 1; 4d (bright vermilion) 1; 5d 1

Sheets: 240 (12×20)

Sold out: 16.7.69 4d blue

Withdrawn: 14.3.71 (locally), 25.11.71 (British Philatelic Counters) 4d

4

Decimal Currency

(Des J. Matthews. Portrait after plaster cast by Arnold Machin. Photo Harrison)

1971 (7 JULY). *Chalk-surfaced paper. One centre phosphor band* (2½p) *or two phosphor bands* (*others*). Perf 15×14 (C)

8	**4**	2½p bright magenta	20	15
9		3p ultramarine	20	15
10		5p reddish violet	80	80
11		7½p chestnut	90	90
8/11		Set of 4	1·10	1·50
		First Day Cover		3·00
		Presentation Pack	3·25	

All values were originally issued on ordinary cream paper, but the 2½p and 3p later appeared on white fluorescent paper.

Cylinder Nos.: (dot and no dot): 2½p 3, phos 5; 3p 1, phos 4; 5p 4, phos 12; 7½p 4, phos 10

Sheets: 200 (10×20)

Withdrawn: 4.7.73 (locally), 4.7.74 (British Philatelic Counters)

INDEPENDENT POSTAL ADMINISTRATION

The Isle of Man established an independent postal administration on 5 July 1973 and introduced its own stamps.

NO WATERMARK. All the following issues are on unwatermarked paper *unless otherwise stated*.

5 Castletown

6 Port Erin

7 Snaefell

8 Laxey

9 Tynwald Hill

10 Douglas Promenade

11 Port St. Mary

12 Fairy Bridge

13 Peel

14 Cregneish

15 Ramsey Bay

16 Douglas Bay

17 Manx Cat

18 Monk's Bridge, Ballasalla

19 Derbyhaven

20 Manx Loaghtyn Ram

21 Manx Shearwater

22 Viking Longship

(Des J. Nicholson. Photo Courvoisier)

1973 (5 JULY)–**75**. *Granite paper*. Perf 11½ (C)

12	**5**	½p multicoloured (*ab*)	10	10
13	**6**	1p multicoloured (*ae*)	10	10
14	**7**	1½p multicoloured (*ak*)	10	10
15	**8**	2p multicoloured (*aj*)	10	10
16	**9**	2½p multicoloured (*a*)	10	10
17	**10**	3p mult (*sage-green border*) (*ac*) .	10	10
		a. Error. Olive-bistre border † . . .	£100	60·00
18	**11**	3½p mult (*olive-brown border*) (*ad*) .	10	10
		a. Error. Grey-brown border † . . .	£100	60·00
19	**12**	4p multicoloured (*a*)	10	10
20	**9**	4½p multicoloured (*f*)	20	15
21	**13**	5p multicoloured (*ah*)	15	10
22	**10**	5½p multicoloured (*g*)	20	15
23	**14**	6p multicoloured (*al*)	20	15
24	**8**	7p multicoloured (*g*)	20	15
25	**15**	7½p multicoloured (*a*)	20	20
26		8p multicoloured (*f*)	25	25

27	**16**	9p multicoloured (an)	20	20
28	**17**	10p multicoloured (an)	35	20
29	**18**	11p multicoloured (l)	35	30
30	**19**	13p multicoloured (l)	40	35
31	**20**	20p multicoloured (an)	50	50
32	**21**	50p multicoloured (an)	1·00	1·10
33	**22**	£1 multicoloured (am)	2·00	2·00
12/33		*Set of 22*	6·00	6·00
		First Day Cover (7)		7·75
		Presentation Pack (6)	9·00

†These errors occur on printings (c) and (d). That on the 3p resembles the border colour of the ½p and that on the 3½p the 2p. Intermediate shades also exist, but are not covered by the listing.

Printings: (a) 5.7.73; (b) 1.11.73; (c) 16.4.74; (d) 29.7.74; (e) 2.9.74; (f) 8.1.75; (g) 28.5.75; (h) 16.6.75; (i) 29.10.75; (j) 1.12.75; (k) 2.2.76; (l) 20.9.76; (m) 16.2.77; (n) 7.7.77

Printings (a) and (i) have thick shiny gum, but all the other printings have matt, almost invisible gum. Printings (f), (g) and (i) are inscribed '1975'. The remainder are inscribed '1973'.

Sheets: 50 (5×10) ½p to 9p, 11p, 13p; (10×5) 10p, 20p to £1

Withdrawn: 31.12.78 (except ½p, 3p and 3½p values in booklets withdrawn 15.5.79. In addition 2p and 3½p values were kept available for use on postal orders after 31.12.78 until finally withdrawn on 30.6.83 (2p) or 31.12.85 (3½p))

23 Vikings Landing on Man, A.D. 938

Inauguration of Postal Independence

(Des J. Nicholson. Photo Harrison)

1973 (5 JULY). Perf 14 (C)

34	**23**	15p multicoloured	35	30
		First Day Cover		1·10
		Presentation Pack	1·40

For 15p inscr 'POST OFFICE DECENNIUM 1983' see No. 256.

Cylinder Nos.: 1A (×4)

Sheets: 50 (10×5)

Quantity sold: 350,000

Sold out: Soon after issue

24 No. 1 *Sutherland*, 1873

25 No. 4 *Caledonia*, 1885

26 No. 13 *Kissack*, 1910

27 No. 3 *Pender*, 1873

Centenary of Steam Railway

(Des J. Nicholson. Photo Harrison)

1973 (4 AUG). Perf 15×14 (C)

35	**24**	2½p multicoloured	15	10
36	**25**	3p multicoloured	15	15
37	**26**	7½p multicoloured	25	25
38	**27**	9p multicoloured	25	25
35/8		*Set of 4*	70	70
		First Day Cover		1·90
		Presentation Pack	1·50

Cylinder Nos.: All values 1A (×5)

Sheets: 50 (5×10)

Quantities sold: 2½p 617,122; 3p 808,173; 7½p 331,695; 9p 324,414

Withdrawn: 3.8.74

28 Leonard Randles, First Winner, 1923 on Sumbeam motorcycle

29 Alan Holmes, Double Winner, 1957 on Norton motorcycle

Golden Jubilee of Manx Grand Prix

(Des J. Nicholson. Litho John Waddington)

1973 (4 SEPT). Perf 14 (C)

39	**28**	3p multicoloured	10	15
40	**29**	3½p multicoloured	15	15
39/40		*Set of 2*	25	25
		First Day Cover		90
		Presentation Pack	70
		Set of 2 Gutter Pairs	60

Plate Nos.: Both values 1A, 1B, 1C, 1D (each ×4)

Sheets: 50 (2 panes 5×5)

Imprint: Central, bottom margin

Quantities sold: 3p 550,347; 3½p 653,355

Withdrawn: 3.9.74

157

30 Princess Anne and
Capt. Mark Philips

Royal Wedding

(Des A. Larkins and litho De La Rue)

1973 (14 NOV). Perf 13½ (C)

41	**30**	25p multicoloured	45	50
		First Day Cover		85
		Presentation Pack	90	
		Gutter Pair	90	

Plate Nos.: 1A, 1B (each ×4)

Sheets: 50 (5 panes 5×5)

Imprint: Right-hand corner, bottom margin

Quantity sold: 400,813

Withdrawn: 13.11.74

31 Badge, Citation and Sir
William Hillary (founder)

32 Wreck of *St. George*,
1830

33 *Manchester & Salford*,
1868–87

34 *Osman Gabriel*

150th Anniversary of Royal National Lifeboat Institution

(Des J. Nicholson. Photo Courvoisier)

1974 (4 MAR). Granite paper. Perf 11½ (C)

42	**31**	3p multicoloured	10	10
43	**32**	3½p multicoloured	15	10
44	**33**	8p multicoloured	25	25
45	**34**	10p multicoloured	30	25
42/5		Set of 4	70	60
		First Day Cover		1·00
		Presentation Pack	1·00	

Sheets: 100 (10×10)

Quantities sold: 3p 674,984; 3½p 849,990; 8p 374,941; 10p 375,043

Withdrawn: 3.3.75

35 Stanley Woods, 1935 on
Motoguzzi motorcycle

36 Freddy Frith, 1937 on
Norton motorcycle

37 Max Deubel and Emil
Horner, 1961 on BMW
500 with Sidecar

38 Mike Hailwood, 1961 on
Honda 125 motorcycle

Tourist Trophy Motorcycle Races (1st issue)

(Des J. Nicholson. Litho De La Rue)

1974 (29 MAY). Perf 13×13½ (C)

46	**35**	3p multicoloured	10	10
47	**36**	3½p multicoloured	10	10
48	**37**	8p multicoloured	25	20
49	**38**	10p multicoloured	25	20
46/9		Set of 4	60	55
		First Day Cover		1·00
		Presentation Pack	1·00	
		Set of 4 Gutter Pairs	1·20	

See also Nos. 63/6.

Plate Nos.: All values 1A, 1B, 1C, 1D (each ×6); 3p also 1A
(×4)–2A–2A, 1B (×4)–2B–2B, 1C (×4)–2C–2C, 1D (×4)–2D–2D; 8p
also 1A–1A–2A–1A (×3), 1B–1B–2B–1B (×3), 1C–1C–2C–1C (×3),
1D–1D–2D–1D (×3)

Sheets: 50 (2 panes 5×5)

Imprint: Right-hand corner, bottom margin

Quantities sold: 3p 578,045; 3½p 816,235; 8p 334,760; 10p 403,177

Withdrawn: 28.5.75

39 Rushen Abbey and Arms

40 Magnus Haraldson rows King Edgar on the Dee

41 King Magnus and Norse Fleet

42 Bridge at Avignon and Bishop's Mitre

Historical Anniversaries

(Des J. Nicholson, from ideas by G. Kneale. Litho Questa (3½p, 10p) or John Waddington (others))

1974 (18 SEPT). Perf 14 (C)

50	**39**	3½p multicoloured	10	10
51	**40**	4½p multicoloured	10	10
52	**41**	8p multicoloured	15	15
53	**42**	10p multicoloured	20	20
50/3		Set of 4	50	50
		First Day Cover		85
		Presentation Pack	85	
		Set of 4 Gutter Pairs	1·00	

Plate Nos.: All values 1A, 1B, 1C, 1D (each ×4)

Sheets: 50 (2 panes 5×5)

Imprint: Right-hand corner, bottom margin and left-hand corner, top margin

Quantities sold: 3½p 931,610; 4½p 1,025,044; 8p 450,418; 10p 425,305

Withdrawn: 17.9.75

43 Churchill and Bugler Dunne at Colenso, 1899

44 Churchill and Government Buildings, Douglas

45 Churchill and Manx A.A Gun Crew

46 Churchill as Freeman of Douglas

Birth Centenary of Sir Winston Churchill

(Des G. Kneale. Photo Courvoisier)

1974 (22 NOV). *Granite paper.* Perf 11½ (C)

54	**43**	3½p multicoloured	10	10
55	**44**	4½p multicoloured	10	10
56	**45**	8p multicoloured	15	15
57	**46**	20p multicoloured	30	25
54/7		Set of 4	60	55
		First Day Cover		85
		Presentation Pack	1·40	
MS58		121×91 mm. Nos. 54/7	75	75
		First Day Cover		1·20

No. **MS**58 is inscribed '30th NOV. 1974.

Sheets: 25 (5×5)

Quantities sold: 3½p 916,748; 4½p 853,537; 8p 424,691; 20p 429,586; miniature sheet 362,089

Withdrawn: 21.11.75

47 Cabin School and Names of Pioneers

48 Terminal Tower Building, John Gill and Robert Carran

49 Clague House Museum and Robert and Margaret Clague

50 *William T. Graves* and Thomas Quayle

Manx Pioneers in Cleveland, Ohio

(Des J. Nicholson. Photo Courvoisier)

1975 (14 MAR). *Granite paper.* Perf 11½ (C)

59	**47**	4½p multicoloured	. . . .	10	10
60	**48**	5½p multicoloured	. . . .	10	10
61	**49**	8p multicoloured	. . . .	15	15
62	**50**	10p multicoloured	. . . .	25	25
59/62		Set of 4	. . . .	55	55
		First Day Cover	. . . .		75
		Presentation Pack	. . . .	80	

Sheets: 50 (5×10)

Quantities sold: 4½p 473,352; 5½p 999,802; 8p 433,352; 10p 447,945

Withdrawn: 13.3.76 (5½p sold out 12.75)

51 Tom Sheard, 1923 and Douglas motorcycle

52 Walter Handley, 1925 and Rex-Acme motorcycle

53 Geoff Duke, 1955 and Gilera motorcycle

54 Peter Williams, 1973 and Norton motorcycle

Tourist Trophy Motorcycle Races (2nd issue)

(Des J. Nicholson. Litho John Waddington)

1975 (28 MAY). Perf 13½ (C)

63	**51**	5½p multicoloured	. . . .	10	10
64	**52**	7p multicoloured	. . . .	15	15
65	**53**	10p multicoloured	. . . .	15	15
66	**54**	12p multicoloured	. . . .	25	20
63/6		Set of 4	. . . .	60	55
		First Day Cover	. . . .		2·40
		Presentation Pack	. . . .	1·00	
		Set of 4 Gutter Pairs	. . . .	1·20	

Plate Nos.: 5½p, 7p 1B, 1D (each ×5); 10p 1A, 1B, 1C (each ×5); 12p 1A, 1C (each ×5)

Sheets: 50 (2 panes 5×5)

Imprint: Right-hand corner, bottom margin

Quantities sold: 5½p 633,250; 7p 520,285; 10p 399,710; 12p 440,208

Withdrawn: 27.5.76

55 Sir George Goldie and Birthplace

56 Goldie and Map of Africa

57 Goldie as President of Royal Geographical Society

58 River Scene on the Niger

50th Death Anniversary of Sir George Goldie

(Des G. Kneale. Photo Courvoisier)

1975 (9 SEPT). *Granite paper.* Perf 11½ (C)

67	**55**	5½p multicoloured	. . . .	10	10
68	**56**	7p multicoloured	. . . .	15	15
69	**57**	10p multicoloured	. . . .	15	15
70	**58**	12p multicoloured	. . . .	25	25
67/70		Set of 4	. . . .	65	65
		First Day Cover	. . . .		90
		Presentation Pack	. . . .	1·00	

Sheets: 50 (10×5) 7p, 10p; (5×10) others

Quantities sold: 5½p 488,317; 7p 426,849; 10p 373,771; 12p 439,843

Withdrawn: 8.9.76

59 Title Page of Manx Bible

60 Rev. Philip Moore and Ballaugh Old Church

61 Bishop Hildesley and Bishops Court

62 John Kelly saving Bible Manuscript

Christmas and Bicentenary of Manx Bible

(Des J. Nicholson. Litho Questa)

1975 (29 OCT). Perf 14 (C)

71	**59**	5½p multicoloured	10	10
72	**60**	7p multicoloured	15	15
73	**61**	11p multicoloured	20	20
74	**62**	13p multicoloured	25	25
71/4		Set of 4	60	60
		First Day Cover		85
		Presentation Pack	1·00	
		Set of 4 Gutter Pairs	1·20	

Plate Nos. 13p 1C, 1D (each ×4); others 1A, 1B (each ×4)

Sheets: 50 (2 panes 5×5)

Quantities sold: 5½p 738,774; 7p 607,377; 11p 405,126; 13p 402,463

63 William Christian listening to Patrick Henry

64 Conveying the Fincastle Resolutions

65 Patrick Henry and William Christian

66 Christian as an Indian Fighter

Bicentenary of American Revolution and Col. William Christian Commemoration

(Des and litho John Waddington)

1976 (12 MAR). Perf 13½ (C)

75	**63**	5½p multicoloured	10	10
76	**64**	7p multicoloured	15	15
77	**65**	13p multicoloured	30	30
		a. Black (face value and inscr) printed double		
78	**66**	20p multicoloured	35	35
75/8		Set of 4	75	80
		First Day Cover		1·00
		Presentation Pack	1·00	
		Set of 4 Gutter Pairs	1·20	
MS79	150×90 mm. Nos. 75/8. Perf 14 (C) .		90	1·00
		First Day Cover		4·00
		Presentation Pack	1·90	

Plate Nos.: 5½p, 20p 1A, 1C (each ×4); others 1B, 1D (each ×4)

Sheets: 50 (2 panes 5×5)

Quantities sold: 5½p 487,310; 7p 524,144; 13p 558,348; 20p 424,728; miniature sheet 209,367

Withdrawn: 11.3.77

67 First Horse Tram, 1876

68 'Toast-rack' Tram, 1890

69 Horse-bus, 1895

70 Royal Tram, 1972

Douglas Horse Trams Centenary

(Des J. Nicholson. Photo Courvoisier)

1976 (26 MAY). Granite paper. Perf 11½ (C)

80	**67**	5½p multicoloured	10	10
81	**68**	7p multicoloured	15	15

161

82	69	11p multicoloured	20	20
83	70	13p multicoloured	25	25
80/3		Set of 4	65	65
		First Day Cover		1·00
		Presentation Pack		1·00

Sheets 25 (5×5)

Quantities sold: 5½p 627,083; 7p 480,417; 11p 391,871; 13p 389,604

Withdrawn: 25.5.77

71 Barroose Beaker

72 Souvenir Teapot

73 Laxey Jug

74 Cronk Aust Food Vessel

75 Sansbury Bowl

76 Knox Urn

Europa. Ceramic Art

(Des J. Nicholson. Photo Courvoisier)

1976 (28 JULY). *Granite paper*. Perf 11½ (C)

84	71	5p multicoloured	20	10
		a. Strip of 3. Nos. 84/6	60	60
85	72	5p multicoloured	20	10
86	73	5p multicoloured	20	10
87	74	10p multicoloured	20	10
		a. Strip of 3 Nos. 87/9	60	60
88	75	10p multicoloured	20	10
89	76	10p multicoloured	20	10
84/9		Set of 6	1·10	1·10
		First Day Cover		2·10
		Presentation Pack		1·50

Sheets: 9 (3×3) containing the three designs of each value horizontally and vertically *se-tenant*

Quantities sold: 5p 256,400 of each design; 10p 262,900 of each design

Sold out: 20.11.76 (5p); 12.76 (10p)

77 Diocesan Banner

78 Onchan Banner

79 Castletown Banner

80 Ramsey Banner

Christmas and Centenary of Mothers' Union

(Des G. Kneale. Litho Questa)

1976 (14 OCT). Perf 14½ (C)

90	77	6p multicoloured	10	10
91	78	7p multicoloured	15	15
92	79	11p multicoloured	20	20
93	80	13p multicoloured	25	25
90/3		Set of 4	65	65
		First Day Cover		80
		Presentation Pack		1·00

Plate Nos.: 6p 1B (×5); 11p 1A (×5); others 1C (×5)

Sheets: 50 (10×5)

Imprint: Right-hand corner, bottom margin and left-hand corner, top margin

Quantities sold: 6p 905,752; 7p 890,762; 11p 397,807; 13p 390,057

Withdrawn: 13.10.77

81 Queen Elizabeth II

82 Queen Elizabeth and Prince Philip

162

83 Queen Elizabeth II

Silver Jubilee

(Des A. Larkins. Litho and recess De La Rue)

1977 (1 MAR). Perf 14×13 (7p) or 13×14 (others), both comb

94	**81**	6p multicoloured	10	10
95	**82**	7p multicoloured	20	20
96	**83**	25p multicoloured	50	50
94/6		*Set of 3*	70	70
		First Day Cover		85
		Presentation pack	1·00	
		Set of 3 Gutter Pairs	1·40	

Plate Nos.: 6p, 7p 1A (×5)–2A, 1B (×5)–2B, 1C (×5)–2C, 1D (×5)–2D; 25p 1B, 1D (each ×6)

Sheets: 50 (2 panes 5×5)

Imprint: Right-hand corner, bottom margin

Quantities sold: 6p 942,356; 7p 911,191; 25p 651,101

Withdrawn: 28.2.78

84 Carrick Bay from 'Tom-the-Dipper'

85 View from Ramsey

Europa. Landscapes

(Des J. Nicholson. Litho Questa)

1977 (26 MAY). Perf 13½×14 (C)

97	**84**	6p multicoloured	15	15
98	**85**	10p multicoloured	25	25
97/8		*Set of 2*	40	40
		First Day Cover		55
		Presentation Pack	75	
		Set of 2 Gutter Pairs	80	

Plate Nos.: 6p 1A, 1B, 1C, 1D, 2A, 2B, 2C, 2D (each ×4); 10p 1A, 1B, 1C, 1D (each ×5), 2A–1A–1A–2A–1A, 2B–1B–1B–2B–1B, 2C–1C–1C–2C–1C, 2D–1D–1D–2D–1D

Sheets: 40 (2 panes 4×5)

Imprint: Right-hand corner, bottom margin and left-hand corner, top margin

Quantities sold: 6p 778,685; 10p 843,525

Withdrawn: 25.5.78

86 F. A. Applebee, 1912 riding Scott motorcycle

87 St. John Ambulance Brigade at Governor's Bridge, c. 1938

88 Scouts working Scoreboard

89 John Williams, 1976 on Norton motorcycle

Linked Anniversaries

(Des J. Nicholson. Litho John Waddington)

1977 (26 MAY). Perf 13½ (C)

99	**86**	6p multicoloured	15	10
100	**87**	7p multicoloured	15	15
101	**88**	11p multicoloured	25	25
102	**89**	13p multicoloured	25	30
99/102		*Set of 4*	70	65
		First Day Cover		85
		Presentation Pack	1·00	
		Set of 4 Gutter Pairs	1·40	

The events commemorated are: 70th anniversary of Manx TT; 70th anniversary of Boy Scouts; centenary of St. John Ambulance Brigade.

Plate Nos.: 11p 1A, 1C (each ×4); others 1B, 1D (each ×4)

Sheets: 50 (2 panes 5×5)

Imprint: Right-hand corner, bottom margin

Quantities sold: 6p 525,703; 7p 875,303; 11p 431,053; 13p 440,403

Withdrawn: 25.5.78

90 Old Summer House, Mount Morrison, Peel

91 Wesley preaching in Castletown Square

92 Wesley preaching outside Bradden Church

93 New Methodist Church, Douglas

97 Sepecat Jaguar over Ramsey, 1977

Bicentenary of the First Visit of John Wesley

(Des and photo Courvoisier)

1977 (19 OCT). *Granite paper.* Perf 11½ (C)

103	**90**	6p multicoloured	15	10
104	**91**	7p multicoloured	15	15
105	**92**	11p multicoloured	25	25
106	**93**	13p multicoloured	25	25
103/6		*Set of 4*	70	65
		First Day Cover		85
		Presentation Pack	1·00	

Sheets: 50 (5×10)

Quantities sold: 6p 661,755; 7p 976,155; 11p 373,805; 13p 366,905

Withdrawn: 18.10.78

R.A.F. Diamond Jubilee

(Des A. Theobald. Litho John Waddington)

1978 (28 Feb). Perf 13½×14 (C)

107	**94**	6p multicoloured	15	10
108	**95**	7p multicoloured	15	15
109	**96**	11p multicoloured	25	25
110	**97**	13p multicoloured	25	25
107/10		*Set of 4*	70	65
		First Day Cover		1·20
		Presentation Pack	1·00	
		Set of 4 Gutter Pairs	1·40	

Plate Nos.: All values 1A, 1C (each ×4)

Sheets: 50 (2 panes 5×5)

Quantities sold: 6p 690,536; 7p 875,811; 11p 416,082; 13p 422,797

Withdrawn: 27.2.79

94 Short Type 184 Seaplane and H.M.S. *Ben-My-Chree*, 1915

98 Watch Tower, Langness

99 Jurby Church

95 Bristol Scout C and H.M.S. *Vindex*, 1915

100 Government Buildings

101 Tynwald Hill

96 Boulton Paul Defiant over Douglas Bay, 1941

102 Milner's Tower

103 Laxey Wheel

164

104 Castle Rushen

105 St. Ninian's Church

106 Tower of Refuge

107 St. German's Cathedral

108 Point of Ayre Lighthouse

109 Corrin's Tower

110 Douglas Head Lighthouse

111 Fuchsia

112 Manx Cat

113 Red-billed Chough

114 Viking Warrior

114a Queen Elizabeth II

Landmarks and Queen's Portrait (£2)

(Des G. Kneale (£2), J. Nicholson (others). Litho Questa (½p to 16p), photo Courvoisier (20p to £2))

1978 (28 FEB)–**81**. (*a*) Perf 14 (C)

111	**98**	½p multicoloured (*a*)	. . . .	10	10
		a. Perf 14½	. . . .	20	10
112	**99**	1p multicoloured (*a*)	. . . .	10	10
		a. Perf 14½	. . . .	20	10
113	**100**	6p multicoloured (*a*)	. . . .	30	30
114	**101**	7p multicoloured (*a*)	. . . .	35	35
		a. Perf 14½	. . . .	8·50	6·50
115	**102**	8p multicoloured (*a*)	. . . .	25	25
		a. Perf 14½	. . . .	35	35
116	**103**	9p multicoloured (*a*)	. . . .	35	35
		a. Perf 14½	. . . .	35	35
117	**104**	10p multicoloured (*a*)	. . . .	40	40
		a. Perf 14½	. . . .	35	35
118	**105**	11p multicoloured (*a*)	. . . .	40	40
		a. Perf 14½	. . . .	40	40
119	**106**	12p multicoloured (*a*)	. . . .	40	25
		a. Perf 14½	. . . .	50	40
120	**107**	13p multicoloured (*a*)	. . . .	60	60
		a. Perf 14½	. . . .	30	25
121	**108**	14p multicoloured (*a*)	. . . .	60	60
		a. Perf 14½	. . . .	30	25
122	**109**	15p multicoloured (*a*)	. . . .	75	75
		a. Perf 14½	. . . .	30	25
123	**110**	16p multicoloured (*a*)	. . . .	55	30
		a. Perf 14½	. . . .	26·00	21·00

(*b*) *Granite paper*. Perf 11½ (C)

124	**111**	20p multicoloured (*b*)	. . . .	50	35
125	**112**	25p multicoloured (*b*)	. . . .	65	45
126	**113**	50p multicoloured (*b*)	. . . .	90	75
127	**114**	£1 multicoloured (*b*)	. . . .	1·90	2·00
128	**114a**	£2 multicoloured (*c*)	. . . .	3·50	3·50
111/28		Set of 18 (*cheapest*)	. . . .	9·00	10·00
		First Day Covers* (5)	. . . . . .		12·00
		Presentation Packs (4)	. . . . . 14·00		

*The most common versions of the three low and medium value first day covers prepared by the Philatelic Bureau were franked with Nos. 111a, 112/15, 116a, 117/18, 119a, 120, 121a, 122 and 123a. Some examples can be found with the ½p as No. 111, the 11p as No. 118a or the 13p as No. 120a. First day covers prepared by dealers or collectors on the island were franked with Nos. 111/18, 119a/20a, 121, 122a and 123.

Printings: (*a*) 28.2.78; (*b*) 18.10.78; (*c*) 29.9.81

Although both perforations of Nos. 111/23 were printed at the same time, some did not appear in use until some time after 28 February 1978. Earliest dates for these are as follows: 1p (112*a*) 8.79, 7p (114*a*) 8.78, 8p (115*a*) 6.80, 10p (117*a*) 8.79, 12p (119) 9.80.

Plate Nos.: ½, 6, 8, 9, 10, 11, 12, 13, 14, 15, 16p 1A, 1B, 1C, 1D (each ×4); 1p 1A, 1B, 1C, 1D (each ×4) (No. 112); 1A–1A–2A–1A, 1B–1B–2B–1B, 1C–1C–2C–1C, 1D–1D–2D–1D; 7p 1A, 1B, 1C, 1D (each ×4) (No. 114); 2A, 2B, 2C, 2D (each ×4), 2B–2B–3B–2B, 2C–2C–3C–2C (No. 114*a*); £2 A1–1–1–1, B1–1–1–1, others none

Sheets: 25 (5×5) (£2); 50 (1, 7, 10, 12, 13, 14, 15, 16p 5×10; others 10×5)

Imprint: ½p to 16p left-hand corner, top margin and right-hand corner, bottom margin; 20p to £1 none; £2 central bottom margin

Withdrawn: 30.6.83 1p to 16p; 31.12.83 20p to £1; 31.12.85 ½p; 30.6.90 £2

115 Queen Elizabeth in Coronation Regalia

25th Anniversary of Coronation

(Des G. Kneale. Litho Questa)

1978 (24 MAY). Perf 14½×14 (C)

132	**115**	25p multicoloured	50	45
		First Day Cover		65
		Presentation Pack	85	
		Gutter Pair	1·00	

Plate Nos.: 1A, 1B (each ×6)

Sheets: 50 (2 panes 5×5)

Imprint: Left-hand corner, top margin and right-hand corner, bottom margin

Quantity sold: 575,996

Withdrawn: 23.5.79

116 Wheel-headed Cross-slab

117 Celtic Wheel-Cross

118 Keeil Chiggyrt Stone

119 Olaf Liotulfson Cross

120 Odd's and Thorleif's Crosses

121 Thor Cross

Europa. Celtic and Norse Crosses

(Des J. Nicholson. Photo Courvoisier)

1978 (24 MAY). *Granite paper.* Perf 11½ (C)

133	**116**	6p multicoloured	10	10
		a. Strip of 3. Nos. 133/5	25	25
134	**117**	6p multicoloured	10	10
135	**118**	6p multicoloured	10	10
136	**119**	11p multicoloured	20	15
		a. Strip of 3. Nos. 136/8	60	60
137	**120**	11p multicoloured	20	15
138	**121**	11p multicoloured	20	15
133/8		Set of 6	85	80
		First Day Cover		1·10
		Presentation Pack	1·20	

Sheets: 9 (3×3) The three designs of each value were printed together, *se-tenant*, in horizontal and vertical strips throughout

Quantities sold: 6p 3,821,152; 11p 3,788,667

Withdrawn: 23.5.79

122 J. K. Ward and Ward Library, Peel

123 Swimmer, Cyclist and Walker

124 American Bald Eagle, Manx Arms and Maple Leaf

125 Lumber Camp at Three Rivers, Quebec

Anniversaries and Events

(Des John Waddington (7p), G. Kneale (11p), J. Nicholson (others). Litho John Waddington)

1978 (10 JUNE). *Invisible gum.* Perf 13½ (C)

139	**122**	6p multicoloured	10	10
140	**123**	7p multicoloured	20	15
141	**124**	11p multicoloured	25	25
142	**125**	13p multicoloured	25	25
139/42		*Set of 4*	70	65
		First Day Covers (3)		1·00
		Presentation Packs (2)	1·00	
		Set of 4 Gutter Pairs	1·40	

Plate Nos.: 6p 1A, 1B, 1C, 1D (each ×4); others 1B, 1D (each ×4)

Sheets: 50 (2 panes 5×5)

Imprint: Central, bottom margin

Quantities sold: 6p 629,041; 7p 873,067; 11p 393,907; 13p 383,048

Withdrawn: 9.6.79

126 Hunt the Wren

Christmas

(Des J. Nicholson. Litho John Waddington)

1978 (18 OCT). Perf 13 (C)

143	**126**	5p multicoloured	20	20
		First Day Cover		40
		Presentation Pack	45	
		Gutter Pair	40	

Plate Nos.: 1B, 1D (each ×4)

Sheets: 50 (2 panes 5×5)

Imprint: Central, bottom margin

Quantity sold: 1,000,000

Sold out: 4.79 (stamp) or 8.79 (presentation pack)

127 P. M. C. Kermode (founder) and *Nassa kermodei*

128 Peregrine Falcon

129 Fulmar

130 *Epitriptus cowini* (fly)

Centenary of Natural History and Antiquarian Society

(Des J. Nicholson. Litho Questa)

1979 (27 FEB). Perf 14 (C)

144	**127**	6p multicoloured	10	10
145	**128**	7p multicoloured	25	15
146	**129**	11p multicoloured	25	30
147	**130**	13p multicoloured	25	35
144/7		*Set of 4*	80	80
		First Day Cover		90
		Presentation Pack	1·00	
		Set of 4 Gutter Pairs	1·40	

Plate Nos.: 6p 1A, 1B, 1C, 1D (each ×4); 13p 1A, 1B (each ×4); others 1C, 1D (each ×4)

Sheets: 50 (2 panes 5×5)

Imprint: Left-hand corner, top margin and right-hand corner, bottom margin

Quantities sold: 6p 642,126; 7p 790,515; 11p 411,863; 13p 390,454

Withdrawn: 26.2.80

131 Postman, 1859

132 Postman, 1979

Europa. Communications

(Des A. Theobald. Litho Questa)

1979 (16 MAY). Perf 14½ (C)

148	**131**	6p multicoloured	15	10
149	**132**	11p multicoloured	40	45
148/9		*Set of 2*	50	50
		First Day Cover		50
		Presentation Pack	85	

Plate Nos.: 6p 1A, 1B (each ×6); 11p 1A, 1B (each ×5)

Sheets: 20 (4×5)

Imprint: Right-hand corner, bottom margin

Quantities sold: 6p 1,301,039; 11p 1,290,318

Sold out: By 10.79 (stamps)

Withdrawn: 15.5.80 (presentation pack)

133 Viking Longship Emblem

134 'Three Legs of Man' Emblem

135 Viking Raid at Garwick

136 10th-century Meeting of Tynwald

137 Tynwald Hill and St. John's Church

138 Procession to Tynwald Hill

Two types of 3p:

Type I. Wrongly inscribed 'INSULAREM'. '1979' imprint date.

Type II. Inscription corrected to 'INSULARUM'. '1980' imprint date.

Millennium of Tynwald

(Des J. Nicholson. Litho Harrison (3, 4p), John Waddington (others))

1979 (16 MAY)–**80**. (*a*) Perf 14½×14 (C)

150	**133**	3p multicoloured (*Type I*) (*a*)		10	10
		a. Booklet pane. Nos. 150×4, 151×2 (4p stamps at top) . . .		60	
		ab. Do. (4p stamps in centre) . . .		1·20	
		b. Type II (*b*)		10	10
		ba. Booklet pane. Nos. 150b×4, 151×2 (4p stamps at bottom)		50	
151	**134**	4p multicoloured (*ab*)		10	10

(*b*) Perf 13 (C)

152	**135**	6p multicoloured (*a*)		15	10
153	**136**	7p multicoloured (*a*)		20	20
154	**137**	11p multicoloured (*a*)		25	25
155	**138**	13p multicoloured (*a*)		30	30
150/5		Set of 6		1·00	1·00
		First Day Cover			95
		Presentation Pack		1·20	
		Set of 6 Gutter Pairs		2·00	

See also Nos. 188/9.

Printings: (*a*) 16.5.79; (*b*) 29.9.80. Inscribed '1980'

Plate Nos.: 3, 4p 1A (×6); 13p 1G (×4); others 1E (×4)

Sheets: 3, 4p 80 (10 panes 2×3, 5 panes 2×2); others 40 (2 panes 4×5). The 3 and 4p values were printed together, *se-tenant*, each pane of 6 containing four 3p and two 4p, the 4p being in either positions 1 and 2 or 3 and 4. The panes of 4 contain the 4p value only. For details of No. 150ba see after No. 189

Imprint: 3, 4p right-hand corner, bottom margin; others central, bottom margin

Quantities sold: 6p 381,334; 7p 465,473; 11p 341,204; 13p 241,162

Withdrawn: 15.5.80 6p to 13p; 25.3.87 3p, 4p

139 Queen and Court on Tynwald Hill

140 Queen and Procession from St. John's Church to Tynwald Hill

Royal Visit

(Des G. Kneale. Litho Questa)

1979 (5 JULY). Perf 14½ (C)

156	**139**	7p multicoloured		15	15
157	**140**	13p multicoloured		25	25
156/7		Set of 2		40	40
		First Day Cover			50
		Presentation pack		75	
		Set of 2 Gutter Pairs		80	

Plate Nos.: 7p 1A, 1B (each ×4); 13p 1C, 1D (each ×4)

Sheets: 50 (2 panes 5×5)

Imprint: Right-hand corner, bottom margin

Quantities sold: 7p 641,930; 13p 436,516

Withdrawn: 4.7.80

141 Odin's Raven

Voyage of Odin's Raven

(Des J. Nicholson. Litho Questa)

1979 (19 OCT). Perf 14×14½ (C)

158	**141**	15p multicoloured	45	30
		First Day Cover		50
		Presentation Pack	75	
		Gutter Pair	90	

See also No. **MS**180.

Plate Nos.: 1A, 1B, 1C, 1D (each ×4)

Sheets: 50 (2 panes 5×5)

Imprint: Right-hand corner, bottom margin

Quantity sold: 412,631

Withdrawn: 18.10.80

142 John Quilliam seized by Press Gang

143 Steering H.M.S. *Victory*, Battle of Trafalgar

144 Captain John Quilliam and H.M.S. *Spencer*

145 Captain John Quilliam (member of the House of Keys)

150th Death Anniversary of Captain John Quilliam

(Des A. Theobald. Litho Questa)

1979 (19 OCT). Perf 14 (C)

159	**142**	6p multicoloured	15	15
160	**143**	8p multicoloured	20	15
161	**144**	13p multicoloured	25	25
162	**145**	15p multicoloured	30	25
159/62		Set of 4	80	70
		First Day Cover		85
		Presentation Pack	1·00	
		Set of 4 Gutter Pairs	1·60	

Plate Nos.: 6p 1C, 1D (each ×4); others 1A, 1B (each ×4)

Sheets: 50 (2 panes 5×5)

Imprint: Right-hand corner, bottom margin

Quantities sold: 6p 608,876; 8p 858,665; 13p 360,821; 15p 360,400

Withdrawn: 18.10.80

146 Young Girl with Teddybear and Cat

147 Father Christmas with Young Children

Christmas and International Year of the Child

(Des Mrs. E. Moore. Litho John Waddington)

1979 (19 OCT). Perf 13 (C)

163	**146**	5p multicoloured	10	10
164	**147**	7p multicoloured	20	20
163/4		Set of 2	30	30
		First Day Cover		50
		Presentation Pack	60	
		Set of 2 Gutter Pairs	60	

Plate Nos.: Both values 1A, 1B, 1C, 1D (each ×4)

Sheets: 50 (2 panes 5×5)

Imprint: Central, left-hand margin

Quantities sold: 5p 1,036,495; 7p 1,087,734

Withdrawn: 18.10.80

148 Conglomerate Arch, Langness

149 Braaid Circle

150 Cashtal-yn-Ard

151 Volcanic Rocks at Scarlett

152 Sugar-loaf Rock

150th Anniversary of Royal Geographical Society

(Des J. Nicholson. Litho Questa)

1980 (5 FEB). Perf 14½ (C)

165	**148**	7p multicoloured	15	15
166	**149**	8p multicoloured	20	20
167	**150**	12p multicoloured	25	25
168	**151**	13p multicoloured	25	25
169	**152**	15p multicoloured	30	25
165/9		*Set of 5*	1·00	1·00
		First Day Cover		1·10
		Presentation Pack	1·40	
		Set of 5 Gutter Pairs	2·00	

Plate Nos.: 12p 1A, 1B, 1C, 1D (each ×4); 15p 1C, 1D (each ×4); others 1A, 1B (each ×4)

Sheets: 50 (2 panes 5×5)

Imprint: Right-hand corner, bottom margin

Quantities sold: 7p 842,859; 8p 837,710; 12p 361,362; 13p 360,261; 15p 360,310

Withdrawn: 4.2.81

153 Mona's Isle I

154 Douglas I

155 H.M.S. *Mona's Queen II* sinking U-boat

156 H.M.S. *King Orry III* at Surrender of German Fleet

157 Ben-My-Chree IV

158 Lady of Mann II

150th Anniversary of Isle of Man Steam Packet Company

(Des J. Nicholson. Photo Courvoisier)

1980 (6 MAY). *Granite paper*. Perf 11½ (C)

170	**153**	7p multicoloured	15	15
171	**154**	8p multicoloured	20	20
172	**155**	11½p multicoloured	20	25
173	**156**	12p multicoloured	25	25
174	**157**	13p multicoloured	35	25
175	**158**	15p multicoloured	40	25
170/5		*Set of 6*	1·20	1·10
		First Day Cover		1·00
		Presentation Pack	2·40	
		Set of 6 Gutter Pairs	2·40	
MS176		180×125 mm. Nos. 170/5	1·20	1·20
		First Day Cover		3·50

No. **MS**176 was issued to commemorate the 'London 1980' International Stamp Exhibition.

Cylinder Nos.: All values A1–1–1–1, B1–1–1–1, C1–1–1–1, D1–1–1–1

Sheets: 40 (2 panes 5×4)

Imprint: Central, bottom margin

Quantities sold: 7p 512,449; 8p 624,090; 11½p 381,466; 12p 367,943; 13p 368,138; 15p 376,596; miniature sheet 300,678

Withdrawn: 5.5.81

159 Stained Glass Window, T. E. Brown Room, Manx Museum

160 Clifton College, Bristol

Europa. Personalities. Thomas Edward Brown (poet and scholar) Commemoration

(Des G. Kneale. Photo Courvoisier)

1980 (6 MAY). *Granite paper*. Perf 11½ (C)

177	**159**	7p multicoloured	15	15
178	**160**	13½p multicoloured	25	25
177/8		*Set of 2*	50	50
		First Day Cover		60
		Presentation Pack	75	
		Set of 2 Gutter Pairs	1·00	

Cylinder Nos.: Both values A1–1–1–1–1, B1–1–1–1–1, C1–1–1–1–1, D1–1–1–1–1

Sheets: 20 (2 panes 2×5)

Imprint: Bottom margin at right-hand corner of left-hand pane

Quantities sold: 7p 1,726,009; 13½p 1,708,590

161 King Olav V and *Norge* (Norwegian royal yacht)

Visit of King Olav V of Norway, August 1979

(Des J. Nicholson. Litho Questa)

1980 (13 JUNE). Perf 14×14½ (C)

179	**161**	12p multicoloured	30	30
		First Day Cover		50
		Presentation Pack	75	
		Gutter Pair	60	
MS180		125×157 mm. Nos. 158 and 179 . .	75	75
		First Day Cover		1·50

No. **MS**180 also commemorates the 'NORWEX 80' stamp exhibition, Oslo.

Plate Nos.: 1C, 1D (each ×4)

Sheets: 40 (2 panes 5×4)

Imprint: Right-hand corner, bottom margin

Quantities sold: 12p 449,267; miniature sheet 401,424

Withdrawn: 12.6.81

162 Winter Wren and View of Calf of Man

163 European Robin and View of Port Erin Marine Biological Station

Christmas and Wildlife Conservation Year

(Des J. Nicholson. Litho John Waddington)

1980 (29 SEPT). Perf 13½×14 (C)

181	**162**	6p multicoloured	15	10
182	**163**	8p multicoloured	30	35
181/2		Set of 2	45	40
		First Day Cover		1·20
		Presentation Pack	80	
		Set of 2 Gutter Pairs	90	

Plate Nos.: 6p 1B, 1D (each ×4); 8p 1A, 1C (each ×4)

Sheets: 40 (2 panes 4×5)

Imprint: Right-hand corner, bottom margin

Quantities sold: 6p 967,976; 8p 942,323

Withdrawn: 28.9.81

164 William Kermode and Brig *Robert Quayle*, 1819

165 'Mona Vale', Van Diemen's Land, 1834

166 Ross Bridge, Tasmania

167 'Mona Vale', Tasmania (completed 1868)

168 Robert Q. Kermode and Parliament Buildings, Tasmania

Kermode Family in Tasmania Commemoration

(Des A. Theobald. Litho Questa)

1980 (29 SEPT). Perf 14½ (C)

183	**164**	7p multicoloured	15	15
184	**165**	9p multicoloured	20	20
185	**166**	13½p multicoloured	25	25
186	**167**	15p multicoloured	30	25
187	**168**	17½p multicoloured	30	30
183/7		Set of 5	1·10	1·00
		First Day Cover		1·00
		Presentation Pack	1·50	
		Set of 5 Gutter Pairs	2·20	

Plate Nos.: All values 1C, 1D (each ×4)

Sheets: 40 (2 panes 5×4)

Imprint: Right-hand corner, bottom margin

Quantities sold: 7p 416,487; 9p 498,880; 13½p 318,353; 15p 314,837; 17½p 315,107

Withdrawn: 28.9.81

169 Peregrine Falcon

170 Loaghtyn Ram

Booklet stamps

(Des J. Nicholson. Litho Harrison)

1980 (29 SEPT). Perf 14½×14 (C)

188	**169**	1p multicoloured	20	20
		a. Booklet pane. Nos. 151, 188 and 189, each ×2	60	
189	**170**	5p multicoloured	30	30
188/9		Set of 2	50	50
		First Day Cover (Nos. 150b ×2, 151×2, 188 and 189) . . .		1·10
		Presentation Pack (Nos.150b ×2, 151×2, 188 and 189) . . .	1·20	

In addition to Booklets SB11/12 Nos. 188/9 also come from special booklet sheets of 60. These sheets contain No. 150ba×5 and No. 188a×5.

Plate Nos.: 1A, 1B (each ×7)

Withdrawn: 25.3.87

171 Luggers passing Red Pier, Douglas

172 Peel Lugger *Wanderer* rescuing survivors from the *Lusitania*

173 Nickeys leaving Port St. Mary Harbour

174 Nobby entering Ramsey Harbour

175 Nickeys *Sunbeam* and *Zebra* at Port Erin

Centenary of Royal National Mission to Deep Sea Fishermen

(Des J. Nicholson. Litho Questa)

1981 (24 FEB). Perf 14 (C)

190	**171**	8p multicoloured	15	15
191	**172**	9p multicoloured	20	20
192	**173**	18p multicoloured	30	30
193	**174**	20p multicoloured	30	30
194	**175**	22p multicoloured	35	35
190/4		Set of 5	1·20	1·20
		First Day Cover		1·50
		Presentation pack	1·50	
		Set of 5 Gutter Pairs	2·50	

Plate Nos.: 8p 1E, 1F (each ×4); 9p 1G, 1H (each ×4); 22p 1A, 1B (each ×4); others 1C, 1D (each ×4)

Sheets: 40 (2 panes 5×4)

Imprint: Right-hand corner, bottom margin

Quantities sold: 8p 566,522; 9p 583,358; 18p 334,765; 20p 315,511; 22p 324,607

Withdrawn: 23.2.82

176 'Crosh Cuirn' Superstition

177 'Bollan Cross' Superstition

Europa. Folklore

(Des J. Nicholson. Litho Questa)

1981 (22 MAY). Perf 14½ (C)

195	**176**	8p multicoloured	15	10
196	**177**	18p multicoloured	30	35
195/6		Set of 2	45	45
		First Day Cover		65
		Presentation Pack	75	
		Set of 2 Gutter Pairs	90	

Plate Nos.: 1A, 1B (each ×4)

Sheets: 24 (2 panes 3×4)

Imprint: Right-hand corner, bottom margin

Quantities sold: 8p 1,261,267; 18p 1,243,459

Withdrawn: 21.5.82

178 Lt. Mark Wilks (Royal Manx Fencibles) and Peel Castle

179 Ensign Mark Wilks and Fort St. George, Madras

180 Governor Mark Wilks and Napoleon, St. Helena

181 Col. Mark Wilks (speaker of the House of Keys) and Estate, Kirby

150th Death Anniversary of Colonel Mark Wilks

(Des A. Theobald. Litho Questa)

1981 (22 MAY). Perf 14 (C)

197	**178**	8p multicoloured	20	20
198	**179**	20p multicoloured	30	30
199	**180**	22p multicoloured	40	35
200	**181**	25p multicoloured	45	35
197/200		Set of 4	1·20	1·10
		First Day Cover		2·50
		Presentation Pack	1·60	
		Set of 4 Gutter Pairs	2·50	

Plate Nos.: 8, 20p 1A, 1B (each ×5); others 1A, 1B (each ×4)

Sheets: 40 (2 panes 5×4)

Imprint: 22p none; others right-hand corner, bottom margin

Quantities sold: 8p 371,280; 20p 278,840; 22p 294,480; 25p 272,640

Withdrawn: 21.5.82

182 Miss Emmeline Goulden (Mrs. Pankhurst) and Mrs. Sophia Jane Goulden

Centenary of Manx Women's Suffrage

(Des A. Theobald. Litho Questa)

1981 (22 MAY). Perf 14 (C)

201	**182**	9p black, olive-grey and stone ..	20	20
		First Day Cover		40
		Presentation Pack	50	
		Gutter Pair	40	

Plate Nos.: 1C, 1D (each ×3)

Sheets: 40 (2 panes 5×4)

Imprint: Right-hand corner, bottom margin

Quantity sold: 657,760

Withdrawn: 21.5.82

183 Prince Charles and Lady Diana Spencer

Royal Wedding

(Des G. Kneale. Litho Harrison)

1981 (29 JULY). Perf 14 (C)

202	**183**	9p black, bright blue & pale blue	15	20
203		25p black, bright blue and pink ..	75	80
202/3		Set of 2	90	1·00
		First Day Cover		1·70
		Presentation Pack	1·70	
		Set of 2 Gutter Pairs	2·00	
MS204		130×183 mm. Nos. 202/3×2	2·00	2·00
		First Day Cover		9·00

Plate Nos.: 9p 1C, 1D (each ×3); 25p 1A, 1B (each ×3)

Sheets: 50 (2 panes 5×5)

Imprint: Central, bottom margin

Quantities sold: 9p 668,864; 25p 474,364; miniature sheet 327,094

Withdrawn: 28.7.82

184 Douglas War Memorial, Poppies and Inscription

185 Major Robert Cain (war hero)

173

186 Festival of Remembrance, Royal Albert Hall

187 T.S.S. *Tynwald* at Dunkirk, May, 1940

60th Anniversary of the Royal British Legion

(Des A. Theobald. Photo Courvoisier)

1981 (29 SEPT). *Granite paper.* Perf 11½ (C)

205	**184**	8p multicoloured	20	20
206	**185**	10p multicoloured	25	25
207	**186**	18p multicoloured	30	30
208	**187**	20p multicoloured	35	35
205/8		Set of 4	1·00	1·00
		First Day Cover		1·20
		Presentation Pack	1·40	
		Set of 4 Gutter Pairs	2·00	

Cylinder Nos.: 8p A1–1–1–1, B1–1–1–1; others A1–1–1–1–1, B1–1–1–1–1

Sheets: 40 (2 panes 4×5)

Imprint: Central, bottom margin

Quantities sold: 8p 314,794; 10p 799,326; 18p 284,059; 20p 261,194

Withdrawn: 28.9.82

188 Nativity Scene (stained glass window, St. George's Church)

189 Children from Special School performing Nativity Play

Christmas

(Des John Waddington (7p), G. Kneale (9p). Litho John Waddington)

1981 (29 SEPT). Perf 14 (C)

209	**188**	7p multicoloured	15	15
210	**189**	9p multicoloured	20	20
209/10		Set of 2	35	35
		First Day Cover		55
		Presentation pack	75	
		Set of 2 Gutter Pairs	70	

The 7p value also commemorates the bicentenary of St. George's Church, Douglas and the 9p the International Year for Disabled Persons.

Plate Nos.: 7p 1A, 1B (each ×6); 9p 1A, 1B, 1C, 1D (each ×6)

Sheets: 40 (2 panes 2×10)

Imprint: Right-hand corner, bottom margin

Quantities sold: 7p 855,407; 9p 862,892

Withdrawn: 28.9.82

190 Joseph and William Cunningham (founders of Manx Boy Scout Movement) and Cunningham House Headquarters

191 Baden-Powell visiting Isle of Man, 1911

192 Baden-Powell and Scout Emblem

193 Scouts and Baden-Powell's Last Message

194 Scout Salute, Handshake, Emblem and Globe

75th Anniversary of Boy Scout Movement and 125th Birth Anniversary of Lord Baden-Powell

(Des G. Kneale. Litho Questa)

1982 (23 FEB). Perf 14×14½ (19½p) or 13½×14 (others), all comb

211	**190**	9p multicoloured	20	15
212	**191**	10p multicoloured	25	25
213	**192**	19½p multicoloured	45	40
214	**193**	24p multicoloured	50	45
215	**194**	29p multicoloured	70	60
211/15		*Set of 5*	1·90	1·70
		First Day Cover		2·00
		Presentation Pack	2·40	
		Set of 5 Gutter Pairs	4·00	

Plate Nos.: 9p 1A, 1B (each ×4); 29p 1A, 1B (each ×5); others 1C, 1D (each ×4)

Sheets: 40 (2 panes 5×4)

Imprint: Right-hand corner, bottom margin

Quantities sold: 9p 748,353; 10p 868,401; 19½p 364,487; 24p 368,346; 29p 370,466

Withdrawn: 22.2.83

195 The Principals and Duties of Christianity (first book printed in Manx, 1707), and Bishop T. Wilson

196 Landing at Derbyhaven (visit of Thomas, 2nd Earl of Derby, 1507)

Europa. Historic Events

(Des A. Theobald. Photo Courvoisier)

1982 (1 JUNE). *Granite paper*. Perf 12×12½ (C)

216	**195**	9p multicoloured	15	10
217	**196**	19½p multicoloured	40	40
216/17		*Set of 2*	55	50
		First Day Cover		85
		Presentation Pack	85	
		Set of 2 Gutter Pairs	1·10	

Cylinder Nos.: Both values A1–1–1–1–1, B1–1–1–1–1

Sheets: 24 (2 panes 3×4)

Imprint: Right-hand corner, bottom margin

Quantities sold: 9p 1,120,457; 19½p 1,129,315

Withdrawn: 31.5.83

197 Charlie Collier (first TT race (single cylinder) winner) and Tourist Trophy Race, 1907

198 Freddie Dixon (Sidecar and Junior TT winner) and Junior TT race, 1927

199 Jimmie Simpson (TT winner and first to lap at 60, 70 and 80 mph) and Senior TT, 1932

200 Mike Hailwood (winner of fourteen TTs) and Senior TT, 1961

201 Jock Taylor (Sidecar TT winner, 1978, 1980 and 1981) and Sidecar TT (with Benga Johansson), 1980

75th Anniversary of Tourist Trophy Motorcycle Races

(Des J. Nicholson. Litho Questa)

1982 (1 JUNE). Perf 14 (C)

218	**197**	9p multicoloured	15	15
219	**198**	10p multicoloured	15	15
220	**199**	24p multicoloured	60	55
221	**200**	26p multicoloured	60	50
222	**201**	29p multicoloured	60	60
218/22		*Set of 5*	1·90	1·80
		First Day Cover		2·10
		Presentation Pack	3·00	
		Stamp Cards (set of 5)	1·20	4·00
		Set of 5 Gutter Pairs	4·00	

Plate Nos.: All values 1B, 1C, 1D (each ×4)

Sheets: 40 (2 panes 5×4)

Imprint: Right-hand corner, bottom margin

Quantities sold: 9p 837,930; 10p 866,223; 24p 351,406; 26p 361,063; 29p 355,690

Withdrawn: 11.6.83

ISLE OF MAN 12p   **202** *Mona I*

ISLE OF MAN 19½p   **203** *Manx Maid II*

150th Anniversary of Isle of Man Steam Packet Company Mail Contract

(Des J. Nicholson. Litho Questa)

1982 (5 OCT). Perf 13½ (C)

223	**202**	12p multicoloured	30	25
224	**203**	19½p multicoloured	45	45
223/4		Set of 2	75	70
		First Day Cover		90
		Presentation Pack	1·20	
		Set of 2 Gutter Pairs	1·50	

Plate Nos.: Both values 1A (×4)

Sheets: 40 (2 panes 5×4)

Imprint: Right-hand bottom margin

Quantities sold: 12p 701,044; 19½p 291,100

Withdrawn: 4.10.83

204 The Three Wise Men

205 Snow Scene and European Robin

Christmas

(Des and litho John Waddington)

1982 (5 OCT). Perf 13 (C)

225	**204**	8p multicoloured	15	15
226	**205**	11p multicoloured	30	30
225/6		Set of 2	45	45
		First Day Cover		70
		Presentation Pack	85	
		Set of 2 Gutter Pairs	1·00	

Plate Nos.: 8p: 1A, 1C (each ×4), 11p 1B, 1D (each ×4)

Sheets: 40 (8p 2 panes 5×4), (11p 2 panes 4×5)

Imprint: Right-hand corner, bottom margin (8p); Top right-hand margin (11p)

Quantities sold; 8p 740,651; 11p 787,552

Withdrawn: 4.10.83

206 Princess Diana with Prince William

21st Birthday of the Princess of Wales and Birth of Prince William

(Des G. Kneale. Litho Questa)

1982 (12 OCT). *Sheet* 100×83 *mm.* Perf 14½×14 (C)

MS227	**206**	50p multicoloured	1·50	1·50
		First Day Cover		4·50
		Presentation Pack	1·70	

Quantity sold: 218,759

Withdrawn: 11.10.83

207 Opening of Salvation Army Citadel, and T. H. Cannell, J.P.

208 Early Meeting Place and Gen. William Booth

209 Salvation Army Band

210 Treating Lepers, and Lt.-Col. Thomas Bridson

Centenary of Salvation Army in Isle of Man

(Des A. Theobald. Photo Courvoisier)

1983 (15 FEB). *Granite paper.* Perf 11½ (C)

228	**207**	10p multicoloured	20	15
229	**208**	12p multicoloured	30	25
230	**209**	19½p multicoloured	45	45
231	**210**	26p multicoloured	65	60
228/31		*Set of 4*	1·40	1·20
		First Day Cover		1·60
		Presentation Pack	2·10	
		Set of 4 Gutter Pairs	2·75	

Cylinder Nos.: All values B1–1–1–1–1

Sheets: 40 (2 panes 4×5)

Imprint: Central, bottom margin

Quantities sold: 10p 467,665; 12p 567,863; 19½p 267,929; 26p 288,069

Withdrawn: 14.2.84

211 Atlantic Puffins

213 Lesser Black-backed Gulls

214 Great Cormorants

215 Black-legged Kittiwakes

216 Shags

217 Grey Herons

218 Herring Gulls

219 Razorbills

220 Greater Black-backed Gulls

221 Common Shelducks

222 Oystercatchers

223 Arctic Terns

224 Common Guillemots

225 Common Redshanks

226 Mute Swans

227 'Queen Elizabeth II' (Ricardo Macarron)

177

Marine Birds and Queen's Portrait (£5)

(Des Colleen Corlett (£5), J. Nicholson (others). Litho Questa)

1983 (15 FEB)–**85**. Perf 14 (20p to £1), 14×13½ (£5) or 14½ (others), all comb

232	**211**	1p multicoloured (a)	30	30
233	**212**	2p multicoloured (a)	30	30
234	**213**	5p multicoloured (a)	60	40
235	**214**	8p multicoloured (a)	60	40
236	**215**	10p multicoloured (a)	60	35
237	**216**	11p multicoloured (a)	60	35
238	**217**	12p multicoloured (a)	70	40
239	**218**	13p multicoloured (a)	70	40
240	**219**	14p multicoloured (a)	70	40
241	**220**	15p multicoloured (a)	80	50
242	**221**	16p multicoloured (a)	80	50
243	**222**	18p multicoloured (a)	80	50
244	**223**	20p multicoloured (b)	1·00	70
245	**224**	25p multicoloured (b)	1·20	75
246	**225**	50p multicoloured (b)	1·70	1·50
247	**226**	£1 multicoloured (b)	2·50	2·75
248	**227**	£5 multicoloured (c)	8·00	8·50
232/48		Set of 17	18·00	19·00
		First Day Covers (4)		25·00
		Presentation Packs (4) ..... 20·00		

Printings: (a) 15.2.83; (b) 14.9.83; (c) 31.1.85

Plate Nos.: 1p to £1 1A, 1B, 1C, 1D (each ×4); £5 1A, 1B (each ×4)

Sheets: 10 (5×2) £5; 50 (5×10) others

Imprint: £5 Right-hand margin; others right-hand corner, bottom margin

Withdrawn: 30.6.88 1p to 18p; 31.12.88 20p to £1; 4.7.94 £5

228 Design Drawings by Robert Casement for the Great Laxey Wheel

229 Robert Casement and the Great Laxey Wheel

Europa. The Great Laxey Wheel

(Des J. Nicholson. Litho Questa)

1983 (18 MAY). Perf 14 (C)

249	**228**	10p black, azure and buff	25	20
250	**229**	20½p multicoloured	50	55
249/50		Set of 2	75	75
		First Day Cover		1·00
		Presentation Pack .... 1·10		
		Set of 2 Gutter Pairs ...... 1·50		

Plate Nos.: 10p 1A, 1B (each ×3); 20½p 1A, 1B (each ×4)

Sheets: 12 (2 panes 2×3)

Imprint: Right-hand corner, bottom margin

Quantities sold: 10p 653,743; 20½p 686,084

Withdrawn 17.5.84

230 Nick Keig (international yachtsman) and Trimaran *Three Legs of Man III*

231 King William's College, Castletown

232 Sir William Bragg (winner of Nobel Prize for Physics) and Spectrometer

233 General Sir George White V.C. and Action at Charasiah

150th Anniversary of King William's College

(Des J. Nicholson (10p, 31p), Colleen Corlett (12p, 28p). Photo Courvoisier)

1983 (18 MAY). *Granite paper.* Perf 11½ (C)

251	**230**	10p multicoloured	15	15
252	**231**	12p multicoloured	20	20
253	**232**	28p multicoloured	55	55
254	**233**	31p multicoloured	65	65
251/4		Set of 4	1·40	1·40
		First Day Cover		1·50
		Presentation Pack .... 2·00		
		Set of 4 Gutter Pairs ...... 3·00		

Cylinder Nos.: 10p C1–1–1–1, D1–1–1–1; 12p C1–1–1–1, D1–1–1–1; 28p A1–1–1–1, B1–1–1–1; 31p A1–1–1–1, B1–1–1–1–1

Sheets: 40 (2 panes 5×4)

Imprint: Central, bottom margin

Quantities sold: 10p 552,573; 12p 693,004; 28p 263,814; 31p 242,393

Withdrawn: 17.5.84

234 New Post Office Headquarters, Douglas

235 Vikings Landing on Man, AD 938

World Communications Year and 10th Anniversary of Isle of Man Post Office Authority

(Des Colleen Corlett (10p), J. Nicholson (15p). Litho Questa)

1983 (5 JULY). Perf 14½ (C)

255	**234**	10p multicoloured	25	25
256	**235**	15p multicoloured	35	40
255/6		Set of 2	60	65
		First Day Cover		90
		Presentation Pack	90	
		Stamp Cards (set of 2)	90	1·40
		Set of 2 Gutter Pairs	1·20	

Plate Nos.: Both values 1A, 1B, 1C, 1D (each ×5)

Sheets: 40 (2 panes 4×5)

Imprint: Central, right-hand margin

Quantities sold: 10p 269,843; 15p 222,013

Withdrawn: 4.7.84

236 Shepherds

237 Three Kings

Christmas

(Des Colleen Corlett. Litho John Waddington)

1983 (14 SEPT). Perf 13 (C)

257	**236**	9p multicoloured	20	20
258	**237**	12p multicoloured	30	30
257/8		Set of 2	50	50
		First Day Cover		85
		Presentation Pack	85	
		Set of 2 Gutter Pairs	1·00	

Plate Nos.: Both values 1A, 1B, 1C, 1D (each ×5)

Sheets: 40 (2 panes 5×4)

Imprint: Right-hand corner, bottom margin

Quantities sold: 9p 642,763; 12p 656,060

Withdrawn: 13.9.84

238 Manx King (full-rigged ship)

239 Hope (barque)

240 Rio Grande (brig)

241 Lady Elizabeth (barque)

242 Sumatra (barque)

243 Wreck of Lady Elizabeth as shown on Falkland Islands Stamp

The Karran Fleet

(Des J. Nicholson (10p to 31p); Colleen Corlett, J. Nicholson and J. Smith (miniature sheet). Litho Questa)

1984 (14 FEB). Perf 14 (C)

259	**238**	10p multicoloured	20	15
260	**239**	13p multicoloured	30	20
261	**240**	20½p multicoloured	45	35
262	**241**	28p multicoloured	65	50
263	**242**	31p multicoloured	75	65
259/63		Set of 5	2·10	1·60
		First Day Cover		2·00
		Presentation Pack	2·75	
		Set of 5 Gutter pairs	4·25	
MS264		103×94 mm. 28p Type **241**; 31p		
		Type **243** (sold at 60p)	2·20	1·50
		First Day Cover		3·00
		Presentation Pack	2·75	

No. **MS**264 was issued to commemorate links between the Isle of Man and the Falkland Islands.

Plate Nos.: All values 1A, 1B (each ×4)

Sheets: 40 (2 panes 5×4)

Imprint: Right-hand corner, bottom margin

Quantities sold: 10p 389,728; 13p 417,637; 20½p 253,949; 28p 238,292; 31p 236,196; miniature sheet 137,031

Withdrawn: 13.2.85

244 C.E.P.T. 25th Anniversary Logo

Europa

(Des J. Larrivière, adapted Colleen Corlett. Photo Courvoisier)

1984 (27 APR). *Granite paper*. Perf 12×11½ (C)

265	**244**	10p dull orange, deep reddish brown and pale orange	30	25
266		20½p lt blue, dp blue & pale blue	50	50
		Set of 2	80	75
		First Day Cover		2·00
		Presentation Pack	2·50	

Cylinder Nos.: 10p B1–1–1; 20½p A1–1–1

Sheets: 20 (4×5)

Imprint: Central, right-hand margin

Quantities sold: 10p 705,410; 20½p 715,479

Withdrawn: 26.4.85

245 Railway Air Services De Havilland D.H.84 Dragon Mk 2

246 West Coast Air Services De Havilland D.H.86A Dragon Express *Ronaldsway*

247 B.E.A. Douglas DC-3

248 B.E.A. Vickers Viscount 800

249 Telair Britten Norman Islander

50th Anniversary of First Official Airmail to the Isle of Man and 40th Anniversary of International Civil Aviation Organization

(Des A. Theobald. Litho Questa)

1984 (27 APR). Perf 14 (C)

267	**245**	11p multicoloured	35	30
268	**246**	13p multicoloured	40	30
269	**247**	26p multicoloured	70	65
270	**248**	28p multicoloured	70	65
271	**249**	31p multicoloured	70	65
267/71		*Set of 5*	2·50	2·20
		First Day Cover		2·75
		Presentation Pack	2·75	
		Set of 5 Gutter Pairs	5·00	

Plate Nos.: All values 1C, 1D (each ×4)

Sheets: 40 (2 panes 5×4)

Imprint: Right-hand corner, bottom margin

Quantities sold: 11p 399,155; 13p 440,623; 26p 234,165; 28p 173,841; 31p 171,890

Withdrawn: 26.4.85

Year Pack 1983

1984. *Comprises Nos.* 228/47, 249/58

Year Pack . . . . 15·00

Withdrawn: 31.3.85

250 Window from Glencrutchery House, Douglas

251 Window from Lonan Old Church

Christmas. Stained-glass Windows

(Des D. Swinton. Litho John Waddington)

1984 (21 SEPT). Perf 14 (C)

272	**250**	10p multicoloured	20	20
273	**251**	13p multicoloured	40	40
272/3		*Set of 2*	60	60
		First Day Cover		90
		Presentation Pack	90	
		Set of 2 Gutter Pairs	1·20	

Plate Nos.: Both values 1A, 1C (each ×6)

Sheets: 40 (2 panes 4×5)

Imprint: Top right-hand margin

Quantities sold: 10p 652,870; 13p 668,084

Withdrawn: 20.9.85

252 William Cain's Birthplace, Ballasalla

253 The *Anna* Leaving Liverpool, 1852

254 Early Australian Railway

255 William Cain as Mayor of Melbourne, and Town Hall

256 Royal Exhibition Buildings, Melbourne

William Cain (civic leader, Victoria) Commemoration

(Des J. Nicholson. Litho Questa)

1984 (21 SEPT). Perf 14½×14 (C)

274	**252**	11p multicoloured	25	20
275	**253**	22p multicoloured	50	50
276	**254**	28p multicoloured	70	65
277	**255**	30p multicoloured	75	65
278	**256**	33p multicoloured	70	65
274/8		Set of 5	2·50	2·40
		First Day Cover		2·75
		Presentation Pack	2·50	
		Set of 5 Gutter Pairs	5·00	

Plate Nos.: All values 1B (×4)

Sheets: 40 (2 panes 5×4)

Imprint: Right-hand corner, bottom margin

Quantities sold: 11p 393,219; 22p 280,598; 28p 223,515; 30p 220,913; 33p 213,933

Withdrawn: 20.9.85

257 Queen Elizabeth II and Commonwealth Parliamentary Association Badge

258 Queen Elizabeth II and Manx Emblem

Links with the Commonwealth. 30th Commonwealth Parliamentary Association Conference

(Des and litho John Waddington)

1984 (21 SEPT). Perf 14 (C)

279	**257**	14p multicoloured	35	35
280	**258**	33p multicoloured	65	65
279/80		Set of 2	1·00	1·00
		First Day Cover		1·50
		Presentation Pack	2·75	
		Set of 2 Gutter Pairs	2·00	

Plate Nos.: Both values 1A, 1C (each ×7)

Sheets: 40 (2 panes 5×4)

Imprint: Right-hand corner, bottom margin

Quantities sold: 14p 373,204; 33p 231,073

Withdrawn: 20.9.85

Year Pack 1984

1985 (1 JAN). *Comprises Nos.* 259/80

Year Pack .... 17·00

Withdrawn: 31.12.85

259 Cunningham House Headquarters, and Mrs. Willie Cunningham and Mrs. Joseph Cunningham (former Commissioners)

260 Princess Margaret, Isle of Man Standard and Guides

261 Lady Olave Baden-Powell opening Guide Headquarters, 1955

262 Guide Uniforms from 1910 to 1985

263 Guide Handclasp, Salute and Early Badge

75th Anniversary of Girl Guide Movement

(Des Colleen Corlett. Photo Courvoisier)

1985 (31 JAN). *Granite paper.* Perf 11½ (C)

281	**259**	11p multicoloured	30	25
282	**260**	14p multicoloured	35	30
283	**261**	29p multicoloured	70	60
284	**262**	31p multicoloured	75	75
285	**263**	34p multicoloured	90	85
281/5		*Set of 5*	2·75	2·50
		First Day Cover		3·00
		Presentation Pack	3·00	
		Set of 5 Gutter Pairs	5·50	

Cylinder Nos.: 11p, 34p A1–1–1–1–1–1, B1–1–1–1–1–1; others A1–1–1–1–1, B1–1–1–1–1

Sheets: 40 (2 panes 4×5)

Imprint: Central, bottom margin of each pane

Withdrawn: 30.1.86

264 Score of Manx National Anthem

265 William H. Gill (lyricist)

266 Score of Hymn 'Crofton'

267 Dr. John Clague (composer)

Europa. European Music Year

(Des D. Swinton. Photo Courvoisier)

1985 (24 APR). *Granite paper.* Perf 11½ (C)

286	**264**	12p black, orange-brn & chestnut	30	15
		a. Horiz pair. Nos. 286/7	75	75
287	**265**	12p black, orange-brn & chestnut	30	15
288	**266**	22p black, brt blue & new bl	80	25
		a. Horiz pair. Nos. 288/9	1·60	1·60
289	**267**	22p black, brt new blue & new bl	80	25
286/9		*Set of 4*	2·10	2·10
		First Day Cover		2·00
		Presentation Pack	2·50	

Cylinder Nos.: Both values A1–1–1, B1–1–1

Sheets: 20 (4×5). The two designs for each value printed together, *se-tenant*, in horizontal pairs throughout the sheets

Imprint: Central, bottom margin

Withdrawn: 23.4.86

268 Charles Rolls in 20 h.p. Rolls Royce Light Twenty tourer (1906 Tourist Trophy Race)

269 W. Bentley in 3 litre Bentley (1922 Tourist Trophy Race)

270 F. Gerard in E.R.A. (1950 British Empire Trophy Race)

271 Brian Lewis in Alfa Romeo (1934 Mannin Moar Race)

272 Jaguar XJ-SC ('Roads Open' Car, 1984 Motorcycle T.T. Races)

273 Tony Pond and Mike Nicholson in Vauxhall Chevette (1981 Rothmans International Rally)

Century of Motoring

(Des A. Theobald. Litho Questa)

1985 (25 MAY). Perf 14 (C)

290	**268**	12p multicoloured	25	15
		a. Horiz pair. Nos. 290/1	60	60
291	**269**	12p multicoloured	25	15
292	**270**	14p multicoloured	30	15
		a. Horiz pair. Nos. 292/3	60	60
293	**271**	14p multicoloured	30	15
294	**272**	31p multicoloured	1·00	40
		a. Horiz pair. Nos. 294/5	2·00	2·00
295	**273**	31p multicoloured	1·00	40
290/5		Set of 6	2·75	2·50
		First Day Cover		2·75
		Presentation Pack	3·25	
		Stamp Cards (set of 6)	3·00	7·25
		Set of 3 Gutter Blocks of 4 .	5·50	

Plate Nos.: All values 1A, 1B (each ×6)

Sheets: 40 (2 panes 4×5). The two designs for each value printed together, *se-tenant*, in horizontal pairs throughout the sheets

Imprint: Right-hand corner, bottom margin of each pane

Withdrawn: 24.5.86

274 Queen Alexandra and Victorian Sergeant with Wife

275 Queen Mary and Royal Air Force Family

276 Earl Mountbatten and Royal Navy Family

277 Prince Michael of Kent and Royal Marine with Parents, 1982

Centenary of the Soldiers', Sailors' and Airmen's Families Association

(Des Colleen Corlett. Litho Questa)

1985 (4 SEPT). Perf 14 (C)

296	**274**	12p multicoloured	25	20
297	**275**	15p multicoloured	35	30
298	**276**	29p multicoloured	65	55
299	**277**	34p multicoloured	90	85
296/9		Set of 4	1·90	1·70
		First Day Cover		3·00
		Presentation Pack	2·50	
		Set of 4 Gutter Pairs	4·00	

Plate Nos. 12p, 34p 1A, 1B, 1C, 1D, 1E, 1F, 1G, 1H (each ×6); others 1A, 1B, 1C, 1D, 1E, 1F, 1G, 1H (each ×5)

Sheets: 40 (2 panes 5×4)

Imprint: Right-hand corner, bottom margin of each pane

Withdrawn: 3.9.86

278 Kirk Maughold (Birthplace)

279 Lieut. Gen. Sir Mark Cubbon

280 Memorial Statue, Bangalore, India

Birth Bicentenary of Lieut.-Gen. Sir Mark Cubbon (Indian administrator)

(Des A. Theobald. Litho Questa)

1985 (2 OCT). Perf 14 (C)

300	**278**	12p multicoloured	30	25
301	**279**	22p multicoloured	70	65
302	**280**	45p multicoloured	1·00	95
300/2		Set of 3	1·70	1·60
		First Day Cover		2·00
		Presentation Pack	2·50	
		Set of 3 Gutter pairs	3·50	

Plate Nos.: All values 1A, 1B, 1C, 1D (each ×4)

Sheets: 40 (2 panes 5×4) 12p or (2 panes 4×5) others

Imprint: Right-hand corner, bottom margin of each pane

Withdrawn: 1.10.86

281 St. Peter's Church, Onchan

282 Royal Chapel of St. John, Tynwald

283 Bride Parish Church

Christmas. Manx Churches

(Des A. Theobald. Litho John Waddington)

1985 (2 OCT). Perf 13×13½ (C)

303	**281**	11p multicoloured	30	25
304	**282**	14p multicoloured	40	35
305	**283**	31p multicoloured	1·00	90
303/5		Set of 3	1·50	1·40
		First Day Cover		1·70
		Presentation Pack	2·00	
		Set of 3 Gutter Pairs	3·00	

Plate Nos.: All values 1A, 1B, 1C, 1D (each ×4)

Sheets: 40 (2 panes 5×4)

Imprint: Right-hand corner, bottom margin of each pane

Withdrawn: 1.10.86

Post Office Yearbook

1985 (9 DEC). Comprises Nos. 248 and 281/305 in slipcase
Yearbook . . . . 28·00

Withdrawn: 9.92

Year Pack 1985

1986 (1 JAN). Comprises Nos. 281/305 with or without No. 248

Year Pack with No. 248 . . . . . 29·00
Year Pack without No. 248 . . 21·00

Withdrawn: 30.12.86

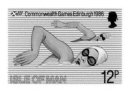

284 Swimming

285 Race Walking

286 Rifle-shooting

287 Cycling

Commonwealth Games, Edinburgh

(Des C. Abbott. Litho Questa)

1986 (5 FEB). Perf 14½ (C)

306	**284**	12p multicoloured	20	15
307	**285**	15p multicoloured	25	30
308	**286**	31p multicoloured	90	95
309	**287**	34p multicoloured	1·00	95
306/9		Set of 4	2·10	2·10
		First Day Cover		2·50
		Presentation Pack	3·00	
		Set of 4 Gutter Pairs	4·25	

No. 309 also commemorates the 50th anniversary of Manx International Cycling Week.

Plate Nos.: All values 1A, 1B, 1C, 1D (each ×5)

Sheets: 40 (2 panes 5×4)

Imprint: Right-hand corner, bottom margin of each pane

Withdrawn: 4.2.87

288 Viking Necklace and Peel Castle

289 Meayll Circle, Rushen

290 Skeleton of Great Deer and Manx Museum

291 Viking Longship Model

292 Open Air Museum, Cregneash

Centenary of Manx Museum

(Des J. Nicholson. Litho Questa)

1986 (5 FEB). Perf 14 (C)

310	**288**	12p multicoloured	20	15
311	**289**	15p multicoloured	25	20
312	**290**	22p multicoloured	65	50
313	**291**	26p multicoloured	80	60
314	**292**	29p multicoloured	90	60
310/14		Set of 5	2·50	1·90
		First Day Cover		2·50
		Presentation Pack	2·75	
		Set of 5 Gutter Pairs	5·00	

Plate Nos.: All values 1A, 1B, 1C, 1D (each ×6)

Sheets: 40 (2 panes 5×4) 12p, 15p, 29p; (2 panes 4×5) others

Imprint: Right-hand corner, bottom margin (12p, 15p, 29p) or bottom left-hand margin (others)

Withdrawn: 4.2.87

293 Viking Longship

294 Celtic Cross Logo

Manx Heritage Year. Booklet stamps

(Des Colleen Corlett. Litho Harrison)

1986 (10 APR). Perf 14½×14 (C)

315	**293**	2p multicoloured	40	40
		a. Booklet pane. Nos. 315×2 and 316×4	2·00	
316	**294**	10p black, apple green and brownish grey	35	35
		a. Booklet pane. No. 316×3 and 3 stamp size labels	1·20	
315/16		Set of 2	90	90
		First Day Cover (Nos. 315×1 and 316×2)		2·00
		Presentation Pack (Nos. 315×1 and 316×2)	1·90	

In addition to Booklets SB14/15 Nos. 315/16 also come from special booklet sheets of 60 containing five each of Nos. 315a and 316a.

Plate Nos.: 1A, 1B (each ×7)

Withdrawn: 25.3.87

295 Usnea articulata (lichen) and Neotinea intacta (orchid), The Ayres

296 Hen Harrier, Calf of Man

297 Manx Stoat, Eary Chuslin

298 Stenobothus stigmaticus (grasshopper), St. Michael's Isle

Europa. Nature and Environment Protection

(Des J. Nicholson and Nancy Corkish. Photo Courvoisier)

1986 (10 APR). Granite paper. Perf 11½ (C)

317	**295**	12p multicoloured	30	15
		a. Horiz pair. Nos. 317/18	60	75
318	**296**	12p multicoloured	30	15
319	**297**	22p multicoloured	60	25
		a. Horiz pair. Nos. 319/20	1·20	1·40
320	**298**	22p multicoloured	60	25
317/20		Set of 4	1·60	1·60
		First Day Cover		2·00
		Presentation Pack	2·10	

Cylinder Nos.: Both values A1–1–1–1–1

Sheets: 20 (4×5). The two designs for each value printed together, se-tenant, in horizontal pairs throughout the sheets

Imprint: Central, right-hand margin

Withdrawn: 9.4.87

299 Ellanbane (home of Myles Standish)

300 Mayflower crossing the Atlantic, 1620

301 Pilgrim Fathers landing at Plymouth, 1620

302 Captain Myles Standish

**'Ameripex '86' International Stamp Exhibition, Chicago.
Captain Myles Standish of the Mayflower**

(Des C. Abbott. Litho Cartor)

1986 (22 MAY). Perf 13½ (C)

321	**299**	12p multicoloured	20	20
322	**300**	15p multicoloured	25	25
323	**301**	31p multicoloured	90	90
324	**302**	34p multicoloured	95	95
321/4		Set of 4	2·10	2·10
		First Day Cover		2·50
		Presentation Pack	2·40	
MS325		100×75 mm. Nos. 323/4. Perf 12½ .	2·10	2·10
		First Day Cover		3·75
		Presentation Pack	2·50	

No. **MS**325 also commemorates the 75th anniversary of
the World Manx Association.

Plate Nos.: All values 1A, 1B, 1C, 1D (each ×5)

Sheets: 20 (5×4)

Imprint: Right-hand corner, bottom margin

Withdrawn: 21.5.87

303 Prince Andrew in Naval Uniform and Miss Sarah Ferguson

304 Engagement Photograph

Royal Wedding

(Des Colleen Corlett. Litho B.D.T.)

1986 (23 JULY). Perf 15×14 (C)

326	**303**	15p multicoloured	25	25
327	**304**	40p multicoloured	1·50	1·50
326/7		Set of 2	1·50	1·50
		First Day Cover		2·00
		Presentation Pack	2·00	

Plate Nos.: Both values 1A, 1B (each ×5)

Sheets: 20 (4×5)

Imprint: Right-hand corner, bottom margin

Withdrawn: 22.7.87

305 Prince Philip

306 Queen Elizabeth II

307 Queen Elizabeth II and Prince Philip

Royal Birthdays

(Des Colleen Corlett. Photo Courvoisier)

1986 (28 AUG). Granite paper. Perf 11½ (C)

328	**305**	15p multicoloured	30	30
		a. Horiz pair. Nos. 328/9	70	70
329	**306**	15p multicoloured	30	30
330	**307**	34p multicoloured	1·10	1·10
328/30		Set of 3	1·60	1·60
		First Day Cover		2·00
		Presentation Pack	2·40	
		Souvenir Folder (complete sheets)		14·00

Nos. 328/30 also commemorate 'Stockholmia '86' and
350th anniversary of Swedish Post Office.

Cylinder Nos.: 15p A1–1–1–1–1–1, B1–1–1–1–1–1, C1–1–1–1–1–1,
D1–1–1–1–1–1; 34p A1–1–1–1–1, B1–1–1–1–1, C1–1–1–1–1,
D1–1–1–1–1

Sheets: 15p 12 (4×3). The two designs printed together, se-tenant,
in horizontal pairs throughout the sheets; 34p 6 (2×3)

Imprint: Central, bottom margin

Withdrawn: 27.8.87

308 European Robins on Globe and 'Peace and Goodwill' in Braille

309 Hands releasing Peace Dove

310 Clasped Hands and 'Peace' in Sign Language

Christmas and International Peace Year

(Des Colleen Corlett. Litho Questa)

1986 (25 SEPT). Perf 14 (C)

331	**308**	11p multicoloured	30	30
332	**309**	14p multicoloured	30	30
333	**310**	31p multicoloured	80	80
331/3		Set of 3	1·20	1·20
		First Day Cover		1·50
		Presentation Pack	1·70	
		Set of 3 Gutter Pairs	2·75	

No. 331 also commemorates the 50th anniversary of Manx Blind Welfare Society.

Plate Nos.: All values 1A, 1B, 1C, 1D (each ×5)

Sheets: 40 (2 panes 4×5)

Imprint: Right-hand corner, bottom margin of each pane

Withdrawn: 24.9.87

Year Pack 1986

1986 (25 SEPT). Comprises Nos. 306/33

Year Pack . . . . 27·00

Withdrawn: 31.12.87

Post Office Yearbook

1986 (DEC). Comprises Nos. 306/14, 315a, 316a, 317/27, 328/30 in complete sheets, and 331/3 in slipcase

Yearbook . . . . 49·00

Sold out 9.90

311 North Quay   **312** Old Fishmarket

313 The Breakwater   **314** Jubilee Clock

315 Loch Promenade   **316** Beach

Victorian Douglas

(Des A. Theobald. Litho Questa)

1987 (21 JAN–26 MAR). Perf 14×14½ (C)

334	**311**	2p multicoloured (a)	10	10
		a. Booklet pane. Nos. 334×2, 335×2 and 336×4 (2p stamps at top) (b)	1·70	
		ab. Ditto, but 2p stamps at bottom (b)	1·70	
		b. Booklet pane. Nos. 334/7, each ×2 (b)	2·00	
		ba. Ditto, but 2p stamps at bottom (b)	2·00	
335	**312**	3p multicoloured (a)	10	10
336	**313**	10p multicoloured (a)	25	25
337	**314**	15p multicoloured (a)	30	30
338	**315**	31p multicoloured (a)	90	80
339	**316**	34p multicoloured (a)	1·00	90
334/9		Set of 6	2·40	2·20
		First Day Cover (Nos. 334/9)		2·50
		First Day Covers (2) (se-tenant strips)		5·50
		Presentation Pack (Nos. 334/9)	3·00	
		Set of 6 Gutter Pairs	5·00	

Printings: (a) 21.1.87; (b) 26.3.87

Plate Nos.: All values 1A, 1B, 1C, 1D (each ×4)

Sheets: 40 (2 panes 5×4). In addition to booklets SB16/17 Nos. 334/7 also come from special booklet sheets of 48 (6×8), containing either 3 each of Nos. 334a/ab or 3 each of Nos. 334b/ba

Imprint: Right-hand corner, bottom margin of each pane

Withdrawn: 20.1.88 sheets; 15.3.88 booklets

317 'The Old Fishmarket and Harbour, Douglas'   **318** 'Red Sails at Douglas'

319 'The Double Corner, Peel'   **320** 'Peel Harbour'

Paintings by John Miller Nicholson

(Des A. Theobald. Litho Cartor)

1987 (18 FEB). Perf 13½ (C)

340	**317**	12p multicoloured	20	20
341	**318**	26p multicoloured	70	60

342	**319**	29p multicoloured	90	80
343	**320**	34p multicoloured	1·00	1·00
340/3		*Set of 4*	2·50	2·40
		First Day Cover		2·75
		Presentation Pack	3·00	
		Set of 4 Gutter Pairs	5·00	

Plate Nos.: All values 1A, 1B, 1C, 1D (each ×5)

Sheets: 40 (2 panes 5×4)

Imprint: Right-hand corner, bottom margin of each pane

Withdrawn: 17.2.88

321 Sea Terminal, Douglas

322 Tower of Refuge, Douglas

323 Gaiety Theatre, Douglas

324 Villa Marina, Douglas

Europa. Architecture

(Des R. Maddox. Litho B.D.T.)

1987 (29 APR). Perf 13½ (C)

344	**321**	12p multicoloured	45	15
		a. Horiz pair. Nos. 344/5	90	1·70
345	**322**	12p multicoloured	45	15
346	**323**	22p multicoloured	65	25
		a. Horiz pair. Nos. 346/7	1·50	2·50
347	**324**	22p multicoloured	65	25
344/7		*Set of 4*	2·20	3·50
		First Day Cover		2·00
		Presentation Pack	2·50	

Plate Nos.: Both values 1A, 1B (each ×5)

Sheets: 10 (2×5). The two designs for each value printed together, *se-tenant*, in horizontal pairs throughout the sheets

Imprint: Central, right-hand margin

Withdrawn: 28.4.88

325 Supercharged BMW 500cc, 1939

326 Manx Kneeler Norton 350cc, 1953

327 MV Agusta 500cc 4, 1956

328 Moto Guzzi 500cc V8, 1957

329 Honda 250cc 6, 1967

80th Anniversary of Tourist Trophy Motor-cycle Races

(Des B. Dix. Litho Cartor)

1987 (27 MAY). Perf 13½×13 (C)

348	**325**	12p multicoloured	45	25
349	**326**	15p multicoloured	50	35
350	**327**	29p multicoloured	90	70
351	**328**	31p multicoloured	90	75
352	**329**	34p multicoloured	1·00	90
348/52		*Set of 5*	3·00	2·75
		First Day Cover		4·00
		Presentation Pack	4·00	
		Stamp Cards (Set of 5)	3·25	4·00
		Set of 5 Gutter Pairs	7·00	
MS353		150×140 mm. Nos. 348/52. Perf 14×13½ (C)	3·00	3·50
		Souvenir Folder	6·00	

Nos. 348/53 also commemorate the centenary of the St. John Ambulance Brigade and the miniature sheet also carries the logo of 'Capex '87' International Stamp Exhibition, Toronto on its margin.

Plate Nos.: 12p, 15p, 29p, 31p, 34p 1A, 1B, 1C, 1D (each ×4); miniature sheet 1A (×4)

Sheets: 40 (2 panes 5×4)

Imprint: Right-hand corner, bottom margin of each pane (sheets) or bottom, right-hand margin (miniature sheet)

Withdrawn: 11.6.88

ISLE of MAN 16ᴾ

330 Fuchsia and
Wild Roses

ISLE of MAN 29ᴾ

331 Field Scabious
and Ragwort

ISLE of MAN 31ᴾ

332 Wood Anemone
and Celandine

ISLE of MAN 34ᴾ

333 Violets and
Primroses

Wild Flowers

(Des Nancy Corkish. Litho Enschedé)

1987 (9 SEPT). Perf 14½×13 (C)

354	**330**	16p multicoloured	50	30
355	**331**	29p multicoloured	90	80
356	**332**	31p multicoloured	90	1·00
357	**333**	34p multicoloured	1·00	1·20
354/7		Set of 4	3·00	3·00
		First Day Cover		3·00
		Presentation Pack	4·00	

Plate Nos.: All values 1A, 1B (each ×4)

Sheets: 20 (5×4)

Imprint: Right-hand corner, bottom margin

Withdrawn: 8.9.88

334 Stirring the
Christmas
Pudding

335 Bringing
Home the
Christmas
Tree

336 Decorating
the Christmas
Tree

Christmas. Victorian Scenes

(Des Colleen Corlett. Litho Questa)

1987 (16 OCT). Perf 14 (C)

358	**334**	12p multicoloured	40	35
359	**335**	15p multicoloured	50	55
		a. Black printed triple		
360	**336**	31p multicoloured	90	90
358/60		Set of 3	1·60	1·60
		First Day Cover		2·10
		Presentation Pack	2·50	
		Set of 3 Gutter Pairs	3·25	

Plate Nos.: All values 1A, 1B, 1C, 1D (each ×4)

Sheets: 40 (2 panes 4×5)

Imprint: Right-hand corner, bottom margin of each pane

Withdrawn: 15.10.88

Year Pack 1987

1987 (16 OCT). Comprises Nos. 334/52 and 354/60
Year Pack . . . . 31·00

Withdrawn: 31.12.88

Post Office Yearbook

1987 (DEC). Comprises Nos. 334/43, 344/7 in complete
sheets, and **MS**353/60 in slipcase
Yearbook . . . . 40·00

Sold out: 5.91

ISLE OF MAN 13ᴾ

337 Russell
Brookes in
Vauxhall Opel
(Manx Rally
winner, 1985)

ISLE OF MAN 26ᴾ

338 Ari Vatanen in
Ford Escort
RS2000 Mk 1
(Manx Rally
winner, 1976)

ISLE OF MAN 31ᴾ

339 Terry Smith in
Repco March
761 (Hill
Climb winner,
1980)

ISLE OF MAN 34ᴾ

340 Nigel Mansell
in Williams/
Honda FW1B
F1 (British
Grand Prix
winner, 1986
and 1987)

Motor Sport

(Des C. Abbott. Litho Enschedé)

1988 (10 FEB). Perf 13½×14½ (C)

361	**337**	13p multicoloured	75	35
362	**338**	26p multicoloured	1·20	1·20
		a. *Black printed double*		
363	**339**	31p multicoloured	1·40	1·50
364	**340**	34p multicoloured	1·60	1·70
361/4		Set of 4	4·50	4·50
		First Day Cover		5·00
		Presentation Pack	4·75	

Plate Nos.: All values 1A, 1B (each ×4)

Sheets: 10 (2×5)

Imprint: Central, right-hand margin

Withdrawn: 9.2.89

341 Horse Tram Terminus, Douglas Bay Tramway

342 Snaefell Mountain Railway

343 Marine Drive Tramway

343a Douglas Cable Tramway

344 Douglas Head Incline Railway

345 Douglas and Laxey Coast Electric Tramway Car at Maughold Head

346 Douglas Cable Tramway

347 Manx Northern Railway No. 4, *Caledonia*, at Gob-y-Deigan

348 Laxey Mine Railway Lewin Locomotive *Ant*

349 Port Erin Breakwater Tramway Locomotive *Henry B. Loch*

350 Ramsey Harbour Tramway

351 Locomotive No. 7, *Tynwald*, on Foxdale Line

351a T.P.O. Special leaving Douglas, 3 July 1991

352 Baldwin Reservoir Tramway Steam Locomotive No. 1, *Injebreck*

353 I.M.R. No. 13, *Kissack*, near St. Johns

353a Manx Northern Railway No. 4, *Caledonia*, at Gob-y-Deigan

353b Double-deck Horse Tram, Douglas

354 I.M.R. No. 12, *Hutchinson*, leaving Douglas

190

355 Groudle Glen Railway Locomotive *Polar Bear*

356 I.M.R. No. 11, *Maitland,* pulling Royal Train, 1963

356a Queen Elizabeth II taking Salute at Trooping the Colour

Manx Railways and Tramways, and Queen's Portrait (£2)

(Des Colleen Corlett (£2), A. Theobald (others). Litho B.D.T. (1p to 19p, 21p, 23p), Questa (20p, 25p to £2))

1988 (10 FEB)–**92**. Perf 13 (1p to 19p, 21p, 23p), 14½×15 (20p, 25p to £1) or 14½ (£2), all comb

365	**341**	1p multicoloured (*a*)	10	10
366	**342**	2p multicoloured (*a*)	10	10
367	**343**	3p multicoloured (*a*)	10	10
		a. Booklet pane. Nos. 367×2, 370 and 373×2 (*b*)	3·00	
		b. Booklet pane. Nos. 367×2, 371×2 and 374 (*d*)	2·50	
367c	**343a**	4p multicoloured (*g*)	20	10
		ca. Booklet pane. Nos. 367c×3, 374 and 377a	4·00	
		cb. Booklet pane. Nos. 367c×3, 374×4 and 377a	4·75	
368	**344**	5p multicoloured (*a*)	20	20
369	**345**	10p multicoloured (*a*)	30	30
370	**346**	13p multicoloured (*a*)	50	50
		a. Booklet pane. Nos. 370×4 and 373×6 (*b*)	4·00	
371	**347**	14p multicoloured (*a*)	50	50
		a. Booklet pane. Nos. 371×4 and 374×6 (*d*)	4·00	
372	**348**	15p multicoloured (*af*)	50	50
		a. Booklet pane. Nos. 372 and 376×2 (*e*)	2·75	
		b. Booklet pane. Nos. 372×4 and 376×6 (*e*)	6·25	
373	**349**	16p multicoloured (*a*)	50	50
374	**350**	17p multicoloured (*ag*)	50	50
375	**351**	18p multicoloured (*a*)	55	55
375a	**351a**	18p multicoloured (*h*)	70	70
		ab. Booklet pane. Nos. 375a×3 and 377b×2	4·00	
		ac. Booklet pane. Nos. 375a×6 and 377b×4	7·00	
376	**352**	19p multicoloured (*af*)	60	60
377	**353**	20p multicoloured (*c*)	60	60
377a	**353a**	21p multicoloured (*g*)	60	60
377b	**353b**	23p multicoloured (*h*)	80	80
378	**354**	25p multicoloured (*c*)	60	60
379	**355**	50p multicoloured (*ci*)	1·30	1·20
380	**356**	£1 multicoloured (*ci*)	2·50	2·50
380a	**356a**	£2 multicoloured (*e*)	5·00	5·00
365/80a		Set of 21	15·00	14·00
		First Day Covers (6)		18·00
		First Day Covers (*se-tenant strips*) (5)		18·00
		Presentation Packs (4) (*ex 4p, 18p (No. 375a), 21p, 23p*)	18·00	
		Stamp Cards (1p to £1 *ex 4p, 18p (No. 375a), 21p, 23p*)	8·00	22·00
		Souvenir Folder (1p to £1 *ex 4p, 18p (No. 375a), 21p 23p*)	11·00	

Printings: (*a*) 10.2.88. Inscribed '1988'; (*b*) 16.3.88. Inscribed '1988'; (*c*) 21.9.88. Inscribed '1988'; (*d*) 16.10.89. Inscribed '1989'; (*e*) 14.2.90. Inscribed '1990'; (*f*) 1.3.90. Inscribed '1990'; (*g*) 9.1.91. Inscribed '1991'; (*h*) 8.1.92. Inscribed '1992'; (*i*) 16.11.92. Inscribed '1992'

Plate Nos.: 20p, 25p, 50p, £1 1A, 1B (each ×4); £2 1A, 1B (each ×5); others 1A, 1B, 1C, 1D (each ×4)

Sheets: 25 (5×5) (£2) or 50 (5×10) (others). In addition to Booklets Nos. SB18/19 and SB21/4 Nos. 367 and 370/4 also come from special booklet sheets of 50 containing either ten examples of the strips of five or five examples of the strips of ten. No. 372a, a strip of three, was taken from the top or bottom of the strip of ten, No. 372b. The 4p value was issued in Booklets Nos. SB26/7 and special booklet sheets of 50 containing five vertical strips of No. 367cb, from which No. 367ca could also be obtained, and five extra examples of both Nos. 367c and 377a. In addition to Booklets Nos. SB29/30 No. 375ac was also issued in special booklet sheets of 50 from which No. 375ab could also be obtained. Nos. 367c and 377a were also issued in a miniature sheet, No. **MS**484.

Imprints: Left-hand margin (£2) or right-hand corner, bottom margin (others).

Withdrawn: 31.12.93 1p to £1; 11.1.94 £2

357 Laying Isle of Man–U.K. Submarine Cable

358 *Flex Service 3* (cable ship)

ISLE OF MAN 22P

359 Earth Station, Braddan

22P ISLE OF MAN

360 'INTELSAT 5' Satellite

Europa. Transport and Communications

(Des C. Abbott. Litho Cartor)

1988 (14 APR). Perf 14×13½ (C)

381	**357**	13p multicoloured	50	45
		a. Horiz pair. Nos. 381/2	1·00	90
382	**358**	13p multicoloured	50	45
383	**359**	22p multicoloured	75	75
		a. Horiz pair. Nos. 383/4	1·50	1·50
384	**360**	22p multicoloured	75	75
381/4		Set of 4	2·20	2·20
		First Day Cover		4·00
		Presentation Pack	3·00	

Plate Nos.: Both values 1A, 1B, 1C, 1D (each ×4)

Sheets: 16 (4×4). The two designs of each value printed together, *se-tenant*, in horizontal pairs throughout the sheets

Imprint: Central, right-hand margin

Withdrawn: 13.4.89

361 *Euterpe* (full-rigged ship) off Ramsey, 1863

362 *Vixen* (topsail schooner) leaving Peel for Australia, 1853

363 *Ramsey* (full-rigged ship) off Brisbane, 1870

364 *Star of India* (formerly *Euterpe*) (barque) off San Diego, 1976

Manx Sailing Ships

(Des J. Nicholson. Litho Questa)

1988 (11 MAY). Perf 14 (C)

385	**361**	16p multicoloured	45	30
386	**362**	29p multicoloured	90	90
387	**363**	31p multicoloured	90	90
388	**364**	34p multicoloured	1·10	1·10
385/8		Set of 4	3·00	3·00
		First Day Cover		3·25
		Presentation Pack	3·75	
MS389		110×85 mm. Nos. 385 and 388 . . .	1·90	2·00
		First Day Cover		3·50
		Presentation Pack	2·50	

Nos. 386/7 also commemorate the Bicentenary of Australian Settlement.

Plate Nos.: All values 1A, 1B (each ×5)

Sheets: 15 (3×5)

Imprint: Bottom, left-hand margin

Withdrawn: 10.5.89

365 'Magellanica'

366 'Pink Cloud'

367 'Leonora'

368 'Satellite'

369 'Preston Guild'

370 'Thalia'

50th Anniversary of British Fuchsia Society

(Des Colleen Corlett. Litho Enschedé)

1988 (21 SEPT). Perf 13½×14 (C)

390	**365**	13p multicoloured	40	25
391	**366**	16p multicoloured	45	35
392	**367**	22p multicoloured	65	50
393	**368**	29p multicoloured	90	90
394	**369**	31p multicoloured	1·00	1·00
395	**370**	34p multicoloured	1·10	1·20
390/5		Set of 6	4·00	3·50
		First Day Cover		3·75
		Presentation Pack	5·00	

Plate Nos.: All values 1A, 1B (each ×5)

Sheets: 20 (4×5)

Imprint: Right-hand margin

Withdrawn: 20.9.89

371 Long-eared Owl

372 European Robin

373 Grey Partridge

Christmas. Manx Birds

(Des Audrey North. Litho Questa)

1988 (12 OCT). Perf 14 (C)

396	**371**	12p multicoloured	. . . .	40	30
397	**372**	15p multicoloured	. . . .	60	65
398	**373**	31p multicoloured	. . . .	1·20	1·20
396/8		*Set of 3*	. . . .	2·00	2·00
		First Day Cover	. . . .		2·50
		Presentation Pack	. . . .	2·75	
		Set of 3 Gutter Pairs	. . . . . .	4·00	

Plate Nos.: All values 1A, 1B, 1C, 1D (each ×5)

Sheets: 40 (2 panes 5×4)

Imprint: Right-hand corner, bottom margin of each pane

Withdrawn: 11.10.89

Year Pack 1988

1988 (1 NOV). *Comprises Nos.* 361/7, 368/75, 376/7, 378/80 *and* 381/98

Year Pack . . . . 40·00

Withdrawn: 31.12.89

Post Office Yearbook

1988 (1 DEC). *Comprises Nos.* 361/7, 368/75, 376/7, 378/80 *and* 381/98 *in slipcase*

Yearbook . . . . 45·00

Sold out: By 9.93

374 Ginger Cat

375 Black and White Cat

376 Tortoiseshell and White Cat

377 Tortoiseshell Cat

Manx Cats

(Des P. Layton. Litho Questa)

1989 (8 FEB). Perf 14 (C)

399	**374**	16p multicoloured	. . . .	50	25
400	**375**	27p multicoloured	. . . .	90	85
401	**376**	30p multicoloured	. . . .	1·20	85
402	**377**	40p multicoloured	. . . .	1·50	1·20
399/402		*Set of 4*	. . . .	3·75	2·75
		First Day Cover	. . . .		3·50
		Presentation Pack	. . . .	4·50	
		Stamp Cards (set of 4)	. . . . .	3·00	8·00
		Set of 4 Gutter Pairs	. . . . . .	7·50	

Plate Nos.: 16p, 27p 1C, 1D, 1G, 1H (each ×4); 30p, 40p 1A, 1B, 1E, 1F (each ×4)

Sheets: 40 (2 panes 5×4)

Imprint: Right-hand corner, bottom margin of each pane

Withdrawn: 7.2.90

378 Tudric Pewter Clock, *c.* 1903

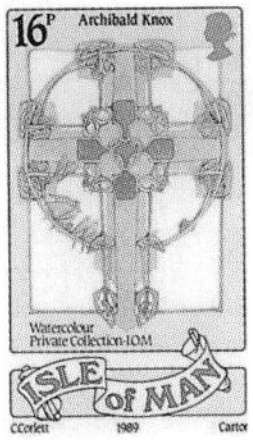

379 'Celtic Cross' Watercolour

380 Silver Cup and Cover, 1902–03

381 Gold and Silver Brooches from Liberty's Cymric Range

382 Silver Jewel Box, 1900

125th Birth Anniversary of Archibald Knox (artist and designer)

(Des Colleen Corlett. Litho Cartor)

1989 (8 FEB). Perf 13 (C)

403	**378**	13p multicoloured	20	20
404	**379**	16p multicoloured	30	25
405	**380**	23p multicoloured	50	50
406	**381**	32p multicoloured	1·20	1·00
407	**382**	35p multicoloured	1·40	1·00
403/7		Set of 5	3·00	2·75
		First Day Cover		3·00
		Presentation Pack	4·00	
		Set of 5 Gutter Pairs	7·50	

Plate Nos.: All values 1A, 1B, 1C, 1D (each ×5)

Sheets: 40 (2 panes 4×5) 13p, 16p, 23p; (2 panes 5×4) others

Imprint: Bottom, left-hand margin of each pane (13p, 16p, 23p) or right-hand corner, bottom margin of each pane

Withdrawn: 7.2.90

383 William Bligh and Old Church, Onchan

384 Bligh and Loyal Crew cast Adrift

385 Pitcairn Islands 1989 Bicentenary 90c. Stamp

386 Norfolk Island 1989 39c. *Bounty* Stamp

387 Midshipman Peter Heywood and Tahiti

388 H.M.S. *Bounty* anchored off Pitcairn

389 Fletcher Christian and Pitcairn Island

Bicentenary of the Mutiny on the Bounty

(Des C. Abbott. Litho B.D.T.)

1989 (28 APR). Perf 14 (C)

408	**383**	13p multicoloured	30	20
		a. Booklet pane. Nos. 408/10 and 412/14	4·25	
		b. Booklet pane. Nos. 408/9 and 411/14	4·00	
409	**384**	16p multicoloured	35	30
410	**385**	23p multicoloured	1·00	1·00
		a. Booklet pane. Nos. 410/11, each ×3	5·50	
411	**386**	27p multicoloured	1·00	1·00
412	**387**	30p multicoloured	50	60
413	**388**	32p multicoloured	50	60
414	**389**	35p multicoloured	50	60
408/14		Set of 7	3·75	4·00
		First Day Cover (ex Nos. 410/11)		4·75
		Presentation Pack (ex Nos. 410/11)	5·50	
MS415		110×85 mm. Nos. 410/11 and 414 .	3·75	3·75
		a. Booklet pane. As No. **MS**415, but 147×101 mm with line of roulettes at left .	4·00	
		First Day Cover		5·00

Plate Nos.: 13p, 16p, 30p, 32p, 35p 1A, 1B (each ×4)

Sheets: 20 (4×5) 13p, 16p, 30p, 32p, 35p. The 23p and 27p values were only issued in £5.30 booklets and in the miniature sheet. Booklet panes Nos. 408a/b and 410a each contain two vertical rows of three stamps, separated by a central gutter

Imprint: 13p, 16p, 30p, 32p, 35p Central, left-hand margin

Withdrawn: 27.4.90 13, 16, 30, 32, 35p

390 Skipping and Hopscotch

391 Wheelbarrow, Leapfrog and Piggyback

392 Building Model House and Blowing Bubbles

393 Girl and Doll and Doll's House

Europa. Childrens Games

(Des Colleen Corlett. Litho Enschedé)

1989 (17 MAY). Perf 13½ (C)

416	**390**	13p multicoloured	45	50
		a. Horiz pair. Nos. 416/17	90	1·00
417	**391**	13p multicoloured	45	50

418	**392**	23p multicoloured	70	75
		a. Horiz pair. Nos. 418/19	1·40	1·50
419	**393**	23p multicoloured	70	75
416/19		Set of 4	2·10	2·20
		First Day Cover		2·75
		Presentation Pack	3·00	

Plate Nos.: Both values 1A, 1B (each ×4)

Sheets: 20 (4×5). The two designs for each value printed together, se-tenant, in horizontal pairs throughout the sheets

Imprint: Central, right-hand margin

Withdrawn: 16.5.90

394 Atlantic Puffin

395 Black Guillemot

396 Great Cormorant

397 Black-legged Kittiwake

Sea Birds

(Des W. Oliver. Litho Questa)

1989 (20 SEPT). Perf 14 (C)

420	**394**	13p multicoloured	55	55
		a. Strip of 4. Nos. 420/3	2·20	
		ab. Black ptd double		
421	**395**	13p multicoloured	55	55
422	**396**	13p multicoloured	55	55
423	**397**	13p multicoloured	55	55
420/3		Set of 4	2·20	2·20
		First Day Cover		3·25
		Presentation Pack	3·00	

In addition to a double image of the black printing on the design some examples of No. 420ab also show three additional impressions of the imprint at the foot of each stamp.

Examples of Nos. 420/3 sold at 'World Stamp Expo '89', held at Washington D.C. between 17 November and 3 December 1989, carried a commemorative inscription on the bottom sheet margin.

Plate Nos.: 1A, 1B, 1C, 1D (each ×4)

Sheets: 16 (4×4). The four designs were printed together, se-tenant, in horizontal and vertical strips throughout the sheet which exists with or without perforations across the side margins

Imprint: Central, right-hand margin

Withdrawn: 19.9.90

398 Red Cross Cadets learning Resuscitation

399 Anniversary Logo

400 Signing Geneva Convention, 1864

401 Red Cross Ambulance

402 Henri Dunant (founder)

125th Anniversary of International Red Cross and Centenary of Noble's Hospital, Isle of Man

(Des A. Theobald. Litho Questa)

1989 (16 OCT). Perf 14 (C)

424	**398**	14p multicoloured	40	30
425	**399**	17p grey and orange-vermilion . .	60	35
426	**400**	23p multicoloured	75	85
427	**401**	30p multicoloured	1·00	1·10
428	**402**	35p multicoloured	1·20	1·20
424/8		Set of 5	3·00	3·25
		First Day Cover		3·75
		Presentation Pack	4·50	
		Set of 5 Gutter Pairs	7·50	

Plate Nos.: 14p, 30p 1A, 1B, 1C, 1D (each ×5); 17p 1A, 1B, 1C, 1D (each ×2); 23p, 35p 1A, 1B, 1C, 1D (each ×4)

Sheets: 40 (2 panes 5×4)

Imprint: Right-hand corner, bottom margin of each pane

Withdrawn: 15.10.90

403 Mother with Baby, Jane Crookall Maternity Home

404 Mother with Child

405 Madonna and Child

406 Baptism, St. Ninian's Church

Christmas. 50th Anniversary of Jane Crookall Maternity Home and 75th Anniversary of St. Ninian's Church, Douglas

(Des Colleen Corlett. Litho Questa)

1989 (16 OCT). Perf 14½ (C)

429	**403**	13p multicoloured	50	45
430	**404**	16p multicoloured	60	60
431	**405**	34p multicoloured	1·10	1·20
432	**406**	37p multicoloured	1·20	1·40
429/32		Set of 4	3·00	3·25
		First Day Cover		3·75
		Presentation Pack	3·75	
		Set of 4 Gutter Pairs	6·00	

Plate Nos.: 13p, 34p 1A, 1B, 1C, 1D (each ×5); 16p, 37p 1A, 1B, 1C, 1D (each ×4)

Sheets: 40 (2 panes 4×5)

Imprint: Right-hand corner, bottom margin of each pane

Withdrawn: 15.10.90

Year Pack 1989

1989 (16 OCT). *Comprises Nos.* 399/409 *and* 412/32
Year Pack . . . . 33·00

Withdrawn: 31.12.90

Post Office Yearbook

1989 (NOV). *Comprises Nos.* 399/409, 412/19, 420/3 *in complete sheet, and* 424/32 *in slipcase*
Yearbook . . . . 41·00

Sold out: By 9.93

407 'The Isle of Man Express going up a Gradient'

408 'A way we have in the Isle of Man'

409 'Douglas – waiting for the Male Boat'

410 'The Last Toast Rack Home, Douglas Parade'

411 'The Last Isle of Man Boat'

Isle of Man Edwardian Postcards

(Des D. Swinton. Litho B.D.T.)

1990 (14 FEB). Perf 14 (C)

433	**407**	15p multicoloured	35	35
434	**408**	19p multicoloured	60	50
435	**409**	32p multicoloured	1·10	1·10
436	**410**	34p multicoloured	1·50	1·50
437	**411**	37p multicoloured	1·60	1·60
433/7		Set of 5	4·50	4·50
		First Day Cover		4·50
		Presentation Pack	5·50	
		Stamp Cards (set of 5)	3·00	6·50
		Set of 5 Gutter Pairs	9·00	

Plate Nos.: All values 1A, 1B, 1C, 1D (each ×4)

Sheets: 40 (2 panes 5×4)

Imprint: Right-hand corner, bottom margin of each pane

Withdrawn: 13.2.91

412 Modern Postman

413 Ramsey Post Office, 1990

414 Postman, 1890

415 Douglas Post Office, 1890

Europa. Post Office Buildings

(Des A. Kellett. Litho Cartor)

1990 (18 APR). Perf 13½ (C)

438	**412**	15p multicoloured	55	20
		a. Horiz pair. Nos. 438/9	1·10	1·10
439	**413**	15p multicoloured	55	20
440	**414**	24p multicoloured	90	25
		a. Horiz pair. Nos. 440/1	1·90	1·75
441	**415**	24p multicoloured	90	25
438/41		Set of 4	2·75	2·40
		First Day Cover		3·00
		Presentation Pack	3·25	

Plate Nos.: Both values 1A, 1B (each ×4)

Sheets: 20 (4×5). The two designs for each value printed together, *se-tenant*, in horizontal pairs throughout the sheets.

Withdrawn 17.4.91

416 Penny Black

417 Wyon Medal, 1837

418 Wyon's Stamp Essay

419 Perkins Bacon Engine-turned Essay, 1839

420 Twopence Blue, 1840

PRICE 1ˢᵗ Per Label. 1/₄ Per Row

421 Marginal Block of Four Penny Blacks

150th Anniversary of the Penny Black

(Des Colleen Corlett. Eng Inge Madlé (No. **MS**447). Recess and litho (No. **MS**447) or litho (others) Enschedé)

1990 (3 MAY). Perf 14×13½ (C)

442	**416**	1p black, buff and gold	15	15
		a. Sheetlet. Horiz strip of 5.		
		Nos. 442/6	4·00	
		b. Sheetlet. No. 442×25	2·20	
		c. Booklet pane. No. 442×8		
		with margins all round	1·10	
443	**417**	19p gold, black and buff	60	50
		a. Booklet pane. Nos. 443/6×2		
		with margins all round	7·00	
444	**418**	32p multicoloured	1·20	1·10
445	**419**	34p multicoloured	1·50	1·10
446	**420**	37p multicoloured	1·60	1·10
442/6		Set of 5	4·50	3·75
		First Day Cover		5·50
		Presentation Pack	5·00	
MS447		100×71 mm. **421** £1 black, gold and buff	4·00	3·50
		a. Booklet pane. As No. **MS**447, but 115×75 mm with line of roulettes at left .	4·00	
		First Day Cover		4·75
		Presentation Pack	4·75	

Sheetlet No. 442a was reissued on 24 August 1990 overprinted 'From STAMP WORLD LONDON '90 to NEW ZEALAND 1990' for sale at the New Zealand exhibition.

The Penny Black stamps shown on Nos. 442b/c each have different corner letters at foot. The sheetlet of 25 was issued in conjunction with a special postal concession which allowed hand-addressed personal mail for the island to be posted for 1p between 10 am and 12 noon on 6 May 1990.

No. **MS**447 also commemorates 'Stamp World London '90' International Stamp Exhibition, London.

Plate Nos.: No. 442b, 1A, 1B (each ×3)

Sheets: 5 (5×1) containing Nos. 442/6 *se-tenant*, or 25 (5×5) No. 442 only

Imprint: No. 442a. Bottom margin, right-hand corner. No. 442b. Central, bottom margin

Withdrawn: 2.5.91

422 Queen Elizabeth the Queen Mother

90th Birthday of Queen Elizabeth the Queen Mother

(Des Colleen Corlett. Litho B.D.T.)

1990 (4 AUG). Perf 13×13½ (C)

448	**442**	90p multicoloured	3·00	3·00
		First Day Cover		3·75
		Presentation Pack	4·00	

Plate Nos.: 1A, 1B (each ×5)

Sheets: 20 (5×4) containing ten stamps and ten *se-tenant* inscribed labels

Imprint: Central, right-hand margin

Withdrawn: 3.8.91

423 Hawker Hurricane Mk 1, Bristol Type 142 Blenheim Mk 1 and Home Defence

424 Supermarine Spitfire, Westland Lysander Mk I and Vickers Walrus with Launch

425 Re-arming Hawker Hurricane Mk I Fighters

426 Ops Room and Scramble

427 Civil Defence Personnel

428 Anti-aircraft Battery

50th Anniversary of the Battle of Britain

(Des A. Theobald. Litho Questa)

1990 (5 SEPT). Perf 14 (C)

449	**423**	15p multicoloured	35	20
		a. Horiz pair. Nos. 449/50	70	70
450	**424**	15p multicoloured	35	20
451	**425**	24p multicoloured	80	25
		a. Horiz pair. Nos. 451/2	1·60	1·60
452	**426**	24p multicoloured	80	25
453	**427**	29p multicoloured	1·00	30
		a. Horiz pair. Nos. 453/4	2·00	2·00
454	**428**	29p multicoloured	1·00	30
449/54		Set of 6	4·00	4·00
		First Day Cover		5·00
		Presentation Pack	4·75	
		Souvenir Folder (complete sheets)	18·00	

Plate Nos.: All values 1A, 1B (each ×4)

Sheets: 8 (2×4). The two designs of each value were printed together, *se-tenant*, in horizontal pairs throughout the sheet, each showing composite panel at foot of Dover cliffs (15p), Weald landscape (24p) or London skyline (29p)

Withdrawn: 4.9.91

429 Churchill with Freedom of Douglas Casket

430 Churchill and London Blitz

431 Churchill and Searchlights over Westminster

432 Churchill with Hawker Hurricane Mk I Fighters

25th Death Anniversary of Sir Winston Churchill

(Des C. Abbott. Litho Cartor)

1990 (5 SEPT). Perf 13½ (C)

455	**429**	19p multicoloured	45	45
456	**430**	32p multicoloured	1·00	1·00
457	**431**	34p multicoloured	1·20	1·20
458	**432**	37p multicoloured	1·20	1·20
455/8		Set of 4	3·50	3·50
		First Day Cover		4·00
		Presentation Pack	4·00	
		Set of 4 Gutter Pairs	7·00	

Plate Nos.: All values 1A, 1B, 1C, 1D (each ×5)

Sheets: 40 (2 panes 5×4)

Imprint: Right-hand corner, bottom margin of each pane

Withdrawn: 4.9.91

433 Boy on Toboggan and Girl posting Letter

434 Girl on Toboggan and Skaters

435 Boy with Snowman

436 Children throwing Snowballs

Christmas

(Des C. Abbott. Litho B.D.T.)

1990 (10 OCT). Perf 13×13½ (C)

459	**433**	14p multicoloured	40	40
460	**434**	18p multicoloured	50	50
461	**435**	34p multicoloured	1·00	1·00
462	**436**	37p multicoloured	1·20	1·20
459/62		Set of 4	2·75	2·75
		First Day Cover		3·50
		Presentation Pack	3·75	
		Set of 4 Gutter Pairs	5·50	

MS463 123×55 mm. As Nos. 459/62 but face values in black . . . . 3·00 3·75

a. Blue (inscriptions) omitted . .£2500

First Day Cover . . . . 3·50

Presentation Pack . . . . 3·75

Plate Nos.: 18p 1A, 1B, 1C, 1D (each ×5); others 1A, 1B, 1C, 1D (each ×6)

Sheets: 40 (2 panes 4×5)

Imprint: Right-hand corner, bottom margin of each pane

Withdrawn: 9.10.91

Year Pack 1990

1990 (10 OCT). Comprises Nos. 380a and 433/63
Year Pack . . . . 41·00

Withdrawn: 31.12.91

Post Office Yearbook

1990 (DEC). Comprises Nos. 380a, 433/41, 422a/b, **MS**447 and 448/63 in slipcase
Yearbook . . . . 50·00

Sold out: By 9.93

437 Henry Bloom Noble and Orphans (Marshall Wane)

438 Douglas (Frederick Frith)

439 Studio Portrait of Three Children (Hilda Newby)

440 Cashtal yn Ard (Christopher Killip)

441 Peel Castle (Colleen Corlett)

Manx Photography

(Des Colleen Corlett. Litho Walsall)

1991 (9 JAN). Perf 14 (C)

464	**437**	17p blackish brn, pale brownish grey and black	35	35
465	**438**	21p deep brown and ochre	50	50
466	**439**	26p blackish brown, stone and brownish black	65	65
467	**440**	31p agate, pale grey-brown & blk	90	90
468	**441**	40p multicoloured	1·10	1·10
464/8		Set of 5	3·25	3·25
		First Day Cover		3·50
		Presentation Pack	3·75	

Plate Nos: 21p 1A–1A, 1B–AB, 40p 1A, 1B (each ×4); others 1A, 1B (each ×3)

Sheets: 20 (4×5)

Imprint: Central, right-hand margin

Withdrawn: 8.1.92

442 Lifeboat, *Sir William Hillary*, Douglas

443 *Osman Gabriel*, Port Erin

444 *Ann and James Ritchie*, Ramsey

445 *The Gough Ritchie*, Port St. Mary

446 *John Batstone*, Peel

447 'Intelsat' Communications Satellite

448 'Ariane' Rocket Launch and Fishing Boats in Douglas Harbour

449 Weather Satellite and Space Station

450 Ronaldsway Airport, Manx Radio Transmitter and Space Shuttle Launch

Manx Lifeboats

(Des A. Peck. Litho Questa)

1991 (13 FEB). Perf 14 (C)

469	**442**	17p multicoloured	45	45
470	**443**	21p multicoloured	55	55
		a. Black ptg double		
471	**444**	26p multicoloured	90	90
472	**445**	31p multicoloured	1·20	1·20
473	**446**	37p multicoloured	1·40	1·40
469/73		Set of 5	4·00	4·00
		First Day Cover		4·50
		Presentation Pack	4·50	
		Set of 5 Gutter Pairs	8·00	

No. 469 is inscribed 'HILARY' and No. 471 'JAMES & ANN RITCHIE', both in error.

Plate Nos.: All values 1A, 1B, 1C, 1D (each ×4)

Sheets: 40 (2 panes 5×4)

Imprint: Right-hand corner, bottom margin of each pane

Withdrawn: 12.2.92

Europa. Europe in Space

(Des D. Miller. Litho B.D.T.)

1991 (24 APR). Perf 14 (C)

474	**447**	17p multicoloured	70	20
		a. Vert pair. Nos. 474/5	1·40	1·40
475	**448**	17p multicoloured	70	20
476	**449**	26p multicoloured	1·00	30
		a. Vert pair. Nos. 476/7	2·00	2·00
477	**450**	26p multicoloured	1·00	30
474/7		Set of 4	3·00	3·00
		First Day Cover		3·75
		Presentation Pack	3·75	

Plate Nos.: Both values 1A, 1B (each ×4)

Sheets: 20 (5×4). The two designs for each value printed together, *se-tenant*, in vertical pairs throughout the sheets, each pair forming a composite design

Imprint: Central, right-hand margin

Withdrawn: 23.4.92

451 Oliver Godfrey with Indian 500cc at Start, 1911

452 Freddie Dixon on Douglas 'Banking' Sidecar, 1923

453 Bill Ivy on Yamaha
125cc, 1968

454 Giacomo Agostini on
MV Agusta 500cc,
1972

455 Joey Dunlop on RVF Honda
750cc, 1985

80th Anniversary of Tourist Trophy Mountain Course

(Des A. Theobald. Litho Enschedé)

1991 (30 MAY). Perf 14½×13 (C)

478	**451**	17p multicoloured	50	40
479	**452**	21p multicoloured	65	60
480	**453**	26p multicoloured	80	80
481	**454**	31p multicoloured	1·20	1·10
482	**455**	37p multicoloured	1·50	1·50
478/82		Set of 5	4·25	4·00
		First Day Cover		4·50
		Presentation Pack	4·75	
		Stamp Cards (set of 5)	3·00	6·00
		Set of 5 Gutter Pairs	8·50	
MS483	149×144 mm. Nos. 478/82		4·00	4·00
		First Day Cover		9·00
		Souvenir Folder	5·50	

No. **MS**483 was reissued on 16 November 1991
overprinted for the Phila Nippon exhibition, Japan.

Plate Nos.: All values 1A, 1B, 1C, 1D (each ×4)

Sheets: 40 (2 panes 5×4)

Imprint: Right-hand corner, bottom margin of each pane

Withdrawn: 29.5.92

Ninth Conference of Commonwealth Postal Administrations, Douglas

(Des Colleen Corlett. Litho B.D.T.)

1991 (1 JULY). Perf 13 (C)

MS484	119×77 mm. Nos. 367c and 377a,			
	each ×2		1·90	2·00
		First Day Cover		2·50
		Presentation Pack	2·75	

Withdrawn: 30.6.92

LAXEY HAND-CART

456 Laxey Hand-cart,
1920

DOUGLAS HORSE DRAWN STEAMER

457 Horse-drawn Steamer,
Douglas, 1909

MERRYWEATHER HATFIELD PUMP

458 Merryweather
Hatfield Pump, 1936

DENNIS F8 PUMPING APPLIANCE

459 Dennis F8 Pumping
Appliance, Peel, 1953

VOLVO TURNTABLE LADDER

460 Volvo Turntable Ladder,
Douglas, 1989

Fire Engines

(Des C. Abbott. Litho Questa)

1991 (18 SEPT). Perf 14½ (C)

485	**456**	17p multicoloured	45	40
486	**457**	21p multicoloured	65	65
487	**458**	30p multicoloured	85	90
488	**459**	33p multicoloured	1·20	1·20
489	**460**	37p multicoloured	1·40	1·50
485/9		Set of 5	4·25	4·25
		First Day Cover		4·75
		Presentation Pack	4·75	
		Set of 5 Gutter Pairs	8·50	

Plate Nos.: All values 1A, 1B, 1C, 1D (each ×5)

Sheets: 40 (2 panes 4×5)

Imprint: Central, gutter margin

Withdrawn: 17.9.92

461 Mute Swans, Douglas
Harbour

462 Black Swans, Curraghs
Wildlife Park

463 Whooper Swans, Bishop's Dub, Ballaugh

464 Tundra ('Bewick's') Swans, Eairy Dam, Foxdale

465 Coscoroba Swans, Curraghs Wildlife Park

466 Whooper ('Trumpeter') Swans, Curraghs Wildlife Park

Swans

(Des Colleen Corlett. Litho Cartor)

1991 (18 SEPT). Perf 13 (C)

490	**461**	17p multicoloured	40	20
		a. Horiz pair. Nos. 490/1	80	1·00
491	**462**	17p multicoloured	40	20
492	**463**	26p multicoloured	1·10	30
		a. Horiz pair. Nos. 492/3	2·10	2·20
493	**464**	26p multicoloured	1·10	30
494	**465**	37p multicoloured	1·20	40
		a. Horiz pair. Nos. 494/5	2·40	2·75
		ab. Black ptg double		
495	**466**	37p multicoloured	1·20	40
490/5		Set of 6	4·50	5·00
		First Day Cover		6·00
		Presentation Pack	5·25	

Plate Nos: All values 1A, 1B (each ×4)

Sheets: 20 (4×5). The two designs of each value were printed together, se-tenant, in horizontal pairs throughout the sheets, with the backgrounds forming composite designs

Imprint: Central, bottom margin

Withdrawn: 17.9.92

467 The Three Kings

468 Mary with Manger

469 Shepherds with Sheep

470 Choir of Angels

Christmas. Paper Sculptures

(Des D. Swinton. Litho Walsall)

1991 (14 OCT). (*a*) Sheet stamps. Perf 14×14½ (C)

496	**467**	16p multicoloured	45	35
497	**468**	20p multicoloured	65	70
498	**469**	26p multicoloured	85	85
499	**470**	37p multicoloured	1·10	1·10
496/9		Set of 4	2·75	2·50
		First Day Cover		3·25
		Presentation Pack	3·50	

Plate Nos: All values 1A, 1B, 1C, 1D (each ×4)

Sheets: 40 (2 panes 4×5)

Imprint: Central, gutter margin

Withdrawn: 13.10.92

(*b*) Booklet stamps. Self-adhesive. Stamps die-cut

500	**467**	16p multicoloured	60	60
		a. Booklet pane. Nos. 500×8 and 501×4	7·50	
501	**468**	20p multicoloured	1·20	1·20

Year Pack 1991

1991 (14 OCT). *Comprises Nos. 367c, 377a, 464/82 and* **MS**484/99

Year Pack .... 40·00

Withdrawn: 31.12.92

Post Office Yearbook

1991 (14 OCT). *Comprises Nos. 367c, 377a, 464/82 and* **MS**484/99

Yearbook .... 45·00

Withdrawn: 30.11.94

471 North African and Italian Campaigns, 1942–43

472 D-Day, 1944

473 Arnhem, 1944

474 Rhine Crossing, 1945

475 Operations in Near, Middle and Far East, 1945–68

476 Liberation of Falkland Islands, 1982

50th Anniversary of Parachute Regiment

(Des A. Theobald. Litho Questa)

1992 (6 FEB). Perf 14 (C)

502	**471**	23p multicoloured	70	25
		a. Horiz pair. Nos. 502/3	1·50	1·50
503	**472**	23p multicoloured	70	25
504	**473**	28p multicoloured	80	30
		a. Horiz pair. Nos. 504/5	1·60	1·70
505	**474**	28p multicoloured	80	30
506	**475**	39p multicoloured	1·20	40
		a. Horiz pair. Nos. 506/7	2·50	2·75
507	**476**	39p multicoloured	1·20	40
502/7		Set of 6	5·00	5·00
		First Day Cover		6·00
		Presentation Pack	6·00	
		Souvenir Folder (complete sheets)	24·00	

Plate Nos: All values 1A, 1B (each ×5)

Sheets: 8 (2×4). The two designs of each value were printed together, se-tenant, in horizontal pairs throughout the sheets

Imprint: Top, left-hand margin

Withdrawn: 5.2.93

477 Queen Elizabeth II at Coronation, 1953

478 Queen visiting Isle of Man, 1979

479 Queen in Evening Dress

480 Queen visiting Isle of Man, 1989

481 Queen arriving for Film Premiere, 1990

40th Anniversary of Accession

(Des D. Miller. Litho B.D.T.)

1992 (6 FEB). Perf 14 (C)

508	**477**	18p multicoloured	45	40
509	**478**	23p multicoloured	60	60
510	**479**	28p multicoloured	70	70
511	**480**	33p multicoloured	1·20	1·40
512	**481**	39p multicoloured	1·40	1·40
508/12		Set of 5	4·00	4·00
		First Day Cover		5·00
		Presentation Pack	5·00	

Plate Nos: All values 1A, 1B (each ×5)

Sheets: 20 (5×4)

Imprint: Central, bottom margin

Withdrawn: 5.2.93

482 Brittle-stars

484 Atlantic Herring

483 Phytoplankton

485 Great Scallop

486 Dahlia Anemone and Delesseria

Centenary of Port Erin Marine Laboratory

(Des Jennifer Toombs. Litho Questa)

1992 (16 APR). Perf 14×14½ (C)

513	**482**	18p multicoloured	40	35
514	**483**	23p multicoloured	60	55
515	**484**	28p multicoloured	60	60
516	**485**	33p multicoloured	1·20	1·20
517	**486**	39p multicoloured	1·50	1·50
513/17		Set of 5	4·00	4·00
		First Day Cover		4·50
		Presentation Pack	4·75	
		Set of 5 Gutter Pairs	8·00	

Plate Nos.: All values 1A, 1B, 1C, 1D (each ×4)

Sheets: 40 (2 panes 5×4)

Imprint: Top right-hand side, gutter margin

Withdrawn: 15.4.93

487 The Pilgrim Fathers embarking at Delfshaven

488 *Speedwell* leaving Delfshaven

489 '*Mayflower* and *Speedwell* at Dartmouth' **490** (L. Wilcox)

Europa. 500th Anniversary of Discovery of America by Columbus

(Des C. Abbott. Litho Enschedé)

1992 (16 APR). Perf 14×13½ (C)

518	**487**	18p multicoloured	40	20
		a. Horiz pair. Nos. 518/19	1·60	1·60
519	**488**	18p multicoloured	40	20
520	**489**	28p multicoloured	75	30
		a. Horiz pair. Nos. 520/1	3·50	3·50

521	**490**	28p multicoloured	75	30
518/21		Set of 4	4·50	4·50
		First Day Cover		5·00
		Presentation Pack	5·25	

Plate Nos.: Both values 1A, 1B (each ×5)

Sheets: 20 (4×5). The two designs of each value were printed together, *se-tenant*, in horizontal pairs throughout the sheets, each pair forming a composite design

Imprint: Central, bottom margin

Withdrawn: 15.4.93

491 Central Pacific Locomotive *Jupiter*, 1869

492 Union Pacific Locomotive No. 119, 1869

493 Union Pacific Locomotive No. 844, 1992

494 Union Pacific Locomotive No. 3985, 1992

495 Golden Spike Ceremony, 10 May 1869 (*illustration reduced. Actual size 105×73 mm*)

Construction of Union Pacific Railroad, 1866–69

(Des A. Peck. Litho Enschedé)

1992 (22 MAY). Perf 13½×14 (C)

522	**491**	33p multicoloured	90	35
		a. Horiz. pair. Nos. 522/3 plus label	2·50	2·50
		b. Booklet pane. Nos. 522/5×2 and **MS**526	12·00	
523	**492**	33p multicoloured	90	35

524	**493**	39p multicoloured	1·20	40
		a. Horiz. pair. Nos. 524/5 plus label	3·00	3·00
525	**494**	39p multicoloured	1·20	40
522/5		Set of 4	4·00	4·50
		First Day Cover		5·00
		Presentation Pack	5·50	
		Souvenir Folder (sheets of 10)	22·00	
		Stamp Cards (set of 4)	3·25	6·50
MS526		105×73 mm. **495** £1.50, mult	3·70	4·50
		First Day Cover		7·00
		Presentation Pack	5·50	
		Stamp Card		70

Nos. 522b and **MS**526 also commemorated the 'World Columbian Stamp Expo'.

Booklet pane No. 522b contains two blocks of four of Nos. 522/5 with No. **MS**526 between them. Miniature sheets from the booklet show a white margin and line of roulettes at left and right. In the blocks of four each horizontal pair is separated by a half stamp-size label.

Plate Nos.: Both values 1A, 1B (each ×4)

Sheets: 10 (2×5). The two designs for each value were printed together in horizontal pairs separated by a half stamp-size label showing Union Pacific emblem or portraits of Dan and Jack Casement (railroad contractors)

Imprint: Central, right-hand margin

Withdrawn: 21.5.93

496 King Orry V in Douglas Harbour

497 Castletown

498 Port St. Mary

499 Ramsey

Manx Harbours

(Des Colleen Corlett. Litho Walsall)

1992 (18 SEPT). Perf 14½×14 (C)

527	**496**	18p multicoloured	45	45
528	**497**	23p multicoloured	55	55
529	**498**	37p multicoloured	1·20	1·20
530	**499**	40p multicoloured	1·40	1·40
527/30		Set of 4	3·25	3·25
		First Day Cover		3·75
		Presentation Pack	4·00	

Plate Nos.: All values 1A, 1B (each ×4)

Sheets: 10 (2×5)

Imprint: Right-hand corner, bottom margin

Withdrawn: 17.9.93

500 King Orry V (ex Saint Eloi) in 1972 and 1992 (illustration reduced. Actual size 111×68 mm)

'Genova '92' International Thematic Stamp Exhibition

(Des Colleen Corlett. Litho Walsall)

1992 (18 SEPT). Sheet 111×68 mm. Perf 14½×14 (C)

MS531	**500**	18p, £1 multicoloured	3·25	3·50
		First Day Cover		3·75
		Presentation Pack	3·75	

Withdrawn: 17.9.93

501 Window, St. German's Cathedral, Peel

502 Reredos, St. Matthew the Apostle, Douglas

503 Window, St. George's, Douglas

504 Reredos, St. Mary of the Isle Catholic Church, Douglas

505 Window, Trinity Methodist Church, Douglas

Christmas. Manx Churches

(Des Colleen Corlett, Litho Questa)

1992 (13 OCT). Perf 14½ (C)

532	**501**	17p multicoloured	45	40
533	**502**	22p multicoloured	65	65
534	**503**	28p multicoloured	80	80
535	**504**	37p multicoloured	95	95
536	**505**	40p multicoloured	1·00	1·00
		a. Gold ptg double		
532/6		Set of 5	3·50	3·50
		First Day Cover		4·00
		Presentation Pack	4·00	
		Set of 5 Gutter Pairs	7·00	

Plate Nos.: 17p, 22p 1A, 1B, 1C, 1D (each ×5); others 1A, 1B (each ×5)

Sheets: 40 (2 panes 4×5)

Imprint: Right-hand corner, bottom margin of each pane

Withdrawn: 12.10.93

Year Pack 1992

1992 (13 OCT). *Comprises Nos. 502/36*
Year Pack .... 40·00

Withdrawn: 31.12.93

Post Office Yearbook

1992 (13 OCT). *Comprises Nos. 375a, 377b, 502/36 and* D25
Yearbook .... 45·00

Withdrawn: 30.11.94

506 Mansell on Lap of Honour, British Grand Prix, 1992

507 Mansell in French Grand Prix, 1992

Nigel Mansell's Victory in Formula 1 World Motor Racing Championship

(Des A. Theobald. Litho Walsall)

1992 (8 NOV). Perf 13½ (C)

537	**506**	20p multicoloured	80	80
538	**507**	24p multicoloured	1·00	1·00
537/8		Set of 2	1·80	1·80
		First Day Cover		2·75
		Presentation Pack	2·75	

Plate Nos.: Both values 1A, 1B (each ×4)

Sheets: 50 (5×10)

Imprint: Bottom margin

Withdrawn: 7.11.93

508 H.M.S. *Amazon* (frigate)

509 *Fingal* (lighthouse tender)

510 *Sir Winston Churchill* (cadet schooner)

511 *Dar Mlodziezy* (full-rigged cadet ship)

512 *Tynwald I* (paddle-steamer)

513 *Ben Veg* (freighter)

514 *Waverley* (paddle-steamer)

515 Royal Yacht *Britannia*

516 *Francis Drake* (ketch)

517 *Royal Viking Sky* (liner)

518 *Lord Nelson* (cadet barque)

519 *Europa* (liner)

520 *Snaefell V* (ferry) leaving Androssan

520a *Seacat* (catamaran ferry)

521 *Lady of Man I* (ferry) off Ramsey

522 *Mona's Queen II* (paddle ferry) leaving Fleetwood

523 *Queen Elizabeth 2* (liner) and *Mona's Queen V* (ferry) off Liverpool

523a Manx Red Ensign

523b Queen Elizabeth II (hologram)

Ships

(Des A. Theobald (1p to 27p), J. Nicholson (30p, 35p, 40p, 50p, £1), Colleen Corlett (£2, £5). Litho Questa (£2), Walsall (£5) (hologram by Applied Holographics), Enschedé (others))

1993 (4 JAN)–**97**. Perf 14½ (£2), 14½×14 (£5) or 13½×13 (others), all comb

539	**508**	1p multicoloured (a)	....	10	10
540	**509**	2p multicoloured (a)	....	10	10
541	**510**	4p multicoloured (a)	....	10	10
		a. Booklet pane. Nos. 541, 544 and 548 each ×2 (g)	......	5·00	
542	**511**	5p multicoloured (a)	....	10	10
543	**512**	20p multicoloured (ae)	....	40	25
		a. Booklet pane. Nos. 543×2 and 547×3	....	3·00	
		b. Booklet pane. Nos. 543×4 and 547×6	....	6·50	
544	**513**	21p multicoloured (ag)	....	50	50
545	**514**	22p multicoloured (a)	....	50	50
546	**515**	23p multicoloured (a)	....	55	55
547	**516**	24p multicoloured (ae)	....	50	35
548	**517**	25p multicoloured (ag)	....	60	60
549	**518**	26p multicoloured (a)	....	65	65
550	**519**	27p multicoloured (a)	....	65	65
551	**520**	30p multicoloured (b)	....	75	75
552	**520a**	35p multicoloured (f)	....	85	85
553	**521**	40p multicoloured (b)	....	1·00	90
554	**522**	50p multicoloured (b)	....	1·20	1·10
555	**523**	£1 multicoloured (bg)	....	2·50	2·40
556	**523a**	£2 multicoloured (c)	....	3·75	4·00
557	**523b**	£5 multicoloured (d)	....	10·00	12·00
539/57		Set of 19	....	22·00	23·00
		First Day Covers (6)			30·00
		Presentation Packs (6)	.....	30·00	
		Stamp Cards (Nos. 539/51, 553/5)	....	8·00	22·00
		Souvenir Folder (Nos. 539/51, 553/5)	....	12·00	

For 4p, 20p and 24p in similar designs, but smaller, see Nos. 687/93.

Printings: (a) 4.1.93. Inscribed '1993'; (b) 15.9.93. Inscribed '1993'; (c) 12.1.94. Inscribed '1994'; (d) 5.7.94. Inscribed '1994'; (e) 8.2.95. Inscribed '1995'; (f) 11.1.1996. Inscribed '1996'; (g) 14.5.97. Inscribed '1997'

Plate Nos.: £2, £5 1A, 1B (each ×4); others 1A, 1B, 1C, 1D (each ×4)

Sheets: 25 (5×5) (£2), 10 (5×2) (£5) or 50 (5×10) (others). In addition to stamp booklets Nos. 543a/b also come from a special booklet sheet of 50 (5×10) which provides either 10 examples of No. 543a or 5 of 543b. No. 541a comes from a special booklet sheet of 30 (5×6)

Imprint: Central, bottom margin (£2, £5) or right-hand corner, bottom margin (others)

Withdrawn: 30.11.98 1p to £1; 12.1.99 £2; 5.7.99 £5

524 No. 1 Motor Car and No. 13 Trailer at Groudle Glen Hotel

525 No. 9 Tunnel Car and No. 19 Trailer at Douglas Bay Hotel

526 No. 19 Motor Car and No. 59 Royal Trailer Special at Douglas Bay

527 No. 33 Motor Car, No. 45 Trailer and No. 13 Van at Derby Castle

Centenary of Manx Electric Railway

(Des A. Theobald. Litho B.D.T.)

1993 (3 FEB). Perf 14 (C)

559	**524**	20p multicoloured	60	60
		a. *Boolet pane. Nos.* 559/62 . .	3·50	
560	**525**	24p multicoloured	90	90
561	**526**	28p multicoloured	1·00	1·00
562	**527**	39p multicoloured	1·40	1·40
559/62		*Set of 4*	3·50	3·50
		First Day Cover		3·75
		Presentation Pack	3·75	

Booklet pane No. 559*a* exists in four versions, which differ in the order of the stamps within the block of four and in the information printed on the pane margin.

Plate Nos.: All values 1A, 1B (each ×4)

Sheets: 10 (2×5)

Imprint: Central, left-hand margin

Withdrawn: 2.2.94

528 'Sir Hall Caine' (statue)

529 'The Brass Bedstead' (painting)

530 Abstract Bronze Sculpture

531 'Polar Bear Skeleton' (drawing)

Europa. Contemporary Art by Bryan Kneale

(Des Colleen Corlett. Litho B.D.T.)

1993 (14 APR). Perf 14 (C)

563	**528**	20p multicoloured	40	20
		a. *Horiz pair. Nos.* 563/4	1·20	1·20
564	**529**	20p multicoloured	40	20

565	**530**	28p multicoloured	75	30
		a. *Horiz pair. Nos.* 565/6	2·00	2·00
566	**531**	28p multicoloured	75	30
563/6		*Set of 4*	3·00	3·00
		First Day Cover		3·50
		Presentation Pack	3·75	

Plate Nos.: Both values 1A, 1B, 1C (each ×4)

Sheets: 20 (4×5). The two designs for each value printed together, *se-tenant*, in horizontal pairs throughout the sheets

Imprint: Central, right-hand margin

Withdrawn: 13.4.94

532 Graham Oates and Bill Marshall (1933 International Six Day Trial) on Ariel Square Four

533 Sergeant Geoff Duke (1947 Royal Signals Display Team) on Triumph 3T Twin

534 Dennis Parkinson (1953 Senior Manx Grand Prix) on Manx Norton

535 Richard Swallow (1991 Junior Classic MGP) on Aermacchi

536 Steve Colley (1992 Scottish Six Day Trial) on Beta Zero

Manx Motor Cycling Events

(Des C. Abbott. Litho Walsall)

1993 (3 JUNE). Perf 13½×14 (C)

567	**532**	20p multicoloured	35	35
568	**533**	24p multicoloured	45	45
569	**534**	28p multicoloured	70	60
570	**535**	33p multicoloured	90	90

571	**536**	39p multicoloured	....	1·00	95
567/71		Set of 5	....	3·00	3·00
		First Day Cover	....		4·00
		Presentation Pack		4·00	
		Stamp Cards (set of 5)	.....	3·00	6·00
MS572		165×120 mm. Nos. 567/71	......	4·50	4·50
		Souvenir Folder	....	4·75	

Plate Nos.: All values 1A, 1B, 1C, 1D (each ×4)

Sheets: 20 (4×5)

Imprint: Right-hand corner, bottom margin

Withdrawn: 2.6.94

537 *Inachis io*
(Peacock)

538 *Argynnis aglaja*
(Dark Green
Fritillary)

539 *Cynthia cardui*
(Painted Lady)

540 *Celastrina argiolus*
(Holly Blue)

541 *Vanessa atalanta* (Red Admiral)

Butterflies

(Des Colleen Corlett. Litho Questa)

1993 (15 SEPT). Perf 14½ (C)

573	**537**	24p multicoloured	....	75	65
		a. Horiz strip of 5. Nos. 573/7	.	3·50	
574	**538**	24p multicoloured	....	75	65
575	**539**	24p multicoloured	....	75	65
576	**540**	24p multicoloured	....	75	65
577	**541**	24p multicoloured	....	75	65
573/7		Set of 5	....	3·50	3·00
		First Day Cover	....		4·25
		Presentation Pack	....	4·00	

Examples of Nos. 573/7 sold at 'Philakorea '94' and 'Singpex '94' come with commemorative cachets on the bottom margin.

Plate Nos.: 1A, 1B (each ×4)

Sheets: 20 (5×4). The five designs for each value printed together, *se-tenant*, in horizontal strips throughout the sheets

Imprint: Right-hand corner, bottom margin

Withdrawn: 14.9.94

542 Children
decorating
Christmas
Tree

543 Girl with
Snowman

544 Boy opening
Presents

545 Girl with
Teddy Bear

546 Children with Toboggan

Christmas

(Des Christine Haworth. Litho Questa)

1993 (12 OCT). Perf 14 (C)

578	**542**	19p multicoloured	....	50	50
579	**543**	23p multicoloured	....	60	60
580	**544**	28p multicoloured	....	70	70
581	**545**	39p multicoloured	....	1·10	1·10
582	**546**	40p multicoloured	....	1·10	1·10
578/82		Set of 5	....	3·50	3·50
		First Day Cover	....		4·00
		Presentation Pack	....	4·25	
		Set of 5 Gutter Pairs	......	7·00	

Nos. 578 and 579 were also issued in booklets, SB35 and SB36.

Plate Nos.: All values 1A, 1B, 1C, 1D (each ×4)

Sheets: 40 (2 panes 4×5)

Imprint: Bottom, right-hand margin of each pane

Withdrawn: 11.10.94

Year Pack 1993

1993 (12 OCT). *Comprises Nos. 539/51, 553/5, 559/71 and 573/82*

Year Pack . . . . 32·00

Withdrawn: 31.12.94

Post Office Yearbook

1993 (12 OCT). *Comprises Nos. 539/51, 553/5, 559/71 and 573/82*

Yearbook . . . . 40·00

Sold out: 8.95

547 White-throated Robin

548 Black-eared Wheatear

549 Goldcrest

550 Northern Oriole

551 River Kingfisher

552 Hoopoe

553 Black-billed Magpie
(*illustration reduced. Actual size* 100×71 *mm*)

Calf of Man Bird Observatory

(Des Colleen Corlett. Litho B.D.T.)

1994 (18 FEB). Perf 13½×13 (No. **MS**589) or 14 (others), both comb

583	**547**	20p multicoloured		50	20
		a. *Pair. Nos. 583/4*		1·00	1·20
584	**548**	20p multicoloured		50	20
585	**549**	24p multicoloured		80	25
		a. *Pair. Nos. 585/6*		1·60	1·70
586	**550**	24p multicoloured		80	25
587	**551**	30p multicoloured		1·00	30
		a. *Pair. Nos. 587/8*		2·00	2·20
588	**552**	30p multicoloured		1·00	30
583/8		*Set of 6*		4·25	4·75
		First Day Cover			5·50
		Presentation Pack		5·00	
		Souvenir Folder (complete sheets)		20·00	
MS589		100×71 mm. **553** £1 multicoloured		3·00	3·50
		First Day Cover			4·50
		Presentation Pack		4·50	

No. **MS**589 also commemorates the 'Hong Kong '94' philatelic exhibition.

Plate Nos.: All values 1A, 1B (each ×4)

Sheets: 10 (2×5). The two designs for each value printed together, *se-tenant*, in horizontal and vertical pairs throughout the sheets

Imprint: Central, right-hand margin

Withdrawn: 17.2.95

554 Gaiety Theatre, Douglas

555 Sports

556 Artist at work and Yachts racing

557 T.T. Races and British Aerospace Hawk T.1s of Red Arrows

558 Musical Instruments

559 Laxey Wheel and Manx Cat

560 Tower of Refuge, Douglas, with Bucket and Spade

561 Cyclist

562 Tynwald Day and Bentley 3 Litre Racing Car (1922)

563 Santa Mince Pie Train, Groudle Glen

566 Edward Forbes and Signature

567 *Solaster moretonis* (fossil starfish)

568 *Adamsia carciniopados* (anemone) on Hermit Crab

569 *Solaster endeca* (starfish)

Manx Tourism Centenary. Booklet Stamps

(Des Colleen Corlett. Litho Cartor)

1994 (18 FEB). Perf 13½ (C)

590	**554**	24p multicoloured	65	60
		a. Booklet pane. Nos. 590/9 with margins all round	6·00	
591	**555**	24p multicoloured	65	60
592	**556**	24p multicoloured	65	60
593	**557**	24p multicoloured	65	60
594	**558**	24p multicoloured	65	60
595	**559**	24p multicoloured	65	60
596	**560**	24p multicoloured	65	60
597	**561**	24p multicoloured	65	60
598	**562**	24p multicoloured	65	60
599	**563**	24p multicoloured	65	60
590/9		Set of 10	6·00	5·50
		First Day Cover		6·50
		Presentation Pack	6·50	
		Stamp Cards (set of 3)	1·50	

Nos. 590/9 were issued in £2.40 stamp booklets, but were also available from the Philatelic Bureau as a loose pane, which was also inserted into the Presentation Pack.

Withdrawn: 17.2.95

564 *Eubranchus tricolor* (sea slug)

565 *Loligo forbesii* (common squid)

Europa. Discoveries of Edward Forbes (marine biologist)

(Des Jennifer Toombs. Litho Enschedé)

1994 (5 MAY). Perf 13×14½ (C)

600	**564**	20p multicoloured	40	20
		a. Horiz strip of 3. Nos. 600/2 .	1·50	1·50
601	**565**	20p multicoloured	40	20
602	**566**	20p multicoloured	40	20
603	**567**	30p multicoloured	75	30
		a. Horiz strip of 3. Nos. 603/5 .	2·75	2·75
604	**568**	30p multicoloured	75	30
605	**569**	30p multicoloured	75	30
600/5		Set of 6	3·75	3·75
		First Day Cover		4·25
		Presentation Pack	4·50	

Plate Nos.: Both values 1A, 1B (each ×4)

Sheets: 15 (3×5). The three designs for each value printed together, *se-tenant*, in horizontal strips of 3 throughout the sheets

Imprint: Central, bottom margin

Withdrawn: 4.5.95

570 Maj.-Gen. Bedell Smith and Naval Landing Force including *Ben-My-Chree IV* (ferry)

571 Admiral Ramsay and Naval Ships including *Victoria* and *Lady of Man* (ferries)

572 Gen. Montgomery and British Landings

573 Lt.-Gen. Dempsey and 2nd Army Landings

574 Air Chief Marshal Leigh-Mallory, U.S. Paratroops and Aircraft

575 Air Chief Marshal Tedder, British Paratroops and Aircraft

576 Lt.-Gen. Bradley and U.S. 1st Army Landings

577 Gen. Eisenhower and American Landings

578 Postman Pat, Jess and Ffinlo at Sea Terminal, Douglas

579 Laxey Wheel

580 Cregneash

581 Manx Electric Railway Trains

582 Peel Harbour

583 Douglas Promenade

50th Anniversary of D-Day

(Des A. Theobald. Litho Questa)

1994 (6 JUNE). Perf 14 (C)

606	**570**	4p multicoloured	10	10
		a. Horiz pair. Nos. 606/7	30	30
607	**571**	4p multicoloured	10	10
608	**572**	20p multicoloured	50	20
		a. Horiz pair. Nos. 608/9	1·40	1·40
609	**573**	20p multicoloured	50	20
610	**574**	30p multicoloured	75	30
		a. Horiz pair. Nos. 610/11	2·00	2·00
611	**575**	30p multicoloured	75	30
612	**576**	41p multicoloured	85	45
		a. Horiz pair. Nos. 612/13	2·50	2·50
613	**577**	41p multicoloured	85	45
606/13		Set of 8	5·50	5·50
		First Day Cover		6·00
		Presentation Pack	6·25	
		Souvenir Folder (complete sheets)	26·00	

Plate Nos.: All values 1A, 1B (each ×5)

Sheets: 8 (2×4). The two designs for each value printed together, se-tenant, in horizontal pairs throughout the sheets

Imprint: Central, left-hand margin

Withdrawn: 5.6.95

584 Postman Pat, Jess, Policeman and Children at Zebra Crossing
(illustration reduced. Actual size 110×85 mm)

Postman Pat visits the Isle of Man

(Des Colleen Corlett. Litho B.D.T.)

1994 (14 SEPT). Perf 13 (No. **MS**620) or 15×14 (others), both comb

614	**578**	1p multicoloured	15	15
		a. *Booklet pane of 2 with margins all round*	50	
615	**579**	20p multicoloured	60	60
		a. *Booklet pane of 2 with margins all round*	1·70	
616	**580**	24p multicoloured	80	80
		a. *Booklet pane of 2 with margins all round*	2·20	
617	**581**	30p multicoloured	90	90
		a. *Booklet pane of 2 with margins all round*	2·50	
618	**582**	36p multicoloured	1·10	1·10
		a. *Booklet pane of 2 with margins all round*	2·75	
619	**583**	41p multicoloured	1·20	1·20
		a. *Booklet pane of 2 with margins all round*	3·25	
614/19		*Set of 6*	4·25	4·25
		First Day Cover		4·50
		Presentation Pack	4·50	
		Stamp Cards (set of 6)	3·00	7·50
MS620		110×85 mm. **584** £1 multicoloured	2·20	2·20
		a. *Booklet pane. As No. **MS**620 but with line of roulettes at left*	2·20	
		First Day Cover		3·00
		Presentation Pack	3·00	

Examples of No. **MS**620 from stamp booklets show a line of roulettes at left.

Plate Nos.: All values 1A, 1B (each ×4)

Sheets: 10 (2×5)

Imprint: Right-hand corner, bottom margin

Withdrawn: 13.9.95

585 Cycling

586 Downhill Skiing

587 Swimming

588 Hurdling

589 Centenary Logo

Centenary of International Olympic Committee

(Des D. Miller. Litho Walsall)

1994 (11 OCT). Perf 14×14½ (C)

621	**585**	10p multicoloured	35	25
622	**586**	20p multicoloured	55	50
623	**587**	24p multicoloured	70	65
624	**588**	35p multicoloured	95	1·00
625	**589**	48p multicoloured	1·60	1·80
621/5		*Set of 5*	3·75	3·75
		First Day Cover		3·75
		Presentation Pack	4·00	

Plate Nos.: 10p 1A (×4); 20p 1B (×4); 24p 1C (×4); 35p 1D (×4); 48p 1E (×4)

Sheets: 20 (5×4)

Imprint: Central, left-hand margin

Withdrawn: 10.10.95

590 Santa Train to Santon

591 Father Christmas and Postman Pat on Mini Tractor, Douglas

592 Father Christmas and Majorettes in Sleigh, Port St. Mary

Christmas. Father Christmas in the Isle of Man

(Des Colleen Corlett. Litho Cartor)

1994 (11 OCT). Perf 13½×14 (23p) or 14×13½ (others), all comb

626	**590**	19p multicoloured	60	60
627	**591**	23p multicoloured	80	80
628	**592**	60p multicoloured	2·00	2·00
626/8		*Set of 3*	3·00	3·00
		First Day Cover		3·50
		Presentation Pack	3·75	
		Set of 3 Gutter Pairs	6·00	

Plate Nos.: All values 1A, 1B, 1C, 1D (each ×4)

Sheets: 40 (2 panes 5×4)

Imprint: Central, side margins of each pane

Withdrawn: 10.10.95

Year Pack 1994

1994 (11 OCT). *Comprises Nos.* 556 *and* 583/628, *with or without No.* 557

Year Pack with No. 557 .... 50·00
Year Pack without No. 557 .. 40·00

Withdrawn: 31.12.95

Post Office Yearbook

1994 (NOV). *Comprises Nos.* 556/7 *and* 583/628
Yearbook .... 55·00

Sold out: 3.96

593 Foden Steam Wagon, Highway Board Depot, Douglas

594 Clayton & Shuttleworth and Fowler engines pulling Dead Whale

595 Wallis & Steevens at Ramsey Harbour

596 Marshall Engine with Threshing Machine, Ballarhenny

597 Marshall Convertible Steam Roller

Steam Traction Engines

(Des A. Peck. Litho Enschedé)

1995 (8 FEB). Perf 13½×13 (C)

629	**593**	20p multicoloured	55	60
630	**594**	24p multicoloured	60	70
631	**595**	30p multicoloured	80	85
632	**596**	35p multicoloured	1·10	1·10
633	**597**	41p multicoloured	1·10	1·20
629/33		*Set of 5*	3·75	4·00
		First Day Cover		4·50
		Presentation Pack	4·50	

Plate Nos.: 35p 1A, 1B, 1C, 1D (each ×4); others 1A, 1B (each ×4)

Sheets: 20 (4×5)

Withdrawn: 7.2.96

598 Car No. 2 and First Train, 1895

599 Car No. 4 in Green Livery and Car No. 3 in Laxey Valley

600 Car No. 6 and Car No. 5 in 1971

601 Goods Car No. 7 and *Caledonia* Steam Locomotive pulling Construction Train

214

602 Passenger Car and Argus Char-a-banc at Bungalow Hotel
(*illustration reduced. Actual size* 110×87 mm)

603 Peace Doves forming Wave and Tower of Refuge, Douglas Bay

604 Peace Dove breaking Barbed Wire

Centenary of Snaefell Mountain Railway

(Des A. Theobald. Litho B.D.T.)

1995 (8 FEB). Perf 14 (C)

634	**598**	20p multicoloured	70	70
		a. *Booklet pane. Nos.* 634/7 *with margins all round*	3·50	
635	**599**	24p multicoloured	80	80
636	**600**	35p multicoloured	1·10	1·10
637	**601**	42p multicoloured	1·20	1·20
634/7		*Set of* 4	3·50	3·50
		First Day Cover		4·25
		Presentation Pack	4·50	
MS638		110×87 mm. **602** £1 multicoloured	3·25	3·25
		a. *Booklet pane. As No.* **MS**638 *with additional margins all round showing further inscriptions at right and left* .	3·75	
		First Day Cover		3·75
		Presentation Pack	4·00	

Booklet pane No. 634*a* exists in three versions which differ in the order of the stamps within the block of four.

Examples of No. **MS**638 from booklet No. SB39 show a white margin, description of the design and line of roulettes at left and an additional inscription, '1895. CENTENARY SNAEFELL MOUNTAIN RAILWAY. 1995', vertically in the margin at right.

Plate Nos.: All values 1A, 1B (each ×4)

Sheets: 10 (2×5)

Imprint: Central, left-hand margin

Withdrawn: 7.2.96

Europa. Peace and Freedom

(Des Colleen Corlett and M. Magleby (20p), Colleen Corlett (30p). Litho Enschedé)

1995 (28 APR). Perf 14×13½ (C)

639	**603**	20p multicoloured	60	75
640	**604**	30p multicoloured	1·00	1·00
639/40		*Set of* 2	1·60	1·70
		First Day Cover		2·20
		Presentation Pack	2·40	

Plate Nos.: Both values 1A, 1B (each ×5)

Sheets: 10 (5×2)

Imprint: Central, bottom margin

Withdrawn: 27.4.96

605 Spitfire, Tank and Medals

606 Typhoon, Anti-aircraft Gun and Medals

607 Lancaster, H.M.S. *Biter* (escort carrier) and Medals

608 Grumman Avenger, Jungle Patrol and Medals

609 Celebrations in
Parliament Square

610 V.E. Day Bonfire

611 Street Party

612 King George VI and
Queen Elizabeth on Isle
of Man in July, 1945

50th Anniversary of End of Second World War

(Des A. Theobald. Litho B.D.T.)

1995 (8 MAY). Perf 14 (C)

641	**605**	10p multicoloured	30	15
		a. Horiz pair. Nos. 641/2	60	60
642	**606**	10p multicoloured	30	15
643	**607**	20p multicoloured	55	25
		a. Horiz pair. Nos. 643/4	1·10	1·10
644	**608**	20p multicoloured	55	25
645	**609**	24p multicoloured	70	25
		a. Horiz pair. Nos. 645/6	1·40	1·40
646	**610**	24p multicoloured	70	25
647	**611**	40p multicoloured	1·10	50
		a. Horiz pair. Nos. 647/8	2·20	2·20
648	**612**	40p multicoloured	1·10	50
641/8		Set of 8	4·75	4·75
		First Day Cover		5·50
		Presentation Pack	6·00	
		Souvenir Folder (complete		
		sheets)	19·00	

Plate Nos.: All values 1A, 1B, 1C (each ×4)

Sheets: 8 (2×4). The two designs for each value printed together, *se-tenant*, in horizontal pairs throughout the sheets

Imprint: Central, left-hand margin

Withdrawn: 7.5.96

613 Reg Parnell in Maserati
4 CLT, 1951

614 Stirling Moss in Frazer
Nash Le Mans Replica
car, 1951

615 Richard Seaman in
Delage, 1936

616 Prince Bira in ERA R2B
Romulus, 1937

617 Kenelm Guinness in
Sunbeam 1, 1914

618 Freddie Dixon in Riley
6 Cylinder Special
Racing Car, 1934

619 John Napier in Arrol Johnston 18 h.p. Racing Car, 1905
(*illustration reduced. Actual size 103×73 mm*)

90th Anniversary of Motor Racing on Isle of Man

(Des N. Sykes. Litho Questa)

1995 (8 MAY). Perf 14 (C)

649	**613**	20p multicoloured	65	60
650	**614**	24p multicoloured	80	75
651	**615**	30p multicoloured	90	85
652	**616**	36p multicoloured	1·10	1·00
653	**617**	41p multicoloured	1·20	1·20
654	**618**	42p multicoloured	1·20	1·50
649/54		Set of 6	5·50	5·50
		First Day Cover		5·75
		Presentation Pack	6·00	
MS655		103×73 mm. **619** £1 multicoloured	3·00	3·00
		First Day Cover		3·25
		Presentation Pack	3·25	

Plate Nos.: All values 1A, 1B (each ×5)

Sheets: 20 (5×4)

Imprint: Right-hand corner, bottom margin

Withdrawn: 7.5.96

620 Thomas the Tank Engine and Bertie Bus being Unloaded

621 Mail Train

622 Bertie and Engines at Ballasalla

623 Viking the Diesel Engine, Port Erin

624 Thomas and Railcar at Snaefell Summit

625 Engines racing past Laxey Wheel

50th Anniversary of Thomas the Tank Engine Stories by Revd. Awdry. 'Thomas the Tank Engine's Dream'

(Des O. Bell. Litho B.D.T.)

1995 (15 AUG). Perf 14 (C)

656	**620**	20p multicoloured	65	60
		a. Booklet pane. Nos. 656/7 with margins all round	1·70	
		b. Booklet pane. Nos. 656 and 661 with margins all round	2·20	
657	**621**	24p multicoloured	80	75
		a. Booklet pane. Nos. 657/8 with margins all round	1·70	
658	**622**	30p multicoloured	90	85
		a. Booklet pane. Nos. 658/9 with margins all round	2·00	
659	**623**	36p multicoloured	1·10	1·00
		a. Booklet pane. Nos. 659/60 with margins all round	2·20	
660	**624**	41p multicoloured	1·20	1·10
		a. Booklet pane. Nos. 660/1 with margins all round	2·50	

661	**625**	45p multicoloured	1·50	1·20
656/61		Set of 6	5·50	5·00
		First Day Cover		5·50
		Presentation Pack	6·00	
		Stamp Cards (set of 6)	3·00	9·00

Plate Nos.: All values 1A, 1B (each ×4)

Sheets: 10 (2×5)

Imprint: Central, bottom margin

Withdrawn: 14.8.96

626 Amanita muscaria

627 Boletus edulis

628 Coprinus disseminatus

629 Pleurotus ostreatus

630 Geastrum triplex

631 Shaggy Ink Cap and Bee Orchid
(illustration reduced. Actual size 100×71 mm)

Fungi

(Des Colleen Corlett. Litho Enschedé)

1995 (1 SEPT). Perf 13½ (C)

662	**626**	20p multicoloured	40	40
663	**627**	24p multicoloured	50	50
664	**628**	30p multicoloured	60	60
665	**629**	35p multicoloured	75	75
666	**630**	45p multicoloured	1·20	1·20
662/6		Set of 5	3·25	3·25
		First Day Cover		4·00
		Presentation Pack	4·75	
MS667		100×71 mm. **631** £1 multicoloured	3·00	3·00
		First Day Cover		3·50
		Presentation Pack	3·50	

No. **MS**667 is inscribed 'Singapore World Stamp Exhibition 1st–10th September 1995' on the sheet margin.

Plate Nos.: All values 1A, 1B, 1C (each ×4)

Sheets: 20 (4×5)

Imprint: Right-hand corner, bottom margin

Withdrawn: 31.8.96

632 St. Catherine's Church, Port Erin

633 European Robin on Holly Branch

634 St. Peter's Church and Wild Flowers

635 Hedgehog hibernating under Farm Machinery

Christmas

(Des Colleen Corlett. Litho B.D.T.)

1995 (10 OCT). Perf 14 (C)

668	**632**	19p multicoloured	55	55
669	**633**	23p multicoloured	70	70
670	**634**	42p multicoloured	1·50	1·50
671	**635**	50p multicoloured	1·70	1·70
668/71		Set of 4	4·00	4·00
		First Day Cover		4·50
		Presentation Pack	4·50	
		Set of 4 Gutter Pairs	8·00	

Plate Nos.: All values 1A, 1B, 1C (each ×4)

Sheets: 40 (2 panes 5×4)

Imprint: Right-hand corner, bottom margin

Withdrawn: 9.10.96

Year Pack 1995

1995 (10 OCT). *Comprises Nos. 629/71*

Year Pack .... 42·00

Withdrawn: 31.12.96

Post Office Yearbook

1995 (OCT). *Comprises Nos. 629/38, 639/40 in sheets of 10 and 641/71*

Yearbook .... 45·00

Sold out: By 5.97

636 Langness Lighthouse

637 Point of Ayre Lighthouse

638 Chicken Rock Lighthouse

639 Calf of Man Lighthouse

640 Douglas Head Lighthouse

641 Maughold Head Lighthouse

Lighthouses

(Des D. Swinton. Litho Questa)

1996 (24 JAN). Perf 14 (C)

672	**636**	20p multicoloured	50	50
		a. Booklet pane. No. 672×4 with margins all round	2·20	
673	**637**	24p multicoloured	60	60
		a. Booklet pane. No. 673×4 with margins all round	3·00	
674	**638**	30p multicoloured	90	90
		a. Booklet pane. Nos. 674 and 676, each ×2, with margins all round	3·75	
675	**639**	36p multicoloured	1·00	1·00
		a. Booklet pane. Nos. 675 and 677, each ×2, with margins all round	4·00	
676	**640**	41p multicoloured	1·10	1·10
677	**641**	42p multicoloured	1·20	1·20
672/7		Set of 6	5·00	5·00
		First Day Cover		5·50
		Presentation Pack	5·50	
		Set of 6 Gutter Pairs	10·00	

Plate Nos.: All values 1A, 1B (each ×5)

Sheets: 40 (2 panes 4×5) 20p, 30p, 41p; (2 panes 5×4) others

Imprint: Central, left-hand margin (20p, 30p, 41p) or central, bottom margin (others)

Withdrawn: 22.1.97

642 White Manx Cat and Celtic Interlaced Ribbons

643 Cat and Union Jack Ribbons

644 Cat on Rug in German Colours, Mouse and Brandenburg Gate

645 Cat, U.S.A. Flag and Statue of Liberty

646 Cat, Map of Australia and Kangaroo

647 Cat and Kittens
(illustration reduced. Actual size 100×71 mm)

Manx Cats

(Des Nancy Corkish. Litho B.D.T.)

1996 (14 MAR). Perf 13×13 (No. **MS**683) or 14 (others), both comb

678	**642**	20p multicoloured	50	50
679	**643**	24p multicoloured	60	60
680	**644**	36p multicoloured	90	90
681	**645**	42p multicoloured	1·10	1·10
682	**646**	48p multicoloured	1·20	1·20
678/82		Set of 5	4·00	4·00
		First Day Cover		5·00
		Presentation Pack	5·00	
		Stamp Cards (set of 5)	2·50	6·50
MS683		100×71 mm. **647** £1.50, mult	3·50	3·50
		First Day Cover		4·50
		Presentation Pack	4·50	

For No. **MS**683 with 'CAPEX '96' logo see No. **MS**712.

Plate Nos.: All values 1A, 1B (each ×4)

Sheets: 10 (2×5)

Imprint: Central, left-hand margin

Withdrawn: 13.3.97

648 Douglas Borough Arms

Centenary of Douglas Borough

(Des Colleen Corlett. Litho B.D.T.)

1996 (14 MAR). Self-adhesive. Die-cut perf 9×10

684	**648**	(20p) multicoloured	70	1·00
		First Day Cover		1·50
		Presentation Pack	1·50	

No. 684 was printed in sheets of 40, each stamp surrounded by white backing paper divided by roulettes. The actual stamps are separated from the backing paper by die-cut perforations. It was initially sold for 20p and was only valid for postage within the Isle of Man.

Plate Nos.: 1A, 1B (each ×4)

Sheets: 40 (8×5)

Imprint: Right-hand corner, bottom margin

Withdrawn: 30.11.98

651 *Sir Winston Churchill* (cadet schooner)

653 *Tynwald I* (paddle-steamer), 1846

657 *Francis Drake* (ketch)

Ships

(Des A. Theobald. Litho Walsall)

1996 (21 APR). *As Nos. 541, 543 and 547, but smaller as T* **651/7**. Perf 14 (C)

687	**651**	4p multicoloured	20	15
		a. Booklet pane. Nos. 687, 689 and 693, each ×2	10·00	
689	**653**	20p multicoloured	60	70
693	**657**	24p multicoloured	90	90
687/93		Set of 3	1·50	1·60
		First Day Cover		2·50
		Presentation Pack	2·50	

The 20p and 24p show the positions of the face value and Queen's head reversed.

Plate Nos.: All values 1A, 1B (each ×4)

Sheets: 100 (10×10)

Imprint: Right-hand corner, bottom margin

Withdrawn: 30.11.98

665 Princess Anne (President, Save the Children Fund) and Children

666 Queen Elizabeth II and People of the Commonwealth

Europa. Famous Women

(Des D. Miller. Litho B.D.T.)

1996 (21 APR). Perf 14 (C)

701	**665**	24p multicoloured	70	75
702	**666**	30p multicoloured	90	1·00
701/2		Set of 2	1·60	1·70
		First Day Cover		2·20
		Presentation Pack	3·50	

The background designs of Nos. 701/2 continue onto the vertical sheet margins.

Plate Nos.: Both values 1A, 1B (each ×4)

Sheets: 10 (2×5)

Withdrawn: 20.4.97

667 Alec Bennett

668 Stanley Woods

669 Artie Bell

670 Joey and Robert Dunlop

671 R.A.F. Red Arrows Display Team (*illustration reduced. Actual size* 100×70 *mm*)

Tourist Trophy Motorcycle Races. Irish Winners

(Des J. Dunne. Litho Questa)

1996 (30 MAY). Perf 14 (C)

703	**667**	20p multicoloured	50	45
704	**668**	24p multicoloured	60	60
705	**669**	45p multicoloured	90	90
706	**670**	60p multicoloured	1·40	1·40
703/6		Set of 4	3·00	3·00
		First Day Cover		3·75
		Presentation Pack	4·00	
		Souvenir Folder	12·00	
		Set of 4 Gutter Pairs	6·00	
MS707		100×70 mm. **671** £1 multicoloured	3·00	3·00
		First Day Cover		4·00
		Presentation Pack	4·00	

The souvenir folder contains Nos. 703/7, together with the stamps and miniature sheet in similar designs issued by Ireland.

Plate Nos.: 20p 1A, 1B (each ×4); 24p 1A (×4); 45p 1C (×4); 60p 1D (×4)

Sheets: 40 (2 panes 2×10)

Imprint: Right-hand corner, bottom margin

Withdrawn: 29.5.97

672 National Poppy Appeal Trophy

673 Manx War Memorial, Braddan

674 Poppy Appeal Collection Box

675 Royal British Legion Badge

75th Anniversary of Royal British Legion

(Des C. Abbott. Litho B.D.T.)

1996 (8 JUNE). Perf 14 (C)

708	**672**	20p multicoloured	65	55
709	**673**	24p multicoloured	70	60
710	**674**	42p multicoloured	1·10	1·20
711	**675**	75p multicoloured	2·00	2·00
708/11		Set of 4	4·00	4·00
		First Day Cover		4·25
		Presentation Pack	4·50	

Plate Nos.: 75p 1A, 1B, 1C (each ×4): others 1A (×4)

Sheets: 40 (8×5)

Imprint: Right-hand corner, bottom margin

Withdrawn: 7.6.97

'CAPEX '96' International Stamp Exhibition, Toronto

1996 (8 JUNE). No. **MS**683 additionally inscribed with 'CAPEX '96' exhibition logo on sheet margin.

MS712	100×71 mm. **647** £1.50, mult	6·00	6·50
	First Day Cover		8·00

Withdrawn: 31.7.97

676 U.N.I.C.E.F. Projects in Mexico

677 Projects in Sri Lanka

678 Projects in Colombia

679 Projects in Zambia

680 Projects in Afghanistan

681 Projects in Vietnam

50th Anniv of U.N.I.C.E.F.

(Des C. Abbott. Litho Enschedé)

1996 (18 SEPT). Perf 13½×14 (C)

713	**676**	24p multicoloured	50	30
		a. Horiz pair. Nos. 713/14	1·30	1·20
714	**677**	24p multicoloured	50	30
715	**678**	30p multicoloured	60	60
		a. Horiz pair. Nos. 715/16	1·60	1·60
716	**679**	30p multicoloured	60	60
717	**680**	42p multicoloured	80	80
		a. Horiz pair. Nos. 717/18	2·50	2·50
718	**681**	42p multicoloured	80	80
713/18		Set of 6	4·75	4·75
		First Day Cover		5·50
		Presentation Pack	5·25	

Plate Nos.: All values 1A, 1B (each ×4)

Sheets: 40 (10×4). The two designs for each value printed together, *se-tenant*, in horizontal pairs throughout the sheets

Imprint: Right-hand corner, bottom margin

Withdrawn: 17.9.97

682 Labrador

683 Border Collie

684 Dalmatian

685 Mongrel

686 English Setter

687 Alsatian

688 Dogs at Work
(*illustration reduced. Actual size 100×71 mm*)

Dogs

(Des Colleen Corlett. Litho Questa)

1996 (18 SEPT). Perf 13½×14 (No. **MS**725) or 14½ (others), both comb

719	**682**	20p multicoloured	60	55
		a. Booklet pane. No. 719×4 with margins all round	2·00	
720	**683**	24p multicoloured	70	65
		a. Booklet pane. No. 720×4 with margins all round	2·20	
721	**684**	31p multicoloured	1·00	90
		a. Booklet pane. Nos. 721/4 with margins all round	3·75	
722	**685**	38p multicoloured	1·10	1·10
723	**686**	43p multicoloured	1·50	1·50
724	**687**	63p multicoloured	2·00	2·00
719/24		Set of 6	6·25	6·25
		First Day Cover		6·50
		Presentation Pack	6·75	
MS725		100×71 mm. **688** £1.20, mult	3·75	3·75
		a. Booklet pane. As No. **MS**725, but with additional white margins all round separated by roulette	4·00	
		First Day Cover		4·25
		Presentation Pack	4·50	

Plate Nos.: All values 1A (×4)

Sheets: 10 (2×5)

Imprint: Left-hand corner, bottom margin

Withdrawn: 17.9.97

689 'Snowman and Pine Trees' (David Bennett)

690 'Three-legged Father Christmas' (Louis White)

691 'Family around Christmas Tree' (Robyn Whelan)

692 'Father Christmas in Sleigh' (Claire Bradley)

Christmas. Children's Paintings

(Adapted Colleen Corlett. Litho Walsall)

1996 (2 NOV). Perf 14×14½ (C)

726	**689**	19p multicoloured	55	50
727	**690**	23p multicoloured	70	65

728	**691**	50p multicoloured	. . . .	1·60	1·60
729	**692**	75p multicoloured	. . . .	2·10	2·20
726/9		Set of 4	. . . .	4·50	4·50
		First Day Cover	. . . .		4·50
		Presentation Pack	. . . .	5·00	

Plate Nos.: All values 1A, 1B (each ×4)

Sheets: 40 (5×8)

Imprint: Right-hand corner, bottom margin

Withdrawn: 1.11.97

Year Pack 1996

1996 (NOV). Comprises Nos. 552 and 672/729
Year Pack . . . . 45·00

Withdrawn: 30.11.98

Post Office Yearbook

1996 (NOV). Comprises Nos. 552 and 672/729
Yearbook . . . . 48·00

Withdrawn: 30.11.98

693 Primroses and
Cashtyl ny Ard

694 Lochtan Sheep
and Lambs

695 Daffodils,
Mallard and
Ducklings

696 Little Grebe with
Young and Frog
on Lily Pad

Spring in Man

(Des Colleen Corlett. Litho B.D.T.)

1997 (12 FEB). Perf 14 (C)

730	**693**	20p multicoloured	. . . .	50	50
731	**694**	24p multicoloured	. . . .	70	70
732	**695**	43p multicoloured	. . . .	1·10	1·10
733	**696**	63p multicoloured	. . . .	1·60	1·60
730/3		Set of 4	. . . .	3·50	3·50
		First Day Cover	. . . .		4·25
		Presentation Pack	. . . . . .	4·25	
		Set of 4 Gutter Pairs	. . . . . .	7·00	

Plate Nos.: All values 1A, 1B (each ×4)

Sheets: 40 (2 panes 5×4)

Imprint: Right-hand corner, bottom margin

Withdrawn: 11.2.98

697 Barn Owl

698 Short-eared Owl

699 Long-eared Owl

700 Little Owl

701 Snowy Owl

702 Eurasian Tawny Owl

703a Long-eared Owl
(illustration reduced. Actual size 100×71 mm)

Owls

(Des J. Paul. Litho B.D.T.)

1997 (12 FEB). Perf 13 (No. **MS**740) or 14 (others), both comb

734	**697**	20p multicoloured	65	60
		a. Booklet pane. No. 734×4		
		with margins all round	1·60	
735	**698**	24p multicoloured	80	75
		a. Booklet pane. No. 735×4		
		with margins all round	2·00	
736	**699**	31p multicoloured	1·00	90
		a. Booklet pane. Nos. 736/9		
		with margins all round	3·75	
737	**700**	36p multicoloured	1·20	1·10
738	**701**	43p multicoloured	1·40	1·50
739	**702**	56p multicoloured	1·60	1·70
734/9		Set of 6	6·00	6·00
		First Day Cover		6·50
		Presentation Pack	6·75	
		Stamp Cards (set of 6)	2·75	7·00
MS740		100×71 mm. **703a** £1.20, mult	4·00	4·25
		a. Booklet pane. As No.		
		MS740 but with additional		
		white margins all round		
		and with line of roulettes at		
		left	4·75	
		First Day Cover		5·50
		Presentation Pack	5·00	

No. **MS**740 includes the 'HONG KONG' '97' International Stamp Exhibition logo on the sheet margin.

Plate Nos.: All values 1A, 1B (each ×4)

Sheets: 10 (5×2)

Imprint: Bottom, right-hand margin

Withdrawn: 11.2.98

704 Moddey Dhoo, Peel Castle

705 Fairies in Tree and Cottage

706 Fairies at Fairy Bridge

707 Giant Finn Maccoil and Calf of Man

708 The Buggane of St. Trinian's

709 Fyonderee and Farm

Europa. Tales and Legends

(Des Colleen Corlett. Litho Enschedé)

1997 (24 APR). Perf 13½×14 (C)

741	**704**	21p multicoloured	55	55
742	**705**	25p multicoloured	65	65
743	**706**	31p multicoloured	85	85
744	**707**	36p multicoloured	1·10	1·10
745	**708**	37p multicoloured	1·10	1·10
746	**709**	43p multicoloured	1·40	1·40
741/6		Set of 6	5·00	5·00
		First Day Cover		5·50
		Presentation Pack	5·75	

Nos. 742/3 include the 'EUROPA' emblem.

Plate Nos.: All values 1A, 1B, 1C, 1D (each ×4)

Sheets: 10 (2×5)

Withdrawn: 23.4.98

710 Sopwith Tabloid

711 Grumman Tiger (1996 Schneider Trophy)

712 BAe ATP (15th anniv of Manx Airlines)

713 BAe 146-200 (15th anniv of Manx Airlines)

714 Boeing 757-200 (largest aircraft to land on Isle of Man)

715 Farman Biplane (1st Manx flight, 1911)

716 Supermarine Spitfire   **717** Hawker Hurricane

Manx Aircraft

(Des R. Carter. Litho Questa)

1997 (24 APR). Perf 14 (C)

747	**710**	21p multicoloured	30	25
		a. Horiz pair. Nos. 747/8	90	90
748	**711**	21p multicoloured	30	25
749	**712**	25p multicoloured	35	25
		a. Horiz pair. Nos. 749/50	1·10	1·10
750	**713**	25p multicoloured	35	25
751	**714**	31p multicoloured	70	35
		a. Horiz pair. Nos. 751/2	1·50	1·50
752	**715**	31p multicoloured	70	35
753	**716**	36p multicoloured	75	40
		a. Horiz pair. Nos. 753/4	1·70	1·70
754	**717**	36p multicoloured	75	40
747/54		Set of 8	5·00	5·00
		First Day Cover		5·50
		Presentation Pack	6·00	
		Souvenir Folder (complete sheets)	20·00	

No. 752 is inscribed 'EARMAN' in error.

Plate Nos.: All values 1A (×4)

Sheets: 8 (2×4) the two designs for each value printed together, se-tenant, in horizontal pairs throughout the sheets, the backgrounds forming composite designs

Withdrawn: 23.4.98

718 14th Hole, Ramsey Golf Club

719 15th Hole, King Edward Bay Golf and Country Club

720 17th Hole, Rowany Golf Club

721 8th Hole, Castletown Golf Links

722a Golf Ball
(illustration reduced. Actual size 100×71 mm)

Golf

(Des D. Swinton. Litho Questa)

1997 (29 MAY). Perf 14 (C)

755	**718**	21p multicoloured	50	50
		a. Booklet pane. No. 755×3 with margins all round	1·70	
756	**719**	25p multicoloured	60	60
		a. Booklet pane. No. 756×3 with margins all round	2·00	
757	**720**	43p multicoloured	1·10	1·10
		a. Booklet pane. Nos. 757/8 each ×2 with margins all round	4·25	
758	**721**	50p multicoloured	1·50	1·50
755/8		Set of 4	3·25	3·25
		First Day Cover		4·00
		Presentation Pack	4·00	
		Set of 4 Gutter Pairs	6·50	
MS759		100×71 mm. **722a** £1.30, mult	3·50	3·50
		a. Booklet pane. As No. **MS**759, but with additional white margins all round	4·00	
		First Day Cover		3·75
		Presentation Pack	3·75	

No. **MS**759 includes the 'PACIFIC 97' International Stamp Exhibition logo on the sheet margin.

Plate Nos.: All values 1A, 1B (each ×4)

Sheets: 40 (2 panes 5×4)

Imprint: Right-hand corner, bottom margin of each pane

Withdrawn: 28.5.98

723a Royal Yacht *Britannia*
(*illustration reduced. Actual size 130×90 mm*)

Return of Hong Kong to China

(Litho Walsall)

1997 (1 JULY). *Sheet 130×90 mm containing stamp as No. 546 with changed imprint date. Wmk Mult Crown CA Diagonal.* Perf 13×13½ (C)

MS760 **723a** 23p multicoloured .... 1·40   1·60

Withdrawn: 30.6.98

724 Steve Colley

725 Steve Saunders

726 Sammy Miller

727 Don Smith

F.I.M. 'Trial des Nations' Motorcycle Team Trials

(Des R. Organ. Litho Cartor)

1997 (17 SEPT). Perf 13½ (C)

761	**724**	21p multicoloured	55	50
762	**725**	25p multicoloured	65	60
763	**726**	37p multicoloured	1·20	1·00
764	**727**	44p multicoloured	1·50	1·20
761/4		*Set of 4*	3·50	3·00
		First Day Cover		4·00
		Presentation Pack	4·50	
		Set of 4 Gutter Pairs	7·00	

Plate Nos.: All values 1A, 1B (each ×4)

Sheets: 40 (2 panes 5×4) 21p, 44p; (2 panes 4×5) 25p, 37p

Imprint: Central, gutter margin

Withdrawn: 16.9.98

728 Angel and Shepherd

729 Angel and King

730 The Nativity

Christmas

(Des Jennifer Toombs. Litho B.D.T.)

1997 (3 NOV). Perf 14 (C)

765	**728**	20p multicoloured	65	55
766	**729**	24p multicoloured	75	70
767	**730**	63p multicoloured	1·80	1·80
765/7		*Set of 3*	3·00	3·00
		First Day Cover		3·00
		Presentation Pack	3·50	

Plate Nos.: 20p, 24p 1A (×5); 63p 1A, 1B (each ×5)

Sheets: 40 (8×5) 20p, 24p; 20 (4×5) 63p

Imprint: Central, left-hand margin

Withdrawn: 2.11.98

731 Engagement of
Princess Elizabeth
and Lieut. Philip
Mountbatten, 1947

732 Wedding Photograph,
1947

733 At Ascot, 1952

734 Golden Wedding
Photograph, 1997

735a Queen Elizabeth and Prince Philip at Peel, 1989

Golden Wedding of Queen Elizabeth and Prince Philip

(Des Colleen Corlett. Litho and die-stamped Questa)

1997 (3 NOV). Perf 14 (No. **MS**772) or 14×14½, both comb

768	**731**	50p sepia and gold	1·00	1·00
		a. Strip of 4. Nos. 768/71	5·00	5·00
769	**732**	50p multicoloured	1·00	1·00
770	**733**	50p multicoloured	1·00	1·00
771	**734**	50p multicoloured	1·00	1·00
768/71		Set of 4	5·00	5·00
		First Day Cover		5·50
		Presentation Pack	5·50	
		Souvenir Folder (complete sheet and **MS**772)	21·00	
MS772		100×72 mm. **735a** £1 multicoloured	3·00	3·00
		First Day Cover		3·50

Plate Nos.: 1A (×5)

Sheets: 16 (4×4). Nos. 768/71 were printed together, *se-tenant*, as
horizontal or vertical strips of 4 throughout the sheets

Imprint: Right-hand corner, bottom margin

Withdrawn: 2.11.98

Year Pack 1997

1997 (3 NOV). *Comprises Nos.* 730/72
Year Pack . . . . 37·00

Withdrawn: 30.11.98

Post Office Yearbook

1997 (3 NOV). *Comprises Nos.* 730/72
Yearbook . . . . 40·00

Sold out: By 8.2001

736 Bearded Iris

737 Daisy

738 Shamrock

739 Silver Jubilee
Rose

740 Oriental
Poppy

741 Heath
Spotted
Orchid

742 Cushag

743 Gorse

744 Princess of
Wales Rose

227

745 Dog Rose

746 Fuchsia 'Lady Thumb'

747 Daffodil

748 Spear Thistle

753 Queen Elizabeth II and Queen Elizabeth the Queen Mother

Two Types of 4p:—
   I. 'WSP' imprint aligns with 'N' of 'MAN' (sheet stamps and 1998 booklet)
   II. 'WSP' ends to right of 'N' of 'MAN' (1999 booklet)

Flowers

(Des Colleen Corlett (1p to £1). Litho Cartor (£2.50), Walsall (others))

1998 (12 FEB)–**99**. Perf 13 (1p, 2p, 10p, 20p, 30p) or 13×13½ (others), both comb

773	**736**	1p multicoloured (b)		10	10
774	**737**	2p multicoloured (b)		10	10
775	**738**	4p multicoloured (I) (a)		10	10
		a. Booklet pane. Nos. 775, 779 and 781, each ×2 (a)	4·00		
		b. Type II (c)		50	60
		ba. Booklet pane. Nos. 775b×2, 780×3 and 782 (c)	3·00		
776	**739**	5p multicoloured (c)		10	15
777	**740**	10p multicoloured (b)		20	25
778	**741**	20p multicoloured (b)		40	30
779	**742**	21p multicoloured (a)		40	45
780	**743**	22p multicoloured (c)		45	50
781	**744**	25p multicoloured (a)		50	40
782	**745**	26p multicoloured (c)		50	40
783	**746**	30p multicoloured (b)		60	60
784	**747**	50p multicoloured (a)		1·00	1·00
785	**748**	£1 multicoloured (a)		2·00	2·00
790	**753**	£2·50 multicoloured (b)		5·00	4·75
773/90		Set of 14		10·50	10·00
		First Day Covers (4)			13·50
		Presentation Packs (4)	13·50		
		Souvenir Folder (Nos. 773/85)	8·00		
		Gutter Pair (No. 790)	10·00		

Printings: (a) 12.2.98. Inscribed '1998'; (b) 2.7.98. Inscribed '1998'; (c) 26.4.99. Inscribed '1999'

Plate Nos.: 4p, 21p, 25p, 50p, £1, £2.50 1A, 1B (each ×4); others 1A (×4)

Sheets: 40 (2 panes 5×4) £2.50, 50 (10×5) (others). In addition to stamp booklets Nos. 775a and 775ba also come from separate special booklet sheets of 36 (6×5), each containing five strips

Imprint: Central, bottom margin

756 Viking Figurehead

757 Viking Longship at Sea

758 Viking Longship on Beach

759 Stern of Ship

760a Viking Ship at Peel Castle
(*illustration reduced. Actual size* 100×71 *mm*)

Viking Longships

(Des A. Bell. Litho B.D.T.)

1998 (14 FEB). Perf 14 (C)

793	**756**	21p multicoloured		55	50
794	**757**	25p multicoloured		75	75
795	**758**	31p multicoloured		90	90
796	**759**	75p multicoloured		2·20	2·50

793/6		Set of 4	4·00	4·25
		First Day Cover		4·25
		Presentation Pack	5·00	
		Set of 4 Gutter Pairs	8·00	
MS797	100×71 mm. **760a** £1 multicoloured		3·00	3·00
		First Day Cover		4·50
		Presentation Pack	4·75	

Plate Nos.: All values 1A, 1B (each ×4)
Sheets: 40 (2 panes 4×5)
Imprint: Central, right-hand margin
Withdrawn: 13.2.99

761 Bottle-nosed Dolphins   762 Basking Shark

763 Front View of Basking   764 Minke Whale
Shark

765 Killer Whale and Calf

U.N.E.S.C.O. International Year of the Ocean

(Des J. Paul. Litho Questa)

1998 (14 MAR). Perf 14 (C)

798	**761**	10p multicoloured	30	30
		a. Booklet pane. Nos. 798/9,		
		each ×3 and 3 labels with		
		margins all round	2·75	
		b. Booklet pane. Nos. 798/9		
		and 800/2, each ×2, and 1		
		central label with margins		
		all round	7·00	
799	**762**	21p multicoloured	50	50
800	**763**	25p multicoloured	65	65
801	**764**	31p multicoloured	75	75
802	**765**	63p multicoloured	1·60	1·60
798/802		Set of 5	3·50	3·50
		First Day Cover		4·25
		Presentation Pack	5·00	
		Souvenir Folder	25·00	
		Stamp Cards (set of 5)	3·00	6·00

Plate Nos.: All values 1A, 1B (each ×4)
Sheets: 10 (2×5)
Withdrawn: 13.3.99

766 Locomotive No. 12   767 Locomotive No. 10
Hutchinson   G. H. Wood

768 Locomotive No. 11   769 Locomotive No. 4 Loch
Maitland

770a Pillar Box and Train at Douglas Station (25p);
Locomotive No. 1 Sutherland (£1)
(illustration reduced. Actual size 120×54 mm)

125th Anniversary of Isle of Man Steam Railway

(Des A. Peck. Litho Questa)

1998 (2 MAY). Perf 14½×14 (C)

803	**766**	21p multicoloured	60	50
		a. Booklet pane. Nos. 803/6		
		with margins all round	3·50	
804	**767**	25p multicoloured	70	60
805	**768**	31p multicoloured	90	80
806	**769**	63p multicoloured	1·60	1·60
803/6		Set of 4	3·50	3·25
		First Day Cover		3·50
		Presentation Pack	4·00	
		Souvenir Folder .... 25·00		
MS807	199×54 mm. **770a** 25p mult; £1 mult		3·00	3·00
		a. Booklet pane. As No. **MS**807,		
		but with additional margins		
		showing diagram all round ..	3·00	
		First Day Cover		3·50
		Presentation Pack	4·00	

Booklet pane No. 803a exists in two versions, which differ
in the order of the stamps within the block of four.

Plate Nos.: All values 1A (×4)
Sheets: 40 (5×8)
Imprints: Right-hand corner, bottom margin
Withdrawn: 31.5.99

771 Purple Helmets Display Team

772 Joey Dunlop

773 Dave Molyneux

774 Naomi Taniguchi

775 Mike Hailwood

Isle of Man T.T. Races and 50th Anniversary of Honda (motorcycle manufacturer)

(Des The Agency. Litho B.D.T.)

1998 (1 JUNE). Perf 14 (C)

808	**771**	21p multicoloured	40	45
809	**772**	25p multicoloured	50	55
810	**773**	31p multicoloured	65	65
811	**774**	43p multicoloured	1·00	1·00
812	**775**	63p multicoloured	1·40	1·50
808/12		Set of 5	3·50	3·75
		First Day Cover		4·50
		Presentation Pack	4·50	
		Souvenir Folder	20·00	
		Set of 5 Gutter Pairs	7·00	

Plate Nos.: All values 1A (×4)

Sheets: 40 (2 panes 5×4 with double gutter)

Withdrawn: 31.5.99

776 Princess Diana wearing Protective Clothing, Angola

777 Receiving Award from United Cerebral Palsy Charity, New York, 1995

778 With Children, South Korea, 1992

779 Wearing Blue Jacket, July 1993

Diana, Princess of Wales Commemoration

(Litho Cartor)

1998 (19 JUNE). Perf 13½×13 (C)

813	**776**	25p multicoloured	50	30
		a. Strip of 4. Nos. 813/16	2·50	2·50
814	**777**	25p multicoloured	50	30
815	**778**	25p multicoloured	50	30
816	**779**	25p multicoloured	50	30
813/16		Set of 4	2·50	2·50
		First Day Cover		3·00
		Presentation Pack	3·00	
		Souvenir Folder	20·00	

Plate Nos.: 1A (×4)

Sheets: 16 (4×4). Nos. 813/16 were printed together, se-tenant, as horizontal or vertical strips of 4 throughout the sheet

Withdrawn: 18.6.99

780 Tynwald Day Ceremony

781 Traditional Dancers, Tynwald Fair

Europa. Festivals

(Des M. Thompson. Litho Cartor)

1998 (2 JULY). Perf 13×13½ (C)

817	**780**	25p multicoloured	50	45
818	**781**	30p multicoloured	1·10	1·20
817/18		Set of 2	1·50	1·50
		First Day Cover		2·00
		Presentation Pack	2·20	

Plate Nos.: Both values 1A (×4)

Sheets: 10 (2×5)

Withdrawn: 30.10.99

782 Father Christmas at North Pole

783 Father Christmas checking List

784 Flying over Spring Valley Sorting Office

785 Passing through Baldrine Village

786 Father Christmas delivering Presents

Christmas. 'A Very Special Delivery'

(Des A. Bell. Litho Enschedé)

1998 (25 Sept). Perf 14½×14 (C)

819	**782**	20p multicoloured	40	30
820	**783**	24p multicoloured	50	45
821	**784**	30p multicoloured	75	75
822	**785**	43p multicoloured	95	95
823	**786**	63p multicoloured	1·40	1·40
819/23		Set of 5	3·75	3·75
		First Day Cover		4·50
		Presentation Pack	4·50	
		Set of 5 Gutter Pairs	7·50	

Plate Nos.: All values 1A (×4)

Sheets: 40 (2 panes 5×4)

Imprint: Right-hand corner, bottom margin

Withdrawn: 30.10.99

Year Pack 1998

1998 (25 SEPT). Comprises Nos. 773/823
               Year Pack . . . . 36·00

Sold out: 9.99

Post Office Yearbook

1998 (25 SEPT). Comprises Nos. 773/823
               Yearbook . . . . 38·00

Sold out: 8.2000

787 Large Oval Pillar Box, Kirk Onchan

788 Wall Box, Ballaterson

789 King Edward VII Pillar Box, Laxey Station

790 Wall Box, Spaldrick

791 Small Oval Pillar Box, Derby Road, Douglas

792 Wall Box, Baldrine Station

Local Post Boxes

(Des The Agency. Litho Walsall)

1999 (4 MAR). Perf 14 (C)

824	**787**	10p multicoloured	25	25
825	**788**	20p multicoloured	45	45
826	**789**	21p multicoloured	50	50
827	**790**	25p multicoloured	85	85
828	**791**	44p multicoloured	1·50	1·50
829	**792**	63p multicoloured	1·75	1·75
824/9		Set of 6	4·50	4·50
		First Day Cover		5·00
		Presentation Pack	5·50	
		Set of 6 Gutter Pairs	9·00	

Plate Nos.: All values 1A, 1B (each ×4)

Sheets: 50 (2 panes 5×5)

Imprint: Right-hand corner, bottom margin

Withdrawn: 3.3.2000

793 Cottage, Ballaglass Glen

794 Glen Maye Waterfall

Europa. Parks and Gardens

(Des Julia Ashby-Smyth. Litho B.D.T.)

1999 (4 MAR). Perf 14 (C)

830	**793**	25p multicoloured	50	50
831	**794**	30p multicoloured	75	80
830/1		Set of 2	1·20	1·30
		First Day Cover		2·00
		Presentation Pack	2·00	

Plate Nos.: Both values 1A, 1B (each ×4)

Sheets: 10 (5×2)

Withdrawn: 3.3.2000

795 Ann and James Ritchie, Ramsey

796 Sir William Hillary, Douglas

797 Ruby Clery, Peel

798 Herbert and Edith (inshore lifeboat), Port Erin

799 1974 150th Anniversary 8p Stamp

800 Gough Ritchie II, Port St. Mary

801 1991 Manx Lifeboats 21p Stamp

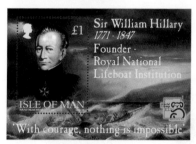

802a Sir William Hillary (founder)
(illustration reduced. Actual size 100×70 mm)

175th Anniversary of Royal National Lifeboat Institution

(Des Mainstream Media (No. **MS**839), R. Tomlinson (others). Litho Questa)

1999 (4 MAR). Perf 13½×14 (No. **MS**839) or 14, both comb

832	**795**	21p multicoloured	50	50
		a. Booklet pane. Nos. 832/5 and 837, plus four printed labels, with margins all round	4·00	
		b. Booklet pane. Nos. 832/4, 836 and 838, plus four printed labels, with margins all round	5·00	
833	**796**	25p multicoloured	55	55
834	**797**	37p multicoloured	80	80
835	**798**	43p multicoloured	90	90
836	**799**	43p multicoloured	1·00	1·00
837	**800**	56p multicoloured	1·20	1·20
838	**801**	56p multicoloured	1·50	1·50
832/8		Set of 7	4·00	4·00
		First Day Cover (Nos. 832/5, 837)		4·50
		Presentation Pack (Nos. 832/5, 837)	5·00	
		Set of 5 Gutter Pairs (Nos. 832/5, 837)	8·00	

MS839   100×70 mm. **802a** £1 multicoloured   4·00   4·00
 a. *Booklet pane. As No.* **MS**839,
  but with additional margins
  showing lifeboats all round .   3·50
  First Day Cover . . . .   4·50
  Presentation Pack . . . .   5·00

Nos. 836 and 838 were available in £4.64 stamp booklets or as a single pane (with no stitch holes), obtainable from the Philatelic Bureau.

No. 832*b* includes an 'iBRA' Stamp Exhibition label and No. **MS**839 the 'Australia '99' World Stamp Exhibition emblem on the sheet margin.

Plate Nos.: All values 1A (×4)

Sheets: 40 (2 panes 5×4)

Withdrawn: 3.3.2000

803 Winter

805 Summer

804 Spring

806 Autumn

Centenary of Yn Cheshaght Ghailckagh (Manx Gaelic Society). The Seasons

(Des C. Alexander. Litho Walsall)

1999 (11 MAY). Perf 14½×14 (C)

840	**803**	22p multicoloured	60	60
841	**804**	26p multicoloured	65	65
842	**805**	50p multicoloured	1·10	1·10
843	**806**	63p multicoloured	1·60	1·60
840/3		*Set of 4*	3·50	3·50
		First Day Cover		4·25
		Presentation Pack	4·50	
		Set of 4 Gutter Pairs	7·00	

Nos. 840/3 are inscribed 'Ellan Vannin', the Manx name for the Isle of Man.

Plate Nos.: All values 1A, 1B (each ×4)

Sheets: 50 (2 panes 5×5)

Imprint: Right-hand corner, bottom margin

Withdrawn: 10.5.2000

807a Queen Victoria; King Edward VII; King George V; King Edward VIII; King George VI; Queen Elizabeth II (*illustration reduced. Actual size* 170×75 *mm*)

British Monarchs of the 20th Century

(Des Colleen Corlett. Litho Walsall)

1999 (2 JUNE). *Sheet* 170×75 *mm.* Perf 14 (C)

MS844	**807a**	26p×6, multicoloured	4·00	4·00
		First Day Cover		5·00
		Presentation Pack	5·00	
		Souvenir Folder (*Nos.* 824/9,		
		MS844)	25·00	

Withdrawn: 1.6.2000

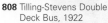

808 Tilling-Stevens Double Deck Bus, 1922

809 Thornycroft BC Single Deck, 1928

810 Cumberland ADC 416 Single Deck, 1927

811 Straker-Squire Single Deck, 1914

812 Thornycroft A2 Single Deck, 1927

813 Leyland Lion LT9 Single Deck, 1938

Manx Buses

(Des P. Hearsey. Litho B.D.T.)

1999 (18 JUNE). Perf 14 (C)

845	**808**	22p multicoloured	50	50
		a. Booklet pane. Nos. 845/6 and 847×2, with margins all round	2·50	
		b. Booklet pane. Nos. 845/6 and 848×2, with margins all round	3·50	
		c. Booklet pane. Nos. 845/6 and 849×2, with margins all round	4·00	
		d. Booklet pane. Nos. 845/6 and 850×2, with margins all round	4·50	
846	**809**	26p multicoloured	55	55
847	**810**	28p multicoloured	65	65
848	**811**	37p multicoloured	1·00	1·00
849	**812**	38p multicoloured	1·20	1·20
850	**813**	40p multicoloured	1·50	1·50
845/50		Set of 6	4·00	4·00
		First Day Cover		4·50
		Presentation Pack	4·50	
		Stamp Cards (set of 6)	3·00	7·50

Plate Nos.: All values 1A (×4)

Sheets: 25 (5×5)

Imprint: Central, bottom margin

Withdrawn: 17.6.2000

814 Miss Sophie Rhys-Jones

815 Leaving St. George's Chapel, Windsor

816 Prince Edward

817 Miss Sophie Rhys-Jones and Prince Edward

818 In Landau

Royal Wedding

(Des Catherine James. Litho B.D.T.)

1999 (19 JUNE–1 SEPT). Perf 14 (C)

851	**814**	22p multicoloured (a)	55	55
852	**815**	26p multicoloured (b)	55	55
853	**816**	39p multicoloured (a)	80	80
854	**817**	44p multicoloured (a)	1·10	1·10
855	**818**	53p multicoloured (b)	1·20	1·20
851/5		Set of 5	3·75	3·75
		First Day Covers (2)		5·00
		Presentation Pack	4·50	

Printings: (a) 19.6.99; (b) 1.9.99

Plate Nos.: All values 1A, 1B (each ×4)

Sheets: 25 (5×5)

Imprint: Central, bottom margin

Withdrawn: 31.8.2000

'PhilexFrance 99' International Stamp Exhibition, Paris

1999 (2 JULY). No. **MS**807 additionally inscribed with 'PhilexFrance' exhibition logo on sheet margin.

MS856 119×54 mm. **770a** 25p mult; £1 mult 7·00 7·00

Withdrawn: 1.7.2000

819 St. Luke's Church, Baldwin

820 St. Mark's Chapel, Malew

821 St. German's Parish Church and Cathedral, Peel

822 Kirk Christ Church, Rushen

Christmas. Churches

(Des N. Sayle. Litho Cartor)

1999 (22 SEPT). Perf 13½ (C)

857	**819**	21p multicoloured	45	45
858	**820**	25p multicoloured	60	60
859	**821**	30p multicoloured	70	70
860	**822**	64p multicoloured	1·50	1·50
857/60		*Set of 4*	3·00	3·00
		First Day Cover		4·00
		Presentation Pack	4·50	
		Set of 4 Gutter Pairs	6·00	

Plate Nos.: All values 1A (×4)
Sheets: 40 (2 panes 4×5)
Imprint: Central, bottom margin
Withdrawn: 21.9.2000

823 'Massachusetts', 1967   **824** 'Words', 1968

825 'I've Gotta Get a Message to You', 1968   **826** 'Ellan Vannin', 1998

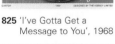

827 'You Win Again', 1987   **828** 'Night Fever', 1978

829a 'Immortality', 1998
(*illustration reduced. Actual size* 119×108 *mm*)

830a 'Stayin' Alive', 1978
(*illustration reduced. Actual size* 119×108 *mm*)

Legends of Music. The Bee Gees (pop group)

(Des The Agency. Litho Cartor (Nos. 861/6), Walsall (No. **MS**867))

1999 (12 OCT). Perf 15 (No. **MS**867) or 13½, both comb

861	**823**	22p multicoloured	60	50
862	**824**	26p multicoloured	70	65
863	**825**	29p multicoloured	75	75
864	**826**	37p multicoloured	90	90
865	**827**	38p multicoloured	90	90
866	**828**	66p multicoloured	1·50	1·70
861/6		*Set of 6*	4·75	5·00
		First Day Cover		5·50
		Presentation Pack	6·00	
		Souvenir Folder (complete sheets)	45·00	

MS867 Two sheets, each 119×108 mm. (a)
829a 60p multicoloured (*circular, 40 mm diam*). (b) **830a** 90p multicoloured, (*circular 40 mm diam*)

Set of 2 sheets	8·00	8·50
First Day Cover		20·00

Sheets: 9 stamps and three labels, arranged 3×4, with the labels in the third horizontal row

Withdrawn: 11.10.2000

Year Pack 1999

1999 (12 OCT). *Comprises Nos.* 776, 780, 782, 824/35, 837 *and* 840/67

Year Pack .... 50·00

Withdrawn: 2.8.2001

Post Office Yearbook

1999 (12 OCT). *Comprises Nos.* 776, 780, 782, 824/35, 837 *and* **MS**839/67

Yearbook .... 58·00

Sold out: 8.2000

831a Sky at Sunset over Calf of Man (50p); Sky at Dawn over Maughold Head (50p); Constellations over Man at Start of New Millennium (£2)
(*illustration reduced. Actual size 169×74 mm*)

New Millennium

(Des H. Parkin and R. Berry. Litho Questa)

1999 (31 DEC). *Sheet* 169×74 mm. Perf 14½ (C)

MS868	**831a**	50p, 50p, £2 multicoloured	8·00	8·00
		First Day Cover		9·00
		Presentation Pack		9·00

The first day cover has three cancellations, one on each stamp, running in a two minute sequence from 23.59 on 31 Dec 99 to 00.01 on 01 Jan 00.

Withdrawn: 30.12.2000

832 Harrison's Chrono-meter, 1735, and Map

833 Daniel's Chrono-meter, 2000, and Clock Face

834 Harrison's Chrono-meter, 1767, Map and Clock

835 Mudge's Chrono-meter, 1769, and Steam Locomotives

836 Arnold's Chrono-meter, 1779, and Map of Africa

837 Earnshaw's Chrono-meter, 1780, and Map of Caribbean

'The Story of Time'

(Des E. Cassidy. Litho Cartor)

2000 (24 JAN). Perf 13×13½ (C)

869	**832**	22p multicoloured	50	55
870	**833**	26p multicoloured	55	60
871	**834**	29p multicoloured	65	70
872	**835**	34p multicoloured	90	90

873	**836**	38p multicoloured	1·20	1·20
874	**837**	44p multicoloured	1·50	1·50
869/74		Set of 6	5·00	5·00
		First Day Cover		5·50
		Presentation Pack	5·50	

Plate Nos.: 29p, 38p 1A, 1B (each ×4); others 1A (×4)

Sheets: 25 (5×5)

Imprint: Top left-hand margin and bottom right-hand margin

Withdrawn: 23.1.2001

838 Duke and Duchess of York on Wedding Day, 1923

839 Queen Elizabeth with Princess Elizabeth, 1940

840 King George VI and Queen Elizabeth visiting Troops, 1944

841 Queen Mother and Queen Elizabeth, 1954

842 Queen Mother with Prince Charles, 1985

843 Queen Mother, 1988

844a Queen Mother visiting Isle of Man

'Queen Elizabeth the Queen Mother's Century'

(Des E.D.L. Litho B.D.T.)

2000 (29 FEB). Perf 14 (C)

875	**838**	22p multicoloured	50	55
		a. Horiz strip of 3. Nos. 875/7 .	2·00	2·00
876	**839**	26p sepia and black	55	60
877	**840**	30p sepia and black	65	70
878	**841**	44p multicoloured	95	80
		a. Horiz strip of 3. Nos. 878/80	3·50	3·50
879	**842**	52p multicoloured	1·00	1·00
880	**843**	64p multicoloured	1·10	1·10
875/80		Set of 6	5·00	5·00
		First Day Cover		5·75
		Presentation Pack	5·50	
		Souvenir Folder (complete sheets and **MS**881)	21·00	
MS881		100×70 mm. **844a** £1 multicoloured	2·50	2·50
		First Day Cover		3·00
		Presentation Pack	3·00	

Plate Nos.: All values 1A (×4)

Sheets: 12 (3×4). Nos. 875/7 and 878/80 were each printed together, *se-tenant*, as horizontal strips of 3 throughout the sheets

Withdrawn: 28.2.2001

845 Barn Swallow

846 Spotted Flycatcher

847 Eurasian Sky Lark

848 Yellowhammer

Endangered Species. Song Birds

(Des Catherine James. Litho Walsall)

2000 (5 MAY). Perf 14½ (C)

882	**845**	22p multicoloured	50	55
		a. Strip of 4. Nos. 882/5	4·50	4·50
883	**846**	26p multicoloured	55	60
884	**847**	64p multicoloured	80	80
885	**848**	77p multicoloured	1·00	1·00
882/5		Set of 4	4·50	4·50
		First Day Cover		5·50
		Presentation Pack	6·00	

Plate Nos.: All values 1A (×4)

Sheets: 20 (4×5). Nos. 882/5 were printed together, *se-tenant*, both horizontally and vertically, within the sheets

Withdrawn: 4.5.2001

'The Stamp Show 2000' International Stamp Exhibition, London

2000 (22 May). *As No.* **MS**881, *but with 'The Stamp Show 2000' multicoloured logo added to the bottom sheet margin.* Perf 14 (C)

MS886 100×70 mm. **844a** £1 multicoloured   5·00   5·00

Withdrawn: 21.5.2001

849 Lieut. John Quilliam and Admiral Lord Nelson, Battle of Trafalgar

850 Ensign Caesar Bacon and Duke of Wellington, Battle of Waterloo

851 Col. Thomas Leigh Goldie and Earl of Cardigan, Crimea

852 Bugler John Dunne and Sir Robert Baden-Powell, Boer War

853 George Kneale and Viscount Kitchener of Khartoum, First World War

854 First Officer Alan Watterson and Sir Winston Churchill, Second World War

855a Two Supermarine Spitfires (60p); Spitfire on Ground, Battle of Britain (60p)
(*illustration reduced. Actual size 170×75 mm*)

Isle of Man at War

(Des P. Hannon (Nos. 887/92), P. Hearsey (No. **MS**893). Litho B.D.T.)

2000 (22 MAY). Perf 15×14 (No. **MS**893) or 13, both comb

887	**849**	22p multicoloured	50	55
		a. Booklet pane. Nos. 887/91	4·75	
		b. Booklet pane. Nos. 887 and 890/2	5·00	
888	**850**	26p multicoloured	55	60
889	**851**	36p multicoloured	75	80
890	**852**	48p multicoloured	1·00	1·10
891	**853**	50p multicoloured	1·10	1·20
892	**854**	77p multicoloured	1·50	1·60
887/92		Set of 6	4·75	5·25
		First Day Cover		6·00
		Presentation Pack	6·00	

MS893   170×75 mm. **855a** 60p multicoloured; 60p multicoloured   2·75   2·75

a. Booklet pane. As No. **MS**893, but with line of roulettes at left   2·75

First Day Cover   3·50

Presentation Pack   3·50

Plate Nos.: All values A1 (×4)

Sheets: 8 (2×4). Nos. 887/8, 889/90 and 891/2 were each printed in sheets containing vertical strips of the two designs separated by a gutter margin

Imprint: Lower left-hand margin

Withdrawn: 21.5.2001

856a Prince William as a Child (22p); With Queen Mother (26p); As a teenager (45p); With Prince Charles and Prince Harry (52p); Wearing ski-suit (56p)
(*illustration reduced. Actual size 170×75 mm*)

18th Birthday of Prince William

(Des The Agency. Litho B.D.T.)

2000 (21 JUNE). *Sheet* 170×75 mm. Perf 14 (C)

MS894 **856a** 22p, 26p, 45p, 52p, 56p multicoloured   4·50   4·50

First Day Cover   5·25

Presentation Pack   5·25

Withdrawn: 20.6.2001

857 Ballet Shoes and Painted Ceiling

858 Comedy Mask and Box Decoration

859 Drama Mask and Statue

860 Pantomime Dame with Wig and Mosaic

861 Opera Glasses and Decoration

862 Top Hat with Cane and Painted Ceiling

Centenary of Gaiety Theatre, Douglas

(Des The Agency. Litho B.D.T.)

2000 (16 JULY). Perf 14 (C)

895	**857**	22p multicoloured	50	55
896	**858**	26p multicoloured	55	60
897	**859**	36p multicoloured	75	80
898	**860**	45p multicoloured	95	1·00
899	**861**	52p multicoloured	1·10	1·20
900	**862**	65p multicoloured	1·40	1·50
895/900		Set of 6	4·75	5·25
		First Day Cover		6·25
		Presentation Pack	6·25	
		Stamp Cards (set of 6)	3·50	9·50

Plate Nos.: All values 1A (×4)

Sheets: 20 (4×5) with enlarged illustrated margin at left

Imprint: Central, right-hand margin

Withdrawn: 14.7.2001

863 Map of Great Britain, Union Jack and Liner

864 Sydney Opera House, Australian Flag and Map

865 New Zealand Map and Flag

866 Map of Buenos Aires and Waterfront

867 U.S. Flag, Map of Boston and Harbour

868 South African Flag, Map and Table Mountain

'BT Global Challenge' Round the World Yacht Race

(Des The Agency. Litho Cartor)

2000 (10 SEPT). Perf 13½ (C)

901	**863**	22p multicoloured	50	55
902	**864**	26p multicoloured	55	60
903	**865**	36p multicoloured	75	80
904	**866**	40p multicoloured	85	90
905	**867**	44p multicoloured	95	1·00
906	**868**	65p multicoloured	1·40	1·50
901/6		Set of 6	4·50	4·75
		First Day Cover		5·75
		Presentation Pack	5·75	
		Set of 6 Gutter Pairs	9·00	

Plate Nos.: All values 1A (×4)

Sheets: 40 (2 panes 2×10)

Imprint: Centre, side margins

Withdrawn: 8.9.2001

869 Sailing and Holiday Tours Poster, 1925

870 'Isle of Man for Happy Holidays'

871 Woman in Swimsuit standing on Isle of Man, 1929

872 Stewardess and Ferry

873 'Isle of Man for Holidays 1931' and Ferry

170th Anniversary of Steam Packet Company. Tourism Posters

(Litho Cartor)

2000 (6 OCT). Perf 13½ (C)

907	**869**	22p multicoloured	50	55
908	**870**	26p multicoloured	55	60
909	**871**	36p multicoloured	75	80
910	**872**	45p multicoloured	1·50	1·50
911	**873**	65p multicoloured	1·90	2·00
907/11		*Set of* 5	4·75	5·00
		First Day Cover		5·00
		Presentation Pack	5·00	

Plate Nos.: All values 1A (×4)

Sheets: 20 (5×4)

Imprint: Centre, side margins

Withdrawn: 5.10.2001

874 Girl with Christingle Candle

875 Children dancing around Christmas Tree

876 'Building Europe'

877 Girl hugging Teddy Bear

878 Children with Stars

Christmas and Europa

(Des R. Wetherall (36p after J.-P. Cousin). Litho Questa)

2000 (7 NOV). Perf 14 (C)

912	**874**	21p multicoloured	45	50
913	**875**	25p multicoloured	55	60
914	**876**	36p multicoloured	75	80
		a. Sheetlet of 10	7·50	
915	**877**	45p multicoloured	1·50	1·50
916	**878**	65p multicoloured	1·90	2·00
912/16		*Set of* 5	4·75	5·00
		First Day Cover		5·00
		Presentation Pack	5·00	
		Set of 5 *Gutter Pairs*	7·50	

Plate Nos.: All values 1A (×4)

Sheets: 40 (2 panes 4×5); 36p also 10 (5×2)

Imprint: Right-hand corner, bottom margin

Withdrawn: 6.11.2001

Year Pack 2000

2000 (7 NOV). *Comprises Nos.* **MS**868/85 *and* 887/916

Year Pack	55·00

Sold out: By 10.2002

Post Office Yearbook

2000 (7 NOV). *Comprises Nos.* **MS**868/85 *and* 887/916

Yearbook	58·00

Sold out: By 10.2003

879 Wyon Medal, Penny Black and Queen Victoria

880 Great Exhibition Medal and Albert Tower, Ramsey

881 Silver Coin and *Great Britain* (early steamship)

882 Manx Coin of 1839, *Oliver Twist* and St. Thomas' Church, Douglas

883 Silver Coin of 1887, Arrival of First Train at Vancouver and Jubilee Lamp Standard

884 Silver Coin of 1893, Joe Mylchreest at Kimberley Diamond Mine and Foxdale Clock Tower

885a St. Patrick and Snakes
(*illustration reduced. Actual size* 110×85 *mm*)

Chinese New Year ('Year of the Snake')

(Des The Agency. Litho and die-stamped Questa)

2001 (22 JAN). *Sheet* 110×85 *mm*. Perf 13½×14 (C)
MS923 **885a** £1 multicoloured . . . . 3·00 3·50
First Day Cover . . . . 4·00
Presentation Pack . . . . 4·00

No. **MS**923 includes the 'Hong Kong 2001' logo on the sheet margin.

Withdrawn: 21.1.2002

Death Centenary of Queen Victoria

(Des Mannin Design. Litho Walsall)

2001 (22 JAN). Perf 13½ (C)
917	**879**	22p multicoloured	50	55
918	**880**	26p multicoloured	55	60
919	**881**	34p multicoloured	75	80
920	**882**	39p multicoloured	1·10	1·20
921	**883**	40p multicoloured	1·10	1·20
922	**884**	52p multicoloured	1·60	1·70
917/22		Set of 6	5·25	5·50
		First Day Cover		5·50
		Presentation Pack	6·00	

Plate Nos.: All values 1A (×4)

Sheets: 20 (4×5)

Imprint: Right-hand corner, bottom margin

Withdrawn: 21.1.2002

886 White-tailed Bumble Bee

887 Seven-spot Ladybird

888 Lesser Mottled Grasshopper

889 Manx Robber Fly

Elephant Hawkmoth, Deilephila elpenor

890 Elephant Hawkmoth

895 Postman, 1983   **896** Postman, 2001

Insects

(Des R. Lewington. Litho Questa)

2001 (1 FEB). Perf 14 (C)

924	**886**	22p multicoloured	50	55
925	**887**	26p multicoloured	55	60
926	**888**	29p multicoloured	80	90
927	**889**	59p multicoloured	1·50	1·60
928	**890**	66p multicoloured	1·90	2·00
924/8		Set of 5	5·00	5·25
		First Day Cover		5·00
		Presentation Pack	5·50	

Plate Nos.: All values 1A, 1B (each ×4)

Sheets: 10 (5×2)

Imprint: Right-hand corner, bottom margin

Withdrawn: 31.1.2002

Postal Uniforms

(Des Colleen Corlett. Litho B.D.T.)

2001 (18 APR). Perf 14 (C)

929	**891**	22p multicoloured	50	55
930	**892**	26p multicoloured	55	60
931	**893**	36p multicoloured	75	80
932	**894**	39p multicoloured	1·10	1·20
933	**895**	40p multicoloured	1·10	1·20
934	**896**	66p multicoloured	1·90	2·00
929/34		Set of 6	5·50	5·75
		First Day Cover		5·50
		Presentation Pack	6·00	

Plate Nos.: All values 1A (×4)

Sheets: 20 (5×4)

Imprint: Central, bottom margin

Withdrawn: 17.4.2002

891 Letter-carrier, 1805   **892** Postman, 1859

897a 1967–70 Great Britain ½d. Machin (29p);
1952–1954 Great Britain 6d. Wilding
(34p); 1971 Isle of Man 2½p. Regional (37p);
1958–68 Isle of Man 4d. Regional (50p)
(*illustration reduced. Actual size 170×75 mm*)

75th Birthday of Queen Elizabeth II

(Des The Agency. Litho B.D.T.)

2001 (18 APR). *Sheet 170×75 mm.* Perf 14 (C)

MS935	**897a**	29p, 34p, 37p, 50p multi-coloured	3·75	3·75
		First Day Cover		4·25
		Presentation Pack	4·25	

893 Postman, 1910   **894** Postman, 1933

Withdrawn: 17.4.2002

898 Joey Dunlop on Rea Yamaha, Parliament Square, 1977 TT Races

899 At Governor's, 1983 TT Races

900 Leaving Ramsey, 1988 TT Races

901 On Honda motorbike, 1991

902 On 250cc Honda at Ballaspur, 1999

903 On the Mountain

904 'The Manx Derby, 1627' (Johnny Jonas)

905 'Post Haste' (Johnny Jonas)

906 'Red Rum' (Hamilton-Rennick)

907 'Hyperion' (Sir Alfred Munnings)

908 'Isle of Man' (Johnny Jonas)

Joey Dunlop (motorcycle champion) Commemoration

(Des Ruth Sutherland. Litho B.D.T.)

2001 (17 MAY). Perf 14 (C)

936	**898**	22p multicoloured	50	55
937	**899**	26p multicoloured	55	60
938	**900**	36p multicoloured	75	80
939	**901**	45p multicoloured	95	1·00
940	**902**	65p multicoloured	1·40	1·50
941	**903**	77p multicoloured	1·60	1·70
936/41		*Set of 6*	5·25	5·75
		First Day Cover		6·50
		Presentation Pack	7·00	
		Souvenir Folder (containing 5 sets of Nos. 936/41, 6 Postcards (PC20/5) and special commemorative cover)	40·00	
		Set of 6 Gutter Pairs	10·50	

Sheets: 20 (2 panes 2×5)

Withdrawn: 16.5.2002

Horse Racing Paintings

(Des The Agency. Litho Cartor)

2001 (18 MAY). Perf 13½ (C)

942	**904**	22p multicoloured	50	55
943	**905**	26p multicoloured	55	60
944	**906**	36p multicoloured	85	80
945	**907**	52p multicoloured	1·50	1·60
946	**908**	63p multicoloured	1·70	1·70
942/6		*Set of 5*	4·50	4·75
		First Day Cover		5·00
		Presentation Pack	5·00	

Plate Nos: All values 1A (×4)

Sheets: 20 (4×5)

Withdrawn: 17.5.2002

909 Beef

910 Queenies with Salmon Caviar

911 Seafood

912 Lamb

913 Kipper Tart

914 Lemon Tart with Raspberries

Europa. Water, a Natural Treasure, Local Dishes prepared by Kevin Woodford

(Des The Agency. Litho B.D.T.)

2001 (10 AUG). Perf 14 (C)

947	**909**	22p multicoloured	50	55
948	**910**	26p multicoloured	55	60
		a. Panel at foot of stamp in pale lilac (R. 2/1)	20·00	
		b. Sheetlet of 10	5·50	
949	**911**	36p multicoloured	75	80
		b. Sheetlet of 10	7·75	
950	**912**	45p multicoloured	1·20	1·20
951	**913**	50p multicoloured	1·30	1·50
952	**914**	66p multicoloured	1·90	2·00
947/52		*Set of 6*	5·75	6·25
		First Day Cover		6·50
		Presentation Pack	7·00	
		Recipe Cards (set of 6)	20·00	

The 26p and 36p show the inscription 'EUROPA 2001' at bottom right.

On Nos. 947/52 the panel at the foot of each stamp, on which the designer and printer imprints occur, is normally white. On R. 2/1 of the 26p in sheets of 25 this panel is in pale lilac.

The set of recipe cards show a strip of 4 stamps plus label and first day of issue postmark.

Plate Nos.: All values 1A (×4)

Sheets: 30 (6×5) containing 25 stamps and 5 stamp-size labels, different for each value, in the first vertical row; 26p, 36p also 10 (2×10)

Withdrawn: 9.8.2002

915 Castletown Police Station

916 'Leafield' (semi-detached house)

917 'The Red House' (Baillie Scott's home)

918 'Ivydene' (detached house)

919 Onchan Village Hall

The Architecture of Mackay Hugh Baillie Scott

(Des Tracey Harding. Litho Cartor)

2001 (3 SEPT). Perf 13½ (C)

953	**915**	22p multicoloured	50	55
954	**916**	26p multicoloured	55	60
955	**917**	37p multicoloured	80	85
956	**918**	40p multicoloured	1·00	1·10
957	**919**	80p multicoloured	2·00	2·10
953/7		*Set of 5*	4·50	4·75
		First Day Cover		5·50
		Presentation Pack	6·00	

Nos. 953/7 are inscribed 'HUGH MACKAY' in error.

Plate Nos.: All values 1A (×4)

Sheets: 20 (4×5) with a further view of the building depicted on the sheet margins

Withdrawn: 2.9.2002

'Hafnia '01' International Stamp Exhibition, Denmark

2001 (16 OCT). *No.* **MS**935 *additionally inscribed with* 'Hafnia '01' *logo in red on sheet margin*

MS958   170×75 mm.   **897a** 29p, 34p, 37p

50p multicoloured . . . .   5·50   5·50
          First Day Cover . . . .   6·00

Sold out: By 8.2003

920 Royal Refreshments at Glasgow

921 Queen on Visit to Lancaster

922 Queen with Labradors, Sandringham

923 Queen meeting Scottish Korean War Veterans

924 Queen at Desk, Sandringham

925 Queen with Bouquet, Oxford

Golden Jubilee (1st issue). 'The Daily Life of the Queen—An Artist's Diary' (paintings by Michael Noakes)

(Adapted The Agency. Litho Questa)

2001 (29 OCT)–**02**. Perf 14 (C)

959	**920**	22p multicoloured (*a*)	50	55
		a. Booklet pane. Nos. 959/61 with margins all round (*b*) . .	2·20	
960	**921**	26p multicoloured (*a*)	55	60
961	**922**	39p multicoloured (*a*)	85	90
962	**923**	40p multicoloured (*a*)	85	90
		a. Booklet pane. Nos. 962/4 with margins all round (*b*) . .	4·00	
963	**924**	45p multicoloured (*a*)	95	1·00
964	**925**	65p multicoloured (*a*)	1·90	2·00
959/64		Set of 6	5·00	5·50
		First Day Cover		6·00
		Presentation Pack	6·25	
		Souvenir Folder (*complete sheets*)	42·00	

See also Nos. 970/5.

Printings: (*a*) 29.10.2001; (*b*) 6.2.2002

Plate Nos.: All values 1A (×4)

Sheets: 8 (4×2) with enlarged illustrated margin at left

Withdrawn: 28.10.2002 (sheets)

926 Christmas Tree Wall Decoration

927 Traditional Wreath

928 Table Decoration

929 Topiary Tree

930 Contemporary Wreath

Christmas. Decorations by Isle of Man Floreat Workshop

(Des The Agency. Litho Questa)

2001 (5 NOV). Perf 14×14½ (C)

965	**926**	21p multicoloured	. . . .	45	50
966	**927**	25p multicoloured	. . . .	55	60
967	**928**	37p multicoloured	. . . .	1·00	1·10
968	**929**	45p multicoloured	. . . .	1·20	1·30
969	**930**	65p multicoloured	. . . .	1·90	2·00
965/9		*Set of 5*	. . . .	4·75	5·00
		First Day Cover	. . . .		5·25
		Presentation Pack	. . . .	5·50	

Plate Nos.: All values 1A, 1B (each ×4)

Sheets: 25 (5×5) with horizontal rows of stamps interspersed by rows of inscribed greetings labels. The 21p and 25p values were also available with personal photographs shown on these labels

Withdrawn: 4.11.2002

Year Folder 2001

2001 (5 NOV). *Comprises Nos.* 917/57 *and* 959/69
Year Folder . . . . 45·00

Sold out: By 11.2003

Year Pack 2001

2001 (5 NOV). *Comprises Nos.* 917/57 *and* 959/69
Year Pack . . . . 55·00

Sold out: By 11.2003

Post Office Yearbook

2001 (5 NOV). *Comprises Nos.* 917/57 *and* 959/69
Yearbook . . . . 60·00

Sold out: By 4.2002

931 'The Coronation, 1953' (Terence Cuneo)

932 'Queen Elizabeth II as Colonel-in-Chief of Grenadier Guards on Imperial, 1962' (Terence Cuneo)

933 'Queen Elizabeth II in Evening Dress, 1981' (June Mendoza)

934 'Queen Elizabeth II in Garter Robes, 2000' (Chen Yan Ning)

935 'The Royal Family' (John Wonnacott)

936a Sculpture of Queen Elizabeth II by David Cregeen (*illustration reduced. Actual size* 110×85 *mm*)

Golden Jubilee (2nd issue). Royal Paintings

(Des The Agency. Litho and die-stamped Questa)

2002 (6 FEB). Perf 14½×14 (No. **MS**975) or 14 (others), both comb

970	**931**	50p multicoloured	. . . .	80	60
		a. Vert strip of 5. Nos. 970/4	. .	5·00	5·50
		b. Booklet pane. Nos. 970/2 with margins all round	. . . . .	3·50	
971	**932**	50p multicoloured	. . . .	80	60
972	**933**	50p multicoloured	. . . .	80	60
973	**934**	50p multicoloured	. . . .	80	60
		b. Booklet pane. Nos. 973/4 with margins all round	. . . . .	2·40	

974	**935**	50p multicoloured	80	60
970/4		*Set of 5*	5·00	5·50
		First Day Cover		6·00
		Presentation Pack	6·00	
		Souvenir Folder (complete sheet)	20·00	
		Gutter Strip	10·50	
MS975	110×85 mm. **936a** £1 multicoloured	2·00	2·10
	b. *Booklet pane. As No.* **MS**975, *but* 152×97 mm *with a line of roulettes at left*	2·40	2·50
		First Day Cover		5·00
		Presentation Pack	3·00	

Plate Nos.: 1A (×4)

Sheets: 20 (2 panes 2×5). Nos. 970/4 were printed together, *se-tenant*, as vertical strips of 5. The panes are separated by an enlarged vertical gutter illustrated with further royal portraits

Withdrawn: 5.2.2003

937 Cycling   **938** Running

939 Javelin and High Jump   **940** Swimming

941 Decathlon   **942** Wheelchair Racing

17th Commonwealth Games, Manchester. Photographic Montages

(Des The Agency. Litho B.D.T.)

2002 (11 MAR). Perf 14 (C)

976	**937**	22p multicoloured	45	50
977	**938**	26p multicoloured	50	55
978	**939**	29p multicoloured	60	65
979	**940**	34p multicoloured	70	75
980	**941**	40p multicoloured	1·00	1·10

981	**942**	45p multicoloured	1·10	1·20
976/81		*Set of 6*	4·25	4·75
		First Day Cover		5·25
		Presentation Pack	5·50	

Plate Nos.: All values 1A (×4)

Sheets: 9 (3×3) with an illustrated gutter between the second and third horizontal rows, and an enlarged right margin

Withdrawn: 10.3.2003

943 'Queen Elizabeth the Queen Mother' (Johnny Jonas)

Queen Elizabeth the Queen Mother Commemoration

(Des The Agency. Litho Cartor)

2002 (23 APR). Perf 13×13½ (C)

982	**943**	£3 multicoloured	6·00	6·25
		First Day Cover		7·00
		Presentation Pack	7·00	

No. 982 was retained in use as a definitive stamp.

Plate Nos.: 1A (×4)

Sheets: 10 (5×2)

944 Ireland v Czech Republic   **945** England v Greece

946 Italy v Belgium   **947** France v Portugal

948 England v Brazil   **949** France v Japan

World Cup Football Championship, Japan and Korea

(Des E. Cassidy. Litho Cartor)

2002 (1 MAY). Perf 13½ (C)

983	**944**	22p multicoloured	45	50
984	**945**	26p multicoloured	50	55
985	**946**	39p multicoloured	80	85
986	**947**	40p multicoloured	80	85
987	**948**	66p multicoloured	1·20	1·40
988	**949**	68p multicoloured	1·40	1·50
983/8		Set of 6	5·00	5·50
		First Day Cover		6·00
		Presentation Pack	6·25	

Plate Nos.: All values 1A (×4)

Sheets: 25 (5×5)

Withdrawn: 30.4.2003

950 'Monk's Bridge, Ballasalla'   **951** 'Laxey'

952 'Langness Lighthouse'   **953** 'King William's College'

954 'The Mull Circle and Bradda Head'

Watercolours by Toni Onley

(Des The Agency. Litho Cartor)

2002 (1 MAY). Perf 13½ (C)

989	**950**	22p multicoloured	45	50
990	**951**	26p multicoloured	50	55
991	**952**	37p multicoloured	75	80
992	**953**	45p multicoloured	1·10	1·20
993	**954**	65p multicoloured	1·50	1·60
989/93		Set of 5	4·25	4·50
		First Day Cover		5·25
		Presentation Pack	5·50	

Plate Nos.: All values 1A (×4)

Sheets: 25 (5×5)

Withdrawn: 30.4.2003

Golden Jubilee Celebrations

2002 (4 JUNE). No. **MS**975 additionally inscribed 'THE ISLE OF MAN CELEBRATES THE JUBILEE 4th JUNE 2002' in purple on the sheet margin

MS994 110×85 mm. **935a** £1 multicoloured 3·00 3·00

Withdrawn: 3.6.2003

955 Magenta Flower on Yellow Background   **956** Green Flower on Pink Background

957 Purple Flower on Green Background   **958** Maroon Flower on Brown Background

959 Red Flower on Blue Background   **960** Orange Flower on Yellow Background

Memories of the Isle of Man

(Des Sir Paul McCartney. Litho Walsall)

2002 (1 JULY). Perf 13½×13 (C)

995	**955**	22p multicoloured	45	50
996	**956**	26p multicoloured	50	55
997	**957**	29p multicoloured	60	65
998	**958**	52p multicoloured	1·00	1·10
999	**959**	63p multicoloured	1·20	1·40
1000	**960**	77p multicoloured	1·50	1·60
995/1000		*Set of 6*	5·25	5·75
		First Day Cover		6·25
		Presentation Pack	6·50	
		Souvenir Folder (complete sheets and first day cover)	50·00	

Plate Nos.: All values 1A (×4)

Sheets: 8 (4×2) with inscribed margins and a photograph of Sir Paul McCartney at left

Withdrawn: 30.6.2003

961 Manx Milestone
(Mrs. B. Trimble)

962 Plough Horses
(Miss D. Flint)

963 Manx Emblem
(Ruth Nicholls)

964 Loaghtan Sheep
(Diana Burford)

965 Fishing Fleet,
Port St. Mary
(Phil Thomas)

966 Peel
(Michael Thompson)

967 Daffodils
(Michael Thompson)

968 Millennium Sword
(Mr. F. K. Smith)

969 Peel Castle
(Kathy Brown)

970 Snaefell Railway
(Joan Burgess)

971 Laxey Wheel
(Kathy Brown)

972 Sheep at Druidale
(John Hall)

973 Carousel at Silverdale
(Colin Edwards)

974 Grandma
(Stephanie Corkhill)

975 Manx Rock
(Ruth Nicholls)

976 T.T. Riders at
Signpost
(Neil Brew)

977 Groudle Railway
(Albert Lowe)

978 Royal Cascade
(Brian Speedie)

979 St. Johns
(John Hall)

980 Niarbyl Cottages
with Poppies
(Cathy Galbraith)

Photography – The People's Choice. Competition Winners

(Des The Agency. Litho Walsall)

2002 (30 AUG–1 OCT). (*a*) *PVA gum.* Perf 14 (C)

1001	**961**	23p multicoloured (*b*)	30	25
		a. Block of 10. *Nos.* 1001/10 .	4·50	5·00
1002	**962**	23p multicoloured (*b*)	30	25
1003	**963**	23p multicoloured (*b*)	30	25
1004	**964**	23p multicoloured (*b*)	30	25
1005	**965**	23p multicoloured (*b*)	30	25
1006	**966**	23p multicoloured (*b*)	30	25
1007	**967**	23p multicoloured (*b*)	30	25
1008	**968**	23p multicoloured (*b*)	30	25
1009	**969**	23p multicoloured (*b*)	30	25
1010	**970**	23p multicoloured (*b*)	30	25
1011	**971**	27p multicoloured (*a*)	35	30
		a. Block of 10. *Nos.* 1011/20 .	5·50	6·00
1012	**972**	27p multicoloured (*a*)	35	30
1013	**973**	27p multicoloured (*a*)	35	30
1014	**974**	27p multicoloured (*a*)	35	30
1015	**975**	27p multicoloured (*a*)	35	30
1016	**976**	27p multicoloured (*a*)	35	30
1017	**977**	27p multicoloured (*a*)	35	30
1018	**978**	27p multicoloured (*a*)	35	30
1019	**979**	27p multicoloured (*a*)	35	30
1020	**980**	27p multicoloured (*a*)	35	30
1001/20		*Set of* 20	10·00	11·00
		First Day Covers (2)		12·00
		Presentation Packs (2)	12·00	

(*b*) *Booklet stamps. Self-adhesive.* Perf 6½ (die-cut)

1021	**961**	23p multicoloured (*b*)	45	50
		a. Booklet pane. Nos. 1021/30	6·50	
1022	**962**	23p multicoloured (*b*)	45	50
1023	**963**	23p multicoloured (*b*)	45	50
1024	**964**	23p multicoloured (*b*)	45	50
1025	**965**	23p multicoloured (*b*)	45	50
1026	**966**	23p multicoloured (*b*)	45	50
1027	**967**	23p multicoloured (*b*)	45	50
1028	**968**	23p multicoloured (*b*)	45	50
1029	**969**	23p multicoloured (*b*)	45	50
1030	**970**	23p multicoloured (*b*)	45	50
1031	**971**	27p multicoloured (*b*)	55	60
		a. Booklet pane. Nos. 1031/40	8·00	
1032	**972**	27p multicoloured (*b*)	55	60
1033	**973**	27p multicoloured (*b*)	55	60
1034	**974**	27p multicoloured (*b*)	55	60
1035	**975**	27p multicoloured (*b*)	55	60
1036	**976**	27p multicoloured (*b*)	55	60
1037	**977**	27p multicoloured (*b*)	55	60
1038	**978**	27p multicoloured (*b*)	55	60
1039	**979**	27p multicoloured (*b*)	55	60
1040	**980**	27p multicoloured (*b*)	55	60
1021/40		*Set of* 20	10·00	11·00

Nos. 1021/30 and 1031/40 were only available in £2.30 and £2.70 stamp booklets with the surplus self-adhesive paper around each stamp retained.

Printings: (*a*) 30.8.02; (*b*) 1.10.02

Plate Nos.: Both values 1A (×5)

Sheets: 40 (5×8) Nos. 1001/10 and 1011/20 were each printed together, *se-tenant*, as blocks of 10, in sheets of 40.

Withdrawn: 29.8.2003 27p sheets; 30.9.2003 23p sheets

981 Father Christmas

982 Virgin Mary
and Jesus

983 Clown

984 Bandsman
playing
Cymbals

985 Fairy

986a 'CHRISTMAS' and Festive Characters
(*illustration reduced. Actual size* 123×55 *mm*)

Christmas. Entertainment

(Des Anthea Radcliffe. Litho Questa)

2002 (5 NOV). Perf 15×14½ (No. **MS**1046) or 14×14½ (others), both comb

1041	**981**	22p multicoloured	45	50
1042	**982**	26p multicoloured	50	55
1043	**983**	37p multicoloured	75	80
1044	**984**	47p multicoloured	95	1·00
1045	**985**	68p multicoloured	1·40	1·50
1041/5		*Set of 5*	4·00	4·25
		First Day Cover		5·00
		Presentation Pack	5·00	
MS1046		123×55 mm. **986a** £1.30, multi-coloured	3·00	3·25
		First Day Cover		4·00
		Presentation Pack	4·25	

The 37p value includes the 'EUROPA' emblem.

Plate Nos.: All values 1A (each ×4)

Sheets: 40 (5×8)

Withdrawn: 4.11.2003

Year Folder 2002

2002 (5 NOV). *Comprises Nos.* 970/93, 995/1020 *and* 1041/5
Year Folder . . . . 45·00

Sold out: By 31.7.2004

Year Pack 2002

2002 (5 NOV). *Comprises Nos.* 970/93, 995/1020 *and* 1041/5
Year Pack . . . . 55·00

Sold out: By 31.7.2004

Post Office Yearbook

2002 (5 NOV). *Comprises Nos.* 970/93, 995/1020 *and* 1041/5
Yearbook . . . . 60·00

Sold out: By 5.2005

987 Dish Aerial and Peel Castle

988 Dish Aerial, Tromode Teleport

989 Camp on Moon and lunar vehicle

990 Astronaut exploring lunar surface

991 *Sea Launch Odyssey* (marine launch platform)

992 *Sea Launch Commander* (assembly and command ship)

993 Loral Telstar 1 satellite

994 Loral Telstar 8 satellite

995a Phobos and American Spaceship (75p); Mars, Astronauts and Transfer Vehicle (75p)
(*illustration reduced. Actual size* 110×85 *mm*)

Isle of Man Involvement in Space Exploration

(Des E. McCall (27p, 75p), E. Gignac (others). Litho Cartor)

2003 (14 FEB). Perf 13½×13 (**MS**1055) or 13½ (others), both comb

1047	**987**	23p multicoloured	45	50
		a. Horiz pair. Nos. 1047/8	90	1·00
1048	**988**	23p multicoloured	45	50

1049	**989**	27p multicoloured	55	60
		a. Horiz pair. Nos. 1049/50 . . .	1·10	1·10
1050	**990**	27p multicoloured	55	60
1051	**991**	37p multicoloured	75	80
		a. Horiz pair. Nos. 1051/2	1·50	1·60
1052	**992**	37p multicoloured	75	80
1053	**993**	42p multicoloured	85	90
		a. Horiz pair. Nos. 1053/4	2·10	2·20
1054	**994**	42p multicoloured	85	90
		Set of 8	6·00	6·00
		First Day Cover		6·50
		Presentation Pack	6·75	

MS1055   110×85 mm. **995a** 75p multi-
coloured . . . . 4·00   4·00
First Day Cover . . . . 4·50
Presentation Pack . . . . 4·50

Plate Nos.: All values 1A (×4)

Sheets: 8 (2×4). Nos. 1047/8, 1049/50, 1051/2 and 1053/4 were each printed together, as horizontal *se-tenant* pairs forming composite designs, in sheets with enlarged illustrated right margins

Withdrawn: 13.2.2004

Post Office Vehicles

(Des P. Hearsey. Litho Questa)

2003 (14 FEB). Perf 14½ (C)

1056	**996**	23p multicoloured	45	50
1057	**997**	27p multicoloured	55	60
1058	**998**	37p multicoloured	1·00	1·10
1059	**999**	42p multicoloured	1·10	1·20
1060	**1000**	89p multicoloured	2·20	2·40
		Set of 5	5·25	5·50
		First Day Cover		6·00
		Presentation Pack	6·00	

Plate Nos.: All values 1A (×4)

Sheets: 25 (5×5)

Imprint: Right-hand side, bottom margin

Withdrawn: 13.2.2004

996 Delivery Handcart (1900–45)

997 Morris Z Van (1942)

1001 Queen Elizabeth II wearing St. Edward's Crown

1002 The Ring

998 Morris L Diesel Van (1960s)

999 DI BSA Bantam Telegraph Delivery Motorbikes

1003 The Orb

1004 Royal Sceptre and Rod of Equity and Mercy

1000 Ford Escort 55 Van

1005 Queen Elizabeth II wearing Imperial State Crown

1006 State Coach

50th Anniversary of Coronation

(Des Diane Fawcett. Litho Walsall)

2003 (12 APR). Perf 13½ (C)

1061	**1001**	50p multicoloured	70	75
		a. Block of 6. Nos. 1061/6	6·00	6·50
1062	**1002**	50p multicoloured	70	75
1063	**1003**	50p multicoloured	70	75
1064	**1004**	50p multicoloured	70	75
1065	**1005**	50p multicoloured	70	75
1066	**1006**	50p multicoloured	70	75
		Set of 6	6·00	6·50
		First Day Cover		7·00
		Presentation Pack	7·00	
		Souvenir Folder	25·00	

Plate Nos.: 1A (×5)

Sheets: 24. Nos. 1061/6 were printed together, *se-tenant*, as four blocks of six with Nos. 1061 and 1065 at either end, 1062/4 in the top row and 1066 at the bottom

Withdrawn: 10.4.2004

1007 De Havilland D.H.83 Fox Moth and Saro Cloud (amphibian)

1008 De Havilland D.H.61 Giant Moth and D.H.80 Puss Moth

1009 Avro Anson Type 652 and Boeing B-17 Flying Fortress

1010 Eurofighter Typhoon and Avro Vulcan

1011 Handley Page Herald and Bristol Wayfarer

1012 Aerospatiale Concorde and projected Airbus Industrie A380

Centenary of Powered Flight

(Des K. Woodcock. Litho B.D.T.)

2003 (9 MAY). Perf 13½ (C)

1067	**1007**	23p multicoloured	45	50
		a. Horiz strip of 3. Nos. 1067/9	1·80	2·00
1068	**1008**	27p multicoloured	60	60
1069	**1009**	37p multicoloured	70	80
1070	**1010**	40p multicoloured	70	85
		a. Horiz strip of 3. Nos. 1070/2	4·00	4·50
1071	**1011**	67p multicoloured	80	1·50
1072	**1012**	89p multicoloured	1·20	1·90
		Set of 6	5·50	6·00
		First Day Cover		6·50
		Presentation Pack	6·75	
		Souvenir Folder (complete sheets and **MS**1073)	28·00	

Plate Nos.: All values 1A (×4)

Sheets: 12 (2 panes 3×2). Nos. 1067/9 and 1070/2 were each printed together, *se-tenant*, as horizontal strips of three, within sheets containing two blocks of six separated by large illustrated gutters.

Withdrawn: 8.5.2004

1012a Avro Lancaster attacking Mohne Dam
(*illustration reduced. Actual size 78×50 mm*)

60th Anniversary of Attack on German Dams by No. 617 ('Dambusters') Squadron

(Des R. Taylor. Litho B.D.T.)

2003 (9 MAY). *Sheet 170×75 mm. Perf 13 (C)*
MS1073 **1012a** £2 multicoloured . . . . 4·00 4·25
First Day Cover . . . . 5·00
Presentation Pack . . . . 5·00

Withdrawn: 8.5.2004

1013 Prince William

1014 Prince William

1015 Prince William

1016 Prince William

21st Birthday of Prince William of Wales

(Des The Agency Ltd. Litho Cartor)

2003 (9 JUNE). *Perf 13½ (C)*
1074	**1013**	42p black and grey	85	90
1075	**1014**	47p black and grey	95	1·00
1076	**1015**	52p black and grey	1·50	1·60
1077	**1016**	68p black and grey	1·90	2·00
		Set of 4	5·00	5·50
		First Day Cover		6·00
		Presentation Pack	6·25	

Plate Nos.: All values 1A (×4)

Sheets: 25 (5×5)

Imprint: Central, side margins

Withdrawn: 8.6.2004

Trilaterale Ticino Exhibition, Locarno, Switzerland

2003 (18 JUNE). *No.* **MS**1073 *additionally inscribed with* 'Ticino 2003' *logo in blue on sheet margin.*
MS1078   £2 multicoloured . . . . 4·75   4·75

Withdrawn: 17.6.2004

1017 *Manx Gold* (Agatha Christie)

1018 *Quatermass and the Pit* (Nigel Kneale)

1019 *Flashman at the Charge* (George MacDonald Fraser)

1020 *The Eternal City* (Hall Caine)

1021 *Peveril of the Peak* (Sir Walter Scott)

1022 *Emma's Secret* (Barbara Taylor Bradford)

'The Manx Bookshelf'. Book Covers

(Des D. Macdonald. Litho Walsall)

2003 (5 JULY). *Perf 13½ (C)*
1079	**1017**	23p multicoloured	45	50
1080	**1018**	27p multicoloured	55	60
1081	**1019**	30p multicoloured	60	65
1082	**1020**	38p multicoloured	75	80

1083	**1021**	40p multicoloured	....	1·00	1·10
1084	**1022**	53p multicoloured	....	1·20	1·30
		Set of 6	....	4·50	5·00
		First Day Cover	....		5·75
		Presentation Pack	....	5·75	

The 38p. value includes the 'EUROPA 2003' emblem.

Plate Nos: All values 1A (×4)

Sheets: 20 (5×4) with small *se-tenant* label giving the author's name at the foot of each stamp; 38p also 10 (5×2)

Withdrawn: 3.7.2004

1023 King Henry VII and Henry Tudor crowned by Sir Thomas Stanley on Bosworth Battlefield

1024 King Henry VIII and Manx Church (Dissolution of the Monasteries)

1025 Queen Elizabeth I and Globe showing Route of Drake's Circumnavigation

1026 King Henry VIII, Cardinal Wolsey and Hampton Court Palace

1027 Queen Mary I and Tudor Rose

1028 Queen Elizabeth I and Ships of Spanish Armada

400th Anniversary of End of the Tudor Reign

(Des D. Kearney. Litho BDT)

2003 (15 SEPT). Perf 14 (C)
1085	**1023**	23p multicoloured	....	45	50
1086	**1024**	27p multicoloured	....	55	60
1087	**1025**	38p multicoloured	....	75	80
1088	**1026**	40p multicoloured	....	80	85

1089	**1027**	47p multicoloured	....	95	1·00
1090	**1028**	67p multicoloured	....	1·40	1·50
		Set of 6	....	4·75	5·25
		First Day Cover	....		5·75
		Presentation Pack	....	5·50	
		Stamp Cards (set of 6)	...	4·25	10·00

Plate Nos.: All values 1A (×4)

Sheets: 25 (5×5)

Withdrawn: 14.9.2004

1029 Henry Bloom Noble and Orphanage Boys

1030 Nurse and Ramsey Cottage Hospital

1031 Children and Children's Home

1032 Bathers at Noble's Baths

1033 Scout and Headquarters

1034 Noble's Hospital, c. 1912

1035 Villa Marina

1036 Noble's Park

1037 St. Ninian's
Church

1038 Noble's
Library

1039 Boy tying Scarf
on Snowman

1040 Snowman
(wearing black
hat and scarf)

1041 Boy and
Snowman
holding Hands

1042 Snowman
(wearing brown
hat and scarf)

1043 Boy flying with Snowman

Centenary of Henry Bloom Noble Trust

(Des Tracey Harding. Litho Walsall)

2003 (1 OCT). (*a*) *PVA gum.* Perf 14 (C)

1091	**1029**	23p multicoloured	40	25
		a. *Horiz strip of 5. Nos.* 1091/5	2·50	2·75
1092	**1030**	23p multicoloured	40	25
1093	**1031**	23p multicoloured	40	25
1094	**1032**	23p multicoloured	40	25
1095	**1033**	23p multicoloured	40	25
1096	**1034**	27p multicoloured	45	30
		a. *Horiz strip of 5. Nos.* 1096/1100	3·00	3·25
1097	**1035**	27p multicoloured	45	30
1098	**1036**	27p multicoloured	45	30
1099	**1037**	27p multicoloured	45	30
1100	**1038**	27p multicoloured	45	30
1091/1100		*Set of* 10	5·00	5·50
		First Day Cover		6·00
		Presentation Pack	6·00	

(*b*) *Self-adhesive booklet stamps.* Roul 6½

1101	**1029**	23p multicoloured	45	50
		a. *Booklet pane. Nos.* 1101/5, *each* × 2	6·00	
1102	**1030**	23p multicoloured	45	50
1103	**1031**	23p multicoloured	45	50
1104	**1032**	23p multicoloured	45	50
1105	**1033**	23p multicoloured	45	50
1106	**1034**	27p multicoloured	55	60
		a. *Booklet pane. Nos.* 1106/1110, *each* × 2	11·00	
1107	**1035**	27p multicoloured	55	60
1108	**1036**	27p multicoloured	55	60
1109	**1037**	27p multicoloured	55	60
1110	**1038**	27p multicoloured	55	60
1101/10		*Set of* 10	5·00	5·50

Plate Nos.: Both values 1A (×4)

Sheets: 50 (5×10). Nos. 1091/5 and 1096/1100 were each printed together, *se-tenant*, in horizontal strips of 5 throughout the sheets Nos. 1101/5 and 1106/1110 were only issued in £2.30 and £2.70 booklets, Nos. SB57/8.

Withdrawn: 30.9.2004 (sheets)

Christmas. The Snowman by Raymond Briggs

(Litho DLR)

2003 (5 NOV). Perf 14½ (C)

1111	**1039**	22p multicoloured	45	50
1112	**1040**	26p multicoloured	50	55
1113	**1041**	38p multicoloured	75	80
1114	**1042**	47p multicoloured	95	1·00
1115	**1043**	68p multicoloured	1·40	1·50
		Set of 5	4·00	4·25
		First Day Cover		5·00
		Presentation Pack	5·25	

Plate Nos.: All values 1A (×4)

Sheets: 40 (5×8)

Withdrawn: 4.11.2004

Year Folder 2003

2003 (12 NOV). *Comprises Nos. 1047/77, 1079/1100 and* 1111/15

Year Folder .... 50·00

Sold out: By 12.2004

Year Pack 2003

2003 (12 NOV). *Comprises Nos.* 1047/77, 1079/1100 *and* 1111/15

Year Pack . . . . 60·00

Sold out: By 5.2005

Post Office Yearbook

2003 (12 NOV). *Comprises Nos.* 1047/77, 1079/1100 *and* 1111/15

Yearbook . . . . 60·00

Sold out: By 12.2006

1044 Aragorn

1045 Gimli

1046 Gandalf

1047 Legolas on Horseback

1048 Gollum

1049 Frodo and Sam

1050 Legolas drawing Bow

1051 Aragorn on Horseback

1052a The Ring
(*illustration reduced. Actual size* 120×78 mm)

Making of The Lord of the Rings *Film Trilogy:* The Return of the King

(Des The Agency Ltd. Litho BDT)

2003 (17 DEC). Perf 13½ (C)

1116	**1044**	23p multicoloured	45	50
1117	**1045**	27p multicoloured	55	60
1118	**1046**	30p multicoloured	60	65
1119	**1047**	38p multicoloured	1·00	90
1120	**1048**	42p multicoloured	1·50	1·00
1121	**1049**	47p multicoloured	2·00	2·00
1122	**1050**	68p multicoloured	3·00	3·50
1123	**1051**	85p multicoloured	3·50	3·00
1116/23		Set of 8	9·75	9·75
		First Day Cover		11·00
		Presentation Pack . . . . 11·00		
		Souvenir Folder (complete sheets and **MS**1124) . . . . 50·00		
		Stamp Cards (pre-paid) (set of 8)	9·50	9·50
MS1124		120×78 mm. **1052a** £2 The Ring (44×40 mm)	5·00	5·50
		First Day Cover		6·00
		Presentation Pack . . . . 6·00		

Plate Nos.: All values 1A (×4)

Sheets: 6 (3×2) with enlarged illustrated margins

Withdrawn: 16.12.2004

1053 *Maitland* (Simon Hall)

1054 *Evening Star* (Terence Cuneo)

1055 *Pen-y-Darren* Tramroad Locomotive (Terence Cuneo)

1056 *Duchess of Hamilton* (Craig Tiley)

1057 *City of Truro* (B. J. Freeman)

1058 *Mallard* (Terence Cuneo)

Bicentenary of Running of First Steam Locomotive. Paintings of Steam Locomotives

(Des Fusion Graphics from paintings. Litho Cartor)

2004 (21 FEB). Perf 13×13½ (C)

1125	**1053**	23p multicoloured	75	75
1126	**1054**	27p multicoloured	90	90
1127	**1055**	40p multicoloured	1·30	1·30
1128	**1056**	57p multicoloured	1·80	1·80
1129	**1057**	61p multicoloured	2·00	2·00
1130	**1058**	90p multicoloured	3·00	3·00
1125/30		Set of 6	9·75	9·75
		First Day Cover		11·00
		Presentation Pack	11·50	

Plate Nos.: All values 1A (×4)

Sheets: 25 (5×5)

Withdrawn: 20.2.2005

1059 Troops on Landing Craft and Tanks going Ashore

1060 Troops leaving Landing Craft and Tanks going Ashore

1061 Troops leaving Landing Craft

1062 Landing Craft and Troops wading Ashore

1063 *Lady of Mann* (ferry used as landing craft carrier)

1064 *Ben-my-Chree* (ferry used as landing craft carrier)

1065 Consolidated B-24 Liberators (bombers) and North American P-51 Mustang (fighter)

1066 Airspeed A.S.51 Horsa Gliders (troop carriers)

1067a Winston Churchill; Troops and Aircraft; Military Vehicles on Street; Soldiers with *France* Guidebook (*illustration reduced. Actual size* 170×75 *mm*)

60th Anniversary of D-Day

(Des B. Sanders (Nos. 1131/8 only) and The Agency Ltd. Litho DLR (Nos. 1131/8) or Enschedé (**MS**1139))

2004 (6 APR). Perf 14 (C)

1131	**1059**	23p multicoloured	50	25
		a. Horiz pair. Nos. 1131/2	1·50	1·50
1132	**1060**	23p multicoloured	50	25
1133	**1061**	27p multicoloured	60	30
		a. Horiz pair. Nos. 1133/4	1·80	1·80
1134	**1062**	27p multicoloured	60	30
1135	**1063**	47p multicoloured	1·00	50
		a. Horiz pair. Nos. 1135/6	3·00	3·00
1136	**1064**	47p multicoloured	1·00	50
1137	**1065**	68p multicoloured	1·20	70
		a. Horiz pair. Nos. 1137/8	5·00	5·00
1138	**1066**	68p multicoloured	1·20	70
1131/8		Set of 8	10·50	10·50
		First Day Cover		12·50
		Presentation Pack	12·50	
		Collectors Folder (complete sheets and **MS**1139)	40·00	

MS1139 170×75 mm. **1067a** 50p×4,
multicoloured. Perf 13½×14 (C) . . . . 6·50   6·50
   First Day Cover . . . .   8·00
   Presentation Pack . . . . 8·25

Plate Nos.: All values 1A (×4)

Sheets: 10 (2×5) Nos. 1131/2, 1133/4, 1135/6 and 1137/8 were each
printed together, *se-tenant*, in horizontal pairs throughout the
sheets, each pair forming a composite design.

Withdrawn: 5.4.2005

1068 Lesser
Celandine

1069 Red Campion

1070 Devil's-bit
Scabious

1071 Northern
Harebell

1072 Wood
Anemone

1073 Common
Spotted Orchid

Bicentenary of Royal Horticultural Society. Wild Flowers

(Des The Agency Ltd. Litho Cartor)

2004 (3 MAY). Perf 13½ (C)

1140	**1068**	25p multicoloured	85	85
1141	**1069**	28p multicoloured	95	95
1142	**1070**	37p multicoloured	1·20	1·20
1143	**1071**	40p multicoloured	1·30	1·30
1144	**1072**	68p multicoloured	2·20	2·20
1145	**1073**	85p multicoloured	2·75	2·75
1140/5		*Set of 6*	9·25	9·25
		First Day Cover		11·00
		Presentation Pack . . . . 11·00		

Plate Nos.: All values 1A (×4)

Sheets: 40 (5×8)

Withdrawn: 2.5.2005

1074 In *No Limit,*
1936

1075 Pushing
Motorcycle

1076 Riding in TT
Race

1077 With Florence
Desmond

1078 On Motorcycle

1079 Close-up of
George Formby

*Birth Centenary of George Formby (entertainer). Scenes
from* **No Limit** *(film)*

(Des Ruth Sutherland. Litho BDT)

2004 (26 MAY). Perf 13½ (C)

1146	**1074**	25p multicoloured	80	80
1147	**1075**	28p multicoloured	90	90
1148	**1076**	40p multicoloured	1·30	1·30
1149	**1077**	43p multicoloured	1·40	1·40
1150	**1078**	50p multicoloured	1·70	1·70
1151	**1079**	74p multicoloured	2·40	2·40
1146/51		*Set of 6*	8·50	8·50
		First Day Cover		10·00
		Presentation Pack . . . . 10·00		

Sheets: 25 (5×5)

Withdrawn: 25.5.2005

1080 Johnny Weissmuller
(gold, 100m & 400m
freestyle), Paris, 1924

1081 Jesse Owens (gold,
100m, 200m, long
jump), Berlin, 1936

1082 John Mark carrying
Olympic Flame,
London, 1948

1083 Fanny Blankers-Koen
(gold, 100m, 200m,
80m hurdles),
London, 1948

1084 James Cracknell,
Steven Redgrave,
Tim Foster and
Matthew Pinsent (gold,
men's coxless fours),
Sydney, 2000

Olympic Games, Athens. Olympic Legends

(Des Fusion Graphics. Litho BDT)

2004 (1 JULY). Perf 14 (C)

1152	**1080**	25p multicoloured	....	85	85
1153	**1081**	28p multicoloured	....	95	95
1154	**1082**	43p multicoloured	....	1·40	1·40
1155	**1083**	55p multicoloured	....	1·80	1·80
1156	**1084**	91p multicoloured	....	3·00	3·00
1152/6		*Set of* 5	....	8·00	8·00
		First Day Cover	....		9·75
		Presentation Pack	.... 10·00		

Plate Nos.: All values 1A (×4)

Sheets: 25 (5×5)

Imprint: Central, bottom margin

Withdrawn: 30.6.2005

1085 Celtic Islanders
and Viking
Invaders

1086 Fisherman
('Ships and the
Sea')

1087 Miner and Laxey
Wheel ('Laxey
Miners')

1088 Soldier with
Longbow and
Castle ('Kings and
Lords of Mann')

1089 Woman with
Spinning Wheel
('Farmers and
Crofters')

1090 Calf of Man

1091 Peel Castle

1092 Laxey Wheel

1093 Castle Rushen

1094 Cregneash

Manx National Heritage 'The Story of Mann'

(Des The Agency Ltd. Litho BDT)

2004 (3 AUG). (a) *PVA gum.* Perf 14 (C)

1157	**1085**	(25p) multicoloured	....	50	25
		a. Horiz strip of 5. Nos.			
		1157/61	....	4·00	4·00
1158	**1086**	(25p) multicoloured	....	50	25
1159	**1087**	(25p) multicoloured	....	50	25
1160	**1088**	(25p) multicoloured	....	50	25
1161	**1089**	(25p) multicoloured	....	50	25
1162	**1090**	(28p) multicoloured	....	60	30
		a. Horiz strip of 5. Nos.			
		1162/6	....	5·00	5·00
1163	**1091**	(28p) multicoloured	....	60	30
1164	**1092**	(28p) multicoloured	....	60	30
1165	**1093**	(28p) multicoloured	....	60	30
1166	**1094**	(28p) multicoloured	....	60	30
1157/66		*Set of* 10	....	8·50	8·50
		First Day Cover	....		10·50
		Presentation Pack	..... 10·50		

(b) *Self-adhesive booklet stamps.* Perf 12½ (die-cut)

1167	**1085**	(25p) multicoloured	....	60	60
		a. Booklet pane. Nos.			
		1167/71, *each* ×2	......	8·00	

1168	**1086**	(25p) multicoloured	60	60
1169	**1087**	(25p) multicoloured	60	60
1170	**1088**	(25p) multicoloured	60	60
1171	**1089**	(25p) multicoloured	60	60
1172	**1090**	(28p) multicoloured	75	75
		a. Booklet pane. Nos. 1172/6, each ×2	9·00	
1173	**1091**	(28p) multicoloured	75	75
1174	**1092**	(28p) multicoloured	75	75
1175	**1093**	(28p) multicoloured	75	75
1176	**1094**	(28p) multicoloured	75	75
1167/76		Set of 10	8·50	8·50

Nos. 1157/61 and 1167/71 are inscribed 'IOM' and were initially sold at 25p. Nos. 1162/6 and 1172/6 are inscribed 'UK' and were initially sold at 28p.

Plate Nos. Both values 1A (×4)

Sheets: 50 (5×10). Nos. 1157/61 and 1162/6 were each printed together, se-tenant, in horizontal strips of 5 throughout the sheets. Nos. 1167/71 and 1172/6 were only issued in £2.50 and £2.80 booklets, Nos. SB59/60.

Withdrawn: 2.8.2005

1095a Laxey Wheel
(illustration reduced. Actual size 120×78 mm)

150th Anniversary of the Great Laxey Wheel

(Des The Agency Ltd. Litho BDT)

2004 (3 AUG). Perf 14 (C)

MS1177	**1095a**	£2 multicoloured	6·50	6·50
		First Day Cover		8·50
		Presentation Pack	8·50	

Withdrawn: 2.8.2005

1096 'Maughold Church'

1097 'Port St. Mary'

1098 'Ballaugh Old Church'

1099 'Douglas Bay (A Midsummer's Night)'

1100 'Point of Ayre'

1101 'Peel Harbour and Castle'

The Isle of Man Watercolours by Alfred Heaton Cooper

(Des The Agency Ltd. Litho Enschedé)

2004 (21 OCT). Perf 13½×13 (C)

1178	**1096**	25p multicoloured	80	80
1179	**1097**	28p multicoloured	90	90
1180	**1098**	40p multicoloured	1·30	1·30
1181	**1099**	41p multicoloured	1·30	1·30
1182	**1100**	43p multicoloured	1·40	1·40
1183	**1101**	74p multicoloured	2·40	2·40
1178/83		Set of 6	8·00	8·00
		First Day Cover		10·00
		Presentation Pack	10·00	

The 28p and 40p values include the 'EUROPA 2004' emblem.

Plate Nos. All values 1A (×4)

Sheets: 25 (5×5); 28p and 40p also 10 (2×5)

Withdrawn: 20.10.2005

Sindelfingen International Stamp Exhibition, Sindelfingen, Germany

2004 (29 OCT). No. **MS**1177 additionally inscribed with SINDELFINGEN logo on the sheet margin.

MS1184	**1095a**	£2 multicoloured	6·50	6·50

Withdrawn: 28.10.2005

1102 Robin on Flower Pot

1103 Robin at Foot of Tree

1104 Robin perched on
Branch among
Bracken

1105 Robin on Window
Ledge

1106 Robin on Snowy Logs

Robins—'Winter's Friends'

(Des Dr. J. Paul. Litho Lowe-Martin, Canada)

2004 (9 NOV). Perf 12½×13 (C)

1185	**1102**	25p multicoloured	80	80
1186	**1103**	28p multicoloured	90	90
1187	**1104**	40p multicoloured	1·30	1·30
1188	**1105**	47p multicoloured	1·50	1·50
1189	**1106**	68p multicoloured	2·30	2·30
1185/9		Set of 5	6·75	6·75
		First Day Cover		8·75
		Presentation Pack	8·75	
		Collectors Folder (**MS**1190 and signed first day cover)	30·00	
MS1190		148×200 mm. Nos. 1185/9×2	8·50	8·50

Plate Nos.: All values 1A (×7)

Sheets: 40 (5×8)

Withdrawn: 8.11.2005

Year Folder 2004

2004 (9 NOV). *Comprises Nos.* 1116/66, **MS**1177/83 *and* 1185/9

Year Folder . . . . 60·00

Sold out: By 7.2005

Year Pack 2004

2004 (9 NOV) *Comprises Nos.* 1116/66, **MS**1177/83 *and* 1185/9

Year Pack . . . . 75·00

Sold out: By 8.2006

Post Office Yearbook

2004 (9 NOV) *Comprises Nos.* 1116/66, **MS**1177/83 *and* 1185/9

Yearbook . . . . 60·00

Sold out: By 12.2006

1107 Harry Potter, Ron
Weasley and
Hermione Granger

1108 Snowy Owl
delivering Owl
Post

1109 Harry Potter and
White Stag

1110 *Hogwarts Express*

1111 Rubeus Hagrid

1112 Purple Triple-decker
Bus

1113 Dementor and
Harry Potter flying

1114 Harry Potter on the
Hippogriff Buckbeak

262

Harry Potter and the Prisoner of Azkaban *(film)*

(Des The Agency Ltd. Litho Enschedé)

2004 (7 DEC). Perf 13½ (C)

1191	**1107**	25p multicoloured	80	80
1192	**1108**	28p multicoloured	90	90
1193	**1109**	39p multicoloured	1·30	1·30
1194	**1110**	40p multicoloured	1·30	1·30
1195	**1111**	49p multicoloured	1·60	1·60
1196	**1112**	55p multicoloured	1·80	1·80
1197	**1113**	57p multicoloured	1·90	1·90
1198	**1114**	68p multicoloured	2·20	2·20
1191/8		*Set of 8*	11·50	11·50
		First Day Cover		13·50
		Presentation Pack	13·50	
		Collectors Folder (contains complete sheets and 'Owl Post Office' first day cover)	50·00	
		Stamp Cards (pre paid) (set of 8)	11·50	11·50

Plate Nos.: All values 1A (×5)

Sheets: 5 (1×5) with enlarged illustrated right margins

Withdrawn: 6.12.2005

1115 'The Nile Campaign'

1116 'The Battle of Copenhagen'

1117 Emma, Horatia and Nelson

1118 Band of Brothers

1119 'Prepare for Battle'

1120 'Victory in Sight'

1121 'The Fall of Nelson'

1122 'The Death of Nelson'

1123 2000 Isle of Man at War 22p Stamp (£1); 1979 150th Death Anniversary of Captain John Quilliam 8p Stamp (£1)

(illustration reduced. Actual size 170×75 mm)

Bicentenary of the Battle of Trafalgar

(Des E. Cassidy. Litho Enschedé (Nos. 1199/1206) or Lowe-Martin (**MS**1207))

2005 (9 JAN). Perf 12½×13 (C)

1199	**1115**	25p multicoloured	50	55
		a. Horiz pair. Nos. 1199/1200	1·00	1·10
1200	**1116**	25p multicoloured	50	55
1201	**1117**	28p multicoloured	55	60
		a. Horiz pair. Nos. 1201/2	1·10	1·20
1202	**1118**	28p multicoloured	55	60
1203	**1119**	50p multicoloured	1·00	1·10
		a. Horiz pair. Nos. 1203/4	2·00	2·20
1204	**1120**	50p multicoloured	1·00	1·10
1205	**1121**	65p multicoloured	1·30	1·40
		a. Horiz pair. Nos. 1205/6	2·50	2·75
1206	**1122**	65p multicoloured	1·30	1·40
1199/1206		*Set of 8*	6·50	7·00
		First Day Cover		8·00
		Presentation Pack	8·00	
		Collectors Folder (complete sheets and **MS**1207*)*	30·00	
MS1207		170×75 mm. **1123** £1 multicoloured; £1 multicoloured	4·00	4·25
		First Day Cover		5·00
		Presentation Pack	5·00	

Plate Nos.: All values 1A (×5)

Sheets: 8 (2×4). Nos. 1199/1200, 1201/2, 1203/4 and 1205/6 were each printed together, *se-tenant*, in horizontal pairs throughout the sheets

Withdrawn: 8.1.2006

1124 Two Couples by Waterside

1125 Group celebrating in the Street

1126 Man trying on Hat

1127 Civil Service Personnel

1128 King George VI and Winston Churchill on Balcony of Buckingham Palace

1129 King George VI and Queen Elizabeth in Carriage

1130 Servicemen

1131 War Graves

1132 The Manx Regiment (£1); Royal Visit, 1945 (£1) (*illustration reduced. Actual size* 170×75 *mm*)

60th Anniversary of the End of World War II

(Des The Agency Ltd. Litho Enschedé)

2005 (15 APR). Perf 13½×14 (C)

1208	**1124**	26p multicoloured	. . . .	45	30
		a. Horiz pair. Nos. 1208/9	. . .	1·00	1·10
1209	**1125**	26p multicoloured	. . . .	45	30
1210	**1126**	29p multicoloured	. . . .	50	30
		a. Horiz. pair. Nos. 1210/11	. .	1·20	1·30

1211	**1127**	29p multicoloured	. . . .	50	30
1212	**1128**	60p multicoloured	. . . .	75	70
		a. Horiz pair. Nos. 1212/13	. .	2·50	2·50
1213	**1129**	60p multicoloured	. . . .	75	70
1214	**1130**	65p multicoloured	. . . .	85	70
		a. Horiz pair. Nos. 1214/15	. .	2·75	2·75
1215	**1131**	65p multicoloured	. . . .	85	70
1208/15		Set of 8	. . . .	7·00	7·75
		First Day Cover	. . . .		8·25
		Presentation Pack	. . . .	8·25	
		Collectors Folder (complete sheets)	. . . .	.40·00	

MS1216 170×75 mm. **1132** £1 multicoloured; £1 multicoloured . . . . 4·00 4·25
First Day Cover . . . . 5·00
Presentation Pack . . . . 5·00

Plate Nos.: All values 1A (×4)

Sheets: 10 (2×5). Nos. 1208/9, 1210/11, 1212/13 and 1214/15 were each printed together, *se-tenant*, in horizontal pairs throughout the sheets

Withdrawn: 14.4.2006

1133 *'Mona's Isle'* (Samuel Walters)

1134 *'Viking'* (Norman Wilkinson)

1135 *'King Orry'* (Robert Lloyd)

1136 *'Mona's Queen'* (Arthur Burgess)

1137 *'Ben-my-Chree'* (John Nicholson)

1138 *'King Orry'* (Robert Lloyd)

1139 *'Ben-my-Chree'* (Robert Lloyd)

1140 *'Lady of Mann'* (Robert Lloyd)

175th Anniversary of Steam Packet Company

(Des Tracey Harding. Litho BDT)

2005 (6 MAY). Perf 14 (C)

1217	**1133**	26p multicoloured	45	30
		a. *Horiz pair. Nos.* 1217/18 . .	1·00	1·00
		b. *Booklet pane. Nos. 1217/20 with margins all round*	2·20	
		c. *Booklet pane. Nos. 1217/18 and 1221/2 with margins all round*	2·50	
1218	**1134**	26p multicoloured	45	30
1219	**1135**	29p multicoloured	50	30
		a. *Horiz pair. Nos.* 1219/20 . .	1·20	1·50
		b. *Booklet pane. Nos. 1219/20 and 1223/4 with margins all round*	3·75	
1220	**1136**	29p multicoloured	50	30
1221	**1137**	40p multicoloured	75	45
		a. *Horiz pair. Nos.* 1221/2 . . .	1·70	1·70
		b. *Booklet pane. Nos. 1221/4 with margins all round* . . .	4·00	
1222	**1138**	40p multicoloured	75	45
1223	**1139**	66p multicoloured	1·00	70
		a. *Horiz pair. Nos.* 1223/4 . . .	2·75	2·75
		b. *Booklet pane. Nos. 1223/4 with margins all round* . . .	2·50	
1224	**1140**	66p multicoloured	1·00	70
1217/24		*Set of 8*	6·25	6·75
		First Day Cover		7·50
		Presentation Pack	7·50	
		Set of 4 Gutter Pairs	13·00	

Plate Nos.: All values 1A (×4)

Sheets: 40 (2 panes 2×10). Nos. 1217/18, 1219/20, 1221/2 and 1223/4 were each printed together, *se-tenant*, as horizontal pairs in sheets containing two vertical columns of pairs separated by an illustrated and inscribed gutter.

Withdrawn: 5.5.2006

1141 Bill Ivy and Phil Read

1142 Joey Dunlop and Ray McCullough

1143 Steve Hislop

1144 Carl Fogarty

1145 David Jefferies

1146 John McGuinness

50th Anniversary of Yamaha

(Des Ruth Sutherland. Litho Enschedé)

2005 (17 MAY). Perf 14 (C)

1225	**1141**	26p multicoloured	50	55
		a. *Sheetlet. Nos.* 1225/30×2	11·50	
1226	**1142**	29p multicoloured	60	65
1227	**1143**	40p multicoloured	80	85
1228	**1144**	42p multicoloured	85	90
1229	**1145**	68p multicoloured	1·40	1·50
1230	**1146**	78p multicoloured	1·60	1·70
1225/30		*Set of 6*	5·75	6·00
		First Day Cover		6·75
		Presentation Pack	6·75	
		Carl Fogarty Folder (sheetlet & signed first day cover)	40·00	

Plate Nos.: All values 1A (×4) (sheets of 25 only)

Sheets: 25 (5×5) or 12 (2 columns 6×1). Nos. 1225/30 were issued in separate sheets of 25 and *se-tenant* in sheetlets of 12 containing two vertical columns separated by an illustrated gutter.

Withdrawn: 16.5.2006

1147 Paul Harris (founder)

1148 Planting Tree, Children grouped and Child drinking

1149 Child being immunised and Boy with Leg Braces and Crutches

1150 Food Preparations

1151 Supply Truck, Children with Volunteer and loading Cases

1152 Child having Eye Test, Group under Rotary Banner and Family

Centenary of Rotary International and Europa Gastronomy

(Des The Agency Ltd. Litho Cartor)

2005 (15 JUNE). Perf 13½×14 (C)

1231	**1147**	26p multicoloured	50	55
1232	**1148**	29p multicoloured	60	65
1233	**1149**	40p multicoloured	80	85
1234	**1150**	42p multicoloured	85	90
1235	**1151**	64p multicoloured	1·30	1·40
1236	**1152**	68p multicoloured	1·40	1·50
1231/6		Set of 6	5·25	5·75
		First Day Cover		6·75
		Presentation Pack	6·75	

The 42p value includes the 'EUROPA 2005' emblem.

Plate Nos.: All values 1A (×4)

Sheets: 25 (5×5); 42p also 10 (2×5).

Withdrawn: 14.6.2006

1153 Guttin' Herrin'

1154 Pickin' Spuds

1155 J. C. Kelly, Master Butcher

1156 Winckles, Foxdale

1157 Palace Ballroom

1158 Land Army

1159 Farmyard, Glen Maye

1160 Eva Kane, Summer Season Stars

1161 Donkey Rides

1162 Alfie Gilmour, 'Give us a go Mister!'

'Time to Remember'

(Des The Agency Ltd. Litho Lowe-Martin)

2005 (12 AUG). (a) PVA gum. Perf 12½×13 (C)

1237	**1153**	26p multicoloured	45	30
		a. Horiz strip of 5. Nos. 1237/41	2·50	2·50
1238	**1154**	26p multicoloured	45	30
1239	**1155**	26p multicoloured	45	30
1240	**1156**	26p multicoloured	45	30
1241	**1157**	26p multicoloured	45	30
1242	**1158**	29p multicoloured	50	30
		a. Horiz strip of 5. Nos. 1242/6	3·50	3·75
1243	**1159**	29p multicoloured	50	30
1244	**1160**	29p multicoloured	50	30
1245	**1161**	29p multicoloured	50	30
1246	**1162**	29p multicoloured	50	30
1237/46		Set of 10	5·50	6·00
		First Day Cover		6·75
		Presentation Pack	6·75	

		(b) Self-adhesive. Perf 12½×13		
1247	**1153**	26p multicoloured	50	55
		a. Horiz strip of 5. Nos. 1247/51	2·50	
		b. Die cut perf 10½	50	55
		ba. Booklet pane. Nos. 1247b/51b, each × 2	5·00	
1248	**1154**	26p multicoloured	50	55
		b. Die-cut perf 10½	50	55
1249	**1155**	26p multicoloured	50	55
		b. Die-cut perf 10½	50	55
1250	**1156**	26p multicoloured	50	55
		b. Die-cut perf 10½	50	55
1251	**1157**	26p multicoloured	50	55
		b. Die-cut perf 10½	50	55

1252	**1158**	29p multicoloured	60	65
		a. *Horiz strip of 5. Nos.*		
		1252/6	3·75	
		b. Die-cut perf 10½	60	65
		ba. *Booklet pane. Nos.*		
		1252b/6b, each × 2	5·75	
1253	**1159**	29p multicoloured	60	65
		b. Die-cut perf 10½	60	65
1254	**1160**	29p multicoloured	60	65
		b. Die-cut perf 10½	60	65
1255	**1161**	29p multicoloured	60	65
		b. Die-cut perf 10½	60	65
1256	**1162**	29p multicoloured	60	65
		b. Die-cut perf 10½	60	65
1247/56		*Set of 10*	5·50	6·00

Plate Nos.: All values 1A (×5)

Sheets: 50 (5×10). Nos. 1237/41, 1242/6, 1247/51 and 1252/6 were each printed together, *se-tenant*, in horizontal strips of five stamps throughout the sheets.
Nos. 1247b/51b and 1252b/6b were only available from £2.60 and £2.90 booklets, Nos. SB62/3.

Withdrawn: 11.8.2006

1163 Obelisk in St Peters Square (42p); St. Peter's Basilica (£1.50)
(*illustration reduced. Actual size 170×75 mm*)

20th World Youth Day

(Des E. Cassidy. Litho BDT)

2005 (15 AUG). *Sheet* 170×75 *mm. Perf* 14×15 (C)
MS1257 **1163** 42p multicoloured; £1.50

	multicoloured	3·75	4·00
	First Day Cover		5·00
	Presentation Pack	5·00	

The stamps within No. **MS**1257 each have labels at left showing Pope John Paul II (42p) and Pope Benedict XVI (£1.50).

Withdrawn: 14.8.2006

1164 Harry Potter

1165 Harry Potter, Hermione, Ron Weasley and Goblet of Fire

1166 Trophy

1167 Hungarian Horntail Dragon

1168 Hogwarts Coat of Arms

1169 Murcus, Chieftainess of the Merpeople

Harry Potter and the Goblet of Fire (film)

(Des The Agency. Litho BDT)

2005 (21 OCT). Perf 13½ (C)

1258	**1164**	26p multicoloured	50	55
1259	**1165**	29p multicoloured	60	65
1260	**1166**	33p multicoloured	65	70
1261	**1167**	64p multicoloured	1·30	1·40
1262	**1168**	68p multicoloured	1·40	1·50
1263	**1169**	75p multicoloured	1·50	1·60
1258/63		*Set of 6*	5·75	6·25
		First Day Cover		7·00
		Presentation Pack	7·00	
		Collectors Folder (complete sheets & special first day cover (silver postmark))		50·00

Plate Nos.: All values 1A (×5)

Sheets: 5 (1×5) with enlarged illustrated right margins

Withdrawn: 20.10.2006

1170 Death of Nelson (Gibraltar £1); Arrival of Nelson's funeral procession at St. Paul's Cathedral, London (£1)
(*illustration reduced. Actual size 170×75 mm*)

Death Bicentenary of Admiral Lord Nelson

(Des and litho Lowe-Martin, Canada)

2005 (21 OCT). *Sheet* 170×75 *mm.* Perf 13½ (C)

MS1264	**1170**	Gibraltar £1 multicoloured;		
		£1 multicoloured	4·00	4·25
		First Day Cover		5·25
		Presentation Pack	5·25	
		Collectors Folder (**MS**1264,		
		Gibraltar miniature sheet,		
		Isle of Man & Gibraltar		
		first day covers) . . . . . .35·00		

The miniature sheet contains a £1 Gibraltar stamp and a £1 Isle of Man stamp. The same miniature sheet was also issued by Gibraltar.

Withdrawn: 20.10.2006

1171 Mary and Jesus

1172 Angel with the Crown of Glory

1173 Shepherds worshipping Christ Child

1174 Nativity

1175 Three Kings

Christmas. Stained-glass Windows from Manx Churches

(Des E. Cassidy. Litho Cartor)

2005 (7 NOV). Perf 13½×13 (C)

1265	**1171**	26p multicoloured	50	55
1266	**1172**	29p multicoloured	60	65
1267	**1173**	42p multicoloured	85	90
1268	**1174**	60p multicoloured	1·20	1·30
1269	**1175**	68p multicoloured	1·40	1·50
1265/9		Set of 5	4·50	4·75
		First Day Cover		5·75
		Presentation Pack	5·75	

Nos. 1265/7 show windows from St. German's Cathedral, Peel and Nos. 1268/9 windows from Kirk Christ, Rushen

Plate Nos.: All values 1A (×4)

Sheets: 50 (10×5)

Withdrawn: 6.11.2006

Year Folder 2005

2005 (7 NOV). *Comprises Nos.* 1191/246 *and* **MS**1257/69

Year Folder . . . . .70·00

Sold out: By 12.2006

Year Pack 2005

2005 (7 NOV). *Comprises Nos.* 1191/246 *and* **MS**1257/69

Year Pack . . . . .85·00

Sold out: By 12.2006

Post Office Yearbook

2005 (7 NOV). *Comprises Nos.* 1191/246, **MS**1257/69 *and* *'Time to Remember' CD including booklets* SB62/3

Yearbook . . . . .70·00

Sold out: By 8.2008

1176 Princess Elizabeth aged Five with Duke and Duchess of York and Princess Margaret, 1931

1177 Princess Elizabeth wearing ATS Uniform, c. 1944

1178 Queen Elizabeth wearing Diadem, 1952

1179 With Princes Philip, Andrew, Edward, Charles and Princess Anne, 1972

1180 With Prince Philip at Balmoral on Silver Wedding Anniversary, 1972

1181 With Regalia in Throne Room, Buckingham Palace, 2001

1182 With Prince William on Buckingham Palace Balcony

1183 With Crowd at Aylesbury, Buckinghamshire on Golden Jubilee Tour, 2002

80th Birthday of Queen Elizabeth II (1st issue)

(Des The Agency. Litho Austrian State Ptg Wks, Vienna)

2006 (16 JAN). Perf 14 (C)

1270	**1176**	20p multicoloured	40	30
		a. *Horiz strip of 4. Nos.* 1270/3	1·70	1·70
1271	**1177**	20p multicoloured	40	30
1272	**1178**	20p multicoloured	40	30
1273	**1179**	20p multicoloured	40	30
1274	**1180**	80p multicoloured	1·60	1·00
		a. *Horiz strip of 4. Nos.* 1274/7	6·75	6·75
1275	**1181**	80p multicoloured	1·60	1·00
1276	**1182**	80p multicoloured	1·60	1·00
1277	**1183**	80p multicoloured	1·60	1·00

1270/7				
	Set of 8	8·00	8·50
	First Day Cover		9·25
	Presentation Pack	9·50	
	Collectors Folder (complete sheets)	32·00	
	Set of 2 Gutter Strips	16·00	

See also No. **MS**1304.

Plate Nos.: Both values 1A (×4)

Sheets: 16 (2 blocks 2×4). Nos. 1270/3 and 1274/7 were each printed together, *se-tenant*, as horizontal strips of four stamps in sheets containing two blocks of 8 separated by a large illustrated gutter.

Withdrawn: 15.1.2007

1184 Jurby Chalice and Jurby Church

1185 Viking Period Gold Pin Head and Peel Castle

1186 Fragment of Early Neolithic Bowl and Meayll Hill, Rushen

1187 Manx Stoat and Cronk Sumark Late Iron Age Hill Fort

1188 Hen Harrier and South Barrule Hill, Malew

1189 Fossil Ammonite, Scarlett Point and Castletown

Manx Study—Isle of Man Natural History and Antiquarian Society

(Des Icon Imaging. Litho Enschedé)

2006 (15 FEB). Perf 14 (C)

1278	**1184**	26p multicoloured	50	55
1279	**1185**	29p multicoloured	60	65
1280	**1186**	64p multicoloured	1·30	1·40
1281	**1187**	68p multicoloured	1·40	1·50

1282	**1188**	78p multicoloured	1·60	1·70
1283	**1189**	97p multicoloured	1·90	2·00
1278/83		Set of 6	7·25	7·75
		First Day Cover		8·50
		Presentation Pack	9·50	

Plate Nos.: All values 1A (×4)

Sheets: 25 (5×5)

Withdrawn: 14.2.2007

1190 Peregrine
Falcon

1191 Puffin

1192 Manx
Shearwater

1193 Chough

1194 Guillemot

1195 Whinchat

1196 Hen Harrier

1197 Goldcrest

1198 Grey Wagtail

1199 Wren

Manx Bird Atlas

(Des Dr. J. Paul and The Agency. Litho Cartor)

2006 (17 APR). (*a*) *PVA gum.* Perf 12½ (C)

1284	**1190**	28p multicoloured	55	35
		a. *Horiz strip of 5. Nos.* 1284/8	3·00	3·00
1285	**1191**	28p multicoloured	55	35
1286	**1192**	28p multicoloured	55	35
1287	**1193**	28p multicoloured	55	35
1288	**1194**	28p multicoloured	55	35
1289	**1195**	31p multicoloured	60	40
		a. *Horiz strip of 5. Nos.* 1289/93	3·50	3·25
1290	**1196**	31p multicoloured	60	40
1291	**1197**	31p multicoloured	60	40
1292	**1198**	31p multicoloured	60	40
1293	**1199**	31p multicoloured	60	40
1284/93		Set of 10	6·00	6·25
		First Day Cover		7·00
		Presentation Pack	7·25	

(*b*) *Self-adhesive.* Perf 12½ (die-cut)

1293a	**1190**	28p multicoloured	55	60
		ab. *Horiz strip of 5. Nos.* 1293a/e	3·25	
1293b	**1191**	28p multicoloured	55	60
1293c	**1192**	28p multicoloured	55	60
1293d	**1193**	28p multicoloured	55	60
1293e	**1194**	28p multicoloured	55	60
1293f	**1195**	31p multicoloured	60	65
		fa. *Horiz strip of 5. Nos.* 1293f/j	4·00	
1293g	**1196**	31p multicoloured	60	65
1293h	**1197**	31p multicoloured	60	65
1293i	**1198**	31p multicoloured	60	65
1293j	**1199**	31p multicoloured	60	65
1293a/j		Set of 10	6·50	6·50

Plate Nos.: Both values 1A (×4)

Sheets: 50 (5×10). Nos. 1284/8, 1289/93, 1293a/e and 1293f/j were each printed together, *se-tenant*, in horizontal strips of five stamps throughout the sheets.

Withdrawn: 16.4.2007

1200 Queen Elizabeth II at Tynwald Ceremony, 2003 (£1); In 1972 (£1)

(*illustration reduced. Actual size* 120×78 *mm*)

80th Birthday of Queen Elizabeth II (2nd issue)

(Des The Agency. Litho BDT)

2006 (21 APR). *Sheet* 120×78 *mm. Perf* 14 (C)
MS1294 £1 multicoloured; £1 multicoloured 4·00 4·25
    First Day Cover . . . . 5·50
    Presentation Pack . . . . 5·50

Withdrawn: 20.4.2007

1201 West German Player

1202 West German Team

1203 Bobby Moore (England captain) with Trophy and Alf Ramsey (manager)

1204 Bobby Moore holding Trophy aloft

1205 West German Players

1206 Victorious England Team

World Cup Football Championship, Germany. 40th Anniversary of England's World Cup Victory

(Des E. Cassidy. Litho Lowe-Martin, Canada)

2006 (2 MAY). *Perf* 12½×13 (C)

1295	**1201**	28p multicoloured	55	60
1296	**1202**	31p multicoloured	60	65
1297	**1203**	44p multicoloured	90	95
1298	**1204**	72p multicoloured	1·40	1·50
1299	**1205**	83p multicoloured	1·70	1·80

1300	**1206**	94p multicoloured	1·90	2·00
1295/300		*Set of* 6	7·00	7·50
		First Day Cover		8·50
		Presentation Pack	8·50	

Nos. 1295/300 each contained a circle of gold imitation perforations.

Plate Nos. All values 1A ×5
Sheets: 20 (4×5)
Withdrawn: 1.5.2007

1207 1977 Isle of Man 10p Europa Stamp (42p); 1990 Isle of Man 15p Europa Stamp (83p) (*illustration reduced. Actual size* 170×75 *mm*)

50th Anniversary of First Europa Stamp

(Des D. Clague. Litho Enschedé)

2006 (2 MAY). *Sheet* 170×75 *mm. Perf* 13½×14 (C)
MS1301 42p multicoloured; 83p multi-
    coloured . . . . 2·50 2·75
    First Day Cover . . . . 4·00
    Presentation Pack . . . . 4·00

Withdrawn: 1.5.2007

1208 Letitia Tyler (First Lady 1841–2)

1209 Joseph Gurney 'Czar' Cannon (Speaker of House of Representatives 1903–11)

1210 Matthew Quay (Civil War hero and Republican Party National Committee chairman)

1211 Mary Clemmer (19th-century journalist)

1212 Ewan Clague (economist)

1213 Henry 'Marse' Watterson (advisor to Pres. Roosevelt)

1218 Manxcar

1219 P1000

Manx Links with Washington

(Des Fusion Design. Litho BDT)

2006 (23 MAY). Perf 14 (C)

1302	**1208**	28p multicoloured	55	60
1303	**1209**	31p multicoloured	60	65
1304	**1210**	45p multicoloured	90	95
1305	**1211**	50p multicoloured	1·00	1·10
1306	**1212**	76p multicoloured	1·50	1·60
1307	**1213**	83p multicoloured	1·70	1·80
1302/7		Set of 6	6·25	6·50
		First Day Cover		7·75
		Presentation Pack	7·75	

Nos. 1302/7 were issued to coincide with the Washington 2006 Stamp Exhibition.

Plate Nos.: All values 1A (×4)

Sheets: 25 (5×5)

Withdrawn: 22.5.2007

Peel Cars

(Des Fusion Design. Litho Lowe-Martin, Canada)

2006 (23 JULY). Perf 13½ (C)

1308	**1214**	28p multicoloured	55	60
1309	**1215**	31p multicoloured	60	65
1310	**1216**	38p multicoloured	75	80
1311	**1217**	41p multicoloured	80	85
1312	**1218**	54p multicoloured	1·10	1·20
1313	**1219**	94p multicoloured	1·90	2·00
1308/13		Set of 6	5·50	6·00
		First Day Cover		7·00
		Presentation Pack	7·25	
		Collectors Folder (top row of 5 and sheet top of each value)	35·00	

Plate Nos.: All values 1A (×4)

Sheets: 25 (5×5)

Withdrawn: 21.7.2007

1214 Peel P50

1215 Trident

1216 Viking Sport

1217 BMC GRP Mini

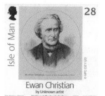

1220 'Ewan Christian'

1221 'Dame Agatha Christie' (John Gay)

1222 'Sir Hall Caine' (Harry Furniss)

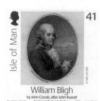

1223 'William Bligh (John Condé, after John Russell)

1224 'Lady Maria
Callcott' (Sir
Thomas Lawrence)

1225 'John Martin'
(Henry Warren)

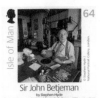

1226 'Sir John Betjeman'
(Stephen Hyde)

1227 'Sir Edward Elgar'
(Herbert Lambert)

150th Anniversary of National Portrait Gallery, London

(Des The Agency. Litho Lowe-Martin, Canada)

2006 (25 AUG). Perf 13½ (C).

1314	**1220**	28p multicoloured	55	60
1315	**1221**	31p multicoloured	60	65
1316	**1222**	38p multicoloured	75	80
1317	**1223**	41p multicoloured	80	85
1318	**1224**	44p multicoloured	90	95
1319	**1225**	54p multicoloured	1·10	1·20
1320	**1226**	64p multicoloured	1·30	1·40
1321	**1227**	96p multicoloured	1·90	2·00
1314/21		Set of 8	7·75	8·25
		First Day Cover		9·25
		Presentation Pack	9·50	

Plate Nos.: All values 1A (×4)

Sheets: 25 (5×5)

Withdrawn: 24.8.2007

1228 Christmas Tree
and Gifts

1229 Tree with Three
Legs of Mann
Decoration at
Top

1230 Tree with
White
Decorations

1231 Monkey-puzzle
Tree and Three
Legs of Mann
Symbols

1232 Tree with
Yellow Three
Legs of Mann
Decorations

1233 Tree with
Brown Three
Legs of Mann
Decorations

Christmas. Trees

(Des Emma Cooke and The Agency. Litho and die-stamped
BDT)

2006 (11 OCT). (a) PVA gum. Perf 14 (C)

1322	**1228**	28p multicoloured	55	60
1323	**1229**	31p multicoloured	60	65
1324	**1230**	41p multicoloured	80	85
1325	**1231**	44p multicoloured	90	95
1326	**1232**	72p multicoloured	1·40	1·50
1327	**1233**	94p multicoloured	1·90	2·00
1322/7		Set of 6	6·00	6·50
		First Day Cover		7·50
		Presentation Pack	7·75	

(b) Size 28×39 mm. Self-adhesive booklet stamps. Perf
9×9½ (die-cut).

1328	**1228**	28p multicoloured	55	60
		a. Booklet pane. No.1328×10	5·50	
1329	**1229**	31p multicoloured	60	65
		a. Booklet pane. No.1329×10	6·00	

Nos. 1323, 1325 and 1329 include the 'EUROPA 2006'
emblem.

Nos. 1328/9 were only available in £2.80 and £3.10
booklets, Nos. SB64/5.

Plate Nos.: All values 1A (×5)

Sheets: 25 (5×5); 31p, 44p also 10 (5×2)

Withdrawn: 10.10.2007

1234 Benjamin Bunny (28p); Jemima Puddle-duck (50p); Peter Rabbit (72p); Jeremy Fisher (75p) (*illustration reduced. Actual size* 170×75 *mm*)

The Tales of Beatrix Potter

(Litho Lowe-Martin, Canada)

2006 (11 OCT). *Sheet* 170×75 *mm.* Perf 13 (C)
MS1330 28p multicoloured; 50p multi-
coloured; 72p multicoloured; 75p multi-
coloured . . . . 4·50   4·75
First Day Cover . . . .   6·00
Presentation Pack . . . . 6·00

Withdrawn: 10.10.2007

Belgica '06 International Stamp Exhibition, Brussels

2006 (11 OCT). *Sheet* 148×210 *mm.* Perf 12½ (C)
MS1331   Nos. 1284/93 . . . . 5·75   6·00

Withdrawn: 10.10.2007

Year Folder 2006

2006 (11 OCT). *Comprises Nos.* 1270/93, **MS**1294/327 *and* **MS**1330
Year Folder . . . . .65·00

Sold out: By 5.2008

Year Pack 2006

2006 (11 OCT). *Comprises Nos.* 1270/93, **MS**1294/327 *and* **MS**1330
Year Pack . . . . .80·00

Sold out: By 5.2008

Post Office Yearbook

2006 (11 OCT). *Comprises Nos.* 1270/93, **MS**1294/327 *and* **MS**1330/1
Yearbook . . . . .70·00

Sold out: By November 2007

1235 Steve Hislop

1236 Joey Dunlop

1237 David Jefferies

1238 Dave Molyneux

1239 John McGuinness

1240 Stanley Woods

1241 Geoff Duke

1242 Bob McIntyre

1243 Giacomo Agostini

1244 Mike Hailwood

Centenary of Isle of Man TT Motor Cycle Races

(Des Ruth Sutherland. Litho BDT)

2007 (1 JAN). Perf 14½ (C)

1332	**1235**	(31p) multicoloured	65	50
		a. Horiz strip of 5. Nos. 1332/6	4·00	4·00
1333	**1236**	(31p) multicoloured	65	50
1334	**1237**	(31p) multicoloured	65	50
1335	**1238**	(31p) multicoloured	65	50
1336	**1239**	(31p) multicoloured	65	50
1337	**1240**	(44p) multicoloured	85	80
		a. Horiz strip of 5. Nos. 1337/41	5·25	5·25
1338	**1241**	(44p) multicoloured	85	80
1339	**1242**	(44p) multicoloured	85	80
1340	**1243**	(44p) multicoloured	85	80
1341	**1244**	(44p) multicoloured	85	80
1332/41		Set of 10	8·75	8·75
		First Day Cover		9·25
		Presentation Pack	9·25	

Collectors Folder (com-
plete sheets) . . . . .45·00
Set of 2 Gutter Strips . . . .20·00
Stamp Cards (pre-paid)
(set of 10) . . . . .16·00   16·00
Deluxe Stamp Cards (set
of 14 Nos. 1332/41 and
4 TT trophy cards) (mint) 25·00

Nos. 1332/6 are inscribed 'UK' and were sold at 31p each.
Nos. 1337/41 are inscribed 'E' and were sold at 44p each.

Plate Nos.: Both values 1A (×4)

Sheets: 20 (2 blocks 5×2). Nos. 1332/6 and 1337/41 were each
printed together, se-tenant, as horizontal strips of five stamps in
sheets containing two blocks of 10 separated by a large illustrated
gutter.

Withdrawn: 31.12.2007

1251 Two Scouts at Camp, 1913 (50p); Scout Camp with
Bell Tent and Open Fire, 1913 (£1.50)
(illustration reduced. Actual size 135×85 mm)

Centenary of Scouting

(Des M. J. Southall. Litho BDT)

1245 Scouts hiking
near South
Barrule

1246 Scout Investiture
on Douglas
Beach

1247 Backpacking
below Cronk-ny-
Arrey-Laa

1248 Manx Scouts on
Parade at St.
Johns

1249 Sea kayaking off
Laxey Beach

1250 Manx Scouts
operating the TT
Scoreboard

2007 (22 FEB). Perf 14 (C)

1342	**1245**	28p multicoloured	65	65
		a. Booklet pane. Nos. 1342/4		
		with margins all round . . .	3·00	
		b. Booklet pane. Nos. 1342,		
		1344 and 1346 with		
		margins all round	4·50	
1343	**1246**	31p multicoloured	75	75
		a. Booklet pane. Nos. 1343,		
		1345 and 1347 with		
		margins all round	6·00	
1344	**1247**	44p multicoloured	1·00	1·00
1345	**1248**	72p multicoloured	1·70	1·70
		a. Booklet pane. Nos. 1345/7		
		with margins all round . . .	7·50	
1346	**1249**	83p multicoloured	2·00	2·00
1347	**1250**	£1 multicoloured	2·40	2·40
1342/7		Set of 6	8·50	8·50
		First Day Cover		9·00
		Presentation Pack	9·00	
		Collectors Folder . . . . . . .45·00		
MS1348		135×85 mm. **1251** 50p, £1.50		
		multicoloured	4·75	4·75
		a. Booklet pane. As No.		
		MS1348, but 155×96 mm		
		with additional margins		
		showing Scout emblems		
		and a line of roulettes at		
		left	4·75	
		First Day Cover		5·25
		Presentation Pack	5·25	

Nos. 1343/4 include the 'EUROPA 2007' emblem.

Plate Nos.: All values 1A (×4)

Sheets: 25 (5×5); 31p, 44p also 10 (5×2)

Withdrawn: 21.2.2008

1252 Wedding, 1947

1253 Queen and Duke of Edinburgh, c 1955

1254 Queen and Duke of Edinburgh, c 1965

1255 Queen and Duke of Edinburgh, c 1977

1256 Queen and Duke of Edinburgh, c 1997

1257 Queen and Duke of Edinburgh, c 2002

Diamond Wedding of Queen Elizabeth II and Duke of Edinburgh

(Des EDL Design. Litho BDT)

2007 (22 FEB). Perf 14 (C)

1349	**1252**	60p multicoloured	1·00	1·00
		a. Horiz strip of 6. Nos. 1349/54	8·50	8·50
1350	**1253**	60p multicoloured	1·00	1·00
1351	**1254**	60p multicoloured	1·00	1·00
1352	**1255**	60p multicoloured	1·00	1·00
1353	**1256**	60p multicoloured	1·00	1·00
1354	**1257**	60p multicoloured	1·00	1·00
1349/54		Set of 6	8·50	8·50
		First Day Cover		9·00
		Presentation Pack	9·00	

Plate Nos.: 1A (×4)

Sheets: 30 (6×5). Nos. 1349/54 were printed together, *se-tenant*, as horizontal strips of six stamps in sheets of 30

Withdrawn: 21.2.2008

1258 'Headland, Cornaa'

1259 'Headland, Sound'

1260 'St Marks Church'

1261 'Castletown Harbour Moonlight'

1262 'Bridge House, Castletown'

1263 'Winter Sun'

1264 'In Ancient Times'

1265 'Bracken Mountain'

Watercolour Paintings by Norman Sayle

(Des EDL. Litho Lowe-Martin, Canada)

2007 (12 APR). (*a*) PVA gum. Perf 12½×13

1355	**1258**	28p multicoloured	65	65
1356	**1259**	28p multicoloured	65	65
1357	**1260**	31p multicoloured	75	75
1358	**1261**	31p multicoloured	75	75
1359	**1262**	42p multicoloured	1·00	1·00
1360	**1263**	44p multicoloured	1·00	1·00
1361	**1264**	65p multicoloured	1·50	1·50
1362	**1265**	75p multicoloured	1·70	1·70
1355/62		Set of 8	8·00	8·00
		First Day Cover		8·50
		Presentation Pack	8·50	

(b) *Self-adhesive.* Die-cut perf 10

1363	**1258**	28p multicoloured	85	85
		a. Booklet pane. Nos. 1363/4, each ×5	8·50	
1364	**1259**	28p multicoloured	85	85
1365	**1260**	31p multicoloured	95	95
		a. Booklet pane. Nos. 1365/6, each ×5	9·25	
1366	**1261**	31p multicoloured	95	95
1363/6		Set of 4	3·50	3·50

Nos. 1363/4 and 1365/6 were only issued in £2.80 or £3.10 stamp booklets, Nos. SB67/8

Plate Nos.: All values 1A (each ×5)

Sheets: 25 (5×5)

Withdrawn: 11.4.2008

1266 King John granting Royal Charter

1267 Liverpool Cathedral and Liverpool Metropolitan Cathedral

1268 Statue of Capt. Noel Chavasse ('Liverpool war heroes')

1269 St. George's Hall

1270 Port of Liverpool

1271 The Wall of Fame

800th Anniversary of the Royal Charter of Liverpool

(Des Fusion Design. Litho BDT)

2007 (20 APR). Perf 14 (C)

1367	**1266**	31p multicoloured	70	70
1368	**1267**	48p multicoloured	1·10	1·10
1369	**1268**	54p multicoloured	1·30	1·30
1370	**1269**	74p multicoloured	1·70	1·70
1371	**1270**	80p multicoloured	1·90	1·90
1372	**1271**	£1 multicoloured	2·30	2·30
1367/72		Set of 6	9·00	9·00
		First Day Cover		9·50
		Presentation Pack	9·50	

The plate numbers for Nos. 1367/72 were omitted from the sheets in error.

Sheets: 20 (5×4)

Withdrawn: 18.4.2008

1272 *Susan Constant* and Map showing Voyage from England to Virginia, 1607

1273 Capt. Christopher Newport and *Susan Constant*, *Godspeed* and *Discovery* on the James River

1274 James Fort and James River, 1607

1275 Algonquin Princess Pocahontas and Capt. John Smith

1276 Jamestown Settlement, 1607

1277 Powhatan Village

400th Anniversary of Jamestown, Virginia, USA

(Des Julia Ashby Smyth. Litho Cartor)

2007 (26 APR). Perf 13½ (C)

1373	**1272**	28p multicoloured	65	65
1374	**1273**	31p multicoloured	75	75
1375	**1274**	44p multicoloured	1·00	1·00
1376	**1275**	54p multicoloured	1·30	1·30
1377	**1276**	78p multicoloured	1·90	1·90

1378	**1277**	90p multicoloured	2·20	2·20
1373/8		Set of 6	7·75	7·75
		First Day Cover		8·25
		Presentation Pack	8·25	

Plate Nos.: All values 1A (×4)

Sheets: 15 (3×5) with enlarged illustrated right margins

Withdrawn: 25.4.2008

1278 James Brown (25p); Joseph Cunningham and Holiday Camp, *c* 1895 (40p); William Gill and First Landing Stage at Liverpool, *c* 1857 (80p); Dalrymple Maitland and 'Liverpool Echo' Newspaper (80p)
(*illustration reduced. Actual size* 170×75 *mm*)

800 Years of Trade between Liverpool and the Isle of Man

(Des Fusion Design. Litho)

2007 (10 MAY). *Sheet* 170×75 *mm*. Perf 14 (C)

MS1379	25p, 40p, 80p, 80p multicoloured	5·25	5·25
	First Day Cover		6·00
	Presentation Pack	6·00	

Withdrawn: 9.5.2008

TT Race Winners

2007 (9 JULY). *Sheet* 180×235 *mm*. Perf 14½ (C)

MS1379*a*	Nos. 1332/41	11·50
	TT Race Winners Folder	30·00

Plate Nos. 1A (×4)

Sheets: 10 (2 blocks 5×1). Nos. 1332/41 were printed together, *se-tenant*, as horizontal strips of five stamps in sheets containing two blocks of five stamps and five *se-tenant* labels separated by a large illustrated gutter.

Withdrawn: 8.7.2008

21st World Scout Jamboree, Chelmsford, England

2007 (26 JULY). No. **MS**1348 additionally inscr with jamboree emblem on the margin.

MS1380	50p, £1.50 multicoloured	4·75	4·75
	Stamp Cards (*prepaid*) (*Nos.* 1342, 1344, 1346, *as No.* **MS**1380)	9·00	9·00

The miniature sheet depicted on the stamp card differs from Type **1251** and **MS**1380. The face value is omitted, the 'centenary of scouting 2007' inscription is at bottom left and the Jamboree emblem at top right.

Withdrawn: 25.7.2008

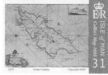

1279 Map by John Speed, 1605

1280 Map by Capt. Greenville Collins, 1693

1281 Map published by John Drinkwater based on Trigonometrical Survey, 1826

1282 Ordnance Survey County Series Map, 1870

1283 Six-inch Series Map based on National Grid, 1975

1284 1:100,000 Map, 2006

Maps of the Isle of Man

(Des Eddie Cassidy. Litho Lowe-Martin)

2007 (1 AUG). Perf 12½×13 (C)

1381	**1279**	28p multicoloured	65	65
1382	**1280**	31p multicoloured	75	75
1383	**1281**	44p multicoloured	1·10	1·10
1384	**1282**	48p multicoloured	1·10	1·10
1385	**1283**	75p multicoloured	1·80	1·80
1386	**1284**	88p multicoloured	2·10	2·10
1381/6		Set of 6	7·50	7·50
		First Day Cover		8·00
		Presentation Pack	8·00	

Plate Nos.: All values 1A (×4)

Sheets: 20 (5×4)

Imprint: Lower side margins

Withdrawn: 31.7.2008

1285 Captain John Ross and *Victory* trapped in Ice

1286 Flares from *Victory* guide returning Exploration Parties

1287 Victory's Crew hunting with Inuit

1288 Hunted Musk Ox

1289 Crew on 300 Mile Trek after abandoning *Victory*

1290 Crew in Whaleboats rescued by Whaler *Isabella*

International Polar Year (1st issue). Voyage of the Victory to the North Pole, 1829–33

(Des Peter Hearsey. Litho Lowe-Martin)

2007 (20 AUG). Perf 12½×13 (C)

1387	**1285**	28p multicoloured	65	65
1388	**1286**	31p multicoloured	70	70
1389	**1287**	55p multicoloured	1·30	1·30
1390	**1288**	75p multicoloured	1·80	1·80
1391	**1289**	90p multicoloured	2·10	2·10
1392	**1290**	117p multicoloured	2·75	2·75
1387/92		Set of 6	9·25	9·25
		First Day Cover		9·75
		Presentation Pack	9·75	

Plate Nos.: All values 1A (×4)

Sheets: 25 (5×5)

Withdrawn: 19.8.2008

1291 'Ben-my-Chree' Log Cabin, Tagish Lake, British Columbia (50p); Graham 'Jimmy' Oates taking Motorcycle and Sidecar along Railroad Track to Hudson Bay, 1932 (50p); Kermode Bear (subspecies of Grizzly Bear) (75p); Dog Sled and Hudson Bay Post Office, 1931–61) (75p)
(*illustration reduced. Actual size 170×75 mm*)

International Polar Year (2nd issue). Manx Connections with Northern Canada

(Des Kcreative. Litho Lowe-Martin)

2007 (20 AUG). *Sheet 170×75 mm.* Perf 13 (C)

MS1393	50p, 50p, 75p, 75p multicoloured	6·00	6·00
	First Day Cover		9·50
	Presentation Pack	9·50	

Withdrawn: 19.8.2008

1292 Harold Leece ploughing Manx Style

1293 John Costain with 1947 Ferguson Tractor and Trailed Plough

1294 Jim Caine with Digger Plough

1295 Herbie Moore with Swing Plough

1296 Jack Clague
ploughing World
Style

1297 Jean Burns
ploughing

1300 Angel wearing
Crown

1301 Angel with
Harp

1302 Angel with Hands clasped in Prayer

European Vintage Ploughing Championships, Isle of Man

(Des Peter Hearsey and Eddie Cassidy. Litho Cartor)

2007 (1 SEPT–1 OCT). Perf 13 (C)

1394	**1292**	28p multicoloured (a)	65	65
1395	**1293**	31p multicoloured (a)	70	70
1396	**1294**	48p multicoloured (b)	1·10	1·10
1397	**1295**	71p multicoloured (a)	1·70	1·70
1398	**1296**	90p multicoloured (a)	2·10	2·10
1399	**1297**	£1.27 multicoloured (a)	3·00	3·00
1394/9		*Set of 6*	9·25	9·25
		First Day Cover		9·75
		Presentation Pack	9·75	

No. 1396 is inscr 'sepac'. This stamp was also available in a folder with 10 other 'sepac' logo stamps issued by other participating administrations.

Plate Nos.: All values 1A (×4)

Sheets: 25 (5×5)

Printings: (*a*) 1.9.07; (*b*) 1.10.07

Withdrawn: 30.9.2008

1298 Angel playing
Trumpet

1299 Angel playing
Lute

Christmas. 'Hark the Herald Angels Sing'

(Des Julia Ashby Smyth. Litho Lowe-Martin, Canada)

2007 (19 OCT). *Self-adhesive. Die-cut perf* 13×13½

1400	**1298**	28p multicoloured	65	65
1401	**1299**	31p multicoloured	75	75
1402	**1300**	69p multicoloured	1·60	1·60
1403	**1301**	78p multicoloured	1·80	1·80
1404	**1302**	£1.24 multicoloured	3·00	3·00
1400/4		*Set of 5*	7·75	7·75
		First Day Cover		8·25
		Presentation Pack	8·25	

The backing paper of Nos. 1400/4 is divided into rectangles by lines of rouletting.

Plate Nos.: All values 1A (each ×5)

Sheets: 20 (5×4)

Withdrawn: 17.10.2008

Year Folder 2007

2007 (19 OCT). *Comprises Nos. 1332/62, 1367/79 and 1381/404*

Year Folder . . . . 80·00

Year Pack 2007

2007 (19 OCT). *Comprises Nos. 1332/62, 1367/79 and 1381/404*

Year Pack £100

Post Office Yearbook

2007 (19 OCT). *Comprises Nos. 1332/62, 1367/79 and 1381/404*

Yearbook . . . . 80·00

1303 *Queen Elizabeth 2*

1304 *Queen Mary 2*

1305 *Queen Victoria*

Cunard Ocean Liners

(Des Kcreative. Litho Enschedé)

2008 (13 JAN). Perf 14×13½ (C)

1405	**1303**	£1 multicoloured	7·00	7·00
1405a	**1304**	£1 multicoloured	7·00	7·00
1405b	**1305**	£1 multicoloured	7·00	7·00
MS1405c	170×75 mm. Nos. 1405/b		7·00	7·00
		First Day Cover		8·75
		Presentation Pack	8·75	
		QE2 Farewell Season Folder (full sheet of No. 1405 and special first day cover) . . . . .50·00		

Nos. 1405/b were only available from the Isle of Man Philatelic Bureau in complete sheetlets, sold for £10 each, or from the miniature sheet.

Plate Nos.: 1A (×6)

Sheets: 10 (2 columns 1×5). Nos. 1405/b were each printed in separate sheetlets of ten stamps and ten labels containing two vertical strips of stamps alternated with two columns of stamp-size labels showing the interior of the ship, so that each stamp is accompanied by a *se-tenant* label at left.

1306 H.P. 0/400 and Bristol F2B Fighter

1307 Avro 504N and Westland Wapiti

1308 Hawker Hurricane and Short Sunderland

1309 Gloster Meteor and Westland Whirlwind

1310 Hawker Hunter and E.E. Canberra

1311 BAE Harrier and Lockheed Hercules

90th Anniversary of the Royal Air Force

(Des Keith Woodcock and Kcreative. Litho BDT)

2008 (15 JAN). Perf 13½ (C)

1406	**1306**	31p multicoloured	60	60
		a. Horiz strip of 3. Nos. 1406/8	2·20	2·20
		b. Booklet pane. Nos. 1406/9 with margins all round . . .	4·25	
		c. Booklet pane. Nos. 1406/7 and 1409/10 with margins all round	5·75	
		d. Booklet pane. Nos. 1406/7 and 1410/11 with margins all round	5·75	
1407	**1307**	31p multicoloured	60	60
1408	**1308**	31p multicoloured	60	60
		a. Booklet pane. Nos. 1408/11 with margins all round	7·25	
1409	**1309**	90p multicoloured	1·70	1·70
		a. Horiz strip of 3. Nos. 1409/11	6·50	6·50
1410	**1310**	90p multicoloured	1·70	1·70
1411	**1311**	90p multicoloured	1·70	1·70
1406/11		Set of 6	8·50	8·50
		First Day Cover		10·00
		Presentation Pack . . . . . . .10·00		
		Souvenir Folder (full sheets) . . . . .35·00		

Plate Nos.: All values 1A (each ×4)

Sheets: 12 (2 blocks 3×2). Nos. 1406/8 and 1409/11 were each printed together, *se-tenant*, as horizontal strips of three stamps in sheets containing two blocks 6 separated by a large illustrated gutter.

1312 The Pagan Lady of Peel

1313 Ship Burial

1314 Godred Crovan ('King Orry')

1315 Gautr Bjornsson the Sculptor

1316 Sigurd the Dragon Slayer

1317 Coming of Christianity

The Viking Age on the Isle of Man

(Des Victor Ambrus and Kcreative. Litho BDT)

2008 (18 FEB). Perf 13½ (C)

1412	**1312**	28p multicoloured	65	65
1413	**1313**	31p multicoloured	75	75
1414	**1314**	44p multicoloured	1·00	1·00
1415	**1315**	54p multicoloured	1·30	1·30
1416	**1316**	69p multicoloured	1·60	1·60
1417	**1317**	£1.24 multicoloured	3·00	3·00
1412/17		Set of 6	8·25	8·25
		First Day Cover		9·75
		Presentation Pack	9·75	

Plate Nos.: All values 1A (each ×4)

Sheets: 25 (5×5)

1318 Isle of Man Bank £1 Note, 1956

1319 Isle of Man Govt £10 Note, 1972

1320 Manx Bank (1882–1900) £1 Note

1321 Isle of Man Govt 50p Decimal Note, 1969

1322 Isle of Man Govt £50 Note, 1983

1323 Parr's Bank £1 Note, 1918

Bank Notes of the Isle of Man

(Des Kcreative. Litho BDT)

2008 (7 APR). (*a*) *PVA gum.* Perf 14

1418	**1318**	30p multicoloured	70	70
1419	**1319**	31p multicoloured	75	75
1420	**1320**	44p multicoloured	1·00	1·00
1421	**1321**	56p multicoloured	1·40	1·40
1422	**1322**	85p multicoloured	2·00	2·00
1423	**1323**	114p multicoloured	2·75	2·75
1418/23		Set of 6	8·50	8·50
		First Day Cover		10·00
		Presentation Pack	10·00	

(*b*) *Self-adhesive. Die-cut perf* 12×12½

1424	**1318**	30p multicoloured	70	70
		a. Booklet pane. No. 1424		
		×10	7·00	

No. 1424 was only issued in £3 stamp booklets, No. SB69.

Plate Nos.: All values 1A (each ×4)

Sheets: 20 (2 columns 1×10). Nos. 1418/23 were each printed in separate sheetlets containing two vertical strips of stamps alternated with two columns of stamp-size labels so that each stamp is accompanied by a *se-tenant* label at left.

1324 Archery (1p); Show-jumping (2p); Cycling (3p); Hand holding Olympic Torch (94p) (*illustration reduced. Actual size* 170×75 mm)

Olympic Games, Beijing

(Des Pobjoy Mint Studio and Solus Strategic Limited. Litho Lowe-Martin, Canada)

2008 (21 APR). *Sheet* 170×75 *mm.* Perf 13½ (C)
MS1425   1p, 2p, 3p, 94p multicoloured .... 2·40   2·40
          First Day Cover . . . .   4·00
          Presentation Pack . . . . 4·00

1325 Cornish Flag

1326 Isle of Man Flag

1327 Scottish Flag

1328 Breton Flag

1329 Irish Flag

1330 Flag of Asturias

1331 Welsh Flag

1332 Flag of Galicia

Interceltique. Flags of Celtic Countries

(Des Pete Jones Design. Litho Lowe-Martin, Canada)

2008 (12 MAY). Perf 13½ (C)
1426	**1325**	20p multicoloured	45	45
1427	**1326**	30p multicoloured	70	70
1428	**1327**	31p multicoloured	70	70
1429	**1328**	48p multicoloured	1·10	1·10
1430	**1329**	50p multicoloured	1·20	1·20
1431	**1330**	56p multicoloured	1·30	1·30
1432	**1331**	72p multicoloured	1·70	1·70
1433	**1332**	£1.13 multicoloured	2·75	2·75
1426/33		*Set of* 8	9·75	9·75
		First Day Cover		11·50
		Presentation Pack . . . . 11·50		
		Stamp Cards (*set of* 8)		
		(1 *Aug*) . . . . 13·00		
		Festival Postcard	1·90	1·90
MS1434		174×210 mm. Nos. 1426/33		
(1 Aug)	. . . .		9·75	9·75

Nos. 1428 and 1430 include the 'EUROPA' emblem.

Plate Nos.: All values 1A (each ×4)

Sheets: 10 (2×5) with enlarged illustrated right margins.

1333 Reg Parnell in Maserati 4CLT

1334 Mike Hawthorn

1335 Tony Brooks in Vanwall

1336 Roy Salvadori in Aston Martin

1337 Stirling Moss at Pit Stop

1338 Jim Clark in Lotus-Climax 25 R4

1339 Aston Martin DB4 GT Zagato, 1961; Ferrari 250 LM, Le Mans, 1965; Ferrari 250 GTO, Goodwood Revival, 1962; Ford GT 40, Goodwood Festival of Speed, 1965; Mercedes-Benz 300 SLR, Mille Miglia Road Race, Italy, 1955; Shelby Cobra, Goodwood Revival, 1964 (*illustration reduced. Actual size 170×75 mm*)

British Motor Racing

(Des Nick Sykes and Kreative (**MS**1441) or Peter Hearsey and Kreative (others). Litho BDT)

2008 (10 JULY). Perf 14 (C)

1435	**1333**	20p multicoloured	45	45
1436	**1334**	30p multicoloured	70	70
1437	**1335**	70p multicoloured	1·60	1·60
1438	**1336**	81p multicoloured	1·90	1·90
1439	**1337**	94p multicoloured	2·20	2·20
1440	**1338**	£1.22 multicoloured	3·00	3·00
1435/40		*Set of 6*	9·75	9·75
		First Day Cover		11·50
		Presentation Pack	11·50	

MS1441   170×75 mm. **1339** 50p×6 multicoloured. Perf 15×14 (C) .... 7·00   7·00
First Day Cover .... 8·75
Presentation Pack .... 8·75

Plate Nos.: All values 1A (each ×4)

Sheets: 25 (5×5)

Imprint: Central, bottom margin

1340 Miss M. L. Wood (founder of Manx Music Festival)

1341 Harry Kelly (last native Manx speaker) and Cottage at Cregneash Folk Museum

1342 Sir Frank Gill (telephony and communications engineer) and Phone Box

1343 Ramsey Gelling Johnson (second deemster (Manx judge), 1947–54)

1344 John Nicholson (artist and designer of Manx stamps, currency notes and gold coinage)

1345 Dr. Dorothy Pantin (Island's first woman doctor and first medical supervisor of Jane Crookall Maternity Home)

1346 Richard Costain (founder of construction company)

1347 Sir William Percy Cowley (first deemster and Clerk of the Rolls, 1947–58)

1348 Revd Fred
Cubbon
(philanthropist)

1349 William Henry Gill
(author, musician
and collector of
Manx folk music)

1350 Orange-tip Butterfly
(*Anthocharis
cardamines*)

1351 Curlew (*Numenius
arquata*)

New Manx Worthies. Personalities from Book

(Des Kreative. Litho Enschedé)

2008 (1 AUG). Perf 13½ (C)

1442	**1340**	31p multicoloured	60	60
		a. Horiz strip of 5. Nos.		
		1442/6	3·75	3·75
1443	**1341**	31p multicoloured	60	60
1444	**1342**	31p multicoloured	60	60
1445	**1343**	31p multicoloured	60	60
1446	**1344**	31p multicoloured	60	60
1447	**1345**	50p multicoloured	1·00	1·00
		a. Horiz strip of 5. Nos.		
		1447/51	6·00	6·00
1448	**1346**	50p multicoloured	1·00	1·00
1449	**1347**	50p multicoloured	1·00	1·00
1450	**1348**	50p multicoloured	1·00	1·00
1451	**1349**	50p multicoloured	1·00	1·00
1442/51		Set of 10	9·50	9·50
		First Day Cover		11·00
		Presentation Pack ....11·00		

Plate Nos.: Both values 1A (each ×4)

Sheets 50 (5×10): Nos. 1442/6 and 1447/51 were each printed
together, *se-tenant*, as horizontal strips of five stamps in sheets of
50.

1352 Birch Bracket Fungus
(*Piptoporus betulinus*)

1353 Large Red Damselfly
(*Pyrrhosoma
nymphula*)

1354 Marsh Cinquefoil
(*Potentilla palustris*)

1355 Royal Fern (*Osmunda
regalis*)

Olympex Olympic Stamp Expo, Beijing

2008 (8 AUG). *No.* **MS**1425 *additionally inscr with 'Beijing
2008' emblem and* 'OLYMPEX, THE OLYMPIC EXPO' *on
the bottom margin*

MS1452	1p, 2p, 3p, 94p multicoloured	2·40	2·40
	Postcard (pre paid)	2·40	

Team GB Olympic Cyclists

2008 (9 AUG). *Sheet* 145×208 *mm.* Perf 13½ (C)

MS1453	3p Cycling; 94p Hand holding		
	Olympic torch	2·40	2·40

No. **MS**1453 contains 3p and 94p designs as in **MS**1425.

A Walk in the Ballaugh Curragh

(Des Richard Lewington and Kcreative. Litho Lowe-Martin)

2008 (1 OCT). Perf 13½ (C)

1454	**1350**	30p multicoloured	70	70
1455	**1351**	31p multicoloured	75	75
1456	**1352**	50p multicoloured	1·20	1·20
1457	**1353**	70p multicoloured	1·70	1·70
1458	**1354**	82p multicoloured	1·90	1·90
1459	**1355**	£1.38 multicoloured	3·25	3·25
1454/9		Set of 6	9·50	9·50
		First Day Cover		11·00
		Presentation Pack ....11·00		

Plate Nos.: All values 1A (each ×4)

Sheets: 25 (5×5)

1356 Second Lt.
Roy F. Corlett,
1916

1357 Second Lt.
John W. Lewis,
1916

1358 Pte Joseph
Killey

1359 Lt. Col. W. A. W.
Crellin, 1917

1360 Lance Cpl Tom
Quilliam, 1918

1361 Pte Robert
Oates, 1914

1362 Manx National War Memorial, St. John's
(*illustration reduced. Actual size 110×70 mm*)

90th Anniversary of the End of World War I. Manx Soldiers and their Letters Home

(Des Mannin Design. Litho BDT)

2008 (1 OCT). Perf 14 (C)

1460	**1356**	30p multicoloured	70	70
1461	**1357**	31p multicoloured	70	70
1462	**1358**	44p multicoloured	1·00	1·00
1463	**1359**	56p multicoloured	1·30	1·30
1464	**1360**	81p multicoloured	1·90	1·90
1465	**1361**	94p multicoloured	2·20	2·20
1460/5		*Set of 6*	7·75	7·75
		First Day Cover		9·50
		Presentation Pack	9·50	

MS1466 110×70 mm. **1362** £2 multi-coloured .... 4·75 4·75

First Day Cover .... 6·25
Presentation Pack ...... 6·25

Plate Nos.: All values 1A (each ×4)

Sheets: 6 (3×2)

1363 Christmas Cards and
Postman on Bicycle

1364 Postman icing
Biscuits and Giant
Biscuit Tin

1365 Offering Postman
Mince Pies and
Decorating Christmas
Tree

1366 Postman holding
Card and Toy Town

1367 Postman on Bicycle
and Winter
Landscape

1368 Postman relaxing at
Home

Christmas. Illustrations from The Jolly Christmas Postman by Janet and Allan Ahlberg

(Des Kcreative. Litho Enschedé)

2008 (20 OCT). Perf 14×14½ (C)

1467	**1363**	28p multicoloured	65	65
1468	**1364**	31p multicoloured	75	75
1469	**1365**	48p multicoloured	1·10	1·10
1470	**1366**	50p multicoloured	1·20	1·20
1471	**1367**	56p multicoloured	1·30	1·30
1472	**1368**	£1.56 multicoloured	3·50	3·50
1467/72		Set of 6	8·50	8·50
		First Day Cover		10·00
		Presentation Pack .... 10·00		

Plate Nos.: All values 1A (each ×4)

Sheets: 25 (5×5)

Year Folder 2008

2008 (20 OCT). *Comprises Nos.* **MS**1405/23, **MS**1425/33, 1435/51 *and* 1454/72

Year Folder .... 85·00

Year Pack 2008

2008 (20 OCT). *Comprises Nos.* **MS**1405/23, **MS**1425/33, 1435/51 *and* 1454/72

Year Pack £100

Post Office Yearbook

2008 (20 OCT). *Comprises Nos.* **MS**1405/23, **MS**1425/33, 1435/51 *and* 1454/72

Yearbook .... 90·00

SOUVENIR POSTAL STATIONERY POSTCARDS

The following postcards were issued by the Isle of Man Postal Authority often in connection with various philatelic exhibitions and, with the exception of Nos. PC8, PC11 and PC15/16 show imprinted stamp designs.

'San Marino 82'

1982 (1 SEPT). *Card showing imprinted stamp design as No.* 217. *Sold at 30p*

PC1   19½p multicoloured .... 1·00   1·20

Withdrawn: 30.4.84

'Tembal 83', Basel

1983 (21 MAY). *Card showing imprinted stamp design as No.* 250. *Sold at 30p*

PC2   20½p multicoloured .... 1·00   1·60

Withdrawn: 20.5.84

'Espana 84', Madrid

1984 (27 APR). *Card showing imprinted stamp design as No.* 266. *Sold at 30p*

PC3   20½p multicoloured .... 1·50   1·70

Withdrawn: 26.4.85

'Ausipex 84', Melbourne

1984 (21 SEPT). *Card showing imprinted stamp design as No.* 278. *Sold at 40p*

PC4   33p multicoloured .... 1·50   2·75

Withdrawn: 20.9.85

'Italia 85', Rome

1985 (25 OCT). *Card showing imprinted stamp designs as Nos.* 292/3. *Sold at 40p*

PC5 14p+14p multicoloured .... 1·50   3·25

Withdrawn: 24.10.86

'Ameripex 86', Chicago

1986 (22 MAY). *Card showing imprinted stamp design as No.* 302. *Sold at 40p*

PC6   34p multicoloured .... 2·20   2·75

Withdrawn: 21.5.87

'Stockholmia 86', Stockholm

1986 (28 AUG). *Card showing imprinted stamp designs as Nos.* 305/6. *Sold at 40p*

PC7   15p+15p multicoloured .... 1·20   2·00

Withdrawn: 27.8.87

'Hafnia 87', Copenhagen

1987 (16 OCT). *Card with Nos.* 358/9 *affixed. Sold at* 50p

PC8   12p+15p multicoloured .... 1·20   1·70

Withdrawn: 15.10.88

'Finlandia 88', Helsinki

1988 (1 JUNE). *Card showing imprinted stamp designs as Nos. 371 and 375. Sold at 50p*
PC9   14p+18p multicoloured . . . .   1·20   1·50

Withdrawn: 31.5.89

'Sydpex 88', Sydney

1988 (30 JULY). *Card showing imprinted stamp designs as Nos. 386/7. Sold at 60p*
PC10   29p +31p multicoloured . . . .   1·50   1·70

Withdrawn: 29.7.89

'Filacept 88', The Hague

1988 (18 OCT). *Card with Nos. 383/4 affixed. Sold at 50p*
PC11   22p+22p multicoloured . . . .   1·20   2·00

Withdrawn: 17.10.89

'Belgica 90', Brussels

1990 (2 JUNE). *Card showing imprinted stamp designs as Nos. 442 and 446. Sold at 50p*
PC12   1p+37p multicoloured . . . .   1·20   1·50

Withdrawn: 2.93

'Essen 94', Centenary of Picture Postcards

1994 (5 MAY). *Cards showing imprinted stamp design as No. 338. Sold at 80p the pair*
PC13   31p multicoloured (Douglas) . . . .   1·20   1·50
PC14   31p multicoloured (Ramsey) . . . .   1·20   1·50

Withdrawn: 4.5.95

'Jakarta 95'

1995 (19 AUG). *Sold at 15p*
PC15   Komodo Dragon   75   1·00

Withdrawn: 6.98

'Beijing 95'

1995 (16 SEPT). *Sold at 15p*
PC16   Great Wall of China   75   1·00

Withdrawn: 6.98

Isle of Man T.T. Races and 50th Anniversary of Honda

1998 (1 JUNE). *Card showing imprinted stamp design as No. 809. Sold at 50p*
PC17   25p multicoloured . . . .   1·00   1·20

Withdrawn: 6.99

'Espana 2000', Madrid

2000 (6 OCT). *Card showing imprinted stamp design as No. 910*
PC18   45p multicoloured . . . .   1·50   1·50

Withdrawn: 6.2002

'Sindelfingen', Germany

2000 (6 OCT). *Card showing imprinted stamp design as No. 911*
PC19   65p multicoloured . . . .   1·50   1·50

Withdrawn: 6.2002

Joey Dunlop (motorcycle champion) Commemoration

2001 (17 MAY). *Cards showing stamp designs and enlarged photographs on the front and Douglas postage paid impression on the reverse. Sold at £5.71*
PC20/5   Set of 6 cards . . . .   11·50   11·50

Withdrawn: 16.5.2002

MANX POSTAL MUSEUM POSTCARDS

1987 (23 MAR). *Sold at 10p*
PM1   Reopening of Regent Street Post Office, Douglas   30   1·00

Sold out: By 2.90

1989 (28 APR). *Sold at 15p*
PM2   Bicentenary of the Mutiny on the Bounty   40   1·50

Sold out: By 1.93

1990 (10 APR). *Sold at 18p*
PM3   'CUNARD 150' Exhibition, Liverpool. Sinking of *Lusitania* (as No. 191)   50   1·50

Sold out: By 2.94

POSTAGE DUE STAMPS

D **1** D **2** D **3** Badge of
Post Office
Authority

(Des and litho Questa)

1973 (5 JULY). Perf 14×13½ (C)

D1	D **1**	½p red, black & bistre-yellow (ab)	1·50	1·10
D2		1p red, black and cinnamon (ab) .	50	60
D3		2p red, black & lt apple-green (ab)	15	20
		a. Positive offset of red ptg on back		
D4		3p red, black and grey (ab)	20	20
D5		4p red, black & carmine-rose (ab)	30	35
D6		5p red, black and cobalt (ab)	30	35
D7		10p red, black & light lavender (ab)	40	40
D8		20p red, black & pale turq-grn (ab) .	75	60
D1/8		Set of 8	3·75	3·50
		Presentation Pack (ptg b)	5·00	

Printings: (a) 5.7.73; (b) 1.9.73. Examples of printing (b) are known used from mid-August onwards.

Prices quoted above are for printing (b), which can be identified by the letter 'A' added after '1973' at the foot of the stamp. Collectors should beware of spurious examples with the 'A' removed. Price for set of 8 from printing (a) £24 mint or used

Plate Nos.: All values 1A, 1B (each ×3)

Sheets: 100 (10×10)

Imprint: Right-hand corner, bottom margin, and left-hand corner, top margin

Sold out: Printing (a) between 13.8.73 and 10.9.73. Printing (b) ½p by 12.74; 1p by 2.75; 2p and 3p by 5.75; others by 31.12.75

(Des and litho Questa)

1975 (8 JAN). Perf 14×13½ (C)

D9	D **2**	½p black, red & greenish yellow	10	10
D10		1p black, red and flesh	10	10
D11		4p black, red and rose-lilac	10	15
D12		7p black, red & lt greenish blue	15	20
D13		9p black, red and brownish grey	25	30
D14		10p black, red and bright mauve .	25	20
D15		50p black, red and orange-yellow	90	90
D16		£1 black, red & turquoise-green	1·50	1·60
D9/16		Set of 8	3·00	3·25
		First Day Cover		4·50
		Presentation Pack	3·50	

Plate Nos.: All values 1A, 1B (each ×3)

Sheets: 100 (10×10)

Imprint: Left-hand corner, bottom margin

Withdrawn: 31.12.82 (1p to £1); 31.12.85 ½p

(Litho B.D.T.)

1982 (5 OCT). Centres multicoloured; background colour given. Perf 14½×14 (C)

D17	D **3**	1p turquoise-green	10	10
D18		2p mauve	10	10
D19		5p greenish blue	10	10
D20		10p reddish lilac	20	25
D21		20p grey	40	45
D22		50p buff	90	1·10
D23		£1 salmon	1·60	2·10
D24		£2 bright blue	3·25	4·25
D17/24		Set of 8	6·00	7·75
		First Day Cover		12·00
		Presentation Pack	8·00	

Plate Nos.: All values 1A (×5)

Sheets: 50 (10×5)

Imprint: Right-hand corner, bottom margin

D **4**

(Des Colleen Corlett. Litho B.D.T.)

1992 (18 SEPT). Perf 13×13½ (C)

D25	D **4**	£5 multicoloured	8·00	8·50
		First Day Cover		12·00
		Presentation Pack	9·50	

Plate Nos.: 1A, 1B (each ×4)

Sheets: 50 (10×5)

Imprint: Right-hand corner, bottom margin

STAMP BOOKLETS

PRICES. Prices are given for complete booklets. All booklets to No. SB7 are stitched.

B **1** Derbyhaven

1973 (5 JULY–17 OCT). *Coloured covers as Type B* **1**, *printed in black*

Type B **1**. *Yellow cover*
SB1 10p booklet containing 2×2½p (No. 16), 2×2p
(No. 15) and 2×½p (No. 12) (*ab*) . . . . 14·00

Ballaugh Church. Green cover
SB2 25p booklet containing 10×2½p (No. 16) (*ab*) . 3·00

Peel Castle. Stone cover
SB3 30p booklet containing 10×3p (No. 17) (*a*) . . 19·00
SB3*a* As SB3 but cover in buff (*b*) . . . . 17·00

Quayside, Douglas. Lavender-grey cover
SB4 50p booklet containing 8×2½p (No. 16) and
10×3p (No. 17) (*a*) . . . . 8·00
SB4*a* As SB4 but grey-green cover (*b*) . . . . 5·50

Nos. SB1/4 were made up from ordinary sheets, the stamps being in vertical pairs with stitching through the side margins. Stamps from both sides of the sheets were used, so that panes come either upright or inverted.

Printings: (*a*) 5.7.73: (*b*) 17.10.73

STAMP SACHETS. These are cardboard covers, with stamps loose inside, contained in clear plastic sachets.

B **2**

1973 (5 JULY–1 NOV). *Stamp Sachets. Covers as Type B* **2**
10p sachet containing 5×½p (No. 12) and 3×2½p (No. 16)
10p sachet containing 2×½p (No. 12) and 3×3p (No. 17)
(1 Nov) (*Price* 1·00 *each*)

B **3** Old Laxey Bridge
(*illustration reduced. Actual size* 89×51 *mm*)

1974 (1 APR*). *Coloured covers as Type B* **3**, *printed in black*

Type B **3**. *Buff cover*
SB5 30p booklet containing 8×½p (No. 12), 4×3p
(No. 17) and 4×3½p (No. 18) . . . . 2·00

Monk's Bridge, Ballasalla. Green cover
SB6 40p booklet containing 4×½p (No. 12), 8×3p
(No. 17) and 4×3½p (No. 18) . . . . 2·00

St. Michael's Chapel, Langness. Red cover
SB7 50p booklet containing 12×3p (No. 17) and
4×3½p (No. 18) . . . . 2·00

Nos. SB5/7 contain panes of four, and were produced in the same way as Nos. SB1/4. 3p panes from SB5/7 exist with either shiny or matt gum. ½p panes are shiny gum and 3½p panes matt gum only (see note after No. 33).

*The booklets were placed on sale at the Interpex stamp exhibition in New York on 22 March 1974 and panes and covers exist cancelled with this date.

1974 (29 JULY). *Stamp Sachets. Cover designs as Nos. SB5/7, but inscriptions redrawn. Contents unchanged*
30p sachet. Pink cover (*Price* 1·50)
40p sachet. Green cover (*Price* 1·60)
50p sachet. Yellow cover (*Price* 1·90)

1975 (25 APR–16 JUNE). *Stamp Sachets. Blue cover showing Post Office badge*
20p sachet containing 3×2p (No. 15) and 4×3½p (No. 18) attached to cover by the selvedge (*Price* 2·20)
20p sachet containing 1×½p (No. 12), 2×1½p (No. 14) and 3×5½p (No. 22), loose or attached to selvedge (28 May) (*Price* 2·70)
20p sachet containing 4×½p (No. 12), 2×1½p (No. 14) and 3×5p (No. 21), loose or attached to selvedge (16 June) (*Price* 2·70)

1976 (20 SEPT)–*79. *Stamp Sachet. Blue cover similar to Type B* **3**, *showing Rushen and Castletown Harbour*
20p sachet containing 2×1p (No. 13) and 3×6p (No. 23) (*Price* 1·10)
20p sachet containing 2×1p (No. 13) and 3×6p (No. 139) (3.79) (*Price* 2·40)

B **4** Viking Longship
  (*illustration reduced. Actual size* 81×49 *mm*)

Millennium of Tynwald

1979 (16 MAY). *Folded card covers as Type* B **4**
SB8   20p booklet containing 4×3p and 2×4p (No.
        150*ab*) (blue cover) . . . .   1·20
SB9   40p booklet containing 8×3p and 4×4p (No.
        150*a*×2) (pink cover) . . . .   1·50
SB10 60p booklet containing 12×3p and 6×4p
        (No. 150*a*×3) (yellow cover) . . . .   2·00

Examples of Nos. SB8/9 are known containing the wrong
pane.

Withdrawn: 28.9.80

1980 (29 SEPT). *Folded card covers as Type* B **4**
SB11 40p booklet containing 2×1p, 4×3p, 4×4p
        and 2×5p (Nos. 150*ba* and 188*a*) (pink cover
        showing Manx Loaghtyn Ram) . . . .   1·00
SB12 80p booklet containing 4×1p, 8×3p, 8×4p
        and 4×5p (Nos. 150*ba* and 188*a* each ×2)
        (green cover showing Peregrine Falcon) . . . .   2·00

Withdrawn: 9.4.86

1985 (12 JUNE). *Booklet No.* SB11 *with cover surcharged*
  50p and an additional loose 10p *stamp inside*
SB13 50p booklet containing Nos. 150*ba*, 188*a* and
        one 10p (No. 236) . . . .   4·50

Withdrawn: 9.4.86

B **5** Celtic Cross Logo
  (*illustration reduced.
  Actual size
  80×48 mm*)

Manx Heritage Year

1986 (10 APR). *Folded card covers as Type* B **5**
SB14 50p booklet containing 2×1p, 2×4p, 2×5p
        and 3×10p (Nos. 188*a* and 316*a*) olive-green
        cover) . . . .   2·00
SB15 £1.14 booklet containing 2×1p, 2×2p, 4×3p,
        4×4p, 2×5p and 7×10p (Nos. 150*ba*, 188*a*,
        315*a* and 316*a*) (greenish blue cover) . . . . . .   4·00

Withdrawn: 25.3.87

B **6** Loch Promenade
  (*illustration reduced. Actual size* 82×48 *mm*)

Victorian Douglas

1987 (26 MAR). *Folded card covers as Type* B **6**
SB16 50p booklet containing either No. 334*a* or
        334*ab* (orange-brown and deep yellow-green
        cover Type B **6**) . . . .   1·70
SB17 £1.10 booklet containing either Nos. 334*a* or
        334*ab*, and 334*b* or 334*ba* (orange-brown
        and bright scarlet cover showing The
        Breakwater) . . . .   3·50

Withdrawn: 15.3.88

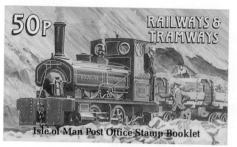

B **7** Baldwin Reservoir Tramway Steam Locomotive *Injebreck*
(*illustration reduced. Actual size* 82×48 mm)

Manx Railways and Tramways

1988 (16 MAR). *Folded multicoloured card covers as Type* B **7**
SB18 50p booklet containing No. 367*a* (cover Type B **7**) .... 3·00
SB19 £1.99 booklet containing Nos. 367*a* and 370*a* (cover showing Manx Electric Railway train at Maughold Head) .... 7·00

Withdrawn: 15.10.89

B **8** 'Mutineers casting Bligh adrift' (Robert Dodd)
(*illustration reduced. Actual size* 155×100 mm)

Bicentenary of The Mutiny on the Bounty

1989 (28 APR). *Multicoloured cover as Type* B **8**. *Booklet contains text and illustrations on interleaving pages. Stitched*
SB20 £5.30 booklet containing Nos. 408*a/b*, 410*a* and **MS**415*a* .... 14·00

Examples of No. **MS**415 from the booklet have wider margins than the normal miniature sheets.

Withdrawn: 2.92

Manx Railways and Tramways

1989 (16 OCT). *Folded multicoloured covers as Type* B **7**
SB21 50p booklet containing No. 367*b* (cover showing Port Erin Breakwater Tramway Locomotive *Henry B. Loch*) .... 2·50

SB22 £2.09 booklet containing Nos. 367*b* and 371*a* (cover showing Douglas Cable Tramway) .... 6·50

Withdrawn: 13.2.90

Manx Railways and Tramways

1990 (14 FEB). *Folded multicoloured covers as Type* B **7**
SB23 50p booklet containing No. 372*a* (cover showing Marine Drive Tramway) .... 2·75
SB24 £1.74 booklet containing No. 372*b* (cover showing Ramsey Harbour Tramway) .... 6·25

Withdrawn: 8.1.91

B **9** Penny Black
(*illustration reduced. Actual size* 125×75 mm)

150th Anniversary of the Penny Black and 'Stamp World London 90' International Stamp Exhibition, London

1990 (3 MAY). *Black and ochre cover as Type* B **9**. *Booklet contains text and illustrations on interleaving pages. Stapled*
SB25 £3.50 booklet containing Nos. 442*c*, 443*a* and **MS**447*a* .... 9·00

Withdrawn: 23.9.93

Manx Railway and Tramways

1991 (9 JAN). *Folded multicoloured covers as Type* B **7**
SB26 50p booklet containing No. 367*ca* (cover, 80×48 mm, showing Groudle Glen Railway steamlocomotive *Polar Bear*) .... 4·00
SB27 £1 booklet containing No. 367*cb* (cover, 56×43 mm, showing I.M.R. No. 11 *Maitland* pulling Royal Train, 1963) .... 4·75

Withdrawn: 7.1.92

B **10** Three Kings
(*illustration reduced. Actual size* 150×105 *mm*)

Christmas

1991 (14 OCT). *Deep violet cover as Type* B **10**. *Stitched*
SB28   £4.16 booklet containing No. 500a×2 . . . . . .   12·50

Withdrawn: 23.9.93

Manx Railways and Tramways

1992 (8 JAN). *Folded multicoloured covers as Type* B **7**, *but*
56×43 *mm*
SB29   £1 booklet containing No. 375ab (cover
   showing double-decker horse tram, Douglas)   4·00
SB30   £2 booklet containing No. 375ac (cover
   showing T.P.O. Special) . . . .   7·00

Withdrawn: 3.1.93

B **11** Union Pacific No. 119, 1869
(*illustration reduced. Actual size* 119×74 *mm*)

Construction of Union Pacific Railroad

1992 (22 MAY). *Multicoloured cover as Type* B **11**. *Pane
attached by selvedge*
SB31   £4.38 booklet containing pane No. 522b . . . .   12·00

Withdrawn: 27.4.94

B **12** *Francis Drake*
(ketch)

Ships

1993 (4 JAN). *Multicoloured covers as Type* B **12**. *Panes
attached by selvedge*
SB32   £1.10 booklet containing pane No. 543a
   (cover Type B **12** . . . .   3·00
SB33   £2.20 booklet containing pane No. 543b
   (cover showing *Tynwald I*) . . . .   6·50

Withdrawn: 20.4.96

B **13** No. 9 Tunnel Car and Crew
(*illustration reduced. Actual size* 160×98 *mm*)

Centenary of Manx Electric Railway

1993 (3 FEB). *Multicoloured cover as Type* B **13**. *Stitched*
SB34   £4.44 booklet containing pane No. 559a×4   .   14·00

Withdrawn: 27.4.94

B **14** (*illustration reduced.
Actual size* 62×95 *mm*)

Christmas

1993 (12 OCT). *Folded multicoloured covers as Type B* **14**.
Panes attached by selvedge

SB35 £1.90 booklet containing No. 578×10 (cover
Type B **14**) .... 4·50

SB36 £2.30 booklet containing No. 579×10 (cover
showing No. 579) .... 6·50

Withdrawn: 10.10.95

B **15** (*illustration reduced. Actual size* 134×85 *mm*)

Manx Tourism Centenary

1994 (18 FEB). *Multicoloured cover as Type B* **15**. *Pane
attached by selvedge*

SB37 £2.40 booklet containing pane No. 590*a* and
pane of 12 (3×4) greetings labels .... 6·00

Sold out: By 9.95

B **16** Postman Pat, Jess, Ferry and Aircraft
(*illustration reduced. Actual size* 152×85 *mm*)

Postman Pat visits the Isle of Man

1994 (14 SEPT). *Multicoloured cover as Type B* **16** *cut out to
show stamps from first pane. Booklet contains text and
illustrations on labels attached to panes. Stitched*

SB38 £4.04 booklet containing Nos. 614*a*/19*a*,
MS620*a* and pane of 8 character labels .... 12·00

Withdrawn: By 2.97

B **17** Car and Passengers at Snaefell Summit
(*illustration reduced. Actual size* 162×97 *mm*)

Centenary of Snaefell Mountain Railway

1995 (8 FEB). *Black, scarlet and grey cover as Type B* **17**.
*Booklet contains text and illustrations on labels attached to
panes. Stitched.*

SB39 £4.63 booklet containing No. 634*a*×3 and
MS638*a* .... 14·00

Withdrawn: By 2.97

B **18** Thomas the Tank Engine
(*illustration reduced. Actual size* 151×80 *mm*)

50th Anniversary of Thomas the Tank Engine Stories by Revd. Awdry. 'Thomas the Tank Engine's Dream'

1995 (15 AUG). *Multicoloured cover as Type B* **18** *cut out to
show stamps from first pane. Stitched*

SB40 £3.92 booklet containing Nos. 656*a*/*b*, 657*a*,
658*a*, 659*a* and 660*a* .... 12·50

Withdrawn: By 2.97

B **19** Aerial view of Langness Lighthouse
(*illustration reduced. Actual size* 130×82 *mm*)

Lighthouses

1996 (24 JAN). *Multicoloured cover as Type B* **19**. *Booklet contains text and illustrations on interleaving pages. Stitched*
SB41   £4.74 booklet containing Nos. 672a/5a ..... 12·00

Withdrawn: By 5.97

Ships

1996 (21 APR). Multicoloured cover as Type B **12**. Pane attached by selvedge
SB42   96p booklet containing pane No. 687a (cover showing *Sir Winston Churchill*) .... 10·00

Sold out: 5.97

B **20** (*illustration reduced. Actual size* 118×81 *mm*)

Dogs

1996 (18 SEPT). *Multicoloured cover as Type B* **20**. *Booklet contains text and illustrations on interleaving pages. Stitched*
SB43   £4.71 booklet containing Nos. 719a, 720a, 721a and **MS**725a .... 12·00

Withdrawn: 17.9.97

B **21** Tawny Owl
(*illustration reduced. Actual size* 152×80 *mm*)

Owls

1997 (12 FEB). *Multicoloured cover as Type B* **21**. *Booklet contains text and illustrations on interleaving pages. Stitched*
SB44   £4.62 booklet containing Nos. 734a/6a and **MS**740a .... 12·00

Withdrawn: 11.2.98

Ships

1997 (14 MAY). *Multicoloured cover as Type B* **12**. *Pane attached by selvedge*
SB45   £1 booklet containing pane No. 541a (cover showing Royal Yacht *Britannia*) .... 5·00
    a. With extra loose 4p stamp and optd inside front cover .... 6·00

No. SB45a was issued from booklet machines until 1 July 1997 when the postal rates were revised. The overprint inside the front cover was applied by handstamp.

Withdrawn: 31.12.97 No. SB45a; 30.11.98 No. SB45

B **22** King Edward Bay Golf and Country Club
(*illustration reduced. Actual size* 160×96 *mm*)

Golf

1997 (29 MAY). *Multicoloured cover as Type B* **22**. *Booklet contains text and illustrations on panes and interleaving pages. Stitched*
SB46   £4.54 booklet containing Nos. 755a/7a and **MS**759a .... 12·00

Withdrawn: 28.5.98

B **23** Cushag

Flowers

1998 (12 FEB). *Multicoloured cover as Type B* **23**. *Pane attached by selvedge*
SB47   £1 booklet containing No. 775a .... 4·00

Withdrawn: 31.8.99

YEAR OF
THE
OCEAN

B **24** Basking Shark
(*illustration reduced. Actual size* 157×105 *mm*)

U.N.E.S.C.O. International Year of the Ocean

1998 (16 MAR). *Multicoloured cover as Type B* **24**. *Booklet contains text and illustrations on interleaving pages. Stitched*

SB48   £3.62 booklet containing No. 798a/b .... 10·00

The price (£3.92) and content details of SB48 are incorrectly stated on the back cover.

Withdrawn: 13.3.99

B **25** Steam Train at Douglas Station
(*illustration reduced. Actual size* 157×105 *mm*)

125th Anniversary of Isle of Man Steam Railway

1998 (2 MAY). *Multicoloured cover as Type B* **25**. *Booklet contains text and illustrations on interleaving pages. Stitched*

SB49   £4.05 booklet containing Nos. 803a×2 and
         MS807a .... 10·00

Sold out: 6.2000

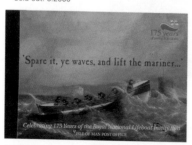

B **26** *Manchester & Salford*, 1868–1887
(*illustration reduced. Actual size* 158×108 *mm*)

175th Anniversary of Royal National Lifeboat Institution

1999 (4 MAR). *Multicoloured cover as Type B* **26**. *Booklet contains text and illustrations on interleaving pages. Stitched*

SB50   £4.64 booklet containing Nos. 832a/b and
         MS839a .... 15·00

Withdrawn: 3.3.2000

Flowers

1999 (26 APR). *Multicoloured cover as Type B* **23**. *Pane attached by selvedge*

SB51   £1 booklet containing pane No. 775ba (cover
         showing Dog Rose) .... 3·00

Sold out: By 31.8.2004

B **27** Bus Radiator and Headlights
(*illustration reduced. Actual size* 158×100 *mm*)

Manx Buses

1999 (18 JUNE). *Multicoloured cover as Type B* **27**. *Booklet contains text and illustrations on panes and interleaving pages. Stitched*

SB52   £4.78 booklet containing panes Nos. 845a/d . 16·00

Sold out: 8.2001

B **28** Flags, Weapons and Military Headgear
(*illustration reduced. Actual size* 180×75 *mm*)

Isle of Man at War

2000 (22 MAY). *Multicoloured cover as Type B* **28**. *Booklet contains text and illustrations on interleaving pages. Stitched*

SB53   £4.99 booklet containing Nos. 887a/b and
         MS893a .... 12·00

Sold out: By 6.2003

B **29** 'The Coronation, 1953' (Terence Cuneo)
(*illustration reduced. Actual size 165×95 mm*)

Golden Jubilee

2002 (6 FEB). *Multicoloured cover as Type B* **29**. *Booklet contains text and illustrations on panes and interleaving pages. Stitched*
SB54   £5.87 booklet containing panes Nos. 959*a*,
         962*a*, 970*b*, 973*b* and **MS**975*b* . . . .   15·00

Withdrawn: 30.4.2004

B **30** Aspects of Isle of Man
(*illustration reduced. Actual size 105×70 mm*)

Photography – The People's Choice

2002 (1 OCT). Multicoloured covers as Type B **30**. *Self-adhesive*
SB55   £2.30 booklet containing No. 1021*a* . . . .   7·00
SB56   £2.70 booklet containing No. 1031*a* . . . .   8·50

Withdrawn: 30.4.2004

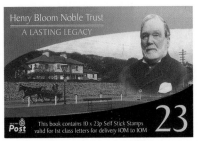

B **31** Henry Bloom Noble and Original Villa Marina
(*illustration reduced. Actual size 104×70 mm*)

Centenary of Henry Bloom Noble Trust

2003 (1 OCT). *Multicoloured covers as Type B* **31**. *Self-adhesive.*
SB57   £2.30 booklet containing No. 1101*a* . . . .   6·00
SB58   £2.70 booklet containing No. 1106*a* . . . .   11·00

Withdrawn: 31.12.2004

B **32** Soldier, Viking, Miner, Spinner and Fisherman
(*illustration reduced. Actual size 102×70 mm*)

Manx National Heritage 'The Story of Mann'

2004 (3 AUG). *Multicoloured covers as Type B* **32**. *Self-adhesive.*
SB59   (£2.50) booklet containing pane No. 1167*a*
         (*cover as Type B* **32**) . . . .   8·00
SB60   (£2.80) booklet containing pane No. 1172*a*
         (*cover showing Cregneash, Calf of Man,
         Castle Rushen, Laxey Wheel and Peel
         Castle*) . . . .   9·00

Withdrawn: 2.8.2005

B **33** 'Mona's Queen' (Arthur Burgess)
(*illustration reduced. Actual size 165×95 mm*)

175th Anniversary of Steam Packet Company

2005 (6 MAY). *Multicoloured cover as Type B* **33**. *Booklet contains text and illustrations on interleaving pages. Stitched.*
SB61   £7.80 booklet containing panes Nos. 1217*b/c*,
         1219*b*, 1221*b* and 1223*b* . . . .   16·00

Withdrawn: 5.5.2006

B **34** Traditional Scenes
(*illustration reduced. Actual size* 107×76 *mm*)

'Time to Remember'

2005 (12 AUG). *Multicoloured covers as Type* B **34** *showing portions of the stamp designs within. Self-adhesive.*

SB62 £2.60 booklet containing pane No. 1247*b* (*cover as Type* B **34**) . . . . 5·00

SB63 £2.90 booklet containing pane No. 1252*b* (*cover showing scenes from stamps*) . . . . . . 5·75

Sold out: By 12.2006

B **35** Christmas Tree with Lights
(*illustration reduced. Actual size* 150×70 *mm*)

Christmas

2006 (11 OCT). *Multicoloured covers as Type* B **35**. *Self-adhesive.*

SB64 £2.80 booklet containing pane No. 1328*a* (*Type* B **35**) . . . . 5·50

SB65 £3.10 booklet containing pane No. 1329*a* (*cover showing tree with Three Legs of Mann decoration at top*) . . . . 6·00

Withdrawn: 10.10.2007

B **36** Scouts hiking near South Barrule
(*illustration reduced. Actual size* 165×96 *mm*)

Centenary of Scouting

2007 (22 Feb). *Multicoloured cover as Type* B **36**. *Booklet contains text and illustrations on interleaving pages. Stitched.*

SB66 £9.16 booklet containing panes Nos. 1342*a*/*b*, 1343*a*, 1345*a* and **MS**1348*a* . . . . 25·00

Withdrawn: 21.2.2008

B **37** 'Headland, Cornaa'
(*illustration reduced. Actual size* 132×67 *mm*)

Watercolour Paintings by Norman Sayle

2007 (12 Apr). *Multicoloured covers as Type* B **37**. *Self-adhesive.*

SB67 £2.80 booklet containing pane No. 1363*a* (*Type* B **37**) . . . . 8·50

SB68 £3.10 booklet containing pane No. 1365*a* (*cover showing 'St. Marks Church'*) . . . . 9·25

B **38** Aircraft
(*illustration reduced. Actual size* 166×96 *mm*)

90th Anniversary of the Royal Air Force

2008 (15 JAN). *Multicoloured cover as Type* B **38**. *Booklet contains text and illustrations on panes and interleaving pages. Stitched.*

SB69 £9.68 booklet containing panes Nos. 1406*b/d* and 1408*a* . . . . 23·00

B **39** Isle of Man Bank £1 Note
(*illustration reduced. Actual size* 98×63 *mm*)

Bank Notes of the Isle of Man

2008 (7 APR). *Multicoloured cover as Type* B **39**. *Self-adhesive.*

SB70 £3 booklet containing pane No. 1424*a* . . . . . 7·00

JERSEY

THE GERMAN OCCUPATION 1940–1945

Soon after the commencement of the occupation of Jersey by German forces on 1 July 1940 orders were given by the German Commandant to the Island's Postmaster for stocks of the currently available stamps to be forwarded to the Jersey printers, J. T. Bigwood, for overprinting with a swastika and 'JERSEY 1940'. All values of the 1937–8 definitives from ½d to 10s, excluding the 1d, were so overprinted as were the 1940 Postal Centenary stamps, excluding the 1d, but whilst this was in progress the Bailiff of Jersey protested to the German Commandant who referred the matter to Berlin and was ordered to destroy the stocks. Four complete sets to 1s, and a few singles, however, are known to exist. At the same time Bigwoods prepared a local 1d. stamp incorporating the ams of Jersey and the words 'ETATS DE JERSEY'. These were printed in imperforate sheets of thirty (10×3) and are known with and without a swastika and '1940' overprint. These also were destroyed with the exception of two sheets of each which have been cut up for collectors and a damaged sheet with the overprint which is complete. There is also a complete sheet of the unoverprinted stamp in the National Postal Museum.

Jersey eventually issued locally printed ½d and 1d stamps, the 1d on 1 April 1941 and the ½d on 29 January 1942. No distinct shades exist though both values come on newsprint paper and, in addition, the 1d is known on chalk-surfaced paper.

In June 1943 a pictorial set of six stamps from ½d to 3d was issued, the designer being the well-known Jersey artist Edmund Blampied. Two values, the 1d and 2½d, are known on newsprint paper.

Both these and the earlier issues remained on sale until 13 April 1946 after which date they could no longer be used.

1

2

The Swastika Overprints

1940. *Prepared for use but not issued. Stamps of Great Britain overprinted by J. T. Bigwood, States' Printers*

(a) On 1937–9 definitive issue

Cat. No.	Type No.		Unused
SW1	**1**	½d. green	£1700
SW2		1½d. red-brown	£1700
SW3		2d. orange	£1700
SW4		2½d. ultramarine	£1700
SW5		3d. violet	£1700

SW6	4d. grey-green	£1700
SW7	5d. brown	£1700
SW8	6d. purple	£1700
SW9	7d. emerald-green	£1700
SW10	8d. bright carmine	£1700
SW11	9d. deep olive-green	£1700
SW12	10d. turquoise-blue	£1700
SW13	1s. bistre-brown	£1700

(b) On 1940 Stamp Centenary issue

SW14	**2**	½d. green	£1700
SW15		1½d. red-brown	£1700
SW16		2d. orange	£1700
SW17		2½d. ultramarine	£1700
SW18		3d. violet	£1700

3

4

(Des R. W. Cutland. Typo J. T. Bigwood)

1940. *Prepared for use but not issued. No wmk. Imperforate*

SW19	**3**	1d. scarlet	£1700
SW20	**4**	1d. scarlet	£1700

5 Arms of Jersey

Stamps issued during the German Occupation

(Des Major N. V. L. Rybot. Typo *Jersey Evening Post*, St. Helier)

1941–43. *White paper. No wmk. Perf 11 (L)*

1	**5**	½d. bright green (29.1.42)	8·00	6·00
		a. *Imperf between (vertical pair)* .	£800	
		b. *Imperf between (horizontal pair)*	£700	
		c. *Imperf (pair)*	£250	
		d. *On greyish paper (1.43)*	12·00	12·00
2		1d. scarlet (1.4.41)	8·00	5·00
		a. *Imperf between (vertical pair)* .	£800	
		b. *Imperf between (horizontal pair)*	£700	
		c. *Imperf (pair)*	£275	
		d. *On chalk-surfaced paper (9.41)*	55·00	48·00
		e. *On greyish paper (1.43)*	14·00	14·00
1		*First Day Cover (plain)*		7·50
2		*First Day Cover (plain)*		8·00

Sheets: 60 (6×10)

Imprint: ½d 'EVENING POST', JERSEY, JANUARY, 1942
1d 'EVENING POST', JERSEY, 17/3/41

Quantities printed: ½d 703,500; 1d 1,030,620

Withdrawn and invalidated: 13.4.46

6 Old Jersey Farm

7 Portelet Bay

8 Corbière
Lighthouse

9 Elizabeth Castle

10 Mont Orgueil
Castle

11 Gathering Vraic
(seaweed)

Pictorial Issue

(Des E. Blampied. Eng H. Cortot. Typo French Govt Printing
Works, Paris)

1943 (1 JUNE)–**44**. *No wmk.* Perf 13½ (C)

3	**6**	½d green	12·00	12·00
		a. Rough, grey paper (6.10.43) . .	15·00	14·00
4	**7**	1d scarlet	3·00	50
		a. On newsprint (28.2.44)	3·50	75
5	**8**	1½d brown (8.6.43)	8·00	5·75
6	**9**	2d orange-yellow (8.6.43)	7·50	2·00
7	**10**	2½d blue (29.6.43)	3·00	1·00
		a. On newsprint (25.2.44)	1·00	1·70
		ba. Thin paper (design shows through on reverse)	£225	
8	**11**	3d violet (29.6.43)	3·00	2·75
3/8		*Set of 6*	30·00	21·00
		First Day Covers (3)		36·00
		Set of 6 Gutter Pairs . . . . 48·00		

Printings: The sheets of the various printings were dated in the sheet
corners as follows:

½d 1st Printing 1/5/43
2nd Printing 3/5/43
3rd Printing 6/10/43
1d 1st Printing 7/5/43
2nd Printing 8/5/43
3rd Printing 7/10/43
4th Printing 28/2/44
1½d 1st Printing 17/5/43
2nd Printing 18/5/43
2d 1st Printing 20/5/43
2nd Printing 21/5/43
2½d 1st Printing 31/5/43
2nd Printing 25/2/44
3d 1st Printing 4/6/43
2nd Printing 5/6/43

Sheets: 60 (2 panes 3×10)

Imprint: None

Quantities printed: ½d (No. 3) 360,000; ½d (No. 3a) 120,000; 1d (No. 4)
960,000; 1d (No. 4a) 240,000; 1½d 360,000; 2d 360,000; 2½d (No. 7)
360,000; 2½d (Nos. 7a/b) 360,000; 3d 360,000

Withdrawn and invalidated: 13.4.46

REGIONAL ISSUES

Although specifically issued for regional use, these issues
were initially valid for use throughout Great Britain. However,
they ceased to be valid in Jersey and Guernsey from 1
October 1969 when these islands each established their own
independent postal administration and introduced their own
stamps.

DATES OF ISSUE. Conflicting dates of issue have been
announced for some of the regional issues, partly explained
by the stamps being released on different dates by the
Philatelic Bureau in Edinburgh or the Philatelic Counter in
London and in the regions. We have adopted the practice of
giving the earliest known dates, since once released the
stamps could have been used anywhere in the U.K.

INVALIDATION. The regional issues of Jersey were
invalidated for use in Jersey and Guernsey on 1 November
1969 (although Guernsey granted a further extension for
British and regional stamps till the end of March 1970). The
stamps continued to be valid for use in the rest of the United
Kingdom until 29 February 1972. Those still current remained
on sale at philatelic sales counters until 30 September 1970.

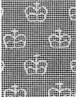

11a Multiple
Crowns

12

13

(Des E. Blampied (Type **12**), W. Gardner (Type **13**). Portrait by Dorothy Wilding Ltd. Photo Harrison)

1958–67 *Wmk Type* **11a**. Perf 15×14 (C)

9	**12**	2½d carmine-red (8.6.64)	30	45
		a. *Imperf three sides* (*pair*) £2000		
10	**13**	3d deep lilac (18.8.58)	30	25
		p. *One centre phosphor band* (9.6.67)	15	15
11		4d ultramarine (7.2.66)	25	30
		p. *Two phosphor bands* (5.9.67) .	15	25
9/11		*Set of 3*	50	75
9		*First Day Cover*		30·00
10		*First Day Cover*		20·00
11		*First Day Cover*		10·00

Cylinder Nos.: 2½d 1; 3d (ord) 1, 2; 3d (phos) 2; 4d (ord) 1; 4d (phos) 1

Sheets: 240 (12×20)

Quantities sold (ordinary only); 2½d 4,770,000; 3d 35,169,720; 4d 6,623,040

Withdrawn: 31.8.66 2½d

Sold out: 10.67 3d (ordinary); 11.67 4d (ordinary); 10.68 3d and 4d (phosphor)

1968–69. *No wmk. Chalk–surfaced paper. One centre phosphor band* (4*d values*) *or two phosphor bands* (5*d*). Perf 15×14 (C)

12	**13**	4d olive-sepia (4.9.68)	15	25
13		4d bright vermilion (26.2.69)	15	25
14		5d Royal blue (4.9.68)	15	50
12/14		*Set of 3*	40	1·00
12, 14		*First Day Cover*		3·00

Cylinder Nos.: 4d (olive-sepia) 1; 4d (bright vermilion) 1; 5d 1

Withdrawn: 30.9.69 (locally), 30.9.70 (British Philatelic Counters) 4d olive-sepia, 4d bright vermilion and 5d

INDEPENDENT POSTAL ADMINISTRATION

Jersey established their own independent postal administration on 1 October 1969 and introduced their own stamps.

NO WATERMARK. All the following issues are on unwatermarked paper.

14 Elizabeth Castle

15 La Hougue Bie (Prehistoric Tomb)

16 Portelet Bay

17 La Corbière Lighthouse

18 Mont Orgueil Castle by Night

19 Arms and Royal Mace

20 Jersey Cow

21 Chart of the English Channel

22 Mont Orgueil Castle by Day

23 Queen Elizabeth II (after Cecil Beaton)

24 Jersey Airport

25 Legislative Chamber

26 The Royal Court

27 Queen Elizabeth II (after Cecil Beaton)

††Printing (f) is the decimal issue which can be positively distinguished by the inscriptions in the left sheet margin which read 'Sheet value £25' at bottom and 'Value per row £5' at top instead of 'Sheet value £25 0s. 0d.' and 'Value per row £5 0s. 0d.' respectively. It exists with more blue in the Queen's dress and less red in the drapery but this printing also includes intermediate shades close to printing (a).

The thinner paper varieties result from a deliberate change as the thicker paper did not adhere well. The two types may be further distinguished by the gum which is creamy on the thicker paper and white on the thinner.

There are a number of shades in this issue which are in part due to the variation in the paper.

There was no postal need for the ½d value as the ½d coin had been withdrawn prior to its issue in anticipation of decimalisation.

(Des V. Whiteley. Photo Harrison (½d to 1s9d), Courvoisier (others))

1969 (1 OCT)–**70**. *Granite paper (2s6d to £1). Multicoloured; frame colours given.* Perf 14 (½d to 1s9d) or 12 (others), all comb

15	**14**	½d ochre (a)	10	60
		a. Thick paper (a)	30	60
16	**15**	1d brown (abc)	10	10
		a. Booklet stamp with blank margins* (a)	75	
		b. Thick paper (a)	80	90
17	**16**	2d claret (a)	10	10
		a. Thinner paper (bc)	50	50
18	**17**	3d ultramarine (a)	10	10
		a. Thinner paper (d)	75	75
		b. Orange omitted	£275	
19	**18**	4d yellow-olive (a)	10	10
		a. Booklet stamp with blank margins* (a)	50	
		b. Thinner paper (c)	50	50
20	**19**	5d bistre (a)	10	10
		a. Thinner paper (c)	50	50
21	**20**	6d yellow-brown (ab)	10	10
		a. Thinner paper (e)	9·00	9·00
22	**21**	9d orange-brown (a)	10	20
		a. Thinner paper (d)	2·75	2·75
23	**22**	1s reddish lilac (a)	25	25
		a. Thinner paper (c)	2·00	2·00
24	**21**	1s6d myrtle-green (a)	80	75
		a. Thinner paper (d)	3·50	3·50
25	**23**	1s9d pale myrtle-green (a)	1·00	1·00
		a. Thinner paper (c)	15·00	15·00
26	**24**	2s6d black and pale mauve (a)	1·60	1·00
27	**25**	5s black and pale blue (a)	6·50	5·00
28	**26**	10s black and pale slate-blue (a)	14·00	12·00
		a. Error. Green border†	£4500	
29	**27**	£1 pale bistre (af)††	1·90	1·60
15/29		Set of 15	20·00	16·00
		First Day Cover		20·00
15/29		Presentation Packs (3)	24·00	

*Nos. 16a and 19a are on medium paper. No. 16b on thick paper comes from 7s and 10s booklets.

†During the final printing of the 10s a sheet was printed in the colours of the 50p, No. 56, ie. green border instead of slate.

Printings: (a) 1.10.69; (b) 18.2.70; (c) 15.4.70; (d) 5.5.70; (e) 27.5.70; (f) 3.73

Cylinder Nos.: ½d, 1d, 2d, 4d, 1s 1A (×5); 3d 1A (×7); 5d, 6d, 9d, 1s6d, 1s9d 1A (×6); 2s6d to £1 None

Sheets: 60 (6×10) ½d to 1s6d; (10×6) 1s9d; 25 (5×5) 2s6d to £1

Quantities sold: ½d 999,439; 1d 1,050,124; 2d 726,837; 3d 635,019; 4d 7,148,849; 5d 4,886,016; 6d 550,766; 9d 954,649; 1s 577,086; 1s6d 419,872; 1s9d 306,674; 2s6d 244,894; 5s 206,629; 10s 179,981; £1 271,194

Withdrawn: 14.2.72 (except ½d, sold out 10.69, and £1 withdrawn 31.8.77)

Invalidated: 14.2.72 (except £1)

28 First Day Cover

Inauguration of Post Office

(Des R. Sellar. Photo Harrison)

1969 (1 OCT). *Multicoloured; background colours given.* Perf 14 (C)

30	**28**	4d magenta	10	15
31		5d new blue	20	10
32		1s6d red-brown	50	75
33		1s9d bright emerald	80	1·00
30/3		Set of 4	1·40	1·80
		First Day Cover		4·00
		Presentation Pack	2·00	

Cylinder Nos.: All values 1A (×4)

Sheets: 60 (6×10)

Quantities sold: 4d 1,483,686; 5d 742,820; 1s6d 272,155; 1s9d 238,856

Withdrawn: 1.10.70

Invalidated: 14.2.72

29 'Lord Coutanche'
(Sir James Gunn)

30 'Sir Winston
Churchill'
(Van Praag)

31 'Liberation' (Edmund
Blampied)

32 S.S. *Vega* (unknown
artist)

25th Anniversary of Liberation

(Des Rosalind Dease from paintings. Photo Courvoisier)

1970 (9 MAY). *Granite paper*. Perf 11½ (C)

34	**29**	4d multicoloured	20	20
35	**30**	5d multicoloured	20	20
36	**31**	1s6d multicoloured	90	1·00
37	**32**	1s9d multicoloured	90	1·00
34/7		Set of 4	2·00	2·00
		First Day Cover		4·00
		Presentation Pack	2·75	

A special Presentation Pack in gold, red and blue-green on olive was given to Jersey schoolchildren (Price £15). The normal Presentation Pack is printed in gold and blue-green.

Sheets: 50 (10×5) 4d, 5d; (5×10) 1s6d, 1s9d

Quantities sold: 4d 1,617,751; 5d 1,296,678; 1s6d 334,468; 1s9d 319,893

Withdrawn: 9.5.71

Invalidated: 14.2.72

33 'A Tribute to Enid
Blyton'

34 'Rags to Riches'

35 'Gourmet's Delight'

36 'We're the Greatest'

'Battle of Flowers' Parade

(Des Jennifer Toombs. Photo Courvoisier)

1970 (28 JULY). *Granite paper*. Perf 11½ (C)

38	**33**	4d multicoloured	20	10
39	**34**	5d multicoloured	20	20
40	**35**	1s6d multicoloured	2·75	2·20
41	**36**	1s9d multicoloured	2·75	2·20
38/41		Set of 4	5·25	4·25
		First Day Cover		4·25
		Presentation Pack	6·50	

Sheets: 50 (5×10)

Quantities sold: 4d 1,905,109; 5d 1,498,301; 1s6d 262,072; 1s9d 231,077

Withdrawn: 27.7.71

Invalidated: 14.2.72

37 Martello Tower,
Archirondel

Decimal Currency

(Des V. Whiteley. Photo Harrison (½ to 9p), Courvoisier (others))

1970–74. *Designs as Type* **37** *etc., but with values inscribed in decimal currency and new design* (6p). *Chalk-surfaced paper* (4½p, 5½p, 8p), *granite paper* (10p, 20p, 50p)

42	**14**	½p multicoloured (bgk)	10	10
		a. Booklet stamp with blank margins (b)	20	
43	**17**	1p multicoloured (bn)	10	10
		a. Orange omitted	£300	
44	**20**	1½p multicoloured (b)	10	10
45	**18**	2p multicoloured (b)	10	10
		a. Booklet stamp with blank margins	60	
46	**19**	2½p multicoloured (bk)	10	10
		a. Booklet stamp with blank margins (b)	60	
		ab. Gold (Mace) omitted	£650	
		ac. Gold (Mace) ptg double	£300	
47	**15**	3p multicoloured (bch)	10	10
		a. Booklet stamp with blank margins (e)	60	
48	**16**	3½p multicoloured (bh)	10	10
		a. Booklet stamp with blank margins (h)	25	
49	**21**	4p multicoloured (bfimo)	10	10
49a	**19**	4½p multicoloured (j)*	75	75
		ab. Uncoated paper	£400	
50	**22**	5p multicoloured (blmo)	10	10
50a	**20**	5½p multicoloured (j)	75	75
51	**37**	6p multicoloured (b)	20	10
52	**21**	7½p multicoloured (b)	50	50
52a	**18**	8p multicoloured (j)	75	75
53	**23**	9p multicoloured (b)	70	70
54	**24**	10p multicoloured (adh)	40	30
55	**25**	20p multicoloured (adh)	90	80
56	**26**	50p multicoloured (al)	1·50	1·20
42/56		Set of 18	4·50	4·50
		First Day Cover (3)		6·50
42/56, 29		Presentation Packs (4)	6·75	

Gum: From 1974 printings appeared with dextrin added to the PVA gum giving a bluish-green tinge and mottled appearance. The ½p, 1p, 2½p, 3p, 3½p, 4p, 5p and 8p all exist both PVA and PVA dextrin. The 4½ and 5½p only come with dextrin, and the 10, 20 and 50p only with gum arabic.

The Presentation Packs for this series exist in two different sizes, 4¼ in×5½ in of the initial supply and 8½×4½ in for replacement stock.

Printings: (a) 1.10.70; (b) 15.2.71; (c) 1.8.72; (d) 15.11.72; (e) 1.12.72; (f) 1.10.73; (g) 3.12.73; (h) 1.7.74; (i) 12.8.74; (k) 31.10.74; (l) 1.11.74; (l) 28.1.75; (m) 1.4.75; (n) 21.4.75; (o) 30.10.75

Plate Nos.: ½p, 2p, 3½p, 6p, 8p 1A (×5); 1p 1A (×7), 2A–1A (×6) (n); 1½p, 2½p, 4½p, 5½p, 7½p, 9p 1A (×6); 3p 1A (×5), (×4)–2A (h); 4p 1A (×6), 2A–1A (×5) (mo); 5p 1A (×5), 2A–1A (×4) (mo); 10p to 50p None

Sheets: 50 (5×10) ½p to 8p; (10×5) 9p; 25 (5×5) 10p to 50p

Quantities sold: ½p 2,247,128; 1p 1,654,860; 1½p 817,871; 2p 2,305,239; 2½p 5,096,912; 3p 4,780,836; 3½p 2,069,095; 4p 3,908,727; 4½p 349,157; 5p 3,593,226; 5½p 333,125; 6p 1,072,224; 7½p 538,810; 8p 329,361; 9p 458,977; 10p 862,524; 20p 765,524; 50p 490,675

Withdrawn: 31.1.77 (½p to 9p); 31.8.77 (others)

38 White Eared-Pheasant

39 Thick-billed Parrot

40 Western Black and White Colobus Monkey

41 Ring-tailed Lemur

Wildlife Preservation Trust (1st series)

(Des Jennifer Toombs. Photo Courvoisier)

1971 (12 MAR). *Granite paper. Perf* 11½ (C)

57	**38**	2p multicoloured	20	10
58	**39**	2½p multicoloured	20	15
59	**40**	7½p multicoloured	2·20	2·20
60	**41**	9p multicoloured	3·00	3·00
57/60		Set of 4	5·00	5·00
		First Day Cover		8·00
		Presentation Pack	6·00	

See also Nos. 73/6, 217/21, 324/9, 447/51 and 824/9.

Sheets: 50 (5×10) 2p, 9p; (10×5) others

Quantities sold: 2p 1,025,544; 2½p 1,363,427; 7½p 233,147; 9p 220,710

Withdrawn: 11.3.72

42 Royal British Legion Badge

43 Poppy Emblem and Field

44 Jack Counter VC, and Victoria Cross

45 Crossed Tricolour and Union Jack

50th Anniversary of Royal British Legion

(Des G. Drummond. Litho Questa)

1971 (15 JUNE). Perf 14 (C)

61	**42**	2p multicoloured	....	20	10
62	**43**	2½p multicoloured	....	20	10
63	**44**	7½p multicoloured	....	1·00	1·10
64	**45**	9p multicoloured	....	1·00	1·10
61/4		Set of 4	....	2·10	2·10
		First Day Cover	....		3·50
		Presentation Pack	....	3·00	

Plate Nos.: 2p, 2½p 1A, 1B (each ×4); others 1A, 1B (each ×5)

Sheets: 50 (5×10)

Imprint: Right-hand corner, bottom margin

Quantities sold: 2p 1,381,873; 2½p 1,529,866; 7½p 239,477; 9p 226,407

Withdrawn: 14.6.72

46 'Tante Elizabeth' (E. Blampied)

47 'English Fleet in the Channel' (P. Monamy)

48 'The Boyhood of Raleigh' (Millais)

49 'The Blind Beggar' (W. W. Ouless)

Paintings

(Des and photo Courvoisier)

1971 (5 OCT). *Granite paper.* Perf 11½ (C)

65	**46**	2p multicoloured	....	15	10
66	**47**	2½p multicoloured	....	20	10
67	**48**	7½p multicoloured	....	1·20	1·40
68	**49**	9p multicoloured	....	1·40	1·50
65/8		Set of 4	....	2·20	2·20
		First Day Cover	....		4·75
		Presentation Pack	....	3·00	

See also Nos. 115/18 and 213/16.

Sheets: 50 (5×10) 2p, 9p; (10×5) others

Quantities sold: 2p 1,243,198; 2½p 1,490,595; 7½p 264,532; 9p 251,770

Withdrawn: 4.10.72

50 Jersey Fern

51 Jersey Thrift

52 Jersey Orchid

53 Jersey Viper's Bugloss

Wild Flowers of Jersey

(Des G. Drummond. Photo Courvoisier)

1972 (18 JAN). *Granite paper.* Perf 11½ (C)

69	**50**	3p multicoloured	....	20	10
70	**51**	5p multicoloured	....	30	20
71	**52**	7½p multicoloured	....	1·20	1·40
72	**53**	9p multicoloured	....	1·20	1·40
69/72		Set of 4	....	2·75	2·75
		First Day Cover	....		4·50
		Presentation Pack	....	3·00	

Sheets: 50 (5×10)

Quantities sold: 3p 1,124,878; 5p 332,764; 7½p 202,404; 9p 196,998

Withdrawn: 17.1.73

54 Cheetah

55 Rothschild's Mynah

60 Shako (5th South-West Regt)

61 Helmet (3rd Jersey Light Infantry)

56 Spectacled Bear

57 Tuatara

Royal Jersey Militia (1st series)

(Des and photo Courvoisier)

1972 (27 JUNE). *Granite paper.* Perf 11½ (C)

77	**58**	2½p multicoloured	. . . .	10	10
78	**59**	3p multicoloured	. . . .	10	10
79	**60**	7½p multicoloured	. . . .	30	20
80	**61**	9p multicoloured	. . . .	50	60
77/80		*Set of 4*	. . . .	90	90
		First Day Cover	. . . .		3·00
		Presentation Pack	. . . .	1·70	

See also Nos. 1253/7

Sheets: 50 (10×5)

Quantities sold: 2½p 1,240,393; 3p 1,857,224; 7½p 300,554; 9p 271,832

Withdrawn: 26.6.73

Wildlife Preservation Trust (2nd series)

(Des Jennifer Toombs. Photo Courvoisier)

1972 (17 MAR). *Granite paper.* Perf 11½ (C)

73	**54**	2½p multicoloured	. . . .	30	10
74	**55**	3p multicoloured	. . . .	25	20
75	**56**	7½p multicoloured	. . . .	50	70
76	**57**	9p multicoloured	. . . .	80	90
73/6		*Set of 4*	. . . .	1·60	1·70
		First Day Cover	. . . .		4·50
		Presentation Pack	. . . .	2·50	

Sheets: 50 (10×5) 3p; (5×10) others

Quantities sold: 2½p 1,223,916; 3p 1,631,752; 7½p 279,935; 9p 235,968

Withdrawn: 16.3.73

62 Princess Anne

63 Queen Elizabeth and Prince Philip

64 Prince Charles

65 The Royal Family

58 Artillery Shako

59 Shako (2nd North Regt)

Royal Silver Wedding

(Des G. Drummond from photographs by D. Groves. Photo Courvoisier)

1972 (1 NOV). *Granite paper.* Perf 11½ (C)

81	62	2½p multicoloured	10	10
82	63	3p multicoloured	10	10
83	64	7½p multicoloured	35	35
84	65	20p multicoloured	35	35
81/4		Set of 4	80	80
		First Day Cover		1·50
		Presentation Pack	1·10	

Sheets: 25 (5×5)

Quantities sold: 2½p 1,743,240; 3p 1,638,566; 7½p 424,029; 20p 418,824

Sold out: by 23.1.73 (7½p, 20p); 16.5.73 (3p)

Withdrawn: 31.10.73 (2½p)

66 Silver Wine Cup and Christening Cup

67 Gold Torque

68 Royal Seal of Charles II

69 Armorican Bronze Coins

Centenary of La Société Jersiaise

(Des G. Drummond. Photo Courvoisier)

1973 (23 JAN). *Granite paper.* Perf 11½ (C)

85	66	2½p violet-blue, new blue and black	10	10
86	67	3p bright cerise, orange-yellow and black	10	10
87	68	7½p multicoloured	25	20
88	69	9p multicoloured	30	30
85/8		Set of 4	70	60
		First Day Cover		1·20
		Presentation Pack	1·20	

Sheets: 50 (10×5) 3p, 7½p; (5×10) others

Quantities sold: 2½p 2,008,923; 3p 2,437,421; 7½p 363,543; 9p 327,917

Sold out: by 31.10.73 (7½p)

Withdrawn: 22.1.74 (2½p, 3p, 9p)

70 Balloon *L'Armee de La Loire* and Letter, Paris, 1870

71 Astra Seaplane, 1912

72 Supermarine Sea Eagle

73 De Havilland D.H.86 Dragon Express *Giffard Bay*

Jersey Aviation History

(Des and photo Courvoisier)

1973 (16 MAY). *Granite paper.* Perf 11½ (C)

89	70	3p multicoloured	10	10
90	71	5p multicoloured	10	10
91	72	7½p multicoloured	35	35
92	73	9p multicoloured	45	45
89/92		Set of 4	90	90
		First Day Cover		1·50
		Presentation Pack	1·20	

Sheets: 50 (5×10)

Quantities sold: 3p 3,085,497; 5p 641,583; 7½p 368,069; 9p 356,379

Sold out: by 31.10.73 (7½p)

Withdrawn: 15.5.74 (3p, 5p, 9p)

74 *North Western*, 1870

75 *Calvados*, 1873

76 *Carteret* at Grouville Station, 1893

77 *Caesarea*, 1873, and Route Map

Centenary of Jersey Eastern Railway

(Des G. Drummond. Photo Courvoisier)

1973 (6 AUG). *Granite paper.* Perf 11½ (C)

93	**74**	2½p multicoloured	....	10	10
94	**75**	3p multicoloured	....	10	10
95	**76**	7½p multicoloured	....	35	35
96	**77**	9p multicoloured	....	45	45
93/6		Set of 4	....	90	90
		First Day Cover	....		1·40
		Presentation Pack	....	1·20	

Sheets: 50 (5×10)

Quantities sold: 2½p 1,591,063; 3p 3,051,097; 7½p 396,919; 9p 365,310

Sold out: by 31.10.73 (7½p)

Withdrawn: 5.8.74 (2½p, 3p, 9p)

78 Princess Anne and Captain Mark Phillips

Royal Wedding

(Des and photo Courvoisier)

1973 (14 NOV). *Granite paper.* Perf 11½ (C)

97	**78**	3p multicoloured	....	10	10
98		20p multicoloured	....	50	50
97/8		Set of 2	....	60	60
		First Day Cover	....		80
		Presentation Pack	....	95	

Sheets: 25 (5×5)

Quantities sold: 3p 1,988,407; 20p 522,793

Withdrawn: 30.11.74

79 Spider Crab

80 Conger Eel

81 Lobster

82 Tuberculate Ormer

Marine Life

(Des Jennifer Toombs. Photo Courvoisier)

1973 (15 NOV). *Granite paper.* Perf 11½ (C)

99	**79**	2½p multicoloured	....	10	10
100	**80**	3p multicoloured	....	10	10
101	**81**	7½p multicoloured	....	30	35
102	**82**	20p multicoloured	....	40	45
99/102		Set of 4	....	80	90
		First Day Cover	....		1·20
		Presentation Pack	....	1·40	

Sheets: 50 (5×10)

Quantities sold: 2½p 1,596,526; 3p 1,243,541; 7½p 501,541; 20p 517,440

Sold out: by 28.2.74 (7½p)

Withdrawn: 30.11.74 (2½p, 3p, 20p)

83 Freesias

84 Anemones

85 Carnations and Gladioli

86 Daffodils and Iris

Spring Flowers

(Des G. Drummond. Photo Courvoisier)

1974 (13 FEB). *Granite paper.* Perf 11½ (C)

103	**83**	3p multicoloured	....	10	10
104	**84**	5½p multicoloured	....	15	15
105	**85**	8p multicoloured	....	25	30
106	**86**	10p multicoloured	....	30	35
103/6		Set of 4	....	70	80
		First Day Cover	....		1·20
		Presentation Pack	....	1·20	

Sheets: 50 (10×5)

Quantities sold: 3p 1,239,968; 5½p 590,376; 8p 475,665; 10p 507,542

Withdrawn: 28.2.75

87 First U.K. Pillar-box and Contemporary Cover

88 Jersey Postmen, 1862 and 1969

89 Modern Pillar-box and Cover

90 Mail Transport, 1874 and 1974

Centenary of Universal Postal Union

(Des G. Drummond. Photo Courvoisier)

1974 (7 JUNE). *Granite paper.* Perf 11½ (C)

107	**87**	2½p multicoloured	10	10
108	**88**	3p multicoloured	10	15
109	**89**	5½p multicoloured	25	20
110	**90**	20p multicoloured	35	40
107/10		Set of 4	70	75
		First Day Cover		95
		Presentation Pack	1·20	

Sheets: 50 (5×10)

Quantities sold: 2½p 461,174; 3p 1,380,018; 5½p 421,674; 20p 386,348

Withdrawn: 30.6.75

91 John Wesley

92 Sir William Hillary

93 Canon Wace

94 Sir Winston Churchill

Anniversaries. Events described on stamps

(Des recess and litho De La Rue)

1974 (31 JULY). Perf 13×14 (C)

111	**91**	3p agate and light cinnamon . . .	10	10
112	**92**	3½p blackish violet & light azure . .	10	10
113	**93**	8p blue-black and pale rose-lilac .	20	20
114	**94**	20p black and pale buff	45	45
		a. Pale buff (background omitted)		
111/14		Set of 4	75	75
		First Day Cover		90
		Presentation Pack	1·20	

Plate Nos.: 3p and 20p 1A–1A, 1B–1B; 3½p and 8p 1A–1A, 1B–1B, 2A–1A, 2B–1B

Sheets: 50 (10×5)

Imprint: Right-hand corner, bottom margin

Quantities sold: 3p 908,852; 3½p 2,355,391; 8p 338,397; 20p 409,291

Withdrawn: 31.7.75

95 *Catherine* and *Mary* (royal yachts)

96 French Two-decker

97 Dutch Vessel

98 Battle of Cap La Hague, 1692

Marine Paintings by Peter Monamy

(Des and photo Courvoisier)

1974 (22 NOV). *Granite paper.* Perf 11½ (C)
115	**95**	3½p multicoloured	10	10
116	**96**	5½p multicoloured	15	10
117	**97**	8p multicoloured	25	20
118	**98**	25p multicoloured	55	55
115/18		*Set* of 4	95	90
		First Day Cover		2·00
		Presentation Pack	1·70	

Sheets: 50 (10×5) 8p; (5×10) others

Quantities sold: 3½p 1,670,994; 5½p 448,137; 8p 416,296; 25p 415,991

Withdrawn: 30.11.75

99 Potato Digger

100 Cider Crusher

101 Six-Horse Plough

102 Hay Cart

Nineteenth-Century Farming

(Des G. Drummond. Photo Courvoisier)

1975 (25 FEB). *Granite paper.* Perf 11½ (C)
119	**99**	3p multicoloured	10	10
120	**100**	3½p multicoloured	10	10
121	**101**	8p multicoloured	20	20
122	**102**	10p multicoloured	35	40
119/22		*Set of* 4	70	75
		First Day Cover		85
		Presentation Pack	90	

Sheets: 50 (5×10)

Quantities sold: 3p 588,185; 3½p 1,025,295; 8p 432,432; 10p 457,196

Withdrawn: 28.2.76

103 H.M. Queen Elizabeth, the Queen Mother (photograph by Cecil Beaton)

Royal Visit

(Des and photo Courvoisier)

1975 (30 MAY). *Granite paper.* Perf 11½ (C)
123	**103**	20p multicoloured	50	45
		First Day Cover		1·70
		Presentation Pack	90	

Cylinder Nos.: A1–1–1–1–1, B1–1–1–1–1

Sheets: 25 (5×5)

Quantity sold: 572,675

Withdrawn: 31.5.76

104 Nautilus Shell

105 Parasol

106 Deckchair

107 Sandcastle with flags of Jersey and the U.K.

Jersey Tourism

(Des A. Games. Photo Courvoisier)

1975 (6 JUNE). *Designs based on holiday posters. Granite paper.* Perf 11½ (C)
124	**104**	5p multicoloured	10	10
125	**105**	8p multicoloured	10	10
126	**106**	10p multicoloured	30	25
127	**107**	12p multicoloured	40	35
124/7		*Set of* 4	80	70
		First Day Cover		1·10
		Presentation Pack	1·70	
MS128		147×69 mm. Nos. 124/7	90	1·10
		First Day Cover		4·00

Cylinder Nos.: All values A1–1–1–1–1, B1–1–1–1–1

Sheets: 50 (10×5)

Quantities sold: 5p 1,377,519; 8p 368,521; 10p 467,278; 12p 389,574; miniature sheet 298,689

Withdrawn: 30.6.76

108 Common Tern

109 British Storm Petrel

110 Brent Geese

111 Shag

Sea Birds

(Des Jennifer Toombs. Photo Courvoisier)

1975 (28 JULY). *Granite paper.* Perf 11½ (C)

129	**108**	4p multicoloured	. . . .	10	10
130	**109**	5p multicoloured	. . . .	15	10
131	**110**	8p multicoloured	. . . .	40	25
132	**111**	25p multicoloured	. . . .	70	50
129/32		Set of 4	. . . .	1·20	85
		First Day Cover	. . . .		1·40
		Presentation Pack	. . . .		1·60

Sheets: 50 (10×5)

Quantities sold: 4p 872,260; 5p 2,871,390; 8p 384,550; 25p 362,160

Withdrawn: 31.7.76

112 Armstrong Whitworth Siskin IIIA

113 Supermarine Southampton I Flying Boat

114 Supermarine Spitfire Mk I

115 Folland Fo. 144 Gnat T. 1

50th Anniversary of Royal Air Forces Association, Jersey Branch

(Des A. Theobald. Photo Courvoisier)

1975 (30 OCT). *Granite paper.* Perf 11½ (C)

133	**112**	4p multicoloured	. . . .	10	10
134	**113**	5p multicoloured	. . . .	15	10
135	**114**	10p multicoloured	. . . .	40	25
136	**115**	25p multicoloured	. . . .	70	50
133/6		Set of 4	. . . .	1·20	85
		First Day Cover	. . . .		1·60
		Presentation Pack	. . . .	1·50	

Cylinder Nos.: All values A1–1–1–1–1, B1–1–1–1–1

Sheets: 50 (5×10)

Quantities sold: 4p 1,496,640; 5p 1,805,624; 10p 581,627; 25p 407,423

Withdrawn: 30.10.76

116 Map of Jersey Parishes

117 Zoological Park

118 St. Mary's Church

119 Seymour Tower

120 La Corbière Lighthouse

121 St. Saviour's Church

122 Elizabeth Castle

123 Gorey Harbour

124 Jersey Airport

125 Grosnez Castle

134 Queen Elizabeth II (photograph by Alex Wilson)

126 Bonne Nuit Harbour

127 Le Hocq Tower

Parish Arms and Views

(Des Courvoisier (£2), G. Drummond (others). Litho Questa (½p to 15p). Photo Courvoisier (others))

1976–80. *Granite paper* (20p to £2). Perf 14½ (½p to 15p) or 12 (others), all comb

128 Morel Farm

129 Parish Arms and Island Scene

137	**116**	½p multicoloured (af)	10	10
138	**117**	1p multicoloured (af)	10	10
		a. *Booklet pane of 4 (No. 138×2 plus 2 se-tenant labels) (b)*	70	
		b. *Booklet pane. No. 138×4 (begh)*	80	
139	**118**	5p multicoloured (ad)	10	10
		a. *Booklet pane of 4 (b)*	40	
140	**119**	6p multicoloured (ad)	10	10
		a. *Booklet pane of 4 (eg)*	40	
141	**120**	7p multicoloured (ad)	10	10
		a. *Booklet pane of 4 (bh)*	40	
142	**121**	8p multicoloured (ad)	15	10
		a. *Booklet pane of 4 (eg)*	80	
143	**122**	9p multicoloured (a)	15	10
		a. *Booklet pane of 4 (h)*	60	
144	**123**	10p multicoloured (af)	20	10
145	**124**	11p multicoloured (a)	25	25
146	**125**	12p multicoloured (a)	25	20
147	**126**	13p multicoloured (a)	25	20
148	**127**	14p multicoloured (a)	30	20
149	**128**	15p multicoloured (a)	30	25
150	**129**	20p multicoloured (c)	45	45
151	**130**	30p multicoloured (c)	55	50
152	**131**	40p multicoloured (c)	80	80
153	**132**	50p multicoloured (c)	1·00	1·00
154	**133**	£1 multicoloured (c)	3·00	3·00
155	**134**	£2 multicoloured (d)	4·00	4·00
137/55		*Set of 19*	11·00	11·00
		First Day Covers (4)		10·50
		Presentation Packs (4)	13·00	

130 Flag and Map

131 Postal H.Q. and Badge

Printings: (a) 29.1.76; (b) 5.4.76; (c) 20.8.76; (d) 16.11.77; (e) 28.2.78; (f) 31.8.78; (g) 1.10.79; (h) 6.5.80

Plate or cylinder Nos.: ½p to 9p, 13p, 14p 1A, 1B, 1C, 1D (each ×4); 10p 1A, 1B, 1C, 1D (each ×4), 1B–1B–1B–2B, 2A–1A–1A–2A, 2B–1B–1B–2B, 2C–1C–1C–2C, 2D–1D–1D–2D; 11p 1A, 1B, 1C, 1D (each ×5); 12p 1A, 1B, 1C, 1D (each ×4), 1A–1A–2A–2A, 1B–1B–2B–2B, 1C–1C–2C–2C, 1D–1D–2D–2D; 15p 1A, 1B, 1C, 1D (each ×4), 1A–2A–1A–1A, 1B–2B–1B–1B, 1C–2C–1C–1C, 1D–2D–1D–1D, 1A–2A–2A–1A, 1B–2B–2B–1B, 1C–2C–1C–1C, 1D–2D–2D–1D, 1A–3A–2A–1A, 1B–3B–2B–1B, 1C–3C–2C–1C,

132 Parliament, Royal Court and Arms

133 Lieutenant-Governor's Flag and Government House

1D–3D–2D–1D; 20p A1–1–1–1–1, B1–1–1–1–1, C1–1–1–1–1, D1–1–1–1–1; 30p, £1 A1–1–1–1–1, B1–1–1–1–1; 40p, 50p A1–1–1–1, B1–1–1–1; £2 A1–1–1–1–1–1–1, B1–1–1–1–1–1–1, C1–1–1–1–1–1–1, D1–1–1–1–1–1–1

Sheets: 50 (5×10) ½p to 15p; 25 (5×5) others

Imprint: Right-hand corner, bottom margin (½p to 15p); central, bottom margin (others)

Withdrawn: 27.2.82 ½p to 9p (sheets); 20.4.82 1p, 5p to 9p (booklets); 31.7.82 10p to 15p; 28.2.83 20p to £1; 31.3.92 £2

135 Sir Walter Ralegh and Map of Virginia

136 Sir George Carteret and Map of New Jersey

137 Philippe D'Auvergne and Long Island Landing

138 John Copley and Sketch

Bicentenary of American Independence

(Des M. Orbell. Photo Courvoisier)

1976 (29 MAY). *Granite paper*. Perf 11½ (C)

160	135	5p multicoloured	10	10
161	136	7p multicoloured	15	10
162	137	11p multicoloured	40	25
163	138	13p multicoloured	50	40
160/3		*Set of 4*	1·00	75
		First Day Cover		1·20
		Presentation Pack	1·40	

Cylinder Nos.: 5p, 11p A1–1–1–1–1, B1–1–1–1–1; others A1–1–1–1, B1–1–1–1

Sheets: 25 (5×5)

Quantities sold: 5p 980,029; 7p 1,352,629; 11p 582,706; 13p 435,561

Withdrawn: 31.5.77

139 Dr. Grandin and Map of China

140 Sampan on the Yangtze

141 Overland Trek

142 Dr. Grandin at Work

Birth Centenary of Dr. Lilian Grandin (medical missionary)

(Des Jennifer Toombs. Photo Courvoisier)

1976 (25 NOV). *Granite paper*. Perf 11½ (C)

164	139	5p multicoloured	10	10
165	140	7p lt yellow, yellow-brown & blk	10	10
166	141	11p multicoloured	35	25
167	142	13p multicoloured	50	40
164/7		*Set of 4*	95	75
		First Day Cover		1·20
		Presentation Pack	1·40	

Cylinder Nos.: 7p A1–1–1, B1–1; 13p A1–1–1–1, B1–1–1–1; others A1–1–1–1, B1–1–1–1

Sheets: 50 (5×10)

Quantities sold: 5p 757,843; 7p 1,043,198; 11p 384,436; 13p 354,096

Withdrawn: 30.11.77

143 Coronation, 1953 (photograph by Cecil Beaton)

144 Visit to Jersey, 1957

145 Queen Elizabeth II (photograph by Peter Grugeon)

Silver Jubilee

(Des G. Drummond. Photo Courvoisier)

1977 (7 FEB). *Granite paper.* Perf 11½ (C)

168	**143**	5p multicoloured	15	10
169	**144**	7p multicoloured	20	15
170	**145**	25p multicoloured	40	55
168/70		*Set of 3*	70	70
		First Day Cover		1·20
		Presentation Pack	1·20	

Cylinder Nos.: All values A1–1–1–1–1, B1–1–1–1–1

Sheets: 25 (5×5)

Imprint: Central, bottom margin

Quantities sold: 5p 1,220,986; 7p 1,212,639; 25p 681,241

Withdrawn: 28.2.78

146 Coins of 1871 and 1877

147 One-twelfth Shilling, 1949

148 Silver Crown, 1966

149 £2 Piece, 1972

Centenary of Currency Reform

(Des D. Henley. Litho Questa)

1977 (25 MAR). Perf 14 (C)

171	**146**	5p multicoloured	10	10
172	**147**	7p multicoloured	15	10
173	**148**	11p multicoloured	30	30
174	**149**	13p multicoloured	35	35
171/4		*Set of 4*	80	75
		First Day Cover		1·10
		Presentation Pack	1·40	

Plate Nos.: 7p 1A, 1B (each ×5), 1A–2A–1A (×3), 1B–2B–1B (×3); others 1A, 1B (each ×5)

Sheets: 50 (5×10)

Imprint: Right-hand corner, bottom margin

Quantities sold: 5p 1,029,661; 7p 923,950; 11p 383,834; 13p 368,249

Withdrawn: 31.3.78

150 Sir William Weston and *Santa Anna*, 1530

151 Sir William Drogo and Ambulance, 1877

152 Duke of Connaught and Rolls-Royce Ambulance, 1917

153 Duke of Gloucester and Stretcher-team, 1977

St. John Ambulance Centenary

(Des A. Theobald. Litho Questa)

1977 (24 JUNE). Perf 14×13½ (C)

175	**150**	5p multicoloured	10	10
176	**151**	7p multicoloured	10	10
177	**152**	11p multicoloured	25	20
178	**153**	13p multicoloured	30	25
175/8		*Set of 4*	70	60
		First Day Cover		1·10
		Presentation Pack	1·20	

Plate Nos.: 5p 1A, 1B, 1C (each ×5); 7p, 11p 1A, 1B, 1C (each ×6); 13p 1A, 1B, 1C (each ×5), 1B–2B–1B–1B–1B

Sheets: 40 (8×5)

Imprint: Bottom corner, right-hand margin

Quantities sold: 5p 849,532; 7p 1,089,526; 11p 421,039; 13p 370,887

Withdrawn: 30.6.78

158 Harry Vardon Statuette and Map of Royal Jersey Course

159 Harry Vardon's Grip and Swing

154 Arrival of Queen Victoria, 1846

155 Victoria College, 1852

160 Harry Vardon's Putt

161 Golf Trophies and Book by Harry Vardon

156 Sir Galahad Statue, 1924

157 College Hall

Centenary of Royal Jersey Golf Club

(Des Jennifer Toombs. Litho Questa)

1978 (28 FEB). Perf 14 (C)

183	**158**	6p multicoloured	10	10
184	**159**	8p multicoloured	15	10
185	**160**	11p multicoloured	35	25
186	**161**	13p multicoloured	40	35
183/6		Set of 4	90	70
		First Day Cover		1·10
		Presentation Pack	1·40	

Plate Nos.: 6p 1A, 1B (each ×5); 8p, 11p 1A, 1B (each ×4); 13p 1A, 1B (each ×4), 2A–1A–1A–1A, 2B–1B–1B–1B

Sheets: 50 (5×10)

Imprint: Right-hand corner, bottom margin

Quantities sold: 6p 837,427; 8p 851,904; 11p 466,343; 13p 368,648

Withdrawn: 28.2.79

125th Anniversary of Victoria College

(Des R. Granger Barrett. Litho Questa)

1977 (29 SEPT). Perf 14½ (C)

179	**154**	7p multicoloured	15	10
180	**155**	10½p multicoloured	20	15
		a. Black ptg double		
181	**156**	11p multicoloured	25	25
182	**157**	13p multicoloured	30	25
179/82		Set of 4	80	70
		First Day Cover		1·10
		Presentation Pack	1·40	

Plate Nos.: 7p 1A, 1B (each ×6), 1A–1A–2A–1A–1A–1A, 1B–1B–2B–1B–1B–1B; 13p 1A, 1B (each ×6); others 1A, 1B (each ×5)

Sheets: 50 (5×10) 7 and 10½p, (10×5) others

Imprint: Right-hand corner, bottom margin

Quantities sold: 7p 1,496,997; 10½p 906,669; 11p 528,293; 13p 371,251

Withdrawn: 30.9.78

162 Mont Orgueil Castle

163 St. Aubin's Fort

164 Elizabeth Castle

Europa Monuments. Castles from Paintings by Thomas Phillips

(Des from paintings by Thomas Philips. Photo Courvoisier)

1978 (1 MAY). Granite paper. Perf 11½ (C)

187	**162**	6p multicoloured	....	10	10
188	**163**	8p multicoloured	....	15	15
189	**164**	10½p multicoloured	....	35	25
187/9		Set of 3	....	55	45
		First Day Cover	....		70
		Presentation Pack	....	80	

Cylinder Nos.: All values A1–1–1–1, B1–1–1–1, C1–1–1–1, D1–1–1–1

Sheets: 20 (5×4)

Imprint: Central, bottom margin

Quantities sold: 6p 2,602,412; 8p 2,592,722; 10½p 2,564,535

Withdrawn: 31.5.79

165 'Gaspé Basin' (P. J. Ouless)

166 Map of Gaspé Peninsula

167 *Century* (brigantine)

168 Early Map of Jersey

169 St. Aubin's Bay, Town and Harbour

Links with Canada

(Des R. Granger Barrett. Litho Questa)

1978 (9 JUNE). Perf 14½ (C)

190	**165**	6p multicoloured	....	10	10
191	**166**	8p multicoloured	....	15	10
192	**167**	10½p multicoloured	....	20	15
193	**168**	11p multicoloured	....	40	25
194	**169**	13p multicoloured	....	45	40
190/4		Set of 5	....	1·10	90
		First Day Cover	....		1·10
		Presentation Pack	....	1·50	

Plate Nos.: 6p 1A, 1B, 1C, 1D (each ×5); others 1A, 1B, 1C, 1D (each ×6)

Sheets: 50 (5×10)

Imprint: Right-hand corner, bottom margin

Quantities sold: 6p 1,047,825; 8p 1,095,489; 10½p 999,002; 11p 443,932; 13p 367,472

Withdrawn: 30.6.79

170 Queen Elizabeth and Prince Philip

171 Hallmarks of 1953 and 1977

25th Anniversary of Coronation

(Des and photo Courvoisier)

1978 (26 JUNE). Granite paper. Perf 11½ (C)

195	**170**	8p silver, black and cerise	.....	20	10
196	**171**	25p silver, black and new blue	..	50	45
195/6		Set of 2	....	70	55
		First Day Cover	....		90
		Presentation Pack	....	95	

Cylinder Nos.: Both values A1–1–1, B1–1–1

Sheets: 50 (10×5)

Quantities sold: 8p 1,060,259; 25p 459,558

Withdrawn: 30.6.79

172 Mail Cutter, 1778–1827

173 *Flamer*, 1831–37

174 *Diana*, 1877–90

175 *Ibex*, 1891–1925

317

176 *Caesarea*, 1960–75

Bicentenary of England–Jersey Government Mail Packet Service

(Des Jersey P.O. Litho Harrison)

1978 (18 OCT). Perf 14½×14 (C)

197	**172**	6p black, yellow-brown and greenish yellow	10	10
198	**173**	8p black, dull yellowish green and pale yellow-green	15	10
199	**174**	10½p black, ultramarine & cobalt .	30	20
200	**175**	11p blk, purple & pale rose-lilac	35	30
201	**176**	13p black, Venetian red and pink	40	40
197/201		Set of 5	1·10	1·00
		First Day Cover		1·40
		Presentation Pack	1·50	

Plate Nos.: All values 1A, 1B (each ×3)

Sheets: 50 (5×10)

Imprint: Right-hand corner, bottom margin

Quantities sold: 6p 1,157,597; 8p 1,149,500; 10½p 528,170; 11p 468,589; 13p 371,210

Withdrawn: 31.10.79

177 Jersey Calf

178 'Ansom Designette' (calf presented to the Queen, 27 June 1978)

9th World Jersey Cattle Bureau Conference

(Des Jersey P.O. and Questa. Litho Questa)

1979 (1 MAR). Perf 13½ (C)

202	**177**	6p multicoloured	10	10
		a. Gold ptg double	£400	
203	**178**	25p multicoloured	50	45
		a. Gold ptg double	£400	
202/3		Set of 2	60	55
		First Day Cover		95
		Presentation Pack	1·10	

Plate Nos.: Both values 1A, 1B, 1C, 1D, 1E, 1F (each ×8)

Sheets: 20 (4×5)

Imprint: Right-hand corner, bottom margin

Withdrawn: 29.2.80

179 Jersey Pillar Box, c. 1860

180 Clearing a Modern Jersey Post Box

181 Telephone Switchboard, c. 1900

182 Modern S.P.C. Telephone System

Europa. Communications

(Des Jennifer Toombs. Litho Questa)

1979 (1 MAR). Thin paper. Perf 14 (C)

204	**179**	8p multicoloured	15	15
		a. Horiz pair. Nos. 204/5	50	50
		b. Thick paper	40	40
		ba. Horiz pair. Nos. 204b/5b . . .	80	90
		c. Perf 14½ (thick paper)	30	30
		ca. Horiz pair. Nos. 204c/5c . . .	60	70
		cb. Yellow omitted*		
205	**180**	8p multicoloured	15	15
		b. Thick paper	40	40
		c. Perf 14½ (thick paper)	30	30
		cb. Pale rose-red omitted*		
206	**181**	10½p multicoloured	15	15
		a. Horiz pair. Nos. 206/7	50	70
		b. Thick paper	70	70
		ba. Horiz pair. Nos. 206b/7b . . .	1·40	1·50
		c. Perf 14½	70	70
		ca. Horiz pair. Nos. 206c/7c . . .	1·40	1·50
207	**182**	10½p multicoloured	15	15
		b. Thick paper	70	70
		c. Perf 14½	70	70
		ca. Greenish blue omitted		
204/7		Set of 4	90	90
		First Day Cover (Nos. 204/5, 206c/7c)		1·10
		First Day Cover (Nos. 204/7)		
		Presentation Pack (either perforation)	1·10	

Although both perforations were supplied to Jersey at the same time the 8p perforated 14½ is not known used before early April.

*Nos. 304*cb* and 305*cb* appear to have only five arcs of colour in the background instead of the usual eight. They come from the same sheet.

Plate Nos.: Both values 1A, 1B, 1C, 1D, 1E, 1F, 1G, 1H (each ×8)

Sheets: 20 (4×5) the two designs of each value were printed together, *se-tenant*, in horizontal pairs throughout

Imprint: Central, bottom margin

Quantities sold: 8p 5,149,852; 10½p 3,047,039

Withdrawn: 29.2.80

183 Percival Mew Gull
Golden City

184 De Havilland D.H.C.1
Chipmunk

185 Druine D.31 Turbulent

186 De Havilland D.H.82A
Tiger Moth

187 North American AT-6
Harvard

25th Anniversary of International Air Rally

(Des A. Theobald. Photo Courvoisier)

1979 (24 APR). *Granite paper.* Perf 11½ (C)

208	**183**	6p multicoloured	10	10
209	**184**	8p multicoloured	25	15
210	**185**	10½p multicoloured	25	20
211	**186**	11p multicoloured	30	25
212	**187**	13p multicoloured	40	35
208/12		Set of 5	1·10	95
		First Day Cover		1·50
		Presentation Pack	1·60	

Cylinder Nos.: 13p A1–1–1–1–1, B1–1–1–1–1, C1–1–1–1–1, D1–1–1–1–1; others A1–1–1–1, B1–1–1–1, C1–1–1–1, D1–1–1–1

Sheets 20 (5×4)

Imprint: Central, bottom margin

Quantities sold: 6p 1,327,279; 8p 1,338,234; 10½p 433,127; 11p 457,566; 13p 426,528

Withdrawn: 30.4.80

188 'My First Sermon'

189 'Orphans'

190 'The Princes in the Tower'

191 'Christ in the House of His Parents'

International Year of the Child and 150th Birth Anniversary of Sir John Millais (painter)

(Des Jersey P.O. and Courvoisier. Photo Courvoisier)

1979 (13 AUG). *Granite paper.* Perf 12×12½ (25p) or 12×11½ (others), all comb

213	**188**	8p multicoloured	20	15
214	**189**	10½p multicoloured	30	20
215	**190**	11p multicoloured	30	30
216	**191**	25p multicoloured	50	40
213/16		Set of 4	1·20	95
		First Day Cover		1·40
		Presentation Pack	1·60	

Cylinder Nos.: 25p A1–1–1–1–1, B1–1–1–1–1; others A1–1–1–1–1, B1–1–1–1–1, C1–1–1–1–1, D1–1–1–1–1

Sheets: 20 (4×5) 25p or (5×4) others

Quantities sold: 8p 1,187,969; 10½p 953,826; 11p 508,316; 25p 463,234

Withdrawn: 30.8.80

192 Pink Pigeon

193 Orang-utan

194 Waldrapp

195 Lowland Gorilla

196 Rodriguez Flying Fox

Wildlife Preservation Trust (3rd series)

(Des Jennifer Toombs. Photo Courvoisier)

1979 (8 NOV). *Granite paper.* Perf 11½ (C)

217	**192**	6p multicoloured	. . . .	10	10
218	**193**	8p multicoloured	. . . .	20	15
219	**194**	11½p multicoloured	. . . .	30	30
220	**195**	13p multicoloured	. . . .	45	35
221	**196**	15p multicoloured	. . . .	45	35
217/21		*Set of 5*	. . . .	1·20	1·10
		First Day Cover	. . . .		1·40
		Presentation Pack	. . . .	1·60	

Cylinder Nos.: All values A1–1–1–1–1, B1–1–1–1–1, C1–1–1–1–1, D1–1–1–1–1

Sheets: 20 (11½p 4×5; others 5×4)

Imprint: Right-hand corner, bottom margin

Quantities sold: 6p 1,128,144; 8p 1,080,889; 11½p 559,534; 13p 443,140; 15p 433,115

Withdrawn: 30.11.80

197 Plan of Mont Orgueil

198 Plan of La Tour de St. Aubin

199 Plan of Elizabeth Castle

200 Map of Jersey showing Fortresses

Jersey Fortresses. Drawings by Thomas Phillips

(Litho Enschedé)

1980 (5 FEB). Perf 13×13½ (25p) or 13½×13 (others), all comb

222	**197**	8p multicoloured	. . . .	20	15
223	**198**	11½p multicoloured	. . . .	30	30
224	**199**	13p multicoloured	. . . .	30	30
225	**200**	25p multicoloured	. . . .	50	45
222/5		*Set of 4*	. . . .	1·20	1·10
		First Day Cover	. . . .		1·40
		Presentation Pack	. . . .	1·60	

Sheets: 20 (4×5)

Imprint: Right-hand corner, bottom margin

Quantities sold: 8p 665,647; 11½p 363,246; 13p 415,790; 25p 379,743

Withdrawn: 28.2.81

201 Sir Walter Raleigh and Paul Ivy (engineer) discussing Elizabeth Castle **202**

203 Sir George Carteret receiving rights to Smith's Island, Virginia, from King Charles II

204 Lady Carteret, maid Jean Chevalier

Europa. Personalities. Links with Britain

(Des Jersey Post Office and Questa. Litho Questa)

1980 (6 MAY). Perf 14 (C)

226	**201**	9p multicoloured	15	15
		a. Horiz. pair. Nos. 226/7	40	50
227	**202**	9p multicoloured	15	15
228	**203**	13½p multicoloured	20	20
		a. Horiz. pair. Nos. 228/9	60	70
229	**204**	13½p multicoloured	20	20
226/9		Set of 4	90	80
		First Day Cover		1·20
		Presentation Pack	1·40	

Plate Nos.: Both values 1A, 1B, 1C, 1D, 1E, 1F (each ×4)

Sheets: 20 (4×5). The two designs of each value were printed together, *se-tenant*, in horizontal pairs throughout, forming composite designs.

Imprint: Central, left-hand margin

Quantities sold: 9p 4,793,980; 13½p 2,638,136

Withdrawn: 31.5.81

205 Planting

206 Digging

207 Weighbridge

Centenary of Jersey Royal Potato

(Des R. Granger Barrett. Litho Questa)

1980 (6 MAY). Perf 14 (C)

230	**205**	7p multicoloured	15	10
231	**206**	15p multicoloured	30	25
232	**207**	17½p multicoloured	30	35
230/2		Set of 3	65	65
		First Day Cover		95
		Presentation Pack	1·20	

Plate Nos.: All values 1A, 1B, 1C, 1D, 1E, 1F (each ×6)

Sheets: 20 (4×5)

Imprint: Central, left-hand margin

Quantities sold: 7p 1,379,048; 15p 383,956; 17½p 375,082

Withdrawn: 31.5.83

208 Three Lap Event

209 Jersey International Road Race

210 Motocross Scrambling

211 Sand Racing (saloon cars)

212 National Hill Climb

60th Anniversary of Jersey Motor-cycle and Light Car Club

(Des A. Theobald. Photo Courvoisier)

1980 (24 JULY). Granite paper. Perf 11½ (C)

233	**208**	7p multicoloured	15	15
234	**209**	9p multicoloured	20	15
235	**210**	13½p multicoloured	30	25
236	**211**	15p multicoloured	30	30
237	**212**	17½p multicoloured	35	35
233/7		Set of 5	1·20	1·10
		First Day Cover		1·60
		Presentation Pack	1·70	

Cylinder Nos.: 7p, 15p A1–1–1–1–1, B1–1–1–1–1, C1–1–1–1–1, D1–1–1–1–1; others A1–1–1–1, B1–1–1–1, C1–1–1–1, D1–1–1–1

Sheets: 20 (5×4)

Imprint: Left-hand corner, bottom margin

Quantities sold: 7p 1,452,280; 9p 1,426,548; 13½p 384,861; 15p 350,608; 17½p 338,658

Withdrawn: 31.7.81

213 *Eye of the Wind*

214 Diving from Inflatable Dinghy

215 Exploration of Papua New Guinea

216 Captain Scott's *Discovery*

217 Using Aerial Walkways, Conservation Project, Sulawesi

218 *Eye of the Wind*, and Goodyear Aerospace Airship *Europa*

Operation Drake and 150th Anniversary of Royal Geographical Society (14p)

(Des G. Drummond. Litho Questa)

1980 (1 OCT). Perf 14 (C)

238	**213**	7p multicoloured	15	15
239	**214**	9p multicoloured	20	20
240	**215**	13½p multicoloured	30	25
241	**216**	14p multicoloured	30	30
242	**217**	15p multicoloured	35	35
		a. Black (face value and inscr) ptg double		
243	**218**	17½p multicoloured	40	40
		a. Black (face value and inscr) ptg double		
238/43		Set of 6	1·50	1·50
		First Day Cover		1·70
		Presentation Pack	2·00	

Plate Nos.: All values 1A, 1B, 1C, 1D, 1E, 1F (each ×6)

Sheets: 20 (5×4)

Imprint: Upper left-hand margin

Quantities sold: 7p 1,631,558; 9p 1,071,684; 13½p 432,201; 14p 357,109; 15p 357,922; 17½p 351,215

Withdrawn: 31.10.81

219

220

221

222

Bicentenary of Battle of Jersey. Details of painting 'The Death of Major Peirson' by J. S. Copley

(Photo Courvoisier)

1981 (6 JAN). *Granite paper*. Perf 12½×12 (C)

244	**219**	7p multicoloured	15	15
245	**220**	10p multicoloured	25	20
246	**221**	15p multicoloured	35	30
247	**222**	17½p multicoloured	40	35
244/7		Set of 4	1·00	90
		First Day Cover		1·40
		Presentation Pack	1·50	
MS248		144×97 mm. Nos. 244/7	1·40	1·60
		First Day Cover		5·50

Stamps from No. **MS248** are without white margins.

Cylinder Nos.: All values A1–1–1–1–1, B1–1–1–1–1

Sheets: 20 (5×4)

Imprint: Right-hand corner, bottom margin

Quantities sold: 7p 997,416; 10p 1,107,456; 15p 367,971; 17½p 359,794; miniature sheet 469,953

Withdrawn: 31.1.82

223 De Bagot

224 De Carteret

225 La Cloche

226 Dumaresq **227** Payn **228** Janvrin

 247 Auvergne

 248 Remon

229 Poingdestre **230** Pipon **231** Marett

250 'Queen Elizabeth II'
(Norman Hepple)

232 Le Breton **233** Le Maistre **234** Bisson

249 Jersey Crest and
Map of Channel

235 Robin **236** Herault **237** Messervy

Arms of Jersey Families

(Des Courvoisier (£5), G. Drummond (others). Litho Questa
(½p to £1). Photo Courvoisier (£5))

1981 (24 FEB)–**88**. *Granite paper* (£5). Perf 15×14 (16p, 17p,
18p, 19p, 26p, 75p), 12½×12 (£5) or 14 (others), all comb

238 Fiott **239** Malet **240** Mabon

241 De St. Martin **242** Hamptonne **243** Badier

244 L'Arbalestier **245** Journeaulx **246** Lempriere

249	**223**	½p black, silver & turq-grn (a) ..	20	20
250	**224**	1p multicoloured (a)	10	10
		a. *Booklet pane of 6 (acf)*	40	
		b. *Perf 15×14 (o)*	30	30
251	**225**	2p multicoloured (a)	10	10
		a. *Booklet pane of 6 (cf)*	70	
		b. *Perf 15×14 (io)*	20	20
		ba. *Booklet pane of 6 (l)*	1·00	
252	**226**	3p multicoloured (a)	10	15
		a. *Booklet pane of 6 (a)*	80	
		b. *Perf 15×14 (ik)*	15	15
		ba. *Booklet pane of 6 (h)*	1·00	
253	**227**	4p black, silver and mauve (a) .	15	15
		a. *Perf 15×14 (k)*	20	20
		ab. *Booklet pane of 6 (mq)*	1·00	
254	**228**	5p multicoloured (a)	15	15
		a. *Perf 15×14 (k)*	30	30
255	**229**	6p multicoloured (a)	20	20
		a. *Perf 15×14 (k)*	40	40
256	**230**	7p multicoloured (a)	25	25
		a. *Booklet pane of 6 (ac)*	1·40	
257	**231**	8p multicoloured (a)	30	30
		a. *Booklet pane of 6 (f)*	1·70	
258	**232**	9p multicoloured (ae)	30	25
		a. *Perf 15×14 (h)*	40	40
		ab. *Booklet pane of 6 (h)*	2·50	
		ac. *'Ghost impression' from No.*		
		261a*		

259	233	10p multicoloured (a)	25	25
		a. Booklet pane of 6 (ac)	1·50	
		b. Perf 15×14 (l)	40	40
		ba. Booklet pane of 6 (l)	1·60	
260	234	11p multicoloured (be)	30	30
		a. Booklet pane of 6 (f)	1·90	
		b. Perf 15×14 (m)	45	45
		ba. Booklet pane of 6 (m)	1·70	
261	235	12p multicoloured (be)	35	30
		a. Perf 15×14 (hq)	50	50
		ab. Booklet pane of 6 (hq)	3·00	
262	236	13p multicoloured (b)	35	35
		a. Perf 15×14 (l)	50	50
263	237	14p multicoloured (b)	40	40
		a. Perf 15×14 (l)	40	40
		ab. Booklet pane of 6 (l)	2·40	
264	238	15p multicoloured (b)	40	40
		a. Perf 15×14 (mo)	45	45
		ab. Booklet pane of 6 (m)	2·20	
265	239	16p multicoloured (jo)	35	35
		a. Booklet pane of 6 (q)	2·20	
266	240	17p multicoloured (j)	45	45
266a	241	18p multicoloured (p)	50	50
266b	242	19p multicoloured (p)	60	60
267	243	20p black, silver and lemon (b) ..	50	50
		a. Perf 15×14 (k)	80	80
268	244	25p black and dull blue (d)	45	45
268a	223	26p black, silver and carmine (p) .	50	50
269	245	30p multicoloured (d)	50	60
		a. Perf 15×14 (k)	1·00	1·00
270	246	40p multicoloured (d)	80	80
		a. Perf 15×14 (m)	1·50	1·40
271	247	50p multicoloured (d)	1·00	1·00
		a. Perf 15×14 (m)	1·90	1·90
272	248	75p multicoloured (n)	1·50	1·50
273	249	£1 multicoloured (d)	2·00	2·00
274	250	£5 multicoloured (g)	10·00	10·00
249/74		Set of 29	20·00	20·00
		First Day Covers (7)		22·00
		Presentation Packs (4)	25·00	

*Examples of No. 258ac show an impression of the blue (shield) plate from the 12p value. The error was caused by an impression of the 12p plate remaining on the transfer roller.
No. 258a only occurs in the £2.16 stamp booklet issued 27 April 1984, No. 259b from the £3.12 booklet of 1 April 1986, No. 260b from the £3.60 booklet of 6 April 1987 and No. 261a from the £2.16 booklet of 27 April 1984 and the £3.84 booklet of 17 May 1988.
No. 252b first occurred in the £2.16 stamp booklet of 27 April 1984, but was subsequently issued in sheets.

Printings: (a) 24.2.81; (b) 28.7.81; (c) 1.12.81; (d) 23.2.82; (e) 11.6.82; (f) 19.4.83; (g) 17.11.83; (h) 27.4.84; (i) 15.11.84; (j) 25.10.85; (k) 4.3.86; (l) 1.4.86; (m) 6.4.87; (n) 23.4.87; (o) 12.1.88; (p) 26.4.88; (q) 17.5.88

Plate and Cylinder Nos.: ½p, 20p 1A, 1B, 1C, 1D, 1E, 1F, 1G, 1H (each ×3); 6p, 11p, 12p, 13p, 14p, 50p, 75p 1A, 1B, 1C, 1D, 1E, 1F, 1G, 1H (each ×4); 10p 1A, 1B, 1C, 1D, 1F, 1G, 1H (each ×5); 2A–1A (×4), 2B–1B (×4), 2C–1C (×4), 2D–1D (×4), 2E–1E (×4), 2F–1F (×4), 2G–1G (×4), 2H–1H (×4); 25p 1A–1A, 1B–1B, 1C–1C, 1D–1D, 1E–1E, 1F–1F, 1G–1G, 1H–1H; 26p 1A, 1B, 1C, 1D, 1F, 1G, 1H (each ×3); £1 1A, 1B, 1C, 1D, 1E, 1F, 1G, 1H (each ×6); £5 A1–1–1–1, B1–1–1–1, C1–1–1–1, D1–1–1–1; others 1A,

1B, 1C, 1D, 1E, 1G, 1H (each ×4)

Sheets: £1 25 (5×5); £5 10 (5×2); others 50 (10×5)

Imprint: Right–hand corner, bottom margin

Withdrawn: 31.12.85 ½p; 30.4.87 £1; 31.3.90 1p to 10p; 31.1.91 11p to 20p; 31.3.91 25p to 75p; 30.4.97 £5

251 Knight of Hambye slaying Dragon

252 Servant slaying Knight and awaiting Execution

253 St. Brelade celebrating Easter on Island

254 Island revealing itself as Huge Fish

Europa. Folklore

(Des Jennifer Toombs. Litho Questa)

1981 (7 APR). Perf 14½ (C)

275	251	10p multicoloured	25	15
		a. Horiz pair. Nos. 275/6	60	60
276	252	10p multicoloured	25	15
277	253	18p multicoloured	50	20
		a. Horiz pair. Nos. 277/8	1·40	1·40
278	254	18p multicoloured	50	20
275/8		Set of 4	1·70	1·70
		First Day Cover		1·50
		Presentation Pack	2·00	

Legends: 10p, Slaying of the Dragon of Lawrence by the Knight of Hambye; 18p. Voyages of St. Brelade.

Plate Nos.: 10p 1A, 1B, 1C, 1D, 1E, 1F, 1G, 1H (each ×6); 18p 1A, 1B, 1C, 1D, 1E, 1F, 1G, 1H (each ×5)

Sheets: 20 (4×5). The two designs of each value were each printed together, se-tenant, in horizontal pairs throughout

Imprint: Central, left-hand margin

Quantities sold: 10p 3,459,902; 18p 2,494,444

Withdrawn: 30.4.82

255 The Harbour by Gaslight

256 The Quay

257 Royal Square

258 Halkett Place

259 Central Market

150th Anniversary of Gas Lighting in Jersey

(Des R. Granger Barrett. Photo Courvoisier)

1981 (22 MAY). *Granite paper.* Perf 11½ (C)

279	**255**	7p multicoloured	20	15
280	**256**	10p multicoloured	25	25
281	**257**	18p multicoloured	40	40
282	**258**	22p multicoloured	45	45
283	**259**	25p multicoloured	55	55
279/83		Set of 5	1·60	1·60
		First Day Cover		1·70
		Presentation Pack	2·00	

Cylinder Nos.: All values A1–1–1–1–1, B1–1–1–1–1, C1–1–1–1–1, D1–1–1–1–1

Sheets: 20 (5×4)

Imprint: Left-hand corner, bottom margin

Quantities sold: 7p 1,433,090; 10p 1,416,051; 18p 384,043; 22p 417,191; 25p 333,402

Withdrawn: 31.5.82

260 Prince Charles and Lady
Diana Spencer

Royal Wedding

(Des Jersey P.O. and Courvoisier. Photo Courvoisier)

1981 (28 JULY). *Granite paper.* Perf 11½ (C)

284	**260**	10p multicoloured	20	20
285		25p multicoloured	75	90
284/5		Set of 2	95	1·10
		First Day Cover		2·50
		Presentation Pack	2·00	

Cylinder Nos.: Both values A1–1–1–1–1, B1–1–1–1–1

Sheets: 20 (5×4)

Imprint: Left-hand corner, bottom margin

Quantities sold: 10p 935,571; 25p 580,597

Withdrawn: 31.7.82

261 Christmas Tree in Royal Square

262 East Window, Parish Church, St. Helier

263 Boxing Day Meet of Jersey Drag Hunt

Christmas

(Des A. Copp. Litho Questa)

1981 (29 SEPT). Perf 14½ (C)

286	**261**	7p multicoloured	15	10
287	**262**	10p multicoloured	25	25
		a. Black (face value, inscr and choir) printed double		
288	**263**	18p multicoloured	30	30
286/8		Set of 3	60	60
		First Day Cover		95
		Presentation Pack	1·20	
		Postcards (set of 3)	1·10	2·50

Plate Nos.: All values 1A, 1B, 1C, 1D, 1E, 1F, 1G, 1H (each ×5)

Sheets: 20 (4×5)

Imprint: Central, left-hand margin

Quantities sold: 7p 1,437,626; 10p 1,386,934; 18p 422,693

Withdrawn: 30.9.82

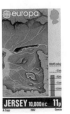

264 Jersey, 16,000 B.C.

265 10,000 B.C.

266 7,000 B.C.

267 4,000 B.C.

Europa. History. Formation of Jersey

(Des A. Copp. Litho Questa)

1982 (20 APR). Perf 14 (C)

289	**264**	11p multicoloured	20	20
290	**265**	11p multicoloured	20	20
291	**266**	19½p multicoloured	45	45
292	**267**	19½p multicoloured	45	45
289/92		*Set of 4*	1·10	1·10
		First Day Cover		1·50
		Presentation Pack	1·50	

Plate Nos.: All values 1A, 1B, 1C, 1D, 1E, 1F (each ×6)

Sheets: 20 (Nos. 289, 292, 4×5; others 5×4)

Imprint: Central, left-hand margin

Quantities sold: 11p (both designs) 3,414,424; 19½p (both designs) 2,307,769

Withdrawn: 30.4.83

268 Rollo, Duke of Normandy, William the Conqueror and 'Clameur de Haro'

269 John of England, Philippe Auguste of France and Siege of Rouen

270 Jean Martell (brandy merchant), early Still and view of Cognac

271 Victor Hugo, 'Le Rocher des Proscrits' (rock where he used to meditate) and Marine Terrace

272 Pierre Teilhard de Chardin (philosopher) and 'Maison Saint Louis' (science institute)

273 Père Charles Rey (scientist), anemo-tachymeter and The Observatory, St. Louis

Links with France

(Des R. Granger Barrett. Litho Questa)

1982 (11 JUNE–7 SEPT). Perf 14 (C)

293	**268**	8p multicoloured	20	15
		a. *Horiz pair.* Nos. 293/4	50	50
		b. *Booklet pane.* Nos. 293/4		
		each ×2 (7.9.82)	1·00	
294	**269**	8p multicoloured	20	15
295	**270**	11p multicoloured	30	15
		a. *Horiz pair.* Nos. 295/6	60	60
		b. *Booklet pane.* Nos. 295/6		
		each ×2 (7.9.82)	1·50	
296	**271**	11p multicoloured	30	15
297	**272**	19½p multicoloured	45	20
		a. *Horiz pair.* Nos. 297/8	90	90
		b. *Booklet pane.* Nos. 297/8		
		each ×2 (7.9.82)	2·20	
		c. *Black* (*face value and inscr*)		
		printed double		
298	**273**	19½p multicoloured	45	20
		c. *Black* (*face value and inscr*)		
		printed double		
293/8		*Set of 6*	1·70	1·70
		First Day Cover		1·80
		Presentation Pack	2·20	

Each booklet pane has margins all round and text, in English or French, printed on the binding selvedge.

Nos. 297c and 298c come from an example of booklet pane No. 297b.

Plate Nos.: All values 1A, 1B, 1C, 1D (each ×4)

Sheets: 20 (4×5). The two designs of each value were printed together, *se-tenant*, in horizontal pairs throughout

Imprint: Central, left-hand margin

Quantities sold (sheet stamps): 8p (both designs) 2,019,854; 11p (both designs) 1,914,536; 19½p (both designs) 828,272

Withdrawn: 30.6.83 (sheets)

274 Sir William Smith and Proclamation of King George V, Jersey, 1910

276 Sir William Smith and Lord Baden-Powell at Boys' Brigade Display, 1903

275 Boys' Brigade Band, Jersey Liberation Parade, 1945

277 Lord and Lady Baden-Powell in St. Helier, 1924

278 Scouts in Summer Camp, Jersey

Youth Organizations

(Des A. Theobald. Photo Courvoisier)

1982 (18 NOV). *Granite paper.* Perf 11½ (C)

299	**274**	8p multicoloured	20	15
300	**275**	11p multicoloured	20	15
301	**276**	24p multicoloured	45	40
302	**277**	26p multicoloured	60	50
303	**278**	29p multicoloured	75	60
299/303		Set of 5	2·00	1·60
		First Day Cover		1·90
		Presentation Pack	2·20	

Nos. 299/303 were issued on the occasion of the 75th anniversary of the Boy Scout Movement, the 125th birth anniversary of Lord Baden-Powell and the centenary of the Boys' Brigade (1983).

Cylinder Nos.: All values A1–1–1–1–1, B1–1–1–1–1, C1–1–1–1–1, D1–1–1–1–1

Sheets: 20 (11p, 26p 5×4; others 4×5)

Imprint: Lower left-hand margin

Quantities sold: 8p 1,006,110; 11p 1,006,206; 24p 242,482; 26p 255,359; 29p 244,746

Withdrawn: 30.11.83

279 H.M.S. *Tamar* with H.M.S. *Dolphin* at Port Egmont

280 H.M.S. *Dolphin* and H.M.S. *Swallow* off Magellan Strait

281 Discovering Pitcairn Island

282 Carteret taking possession of English Cove, New Zealand

283 H.M.S. *Swallow* sinking a Pirate, Macassar Strait

284 H.M.S. *Endymion* leading Convoy from West Indies

Jersey Adventurers (1st series). 250th Birth Anniv of Philippe de Carteret

(Des R. Granger Barrett. Litho Questa)

1983 (15 FEB). Perf 14×14½ (C)

304	**279**	8p multicoloured	20	15
		a. Black (*face value and inscr*) printed double		
305	**280**	11p multicoloured	25	15
		a. Black (*face value and inscr*) printed double		
306	**281**	19½p multicoloured	40	35
307	**282**	24p multicoloured	45	45
		a. Black (*face value and inscr*) printed double		
308	**283**	26p multicoloured	50	50
		a. Black (*face value and inscr*) printed double		
309	**284**	29p multicoloured	65	60
304/9		Set of 6	2·20	2·00
		First Day Cover		2·75
		Presentation Pack	3·50	

See also Nos. 417/21 and 573/8.

Plate Nos.: All values 1A, 1B, 1C, 1D, 1E, 1F (each ×6)

Sheets: 20 (4×5)

Imprint: Central, left-hand margin

Quantities sold: 8p 983,227; 11p 979,640; 19½p 377,535; 24p 264,595; 26p 279,424; 29p 254,023

Withdrawn: 29.2.84

285 1969 5s. Legislative Chamber Definitive

286 Royal Mace

287 1969 10s. Royal Court Definitive showing Green Border Error

288 Bailiff's Seal

Europa. Great Works of Human Genius

(Des G. Drummond. Litho Questa)

1983 (19 APR). Perf 14½ (C)

310	**285**	11p multicoloured	25	30
		a. Horiz pair. Nos. 310/11	80	80
311	**286**	11p multicoloured	25	30
312	**287**	19½p multicoloured	35	35
		a. Horiz pair. Nos. 312/13	90	90
313	**288**	19½p multicoloured	35	35
310/13		Set of 4	1·50	1·50
		First Day Cover		2·00
		Presentation Pack	2·20	

Plate Nos.: Both values 1A, 1B, 1C, 1D, 1E, 1F (each ×6)

Sheets: 20 (4×5). The two designs of each value were printed together, se-tenant, in horizontal pairs throughout

Imprint: Central, left-hand margin

Quantities sold: 11p (both designs) 2,973,691; 19½p (both designs) 1,301,579

Withdrawn: 30.4.84

289 Charles Le Geyt and Battle of Minden (1759)

290 London to Weymouth Mail Coach

291 P.O. Mail Packet *Chesterfield* attacked by French Privateer

292 Mary Godfray and the Hue Street Post Office

293 Mail Steamer leaving St. Helier Harbour

World Communications Year and 250th Birth Anniversary of Charles Le Geyt (first Jersey postmaster)

(Des A. Copp. Litho Questa)

1983 (21 JUNE). Perf 14 (C)

314	**289**	8p multicoloured	20	20
315	**290**	11p multicoloured	30	30
316	**291**	24p multicoloured	55	55
317	**292**	26p multicoloured	65	65
318	**293**	29p multicoloured	80	80
314/18		Set of 5	2·20	2·20
		First Day Cover		2·50
		Presentation Pack	2·75	

Plate Nos.: All values 1A, 1B, 1C, 1D (each ×5)

Sheets: 20 (4×5)

Imprint: Central, left-hand margin

Quantities sold: 8p 1,136,008; 11p 961,725; 24p 244,690; 26p 247,654; 29p 230,325

Withdrawn: 30.6.84

294 Assembly Emblem

13th General Assembly of the A.I.P.L.F. (Association Internationale des Parlementaires de Langue Francaise)

(Des A. Copp. Litho Questa)

1983 (21 JUNE). Perf 14½ (C)

319	**294**	19½p multicoloured	50	50
		First Day Cover		95
		Presentation Pack	1·20	

Plate Nos.: 1A, 1B, 1C, 1D (each ×5)

Sheets: 20 (4×5)

Imprint: Central, left-hand margin

Quantity sold: 312,304

Withdrawn: 30.6.84

295 'Cardinal Newman'

296 'Incident in the French Revolution'

297 'Thomas Hardy'

298 'David with the Head of Goliath'

50th Death Anniversary of Walter Ouless (artist)

(Des and photo Courvoisier)

1983 (20 Sept). *Granite paper.* Perf 11½ (C)

320	**295**	8p multicoloured	20	20
321	**296**	11p multicoloured	30	30
322	**297**	20½p multicoloured	50	50
323	**298**	31p multicoloured	80	80
320/3		Set of 4	1·60	1·60
		First Day Cover		2·00
		Presentation Pack	2·20	

Cylinder Nos.: All values 1A, 1B (each ×5)

Sheets: 20 (4×5) 31p or (5×4) others

Imprint: Central, left-hand margin

Quantities sold: 8p 1,054,200; 11p 1,055,429; 20½p 424,049; 31p 216,128

Withdrawn: 30.9.84

299 Golden Lion Tamarin

300 Snow Leopard

301 Jamaican Boa

302 Round Island Gecko

303 Coscoroba Swan

304 St. Lucia Amazon

Wildlife Preservation Trust (4th series)

(Des W. Oliver. Litho Questa)

1984 (17 JAN). Perf 13½×14 (C)

324	**299**	9p multicoloured	25	10
325	**300**	12p multicoloured	25	15
326	**301**	20½p multicoloured	45	40
327	**302**	26p multicoloured	75	65
328	**303**	28p multicoloured	80	70
329	**304**	31p multicoloured	1·00	90
324/9		Set of 6	3·25	2·50
		First Day Cover		4·25
		Presentation Pack	3·75	

Plate Nos.: 20½p, 28p 1B, 1C, 1E, 1F (each ×4); others 1A, 1B, 1C, 1D, 1E, 1F (each ×4)

Sheets: 20 (5×4)

Imprint: Central, left-hand margin

Quantities sold: 9p 1,229,713; 12p 1,365,973; 20½p 266,444; 26p 239,180; 28p 255,205; 31p 221,422

Withdrawn: 31.1.85

305 C.E.P.T. 25th Anniversary Logo

Europa

(Des J. Larrivière. Litho Questa)

1984 (12 MAR). Perf 14½×15 (C)

330	**305**	9p cobalt, ultramarine & black .	20	15
331		12p light green, green and black	30	25
332		20½p rose-lilac, dp magenta & blk	60	50
330/2		*Set of 3*	1·00	80
		First Day Cover		1·50
		Presentation Pack	1·60	

Plate Nos.: All values 1A, 1B, 1C, 1D, 1E, 1F (each ×3)

Sheets: 20 (4×5)

Imprint: Central, left-hand margin

Quantities sold: 9p 1,352,245; 12p 1,388,802; 20½p 742,046

Withdrawn: 31.3.85

306 Map showing Commonwealth

Links with the Commonwealth

(Des A. Copp. Litho Questa)

1984 (12 MAR). *Sheet* 108×74 *mm*. Perf 15×14½ (C)

MS333	**306**	75p multicoloured	2·00	2·00
		First Day Cover		2·50
		Presentation Pack	2·75	

Quantity sold: 215,566

Withdrawn: 31.3.85

307 *Sarah Bloomshoft* at Demie de Pas Light, 1906

308 *Hearts of Oak* and *Maurice Georges*, 1949

309 *Elizabeth Rippon* and *Hanna*, 1949

310 *Elizabeth Rippon* and *Santa Maria*, 1951

311 *Elizabeth Rippon* and *Bacchus*, 1973

312 *Thomas James King* and *Cythara*, 1983

Centenary of the Jersey R.N.L.I. Lifeboat Station

(Des G. Palmer. Litho Questa)

1984 (1 JUNE). Perf 14½ (C)

334	**307**	9p multicoloured	25	15
335	**308**	9p multicoloured	25	15
336	**309**	12p multicoloured	35	30
337	**310**	12p multicoloured	35	30
338	**311**	20½p multicoloured	60	70
339	**312**	20½p multicoloured	60	70
334/9		*Set of 6*	2·10	2·20
		First Day Cover		3·00
		Presentation Pack	3·25	
		Postcard (as No. 339)	1·20	2·20

Plate Nos.: All values 1A, 1B, 1C, 1D, 1E, 1F (each ×5)

Sheets: 20 (4×5)

Imprint: Central, left-hand margin

Quantities sold: 9p (No. 334) 485,538; 9p (No. 335) 435,647; 12p (No. 336) 534,920; 12p (No. 337) 518,807; 20½p (No. 338) 298,935; 20½p (No. 339) 290,945

Withdrawn: 30.6.85

313 Bristol Type 170 Freighter Mk 32

314 Airspeed A.S.57 Ambassador 2

315 De Havilland D.H.114 Heron 1B

316 De Havilland D.H.89A Dragon Rapide

40th Anniversary of International Civil Aviation Organization

(Des G. Drummond. Litho Questa)

1984 (24 JULY). Perf 14 (C)

340	**313**	9p multicoloured	20	15
341	**314**	12p multicoloured	35	35

342	**315**	26p multicoloured	. . . .	75	75
343	**316**	31p multicoloured	. . . .	1·00	1·00
340/3		Set of 4	. . . .	2·10	2·00
		First Day Cover	. . . .		2·75
		Presentation Pack	. . . .	3·25	

Plate Nos.: All values 1A, 1B, 1C, 1D (each ×4)

Sheets: 20 (4×5)

Imprint: Central, left-hand margin

Quantities sold: 9p 563,394; 12p 751,072; 26p 262,640; 31p 193,703

Withdrawn: 31.7.85

317 'Robinson Crusoe leaves the Wreck'

318 'Edinburgh Castle'

319 'Maori Village'

320 'Australian Landscape'

321 'Waterhouse's Corner, Adelaide'

322 'Captain Cook at Botany Bay'

Links with Australia. Paintings by John Alexander Gilfillan

(Des R. Granger Barrett. Photo Courvoisier)

1984 (21 SEPT). *Granite paper.* Perf 11½×12 (C)

344	**317**	9p multicoloured	. . . .	25	20
345	**318**	12p multicoloured	. . . .	30	20
346	**319**	20½p multicoloured	. . . .	60	50
347	**320**	26p multicoloured	. . . .	70	60
348	**321**	28p multicoloured	. . . .	80	80
349	**322**	31p multicoloured	. . . .	80	80
344/9		Set of 6	. . . .	3·00	2·75
		First Day Cover	. . . .		3·75
		Presentation Pack	. . . .	3·75	
		Postcards (Set of 3 as Nos. 347/9)	. . . .	1·70	4·50

Cylinder Nos.: All values A1, B1 (each ×6)

Sheets: 20 (4×5)

Imprint: Central, left-hand margin

Quantities sold: 9p 541,384; 12p 635,192; 20½p 210,119; 26p 234,836; 28p 188,052; 31p 192,353

Withdrawn: 30.9.85

323 'B.L.C. St. Helier'

324 'Oda Mt Bingham'

Christmas. Jersey Orchids (1st series)

(Photo Courvoisier)

1984 (15 NOV). *Granite paper.* Perf 12×11½ (C)

350	**323**	9p multicoloured	. . . .	25	20
351	**324**	12p multicoloured	. . . .	50	50
350/1		Set of 2	. . . .	75	70
		First Day Cover	. . . .		1·50
		Presentation Pack	. . . .	1·50	

See also Nos. 433/7, 613/17, 892/7 and 1143/**MS**1149.

Cylinder Nos.: Both values A1, B1, C1, D1 (each ×6)

Sheets: 20 (4×5)

Imprint: Central, left-hand margin

Quantities sold: 9p 1,197,796; 12p 1,116,097

Withdrawn: 30.11.85

325 '*Hebe* off Corbière, 1874'

326 'The *Gaspe* engaging the *Diomede*'

327 'The Paddle-steamer *London* entering Naples, 1856'

328 'The *Rambler* entering Cape Town, 1840'

329 'St. Aubin's Bay from Mount Bingham, 1871'

Death Centenary of Philip John Ouless (*artist*)

(Photo Harrison)

1985 (26 FEB). Perf 14×15 (C)

352	**325**	9p multicoloured	25	20
353	**326**	12p multicoloured	30	30
354	**327**	22p multicoloured	65	60
355	**328**	31p multicoloured	1·00	90
356	**329**	34p multicoloured	1·20	1·00
352/6		Set of 5	3·00	2·75
		First Day Cover		3·50
		Presentation Pack	4·00	

Cylinder Nos.: 31p 1B (×5); others 1A, 1B (each ×5)

Sheets: 20 (4×5)

Imprint: Central, left-hand margin

Quantities sold: 9p 463,589; 12p 405,133; 22p 407,598; 31p 193,772; 34p 185,467

Withdrawn: 28.2.86

330 John Ireland (composer) and Faldouet Dolmen

331 Ivy St. Helier (actress) and His Majesty's Theatre, London

332 Claude Debussy (composer) and Elizabeth Castle

Europa. European Music Year

(Des Jennifer Toombs. Litho Questa)

1985 (23 APR). Perf 14 (C)

357	**330**	10p multicoloured	30	30
358	**331**	13p multicoloured	45	45
359	**332**	22p multicoloured	80	80
357/9		Set of 3	1·40	1·40
		First Day Cover		1·90
		Presentation Pack	2·00	

Plate Nos.: 10p 1A, 1B, 1C, 1D, 1E, 1F (each ×5); 13p 1A, 1C, 1D, 1E, 1F (each ×5); 22p 1A, 1B, 1D, 1E, 1F (each ×5)

Sheets: 20 (4×5)

Imprint: Central, left-hand margin

Quantities sold: 10p 916,040; 13p 766,179; 22p 620,375

Withdrawn: 30.4.86

333 Girls' Brigade

334 Girl Guides (75th anniversary)

335 Prince Charles and Jersey Youth Service Activities Base

336 Sea Cadet Corps

337 Air Training Corps

International Youth Year

(Des A. Theobald. Litho Questa)

1985 (30 MAY). Perf 14½×14 (C)

360	**333**	10p multicoloured	30	30
361	**334**	13p multicoloured	40	40
362	**335**	29p multicoloured	70	70
363	**336**	31p multicoloured	75	75
364	**337**	34p multicoloured	90	90
360/4		Set of 5	2·75	2·75
		First Day Cover		3·25
		Presentation Pack	3·75	

Plate Nos.: All values 1A, 1B, 1C, 1D, 1E, 1F (each ×4)

Sheets: 20 (5×4)

Imprint: Central, left-hand margin

Quantities sold: 10p 943,351; 13p 944,724; 29p 175,365; 31p 183,551; 34p 175,842

Withdrawn: 30.5.86

338 *Duke of Normandy* at Cheapside

339 Saddletank at First Tower

340 *La Moye* at Millbrook

341 *St Heliers* at St. Aubin

342 *St Aubyns* at Corbière

Jersey Western Railway

(Des G. Palmer. Photo Courvoisier)

1985 (16 JULY). *Granite paper.* Perf 11½ (C)

365	**338**	10p multicoloured	45	45
366	**339**	13p multicoloured	50	50
367	**340**	22p multicoloured	90	90
368	**341**	29p multicoloured	95	95
369	**342**	34p multicoloured	1·00	1·00
365/9		Set of 5	3·50	3·50
		First Day Cover		3·75
		Presentation Pack	4·00	

Cylinder Nos.: 10p, 13p A1, B1 (each ×5); others A1 (×5)

Sheets: 20 (4×5)

Imprint: Central, left-hand margin

Quantities sold: 10p 708,912; 13p 706,189; 22p 249,659; 29p 179,849; 34p 179,977

Withdrawn: 31.7.86

343 Memorial Window to Revd. James Hemery (former Dean) and St. Helier Parish Church

344 Judge Francis Jeune, Baron St. Helier, and Houses of Parliament

345 Silverware by Pierre Amiraux

346 Francis Voisin (merchant) and Russian Port

347 Robert Brohier, Schweppes Carbonation Plant and Bottles

348 George Ingouville, V.C., R.N., and Attack on Viborg

Plate Nos.: 13p (No. 372) 1A, 1B, 1C, 1D (each ×4); 22p (No. 375) 1A, 1C, 1D (each ×5); others 1A, 1B, 1C, 1D (each ×5)

Sheets: 20 (4×5)

Imprint: Central, left-hand margin

Quantities sold (sheets): 10p (No. 370) 308,085; 10p (No. 371) 310,475; 13p (No. 372) 488,224; 13p (No. 373) 477,764; 22p (No. 374) 259,921; 22p (No. 375) 253,607

Withdrawn: 30.9.86 (sheets)

349 Howard Davis Hall, Victoria College

350 Racing Schooner *Westward*

351 Howard Davis Park, St. Helier

352 Howard Davis Experimental Farm, Trinity

300th Anniversary of Huguenot Immigration

(Des R. Granger Barrett. Litho Questa)

1985 (10 SEPT). Perf 14 (C)

370	**343**	10p multicoloured	30	30
		a. Booklet pane of 4	1·20	
371	**344**	10p multicoloured	30	30
		a. Booklet pane of 4	1·20	
372	**345**	13p multicoloured	40	40
		a. Booklet pane of 4	1·60	
373	**346**	13p multicoloured	40	40
		a. Booklet pane of 4	1·60	
		ab. Black (face value and inscr) printed double		
374	**347**	22p multicoloured	55	50
		a. Booklet pane of 4	2·20	
		b. Black (inscr) printed double		
375	**348**	22p multicoloured	55	50
		a. Booklet pane of 4	2·20	
370/5		Set of 6	2·20	2·10
		First Day Cover		2·75
		Presentation Pack	2·75	

Each booklet pane has margins all round and text printed on the binding selvedge.

Thomas Davis (philanthropist) Commemoration

(Des A. Copp. Litho Cartor)

1985 (25 OCT). Perf 13½ (C)

376	**349**	10p multicoloured	35	35
377	**350**	13p multicoloured	50	50
378	**351**	31p multicoloured	70	70
379	**352**	34p multicoloured	85	85
376/9		Set of 4	2·20	2·20
		First Day Cover		2·75
		Presentation Pack	3·00	

Plate Nos.: 10p 1A, 1B, 1C, 1D (each ×5); 13p 2A, 2B, 2C, 2D (each ×5); 31p 3A, 3B, 3C, 3D (each ×5); 34p 4A, 4B, 4C, 4D (each ×5)

Sheets: 20 (4×5)

Imprint: Central, left-hand margin

Quantities sold: 10p 939,104; 13p 831,351; 31p 170,020; 34p 156,653

Withdrawn: 31.10.86

357 Aspects of Communications in 1910 and 1986 on TV Screens

353 *Amaryllis belladonna* (Pandora Sellars)

354 'A Jersey Lily' (Lily Langtry) (Sir John Millais)

Jersey Lilies

(Des C. Abbott. Litho Questa)

1986 (28 JAN). Perf 15×14½ (C)

380	**353**	13p multicoloured	45	45
381	**354**	34p multicoloured	1·00	1·10
380/1		*Set of 2*	1·40	1·50
		First Day Cover		2·00
		Presentation Pack	2·20	
MS382		140×96 mm. Nos. 380×4 and 381	2·75	3·00
		First Day Cover		6·50
		Presentation Pack	4·00	

Plate Nos.: 13p 1A, 1B, 1C, 1D, 1E, 1F, 1G, 1H (each ×6); 34p 1A, 1B, 1C, 1D (each ×5)

Sheets: 20 (4×5); (5×4) 34p

Imprint: Central, left-hand margin

Quantities sold: 13p 444,175; 34p 169,811; miniature sheet 157,575

Withdrawn: 31.1.87

355 King Harold, William of Normandy and Halley's Comet, 1066 (from Bayeux Tapestry)

356 Lady Carteret, Edmond Halley, Map and Comet

Appearance of Halley's Comet

(Des Jennifer Toombs. Litho Cartor)

1986 (4 MAR). Perf 13½×13 (C)

383	**355**	10p multicoloured	35	35
384	**356**	22p multicoloured	80	85
385	**357**	31p multicoloured	1·00	1·10
383/5		*Set of 3*	1·90	2·10
		First Day Cover		2·20
		Presentation Pack	2·75	

Plate Nos.: All values 1A, 1B, 1C, 1D (each ×5)

Sheets: 20 (4×5)

Imprint: Central, left-hand margin

Quantities sold: 10p 552,062; 22p 245,111; 31p 182,390

Withdrawn: 31.3.87

358 Dwarf Pansy

359 Sea Stock

360 Sand Crocus

Europa. Environmental Conservation

(Des Pandora Sellars. Litho Questa)

1986 (21 APR). Perf 14½×14 (C)

386	**358**	10p multicoloured	35	35
387	**359**	14p multicoloured	45	45
388	**360**	22p multicoloured	70	70
386/8		*Set of 3*	1·40	1·40
		First Day Cover		1·70
		Presentation Pack	2·20	

Plate Nos.: 22p 1A, 1B, 1C, 1E, 1F (each ×5); others 1A, 1B, 1C, 1D, 1E, 1F (each ×5)

Sheets: 20 (5×4)

Imprint: Central, left-hand margin

Quantities sold: 10p 892,977; 14p 892,631; 22p 612,513

Withdrawn: 30.4.87

361 Queen Elizabeth II (from photo by Karsh)

60th Birthday of Queen Elizabeth II

(Photo Courvoisier)

1986 (21 APR). *Granite paper*. Perf 14½ (C)

389	**361**	£1 multicoloured	. . . .	2·50	2·00
		First Day Cover	. . . .		3·25
		Presentation Pack	. . . .	3·00	

No. 389 was retained in use as part of the current definitive series until replaced by No. 500.

For a £2 value in this design see No. 491*b*.

Cylinder Nos.: 1A, 1B, 1C, 1D (each ×6)

Sheets: 20 (4×5)

Imprint: Central, left-hand margin

Quantity sold: 431,591

Withdrawn: 31.5.90

362 Le Rât Cottage

363 The Elms (Trust Headquarters)

364 Morel Farm

365 Quétivel Mill

366 La Vallette

50th Anniversary of the National Trust for Jersey

(Des A. Copp. Litho Cartor)

1986 (17 JUNE). Perf 13½×13 (C)

390	**362**	10p multicoloured	. . . .	25	20
391	**363**	14p multicoloured	. . . .	35	30
392	**364**	22p multicoloured	. . . .	65	65
393	**365**	29p multicoloured	. . . .	70	70
394	**366**	31p multicoloured	. . . .	75	75
390/4		Set of 5	. . . .	2·40	2·40
		First Day Cover	. . . .		2·75
		Presentation Pack	. . . .	3·75	

Plate Nos.: All values 1A, 1B, 1C, 1D (each ×5)

Sheets: 20 (4×5)

Imprint: Central, left-hand margin

Quantities sold: 10p 946,735; 14p 919,823; 22p 427,370; 29p 173,763; 31p 178,353

Withdrawn: 30.6.87

367 Prince Andrew and Miss Sarah Ferguson

Royal Wedding

(Des A. Copp. Litho Cartor)

1986 (23 JULY). Perf 13½ (C)

395	**367**	14p multicoloured	. . . .	35	35
396		40p multicoloured	. . . .	1·20	1·20
395/6		Set of 2	. . . .	1·50	1·50
		First Day Cover	. . . .		2·00
		Presentation Pack	. . . .	2·20	

Plate Nos.: Both values 1A, 1B, 1C, 1D (each ×6)

Sheets: 20 (5×4)

Imprint: Central, left-hand margin

Quantities sold: 14p 991,943; 40p 267,312

Withdrawn: 31.7.87

368 'Gathering Vraic'

369 'Driving Home in the Rain'

370 'The Miller'

371 'The Joy Ride'

372 'Tante Elizabeth'

Birth Centenary of Edmund Blampied (artist)

(Des A. Copp. Litho Questa)

1986 (28 AUG). Perf 14 (C)

397	**368**	10p multicoloured	25	25
398	**369**	14p black, brownish grey & lt bl .	40	40
399	**370**	29p multicoloured	75	75
400	**371**	31p black, brownish grey and pale orange	90	90
401	**372**	34p multicoloured	95	95
397/401		*Set of 5*	3·00	3·00
		First Day Cover		3·75
		Presentation Pack	4·00	

Plate Nos.: 14p, 31p 1A, 1B, 1C, 1D (each ×3); others 1A, 1B, 1C, 1D (each ×5)

Sheets: 20 (4×5)

Imprint: Central, left-hand margin

Quantities sold: 10p, 885,979; 14p 675,290; 29p 163,085; 31p 157,559; 34p 151,128

Withdrawn: 31.8.87

373 Island Map on Jersey Lily, and Dove holding Olive Branch

374 Mistletoe Wreath encircling European Robin and Dove

375 Christmas Cracker releasing Dove

Christmas. International Year of Peace

(Des G. Taylor. Litho Questa)

1986 (4 NOV). Perf 14½×14 (C)

402	**373**	10p multicoloured	20	20
403	**374**	14p multicoloured	40	40
404	**375**	34p multicoloured	95	95
402/4		*Set of 3*	1·40	1·40
		First Day Cover		2·20
		Presentation Pack	2·00	

Plate Nos.: All values 1A, 1B, 1C, 1D, 1E, 1F (each ×6)

Sheets: 20 (5×4)

Imprint: Central, left-hand margin

Quantities sold: 10p 947,614; 14p 940,123; 34p 169,269

Withdrawn: 30.11.87

Post Office Yearbook

1986 (4 NOV). *Comprises Nos.* 380/404

Yearbook . . . . 45·00

Withdrawn: 31.1.88

376 *Westward* under Full Sail

377 T. B. Davis at the Helm

378 *Westward* overhauling
Britannia

379 *Westward* fitting-out at
St. Helier

Racing Schooner Westward

(Des A. Copp. Litho Cartor)

1987 (15 JAN). Perf 13½ (C)

405	**376**	10p multicoloured	40	35
406	**377**	14p multicoloured	50	55
407	**378**	31p multicoloured	95	95
408	**379**	34p multicoloured	95	95
405/8		*Set of* 4	2·50	2·50
		First Day Cover		2·75
		Presentation Pack	3·75	

Plate Nos.: All values 1A, 1B, 1C, 1D (each ×5)

Sheets: 20 (4×5)

Imprint: Central, left-hand margin

Quantites sold: 10p 519,330; 14p 370,229; 31p 173,046; 34p 158,754

Withdrawn: 31.1.88

380 De Havilland D.H.86
Dragon Express
Belcroute Bay

381 Boeing 757 and
Douglas DC-9-15

382 Britten Norman 'long
nose' Trislander and
Islander

383 Shorts 330 and Vickers
Viscount 800

384 B.A.C. One Eleven 500 and
Handley Page H.P.R.7 Dart
Herald

50th Anniversary of Jersey Airport

(Des G. Palmer. Litho Questa)

1987 (3 MAR). Perf 14 (C)

409	**380**	10p multicoloured	25	25
410	**381**	14p multicoloured	40	45
411	**382**	22p multicoloured	55	50
412	**383**	29p multicoloured	90	90
413	**384**	31p multicoloured	95	95
409/13		*Set of* 5	2·75	2·75
		First Day Cover		4·00
		Presentation Pack	3·75	

Plate Nos.: All values 1A, 1B, 1C, 1D (each ×4)

Sheets: 20 (4×5)

Imprint: Central, left-hand margin

Quantities sold: 10p 313,733; 14p 281,226; 22p 368,486; 29p
155,159; 31p 167,709

Withdrawn: 31.3.88

385 St. Mary and St.
Peter's Roman
Catholic Church

386 Villa Devereux,
St. Brelade

387 Fort Regent
Leisure Centre,
St. Helier

Europa. Modern Architecture

(Des A. Copp. Litho Questa)

1987 (23 APR). Perf 15×14 (C)

414	**385**	11p multicoloured	40	40
415	**386**	15p multicoloured	50	45
416	**387**	22p multicoloured	75	75
414/16		*Set of* 3	1·50	1·40
		First Day Cover		2·00
		Presentation Pack	2·20	

Plate Nos.: 11p, 15p 1A, 1B, 1C, 1D, 1E, 1F, 1G, 1H, 1I, 1J (each ×6);
22p 1A, 1B, 1C, 1D, 1E, 1F, 1G, 1H (each ×6)

Sheets: 10 (2×5)

Imprint: Central, left-hand margin

Quantities sold: 11p 847,735; 15p 883,825; 22p 467,615

Withdrawn: 30.4.88

388 H.M.S. *Racehorse* and H.M.S. *Carcass* (bomb-ketches) trapped in Arctic

389 H.M.S. *Alarm* on Fire, Rhode Island

390 H.M.S. *Arethusa* wrecked off Ushant

391 H.M.S. *Rattlesnake* stranded on Isle de Trinidad

392 Mont Orgueil Castle and Fishing Boats

Jersey Adventurers (2nd series). Philippe D'Auvergne

(Des R. Granger Barrett. Litho Questa)

1987 (9 JULY). Perf 14 (C)

417	**388**	11p multicoloured	30	35
418	**389**	15p multicoloured	40	45
419	**390**	29p multicoloured	70	75
420	**391**	31p multicoloured	80	90
421	**392**	34p multicoloured	85	95
417/21		Set of 5	2·75	3·00
		First Day Cover		3·25
		Presentation Pack	4·25	

See also Nos. 501/6 and 539/44.

Plate Nos.: All values 1A, 1B, 1C, 1D (each ×4)

Sheets: 20 (4×5)

Imprint: Central, left-hand margin

Quantities sold: 11p 694,506; 15p 897,162; 29p 138,711; 31p 144,518; 34p 140,968

Withdrawn: 31.7.88.

393 Grant of Lands to Normandy, 911 and 933

394 Edward the Confessor and Duke Robert I of Normandy landing on Jersey, 1030

395 King William's Coronation, 1066, and Fatal Fall, 1087

396 Death of William Rufus, 1100, and Battle of Tinchebrai, 1106

397 Civil War between Matilda and Stephen, 1135–41

398 Henry inherits Normandy, 1151: John asserts Ducal Rights in Jersey, 1213

900th Death Anniversary of William the Conqueror

(Des Jennifer Toombs, Litho Cartor)

1987 (9 SEPT–16 OCT). Perf 13½ (C)

422	**393**	11p multicoloured (a)	30	30
		a. Booklet pane of 4 (b)	1·20	
423	**394**	15p multicoloured (a)	35	35
		a. Booklet pane of 4 (b)	1·40	
424	**395**	22p multicoloured (a)	70	65
		a. Booklet pane of 4 (b)	2·75	

425	**396**	29p multicoloured (a)	75	75
		a. *Booklet pane of 4* (b)	3·00	
426	**397**	31p multicoloured (a)	85	85
		a. *Booklet pane of 4* (b)	3·25	
427	**398**	34p multicoloured (a)	95	95
		a. *Booklet pane of 4* (b)	3·75	
422/7		*Set of 6*	3·50	3·50
		First Day Cover		3·75
		Presentation Pack	4·50	

Each booklet pane has margins all round and text printed on the binding selvedge.

Printings: (a) 9.9.87; (b) 16.10.87

Plate Nos.: All values 1A, 1B, 1C, 1D (each ×6)

Imprint: Central, left-hand margin

Quantities sold (sheets): 11p 869,726; 15p 968,815; 22p 217,160; 29p 139,905; 31p 147,527; 34p 143,684

Withdrawn: 30.9.88 (sheets)

399 'Grosnez Castle'

400 'St. Aubin's Bay'

401 'Mont Orgueil Castle'

402 'Town Fort and Harbour, St. Helier'

403 'The Hermitage'

Christmas. Paintings by John Le Capelain

(Photo Courvoisier)

1987 (3 NOV). *Granite paper*. Perf 11½ (C)

428	**399**	11p multicoloured	35	30
429	**400**	15p multicoloured	50	50
430	**401**	22p multicoloured	65	65
431	**402**	31p multicoloured	90	80
432	**403**	34p multicoloured	1·00	1·00
428/32		*Set of 5*	3·00	3·00
		First Day Cover		3·75
		Presentation Pack	4·00	

Cylinder Nos.: 11p, 15p, 22p 1A, 1B (each ×6); 31p, 34p 1A (×6)

Sheets: 20 (5×4)

Imprint: Central, left-hand margin

Quantities sold: 11p 951,916; 15p 874,209; 22p 371,992; 31p 154,824; 34p 145,550

Withdrawn: 30.11.88

Post Office Yearbook

1987 (3 NOV). *Comprises Nos. 272 and 405/32*
Yearbook .... 38·00

Withdrawn: 28.2.89

404 *Cymbidium pontac*

405 *Odontioda* Eric Young

406 *Lycaste auburn* Seaford and Ditchling

407 *Odontoglossum* St. Brelade

408 *Cymbidium mavourneen* Jester

Jersey Orchids (2nd series)

(Litho Questa)

1988 (12 JAN). Perf 14 (C)

433	**404**	11p multicoloured	40	35
434	**405**	15p multicoloured	45	45
435	**406**	29p multicoloured	70	70
436	**407**	31p multicoloured	80	80
437	**408**	34p multicoloured	95	95
433/7		*Set of 5*	3·00	3·00
		First Day Cover		3·50
		Presentation Pack	3·75	

Plate Nos.: All values 1A, 1B, 1C, 1D (each ×5)

Sheets: 20 (4×5) 11p, 29p, 34p; (5×4) 15p, 31p

Imprint: Central, left-hand margin

Quantities sold: 11p 558,185; 15p 374,117; 29p 143,613; 31p 162,096; 34p 151,193

Withdrawn: 31.1.89

409 Labrador Retriever

410 Wire-haired Dachshund

411 Pekingese

412 Cavalier King Charles Spaniel

413 Dalmatian

414 De Havilland D.H.C.7 Dash Seven, London Landmarks and Jersey Control Tower

415 Weather Radar and Jersey Airport Landing System

416 Hydrofoil, St. Malo, and Elizabeth Castle, St. Helier

417 Port Control Tower and Jersey Radio Maritime Communication Centre, La Moye

Centenary of Jersey Dog Club

(Des P. Layton. Litho Questa)

1988 (2 MAR). Perf 14 (C)

438	**409**	11p multicoloured	40	30
439	**410**	15p multicoloured	60	30
440	**411**	22p multicoloured	80	80
441	**412**	31p multicoloured	90	95
442	**413**	34p multicoloured	1·00	1·00
438/42		Set of 5	3·25	3·25
		First Day Cover		3·75
		Presentation Pack	4·25	

Plate Nos.: All values 1A, 1B, 1C, 1D (each ×4)

Sheets: 20 (4×5)

Imprint: Central, left-hand margin

Quantities sold: 11p 371,583; 15p 374,953; 22p 178,132; 31p 154,530; 34p 146,628

Withdrawn: 31.3.89

Europa. Transport and Communications

(Des A. Copp. Litho Cartor)

1988 (26 APR). Perf 14×13½ (horiz) or 13½×14 (vert), both comb

443	**414**	16p multicoloured	40	45
444	**415**	16p multicoloured	40	45
445	**416**	22p multicoloured	75	75
446	**417**	22p multicoloured	75	75
443/6		Set of 4	2·10	2·40
		First Day Cover		2·75
		Presentation Pack	3·00	

Plate Nos.: Nos. 443/4, 446 1A, 1B, 1C, 1D (each ×5); No. 445 1A, 1B, 1C, 1D (each ×6)

Sheets: 20 (4×5) Nos. 443, 445; (5×4) Nos. 444, 446

Imprint: Central, left-hand margin

Quantities sold: 16p (No. 443) 881,324; 16p (No. 444) 865,868; 22p (No. 445) 509,086; 22p (No. 446) 510,104

Withdrawn: 30.4.89

418 Rodriguez Fody

419 Volcano Rabbit

420 White-faced
Marmoset

421 Ploughshare Tortoise

422 Mauritius Kestrel

423 Rain Forest Leaf Frog,
Costa Rica

424 Archaeological Survey,
Peru

425 Climbing Glacier,
Chile

426 Red Cross Centre,
Solomon Islands

427 Underwater
Exploration, Australia

428 *Zebu* (brigantine)
returning to St. Helier

Wildlife Preservation Trust (5th series)

(Des W. Oliver. Litho Cartor)

1988 (6 JULY). Perf 13½×14 (vert) or 14×13½ (horiz), both comb

447	**418**	12p multicoloured	45	45
448	**419**	16p multicoloured	55	50
449	**420**	29p multicoloured	90	1·00
450	**421**	31p multicoloured	1·10	1·10
451	**422**	34p multicoloured	1·20	1·20
447/51		Set of 5	3·75	3·75
		First Day Cover		4·50
		Presentation Pack	4·50	

Plate Nos.: All values 1A, 1B, 1C, 1D (each ×6)

Sheets: 20 (5×4) 12p, 29p, 34p; (4×5) 16p, 31p

Imprint: Central, left-hand margin

Quantities sold: 12p 875,722; 16p 969,800; 29p 146,567; 31p 155,348; 34p 151,723

Withdrawn: 31.7.89

Operation Raleigh

(Des V. Ambrus. Photo Courvoisier)

1988 (27 SEPT). *Granite paper.* Perf 12 (C)

452	**423**	12p multicoloured	35	25
453	**424**	16p multicoloured	40	40
454	**425**	22p multicoloured	60	60
455	**426**	29p multicoloured	70	70
456	**427**	31p multicoloured	80	90
457	**428**	34p multicoloured	90	1·00
452/7		Set of 6	3·50	3·50
		First Day Cover		3·75
		Presentation Pack	4·50	

No. 455 also commemorates the 40th anniversary of the World Health Organization.

Cylinder Nos.: All values 1A (×5)

Sheets: 20 (5×4)

Imprint: Central, left-hand margin

Quantities sold: 12p 706,594; 16p 507,077; 22p 226,791; 29p 127,647; 31p 127,658; 34p 128,055

Withdrawn: 30.9.89

429 St. Clement

430 St. Ouen

431 St. Brelade

432 St. Lawrence

435 Austin 7 'Chummy', 1926

436 Ford 'Model T', 1926

437 Bentley 8 Litre, 1930

438 Cadillac '452A-V16 Fleetwood Sports Phaeton', 1931

Christmas. Jersey Parish Churches (1st series)

(Des P. Layton. Litho B.D.T.)

1988 (15 NOV). Perf 13½ (C)

458	**429**	12p multicoloured	30	15
459	**430**	16p multicoloured	45	30
460	**431**	31p multicoloured	90	90
461	**432**	34p multicoloured	85	95
458/61		*Set of 4*	2·20	2·20
		First Day Cover		2·75
		Presentation Pack	3·75	
		Postcards (set of 4)	2·00	5·50

See also Nos. 535/8 and 597/600.

Plate Nos.: All values 1A, 1B, 1C, 1D (each ×5)

Sheets: 20 (4×5)

Imprint: Central, left-hand margin

Quantities sold: 12p 964,161; 16p 917,883; 31p 170,477; 34p 159,688

Withdrawn: 30.11.89

Post Office Yearbook

1988 (15 NOV). *Comprises Nos. 266a/b, 268a and 433/61*
Yearbook . . . . 42·00

Withdrawn: 23.10.89

433 Talbot Type 4 CT Tourer, 1912

434 De Dion Bouton Type 1-D, 1920

Vintage Cars (1st series)

(Des A. Copp. Litho Questa)

1989 (31 JAN). Perf 14 (C)

462	**433**	12p multicoloured	35	30
463	**434**	16p multicoloured	50	45
464	**435**	23p multicoloured	60	55
		a. Black (inscr etc) printed double		
465	**436**	30p multicoloured	80	80
466	**437**	32p multicoloured	1·00	1·00
467	**438**	35p multicoloured	1·00	1·00
462/7		*Set of 6*	3·75	3·75
		First Day Cover		4·25
		Presentation Pack	4·50	

See also Nos. 591/6 and 905/10.

Plate Nos.: 12p, 30p 1A, 1B (each ×4); 16p, 32p 1C, 1D (each ×4); 23p, 35p 1A, 1B, 1C, 1D (each ×4)

Sheets: 20 (4×5)

Imprint: Central, left-hand margin

Quantities sold: 12p 253,257; 16p 230,695; 23p 228,895; 30p 130,974; 32p 144,798; 35p 148,189

Withdrawn: 31.1.90

439 Belcroute Bay

440 High Street, St. Aubin

441 Royal Jersey Golf Course

442 Portelet Bay

443 Les Charrières D'Anneport

444 St. Helier Marina

445 Sand Yacht Racing, St. Ouen's Bay

446 Rozel Harbour

447 St. Aubin's Harbour

448 Jersey Airport

449 Corbière Lighthouse

450 Val de la Mare

451 Elizabeth Castle

452 Greve de Lecq

453 Samarès Manor

454 Bonne Nuit Harbour

455 Grosnez Castle

456 Augrès Manor

457 Central Market

458 St. Brelade's Bay

459 St. Ouen's Manor

460 La Hougue Bie

461 Mont Orgueil Castle

462 Royal Square, St. Helier

463 Queen Elizabeth II (from photo by Karsh)

464 Arms of King George VI

Jersey Scenes

(Des G. Drummond (1p to 75p). Photo Courvoisier (£2), Litho Questa (£4), B.D.T. (others))

1989 (21 MAR)–**95**. Perf 11½×12 (£2), 15×14 (£4) or 13×13½ (others), all comb

468	**439**	1p multicoloured (a)	10	10
469	**440**	2p multicoloured (a)	10	10
470	**441**	4p multicoloured (a)	10	10
		a. Booklet pane of 6 with margins all round (d)	60	
471	**442**	5p multicoloured (a)	10	15
		a. Booklet pane of 6 with margins all round (f)	75	
472	**443**	10p multicoloured (a)	30	30
473	**444**	13p multicoloured (a)	40	45
474	**445**	14p multicoloured (ae)	40	45
		a. Booklet pane of 6 with margins all round (d)	2·00	
		b. Booklet pane of 8 with margins all round (i)	2·75	
475	**446**	15p multicoloured (ae)	45	50
		a. Booklet pane of 6 with margins all round (f)	2·00	
476	**447**	16p multicoloured (ah)	50	55
		a. Booklet pane of 8 with margins all round (i)	3·50	
477	**448**	17p multicoloured (aj)	50	55
478	**449**	18p multicoloured (akm)	55	60
		a. Booklet pane of 6 with margins all round (d)	2·50	
479	**450**	19p multicoloured (ano)	55	60
480	**451**	20p multicoloured (ae)	45	45
		a. Booklet pane of 6 with margins all round (f)	3·00	
481	**452**	21p multicoloured (b)	50	55
482	**453**	22p multicoloured (bh)	45	50
		a. Booklet pane of 8 with margins all round (i)	4·50	
483	**454**	23p multicoloured (bjkmo)	75	55
484	**455**	24p multicoloured (b)	60	60
485	**456**	25p multicoloured (b)	70	75
486	**457**	26p multicoloured (bh)	75	80
487	**458**	27p multicoloured (b)	80	90
488	**459**	30p multicoloured (c)	85	90
489	**460**	40p multicoloured (c)	1·00	1·00
490	**461**	50p multicoloured (c)	1·20	1·40
491	**462**	75p multicoloured (c)	2·00	1·50
491b	**463**	£2 multicoloured (g)	4·00	3·25
491c	**464**	£4 multicoloured (l)	7·00	6·75
468/91c		Set of 26	22·00	22·00
		First Day Covers (5)		28·00
		Presentation Packs (5)	27·00	

For £1 value as No. 491b see No. 389.

Printings: (a) 21.3.89; (b) 16.1.90; (c) 13.3.90; (d) 3.5.90; (e) 13.11.90; (f) 12.2.91; (g) 19.3.91; (h) 7.1.92; (i) 22.5.92; (j) 11.1.93; (k) 18.2.94; (l) 24.1.95; (m) 21.3.95; (n) 1.9.95; (o) 12.11.96

Cylinder or Plate Nos.: £2 A1, B1, C1, D1 (each ×6); £4 1A (×5); others 1A, 1B, 1C, 1D, 1E, 1F (each ×4)

Sheets: £2 20 (4×5); £4 10 (5×2); others 50 (5×10)

Imprint: Left-hand corner, bottom margin (£4) or central, left-hand margin (others)

Withdrawn: 31.3.99 1p to £2

465 Agile Frog

466 *Heteropterus morpheus* (butterfly)

467 Barn Owl

468 Green Lizard

Endangered Jersey Fauna

(Des W. Oliver. Litho Cartor)

1989 (25 APR). Perf 13½×13 (Nos. 492 and 495), 13×13½ (No. 493) or 13½×14 (No. 494), all comb

492	**465**	13p multicoloured	80	85
493	**466**	13p multicoloured	80	85
494	**467**	17p multicoloured	80	85
495	**468**	17p multicoloured	80	85
492/5		Set of 4	2·75	3·00
		First Day Cover		4·00
		Presentation Pack	3·75	

Plate Nos.: All designs 1A, 1B, 1C, 1D (each ×5)

Sheets: 20 (4×5) Nos. 492 and 495; (5×4) Nos. 493/4

Imprint: Central, left-hand margin

Quantities sold: 13p (No. 492) 650,061; 13p (No. 493) 589,329; 17p (No. 494) 552,582; 17p (No. 495) 515,262

Withdrawn: 30.4.90

469 Toddlers' Toys

470 Playground Games

471 Party Games

472 Teenage Sports

Europa. Children's Toys and Games

(Des from clay plaques by Clare Luke. Litho Questa)

1989 (25 APR). Perf 14 (C)

496	**469**	17p multicoloured	45	45
497	**470**	17p multicoloured	45	45
498	**471**	23p multicoloured	80	80
499	**472**	23p multicoloured	80	80
496/9		Set of 4	2·20	2·20
		First Day Cover		2·50
		Presentation Pack	2·75	

Plate Nos.: All designs 1A, 1B, 1C, 1D, 1E, 1F (each ×4)

Sheets: 20 (4×5)

Imprint: Central, left-hand margin

Quantities sold: 17p (No. 496) 473,930; 17p (No. 497) 471,124; 23p (No. 498) 424,212; 23p (No. 499) 424,340

Withdrawn: 30.4.90

473 Queen Elizabeth II and Royal Yacht *Britannia* in Elizabeth Harbour

Royal Visit

(Des A. Copp. Litho Questa)

1989 (24 MAY). Perf 14½ (C)

500	**473**	£1 multicoloured	2·50	2·50
		First Day Cover		3·00
		Presentation Pack	3·00	

No. 500 was retained in use as part of the current definitive series until replaced by No. 634.

Sheets: 20 (4×5)

Imprint: Central, left-hand margin

Withdrawn: 30.6.94

474 Philippe D'Auvergne presented to Louis XVI, 1786

475 Storming the Bastille, 1789

476 Marie de Bouillon and
Revolutionaries, 1790

477 D'Auvergne's
Headquarters at Mont
Orgueil, 1795

478 Landing Arms for
Chouan Rebels, 1796

479 The Last Chouan
Revolt, 1799

**Bicentenary of the French Revolution. Philippe
D'Auvergne**

(Des V. Ambrus. Litho Cartor)

1989 (7 JULY). Perf 13½ (C)

501	**474**	13p multicoloured	40	30
		a. Booklet pane of 4	1·20	
502	**475**	17p multicoloured	50	40
		a. Booklet pane of 4	2·00	
503	**476**	23p multicoloured	60	50
		a. Booklet pane of 4	2·20	
504	**477**	30p multicoloured	95	1·00
		a. Booklet pane of 4	3·75	
505	**478**	32p multicoloured	1·00	1·10
		a. Booklet pane of 4	4·00	
506	**479**	35p multicoloured	1·20	1·30
		a. Booklet pane of 4	5·00	
501/6		Set of 6	4·25	4·00
		First Day Cover		4·25
		Presentation Pack	4·50	

Each booklet pane has margins all round and text printed on
the binding selvedge.
See also Nos. 539/44.

Plate Nos.: All values 1A, 1B, 1C, 1D (each ×4)

Sheets: 20 (5×4)

Imprint: Central, left-hand margin

Quantities sold: 13p 637,422; 17p 840,904; 23p 408,967; 30p
133,642; 32p 148,474; 35p 151,639

Withdrawn: 31.7.90

480 St. Helier off Elizabeth
Castle

481 Caesarea II off
Corbière Lighthouse

482 Reindeer in St. Helier
Harbour

483 Ibex racing Frederica
off Portelet

484 Lynx off Noirmont

**Centenary of Great Western Railway Steamer Service to
Channel Islands**

(Des G. Palmer. Litho Questa)

1989 (5 SEPT). Perf 13½×14 (C)

507	**480**	13p multicoloured	30	30
508	**481**	17p multicoloured	35	35
509	**482**	27p multicoloured	80	80
510	**483**	32p multicoloured	95	95
511	**484**	35p multicoloured	1·10	1·10
507/11		Set of 5	3·25	3·25
		First Day Cover		3·75
		Presentation Pack	4·00	

Plate Nos.: 13p, 27p 1A, 1B (each ×4); 17p, 32p 1C, 1D (each ×4);
35p 1A, 1B, 1C, 1D (each ×4)

Sheets: 20 (4×5)

Imprint: Central, left-hand margin

Quantities sold: 13p 265,382; 17p 294,992; 27p 135,226; 32p
128,966; 35p 134,800

Withdrawn: 28.9.90

485 Gorey Harbour

486 La Corbière

487 Grève de Lecq

488 Bouley Bay

489 Mont Orgueil

490 Head Post Office, Broad Street, 1969

491 Postal Headquarters, Mont Millais, 1990

492 Hue Street Post Office, 1815

493 Head Post Office, Halkett Place, 1890

150th Birth Anniversary of Sarah Louisa Kilpack (artist)

(Litho Enschedé)

1989 (24 OCT). Perf 13×12½ (C)

512	**485**	13p multicoloured	25	25
513	**486**	17p multicoloured	30	30
514	**487**	23p multicoloured	80	75
515	**488**	32p multicoloured	85	85
516	**489**	35p multicoloured	90	1·00
512/16		Set of 5	2·75	2·75
		First Day Cover		3·25
		Presentation Pack	4·00	

Plate Nos.: 13p, 17p, 1A, 1B, 1C (each ×5); 23p, 32p, 35p 1A, 1B (each ×5)

Sheets: 20 (4×5)

Imprint: Central, left-hand margin

Quantities sold: 13p 649,308; 17p 571,503; 23p 159,487; 32p 138,562; 35p 137,950

Withdrawn: 31.10.90

Post Office Yearbook

1989 (24 OCT). *Comprises Nos.* 462/80 *and* 492/516

Yearbook . . . . 37·00

Sold out: 12.11.90

Europa. Post Office Buildings

(Des P. Layton. Litho Cartor)

1990 (13 MAR). Perf 13½×14 (vert) or 14×13½ (horiz), both comb

517	**490**	18p multicoloured	50	40
518	**491**	18p multicoloured	50	50
519	**492**	24p multicoloured	65	65
520	**493**	24p multicoloured	65	65
517/20		Set of 4	2·10	2·00
		First Day Cover		2·50
		Presentation Pack	3·00	

Plate Nos.: All designs 1A, 1B, 1C, 1D (each ×5)

Sheets: 20 (5×4) 18p; (4×5) 24p

Imprint: Central, left-hand margin

Quantities sold: 18p (No. 517) 596,221; 18p (No. 518) 595,918; 24p (No. 519) 400,441; 24p (No. 520) 406,656

Withdrawn: 31.3.91

494 'Battle of Flowers' Parade

495 Sports

496 Mont Orgueil Castle and German Underground Hospital Museum

497 Salon Culinaire

500 Radio Jersey Broadcaster

501 Channel Television Studio Cameraman

Festival of Tourism

(Des A. Copp. Litho Enschedé)

1990 (3 MAY). Perf 14×13½ (C)

521	**494**	18p multicoloured	55	55
522	**495**	24p multicoloured	70	70
523	**496**	29p multicoloured	85	85
524	**497**	32p multicoloured	90	90
521/4		*Set of 4*	2·75	2·75
		First Day Cover		3·25
		Presentation Pack	4·00	
MS525		151×100 mm. Nos. 521/4	2·75	3·00
		First Day Cover		6·50
		Presentation Pack	4·50	

Plate Nos.: 18p 1A, 1B, 1C, 1D, 1E (each ×5); 24p 1A, 1B, 1C, 1D (each ×5); 29p 1A (×5); 32p 1A, 1B (each ×5)

Sheets: 20 (5×4)

Imprint: Central, left-hand margin

Quantities sold: 18p 630,610; 24p 252,670; 29p 168,528; 32p 127,334; miniature sheet 110,177

Withdrawn: 31.5.91

International Literacy Year. Jersey News Media

(Des A. Copp. Litho Cartor)

1990 (26 JUNE). Perf 13½ (C)

526	**498**	14p multicoloured	45	45
527	**499**	18p multicoloured	45	45
528	**500**	34p multicoloured	90	90
529	**501**	37p multicoloured	95	95
526/9		*Set of 4*	2·50	2·50
		First Day Cover		2·75
		Presentation Pack	3·50	

Plate Nos.: All values 1A, 1B, 1C, 1D (each ×4)

Sheets: 20 (4×5)

Imprint: Central, left-hand margin

Quantities sold: 14p 926,906; 18p 795,733; 34p 121,842; 37p 129,468

Withdrawn: 30.6.91

498 Early Printing Press and Jersey Newspaper Mastheads

502 British Aerospace Hawk T.1

503 Supermarine Spitfire

499 Modern Press, and Offices of *Jersey Evening Post* in 1890 and 1990

504 Hawker Hurricane Mk I

505 Vickers-Armstrong Wellington

JERSEY

Lancaster

37P

50th Anniversary Battle of Britain

506 Avro Lancaster

50th Anniversary of Battle of Britain

(Des G. Palmer. Litho Questa)

1990 (4 SEPT). Perf 14 (C)

530	**502**	14p multicoloured	40	45
531	**503**	18p multicoloured	55	60
532	**504**	24p multicoloured	85	85
533	**505**	34p multicoloured	1·50	1·60
534	**506**	37p multicoloured	1·60	1·60
530/4		Set of 5	4·50	4·50
		First Day Cover		5·25
		Presentation Pack	5·25	

Plate Nos.: 14p, 34p 1A, 1B (each ×5); 18p, 37p 1C, 1D (each ×5); 24p 1A, 1B, 1C, 1D (each ×5)

Sheets: 20 (4×5)

Imprint: Central, left-hand margin

Quantities sold: 14p 495,815; 18p 519,684; 24p 206,541; 34p 136,330; 37p 134,747

Withdrawn: 30.9.91

507 St. Helier

508 Grouville

509 St. Saviour

510 St. John

Christmas. Jersey Parish Churches (2nd series)

(Des P. Layton. Litho B.D.T.)

1990 (13 NOV). Perf 13½ (C)

535	**507**	14p multicoloured	45	40
536	**508**	18p multicoloured	45	40
		a. deep blue-green (Queen's head, value and "JERSEY") omitted £1500		

537	**509**	34p multicoloured	1·00	1·10
538	**510**	37p multicoloured	1·20	1·40
535/8		Set of 4	3·00	3·00
		First Day Cover		3·50
		Presentation Pack	4·00	
		Postcards (set of 4)	2·20	5·00

Plate Nos.: All values 1A, 1B, 1C, 1D (each ×5)

Sheets: 20 (4×5)

Imprint: Central, left-hand margin

Quantities sold: 14p 948,076; 18p 690,282; 34p 141,514; 37p 147,768

Withdrawn: 30.11.91

Post Office Yearbook

1990 (13 NOV). Comprises Nos. 481/91 and 517/38

Yearbook .... 35·00

Withdrawn: 30.11.91

JERSEY 15

PHILIPPE D'AUVERGNE   Prince's Tower, La Hougue Bie

511 Prince's Tower, La Hougue Bie

JERSEY 20

PHILIPPE D'AUVERGNE   Arrested in Paris

512 D'Auvergne's Arrest in Paris

JERSEY 26

PHILIPPE D'AUVERGNE   Plotting against Napoleon

513 D'Auvergne plotting against Napoleon

JERSEY 31

PHILIPPE D'AUVERGNE   Cadoudal to the Guillotine

514 Execution of George Cadoudal

JERSEY 37

PHILIPPE D'AUVERGNE   H.M. Cutter 'Surly' in Action

515 H.M.S. Surly (cutter) attacking French Convoy

JERSEY 44

PHILIPPE D'AUVERGNE   Prince de Bouillon - the end

516 D'Auvergne's Last Days in London

175th Death Anniversary of Philippe D'Auvergne

(Des V. Ambrus. Litho Cartor)

1991 (22 JAN). Perf 13½ (C)

539	**511**	15p multicoloured	45	40
540	**512**	20p multicoloured	55	55
541	**513**	26p multicoloured	70	75

542	**514**	31p multicoloured	....	90	90
543	**515**	37p multicoloured	....	1·10	1·10
544	**516**	44p multicoloured	....	1·20	1·20
539/44		*Set of 6*	....	4·50	4·50
		First Day Cover	....		4·75
		Presentation Pack	....	5·00	

Plate Nos.: All values 1A, 1B, 1C, 1D (each ×4)

Sheets: 20 (4×5)

Imprint: Central, left-hand margin

Quantities sold: 15p 709,403; 20p 454,921; 26p 159,902; 31p 140,379; 37p 341,103; 44p 153,157

Withdrawn: 31.1.92

517 'Landsat 5' and Thematic Mapper Image over Jersey

518 'ERS-1' Earth Resources Remote Sensing Satellite

519 'Meteosat' Weather Satellite

520 'Olympus Direct Broadcasting Satellite

Europa. Europe in Space

(Des A. Copp. Litho Enschedé)

1991 (19 MAR). Perf 14½×13 (C)

545	**517**	20p multicoloured	....	50	50
546	**518**	20p multicoloured	....	50	50
547	**519**	26p multicoloured	....	80	85
548	**520**	26p multicoloured	....	80	85
545/8		*Set of 4*	....	2·40	2·40
		First Day Cover	....		2·75
		Presentation Pack	....	3·00	

Plate Nos.: All designs 1A, 1B, 1C (each ×5)

Sheets: 20 (5×4)

Imprint: Central, left-hand margin

Quantities sold: 20p (No. 545) 682,799; 20p (No. 546) 690,871; 26p (No. 547) 442,476; 26p (No. 548) 439,415

Withdrawn: 31.3.92

521 1941 1d. Stamp (50th anniv of first Jersey postage stamp)

522 Steam Train (centenary of Jersey Eastern Railway extension to Gorey Pier)

523 Jersey Cow and Herd Book (125th anniv of Jersey Herd Book)

524 Stone-laying Ceremony (painting by P. Ouless) (150th anniv of Victoria Harbour)

525 Marie Bartlett and Hospital (250th anniversary of Marie Bartlett's hospital bequest)

Anniversaries

(Des A. Copp. Litho Cartor)

1991 (16 MAY). Perf 13½ (C)

549	**521**	15p multicoloured	....	30	30
550	**522**	20p multicoloured	....	50	55
551	**523**	26p multicoloured	....	60	70
552	**524**	31p multicoloured	....	75	80
553	**525**	53p multicoloured	....	1·70	1·70
549/53		*Set of 5*	....	3·50	3·75
		First Day Cover	....		4·25
		Presentation Pack	....	4·50	

Plate Nos.: All values 1A, 1B, 1C, 1D (each ×4)

Sheets: 20 (5×4)

Imprint: Central, left-hand margin

Quantities sold: 15p 618,479; 20p 608,585; 26p 245,772; 31p 133,604; 53p 135,394

Withdrawn: 30.5.92

526 *Melitaea cinxia*

527 *Euplagia quadripunctaria*

528 *Deilephila porcellus*

529 *Inachis io*

Butterflies and Moths

(Des W. Oliver. Litho Enschedé)

1991 (9 JULY). Perf 13×12½ (C)

554	**526**	15p multicoloured	35	35
555	**527**	20p multicoloured	45	30
556	**528**	37p multicoloured	1·40	1·50
557	**529**	57p multicoloured	1·70	1·90
554/7		Set of 4	3·50	3·75
		First Day Cover		4·50
		Presentation Pack	4·50	

Plate Nos.: All values 1A, 1B, 1C (each ×4)

Sheets: 20 (4×5)

Imprint: Central, left-hand margin

Quantities sold: 15p 489,632; 20p 646,607; 37p 130,494; 57p 142,646

Withdrawn: 31.7.92

530 Drilling for Water, Ethiopia

531 Building Construction, Rwanda

532 Village Polytechnic, Kenya

533 Treating Leprosy, Tanzania

534 Ploughing, Zambia

535 Immunisation Clinic, Lesotho

Overseas Aid

(Des A. Theobald. Litho B.D.T.)

1991 (3 SEPT). Perf 13½×14 (C)

558	**530**	15p multicoloured	45	40
559	**531**	20p multicoloured	50	45
560	**532**	26p multicoloured	70	70
561	**533**	31p multicoloured	85	90
562	**534**	37p multicoloured	1·10	1·10
563	**535**	44p multicoloured	1·20	1·40
558/63		Set of 6	4·50	4·50
		First Day Cover		5·00
		Presentation Pack	5·00	

Plate Nos.: All values 1A, 1B (each ×4)

Sheets: 20 (4×5)

Imprint: Central, left-hand margin

Quantities sold: 15p 517,917; 20p 644,721; 26p 177,179; 31p 115,769; 37p 111,112; 44p 142,024

Withdrawn: 30.9.92

536 'This is the Place for Me'

537 'The Island Come True'

538 'The Never Bird'

539 'The Great White Father'

543 Northern Lapwing

544 Fieldfare

Christmas. Illustrations by Edmund Blampied for J. M. Barrie's 'Peter Pan'

(Litho Questa)

1991 (5 NOV). Perf 14 (C)

564	**536**	15p multicoloured	40	40
565	**537**	20p multicoloured	65	65
566	**538**	37p multicoloured	1·20	1·20
567	**539**	53p multicoloured	1·60	1·60
564/7		Set of 4	3·50	3·50
		First Day Cover		4·00
		Presentation Pack	4·50	

Sheets: 20 (5×4)

Imprint: Central, left-hand margin

Quantities sold: 15p 917,860; 20p 693,203; 37p 128,585; 53p 117,877

Withdrawn: 30.11.92

Winter Birds

(Des W. Oliver. Litho Cartor)

1992 (7 JAN). Perf 13½×14 (C)

568	**540**	16p multicoloured	50	25
569	**541**	22p multicoloured	70	55
570	**542**	28p multicoloured	80	85
571	**543**	39p multicoloured	1·20	1·20
572	**544**	57p multicoloured	1·70	1·70
568/72		Set of 5	4·50	4·25
		First Day Cover		5·25
		Presentation Pack	5·50	

See also Nos. 635/9.

Plate Nos.: All values 1A, 1B, 1C, 1D (each ×4)

Sheets: 20 (5×4)

Imprint: Central, left-hand margin

Quantities sold: 16p 481,678; 22p 462,647; 28p 268,973; 39p 151,671; 57p 132,065

Withdrawn: 30.1.93

Post Office Yearbook

1991 (5 NOV). *Comprises Nos. 491b and 539/67*

Yearbook . . . . 32·00

Sold out: By 9.93

540 Pied Wagtail

541 Firecrest

542 Common Snipe

545 Shipping at Shanghai, 1860

546 Mesny's Junk running Taiping Blockade, 1862

547 General Mesny outside River Gate, 1874

548 Mesny in Burma, 1877

549 Mesny and Governor Chang, 1882

550 Mesny in Mandarin's Sedan Chair, 1886

Jersey Adventures (3rd series). 150th Birth Anniversary of William Mesny

(Des V. Ambrus. Litho Cartor)

1992 (25 FEB). Perf 13½ (C)

573	**545**	16p multicoloured	40	45
		a. Black printed double		
		b. Booklet pane of 4	1·50	
574	**546**	16p multicoloured	40	45
		a. Booklet pane of 4	1·50	
575	**547**	22p multicoloured	65	65
		a. Booklet pane of 4	2·00	
576	**548**	22p multicoloured	65	65
		a. Booklet pane of 4	2·00	
577	**549**	33p multicoloured	90	95
		a. Booklet pane of 4	3·00	
578	**550**	33p multicoloured	90	95
		a. Booklet pane of 4	3·00	
573/8		Set of 6	3·50	3·75
		First Day Cover		4·25
		Presentation Pack	4·50	

Each booklet pane has margins all round and text printed on the binding selvedge.

Plate Nos.: All values 1A, 1B, 1C, 1D (each ×4)

Sheets: 20 (4×5)

Imprint: Central, left-hand margin

Quantities sold: 16p (No. 573) 346,732; 16p (No. 574) 336,655; 22p (No. 575) 377,299; 22p (No. 576) 360,220; 33p (No. 577) 129,904; 33p (No. 578) 130,637

Withdrawn: 27.2.93 (sheets)

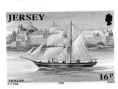

551 Tickler (brigantine)

552 Hebe (brig)

553 Gemini (barque)

554 Percy Douglas (full-rigged ship)

Jersey Shipbuilding

(Des A. Copp. Litho Questa)

1992 (14 APR). Perf 14 (C)

579	**551**	16p multicoloured	45	40
580	**552**	22p multicoloured	70	75
581	**553**	50p multicoloured	1·40	1·50
582	**554**	57p multicoloured	1·60	1·70
579/82		Set of 4	3·75	4·00
		First Day Cover		4·50
		Presentation Pack	4·50	
MS583		148×98 mm. Nos. 579/82	4·00	4·25
		First Day Cover		4·50
		Presentation Pack	4·50	

Plate Nos.: 16p 1A, 1B, 1C, 1D, 1E, 1F (each ×4); 22p, 57p 1A, 1B, 1C, 1D (each ×4); 50p 1A, 1B (each ×4)

Sheets: 20 (5×4)

Imprint: Central, left-hand margin

Quantities sold: 16p 673,830; 22p 462,972; 50p 138,158; 57p 111,044; miniature sheet 126,594

Withdrawn: 30.4.93

555 John Bertram (ship owner) and Columbus

556 Sir George Carteret (founder of New Jersey)

557 Sir Walter Ralegh (founder of Virginia)

Europa. 500th Anniversary of Discovery of America by Columbus

(Des V. Ambrus. Litho Questa)

1992 (14 APR). Perf 14×14½ (C)

584	**555**	22p multicoloured	65	50
585	**556**	28p multicoloured	75	80
586	**557**	39p multicoloured	1·10	1·40
584/6		Set of 3	2·20	2·40
		First Day Cover		3·00
		Presentation Pack	3·25	

Plate Nos.: 22p 1A, 1B (each ×5); 28p 1A, 1B, 1C, 1D (each ×5); 39p 1C, 1D (each ×5)

Sheets: 20 (4×5)

Imprint: Central, left-hand margin

Quantities sold: 22p 459,817; 28p 664,537; 39p 298,597

Withdrawn: 30.4.93

558 'Snow Leopards' (Allison Griffiths)

559 'Three Elements' (Nataly Miorin)

560 'Three Men in a Tub' (Amanda Crocker)

561 'Cockatoos' (Michelle Millard)

Batik Designs

(Litho Questa)

1992 (23 JUNE). Perf 14½ (C)

587	**558**	16p multicoloured	45	40
588	**559**	22p multicoloured	65	45
589	**560**	39p multicoloured	1·10	1·20
590	**561**	57p multicoloured	1·50	1·70
587/90		Set of 4	3·25	3·50
		First Day Cover		4·00
		Presentation Pack	4·25	

Plate Nos.: 16p, 39p 1A, 1B (each ×4); 22p, 57p 1C, 1D (each ×4)

Sheets: 20 (5×4)

Imprint: Central, left-hand margin

Quantities sold: 16p 427,970; 22p 472,443; 39p 112,188; 57p 113,465

Withdrawn: 30.6.93

562 Morris Cowley 'Bullnose', 1925

563 Rolls-Royce 20/25, 1932

564 Chenard and Walcker T5, 1924

565 Packard 900 series Light Eight, 1932

566 Lanchester 21, 1927

567 Buick 30 Roadster, 1913

Vintage Cars (2nd series)

(Des A. Copp. Litho Enschedé)

1992 (8 SEPT). Perf 13×12½ (C)

591	**562**	16p multicoloured	30	30
592	**563**	22p multicoloured	45	45
593	**564**	28p multicoloured	70	75
594	**565**	33p multicoloured	90	95
595	**566**	39p multicoloured	1·00	1·10
596	**567**	50p multicoloured	1·50	1·70
591/6		Set of 6	4·50	4·75
		First Day Cover		5·00
		Presentation Pack	5·25	

Plate Nos.: All values 1A, 1B (each ×4)

Sheets: 20 (4×5)

Imprint: Central, left-hand margin

Quantities sold: 16p 434,984; 22p 426,734; 28p 290,202; 33p 134,477; 39p 124,759; 50p 127,917

Withdrawn: 30.9.93

568 Trinity

569 St. Mary

570 St. Martin   **571** St. Peter

Christmas. Jersey Parish Churches (3rd series)

(Des P. Layton. Litho B.D.T.)

1992 (3 NOV). Perf 13½ (C)

597	**568**	16p multicoloured	40	30
598	**569**	22p multicoloured	55	50
599	**570**	39p multicoloured	1·10	1·10
600	**571**	57p multicoloured	1·50	1·50
597/600		Set of 4	3·25	3·25
		First Day Cover		3·75
		Presentation Pack	4·00	
		Postcards (set of 4)	2·00	5·00

Plate Nos.: All values 1A, 1B, 1C, 1D (each ×5)

Sheets: 20 (4×5)

Imprint: Central, left-hand margin

Quantities sold: 16p 894,098; 22p 729,413; 39p 93,764; 57p 95,936

Withdrawn: 30.11.93

Post Office Yearbook

1992 (3 NOV). *Comprises Nos. 568/600*

Yearbook . . . . 32·00

Sold out: By 10.95

572 Farmhouse   **573** Trinity Church   **574** Daffodils and Cows

575 Jersey Cows   **576** Sunbathing   **577** Windsurfing

578 Crab (Queen's head at left)   **579** Crab (Queen's head at right)   **580** 'Singin' in the Rain' Float

581 'Dragon Dance' Float   **582** 'Bali, Morning of the World' Float   **583** 'Zulu Fantasy' Float

Booklet Stamps

(Des A. Copp. Litho B.D.T.)

1993 (11 JAN). Perf 13 (C)

601	**572**	(–) multicoloured	60	70
		a. Booklet pane. Nos. 601/4, each ×2, with margins all round . . .	5·00	
602	**573**	(–) multicoloured	60	70
603	**574**	(–) multicoloured	60	70
604	**575**	(–) multicoloured	60	70
605	**576**	(–) multicoloured	70	60
		a. Booklet pane. Nos. 605/8, each ×2, with margins all round . . .	5·50	
606	**577**	(–) multicoloured	70	60
607	**578**	(–) multicoloured	70	60
608	**579**	(–) multicoloured	70	60
609	**580**	(–) multicoloured	85	80
		a. Booklet pane. Nos. 609/12, each ×2, with margins all round . . .	7·00	
610	**581**	(–) multicoloured	85	80
611	**582**	(–) multicoloured	85	80
612	**583**	(–) multicoloured	85	80
601/12		Set of 12	7·75	7·50
		First Day Cover		16·00
		Presentation Pack . . . . 10·00	

The above do not show face values, but are inscribed 'BAILIWICK POSTAGE PAID' (Nos. 601/4), 'U.K. MINIMUM POSTAGE PAID' (Nos. 605/8) or 'EUROPE POSTAGE PAID' (Nos. 609/12). They were initially sold at 17p, 23p or 28p, but Nos. 601/4 and 609/12 were increased to 18p and 30p on 10 January 1994 and Nos. 601/4 to 19p on 4 July 1995. On 10 March 1997 Nos. 601/4 were increased to 20p, Nos. 605/8 to 24p and Nos. 609/12 to 31p.

Withdrawn: 30.9.99

584 *Phragmipedium* Eric Young 'Jersey'   **585** *Odontoglossum* Augres 'Trinity'

586 *Miltonia* St. Helier 'Colomberie'

587 *Phragmipedium pearcei*

588 *Calanthe* Grouville 'Gorey'

Jersey Orchids (3rd series)

(Litho Enschedé)

1993 (26 JAN). Perf 14×13 (C)

613	**584**	17p multicoloured	45	35
		a. Black printed double		
614	**585**	23p multicoloured	70	65
		a. Black printed double		
615	**586**	28p multicoloured	80	75
		a. Black printed double		
616	**587**	39p multicoloured	1·20	1·40
617	**588**	57p multicoloured	1·70	1·90
		a. Black printed double		
613/17		Set of 5	4·50	4·50
		First Day Cover		5·00
		Presentation Pack	5·25	

Plate Nos.: 17p, 23p 1A, 1B, 1C (each ×5); 28p, 39p, 57p 1A, 1B (each ×5)

Sheets: 20 (5×4)

Imprint: Central, left-hand margin

Quantities sold: 17p 391,802; 23p 391,444; 28p, 188,149; 39p 141,610; 57p 141,463

Withdrawn: 31.1.94

589 Douglas Dakota

590 Wight Seaplane

591 Avro Shackleton A.E.W.2

592 Gloster Meteor Mk III and De Havilland D.H.100 Vampire FB.5

593 BAe Harrier GR.1A

594 Panavia Tornado F.3

75th Anniversary of Royal Air Force

(Des A. Theobald. Litho Questa)

1993 (1 APR). Perf 14 (C)

618	**589**	17p multicoloured	45	30
619	**590**	23p multicoloured	60	65
620	**591**	28p multicoloured	70	70
621	**592**	33p multicoloured	80	85
622	**593**	39p multicoloured	1·00	1·10
623	**594**	57p multicoloured	1·50	1·60
618/23		Set of 6	4·50	4·75
		First Day Cover		6·00
		Presentation Pack	5·25	
MS624		147×98 mm. Nos. 619 and 623	4·50	4·75
		First Day Cover		6·00
		Presentation Pack	5·25	

Nos. 618/24 also commemorate the 50th anniversary of the Royal Air Force Association and the 40th anniversary of the first air display on Jersey.

Plate Nos.: 17p, 23p 1A, 1B, 1C, 1D (each ×4); 28p, 33p, 39p, 57p 1A, 1B (each ×4)

Sheets: 20 (5×4)

Imprint: Central, left-hand margin

Quantities sold: 17p, 578,871; 23p 581,661; 28p 184,066; 33p 140,430; 39p 144,522; 57p 159,447; miniature sheet 113,236

Withdrawn: 30.4.94

JERSEY

EUROPA 23ᵖ

595 'Jersey's Opera House' (Ian Rolls)

JERSEY

EUROPA 28ᵖ

596 'The Ham and Tomato Bap' (Jonathan Hubbard)

JERSEY

EUROPA 39ᵖ

597 'Vase of Flowers' (Neil MacKenzie)

Europa. Contemporary Art

(Litho Cartor)

1993 (1 APR). Perf 13½×14 (C)

625	**595**	23p multicoloured	60	60
626	**596**	28p multicoloured	70	70
627	**597**	39p multicoloured	1·10	1·10
625/7		Set of 3	2·20	2·20
		First Day Cover		2·75
		Presentation Pack	2·75	

Plate Nos.: All values 1A, 1B, 1C, 1D (each ×4)

Sheets: 20 (5×4)

Imprint: Central, left-hand margin

Quantities sold: 23p 422,536; 28p 340,206; 39p 230,510

Withdrawn: 30.4.94

598 1943 Occupation ½d Stamp

599 1943 1d Stamp

600 1943 1½d Stamp

601 1943 2d Stamp

602 1943 2½d Stamp

603 1943 3d Stamp

50th Anniversary of Edmund Blampied's Occupation Stamps

(Des G. Drummond. Litho Cartor)

1993 (2 JUNE). Perf 13½ (C)

628	**598**	17p myrtle-green, pale grn & blk	35	35
629	**599**	23p vermilion, salmon-pink & blk	50	50
630	**600**	28p chocolate, cinnamon & black	70	70
631	**601**	33p reddish orge, salmon & blk .	85	85
632	**602**	39p royal blue, cobalt and black .	1·20	1·20
633	**603**	50p bright magenta, pale mauve and black	1·40	1·40
628/33		Set of 6	4·50	4·50
		First Day Cover		4·75
		Presentation Pack	5·25	

Plate Nos.: All values 1A, 1B, 1C, 1D (each ×3)

Sheets: 20 (4×5)

Imprint: Central, left-hand margin

Quantities sold: 17p 549,708; 23p 565,711; 28p 174,159; 33p 120,570; 39p 93,502; 50p 99,135

Withdrawn: 30.6.94

604 Queen Elizabeth II (from painting by Mara McGregor)

40th Anniversary of Coronation

(Litho Questa)

1993 (2 JUNE). Perf 14½ (C)

634	**604**	£1 multicoloured (ab)	.... 2·75	2·75
		First Day Cover	....	3·00
		Presentation Pack	.... 3·50	

No. 634 was retained in use as part of the current definitive series until replaced by No. 804.

Printings: (a) 2.6.93; (b) 1.9.95

Plate Nos.: 1A, 1B, 1C, 1D (each ×4)

Sheets: 20 (5×4)

Imprint: Central, left-hand margin

Withdrawn: 31.3.99 but used again by the Philatelic Bureau for a Millennium cover, issued 31.12.99

  [third bird stamp 28p]

605 Short-toed Treecreeper   **606** Dartford Warbler   **607** Northern Wheatear

608 Cirl Bunting   **609** Jay

Summer Birds

(Des W. Oliver. Litho Cartor)

1993 (7 SEPT). Perf 13½×14 (C)

635	**605**	17p multicoloured	45	50
636	**606**	23p multicoloured	70	75
637	**607**	28p multicoloured	80	85
638	**608**	39p multicoloured	1·20	1·20
639	**609**	57p multicoloured	1·70	1·70
635/9		Set of 5	4·50	4·50
		First Day Cover		5·25
		Presentation Pack .... 5·00		

Plate Nos.: All values 1A, 1B, 1C, 1D (each ×4)

Sheets: 20 (5×4)

Imprint: Central, left-hand margin

Quantities sold: 17p 495,975; 23p 496,942; 28p 170,135; 39p 139,630; 57p 138,994

Withdrawn: 30.9.94

610 Two Angels holding 'Hark the Herald Angels Sing' Banner   **611** Two Angels playing Harps

612 Two Angels playing Violins   **613** Two Angels holding 'Once in Royal David's City' Banner

Christmas. Stained Glass Windows by Henry Bosdet from St. Aubin on the Hill Church

(Des N. Mackenzie. Litho Enschedé)

1993 (2 NOV). Perf 14×13 (C)

640	**610**	17p multicoloured	40	35
641	**611**	23p multicoloured	60	60
642	**612**	39p multicoloured	1·10	1·20
643	**613**	57p multicoloured	1·70	1·90
640/3		Set of 4	3·50	3·75
		First Day Cover		4·00
		Presentation Pack .... 4·25		

Plate Nos.: All values 1A, 1B, 1C (each ×4)

Sheets: 20 (5×4)

Imprint: Central, left-hand margin

Quantities sold: 17p 877,806; 23p 744,661; 39p 110,131; 57p 108,703

Withdrawn: 30.11.94

Post Office Yearbook

1993 (2 NOV). Comprises Nos. 601/43

Yearbook .... 33·00

Sold out: By 9.97

614 *Coprinus comatus*

615 *Amanita muscaria*

616 *Cantharellus cibarius*

617 *Macrolepiota procera*

618 *Clathrus ruber*

Fungi

(Des W. Oliver. Litho Questa)

1994 (11 JAN). Perf 14½ (C)

644	**614**	18p multicoloured	45	40
645	**615**	23p multicoloured	65	70
646	**616**	30p multicoloured	80	85
647	**617**	41p multicoloured	1·20	1·20
648	**618**	60p multicoloured	1·60	1·60
644/8		*Set of 5*	4·25	4·25
		First Day Cover		4·50
		Presentation Pack	4·75	

Plate Nos.: 18p 1A (×4); 23p 1B (×4); 30p 1C (×4); 41p 1D (×4); 60p 1E (×4)

Sheets: 20 (5×4)

Imprint: Central, left-hand margin

Quantities sold: 18p 735,158; 23p 482,461; 30p 188,095; 41p 184,418; 60p 137,309

Withdrawn: 30.1.95

619a Pekingese
  (*illustration reduced. Actual size* 110×75 *mm*)

'Hong Kong '94' International Stamp Exhibition. 'Chinese Year of the Dog'

(Des P. Layton, adapted A. Copp. Litho Questa)

1994 (18 FEB). *Sheet* 110×75 *mm. Perf* 15×14½ (C)

MS649	**619a**	£1 multicoloured	2·50	2·75
		First Day Cover		3·00
		Presentation Pack	3·50	

Quantity sold: 120,029

Withdrawn: 28.2.95

620 Maine Coon

621 British Shorthair

622 Persian

623 Siamese

624 Non-pedigree

21st Anniversary of Jersey Cat Club

(Des P. Layton. Litho B.D.T.)

1994 (5 APR). Perf 14 (C)

650	**620**	18p multicoloured	40	30
651	**621**	23p multicoloured	60	50
652	**622**	35p multicoloured	80	80
653	**623**	41p multicoloured	1·10	1·20
654	**624**	60p multicoloured	1·60	1·70
650/4		Set of 5	4·00	4·25
		First Day Cover		4·50
		Presentation Pack	4·50	

Plate Nos.: 35p 1A, 1B, 1C, 1D (each ×4); others 1A, 1B (each ×4)

Sheets: 20 (5×4) 18p, 35p, 60p; (4×5) 23p, 41p

Imprint: Central, left-hand margin

Quantities sold: 18p 491,500; 23p 490,820; 35p 221,769; 41p 185,206; 60p 132,276

Withdrawn: 29.4.95

625 Mammoth Hunt, La Cotte de St. Brelade

626 Stone Age Hunters pulling Mammoth into Cave

627 Chambered Passage, La Hougue Bie

628 Transporting Stones

Europa. Archaeological Discoveries

(Des A. Copp. Litho Enschedé)

1994 (5 APR). Perf 13½×14 (C)

655	**625**	23p multicoloured	50	55
		a. Horiz pair. Nos. 655/6	1·00	1·10
656	**626**	23p multicoloured	50	55
657	**627**	30p multicoloured	75	85
		a. Horiz pair. Nos. 657/8	1·50	1·70
658	**628**	30p multicoloured	75	85
655/8		Set of 4	2·20	2·50
		First Day Cover		3·00
		Presentation Pack	3·00	

Plate Nos.: Both values 1A, 1B (each ×4)

Sheets: 20 (4×5) the two horizontal designs for each value printed together, *se-tenant*, in horizontal pairs throughout the sheets

Imprint: Central, left-hand margin

Quantities sold: No. 655, 371,149; No. 656, 373,190; No. 657, 273,889; No. 658, 275,833

Withdrawn: 29.4.95

629 Gliders and Towing Aircraft approaching France

630 Landing Craft approaching Beaches

631 Disembarking from Landing Craft on Gold Beach

632 British Troops on Sword Beach

633 Spitfires over Beaches

634 Invasion Map

50th Anniversary of D-Day

(Des A. Theobald. Litho B.D.T.)

1994 (6 JUNE). Perf 13½×14 (C)

659	**629**	18p multicoloured	55	50
		a. Booklet pane. Nos. 659/60, each ×3, with margins all round	3·00	
		b. Booklet pane. Nos. 659/64, with margins all round	4·50	
660	**630**	18p multicoloured	55	50
661	**631**	23p multicoloured	75	70
		a. Booklet pane. Nos. 661/2, each ×3, with margins all round	5·00	
662	**632**	23p multicoloured	75	70

663	**633**	30p multicoloured	80	75
		a. *Booklet pane. Nos. 663/4,*		
		each ×3, *with margins all*		
		round	5·00	
664	**634**	30p multicoloured	80	75
659/64		*Set of 6*	3·75	3·50
		First Day Cover		4·25
		Presentation Pack	4·50	

No. 659*b* was also available as a loose pane (with no stitch holes) from the Philatelic Bureau.

Plate Nos.: All values 1A, 1B (each ×4)

Sheets: 20 (4×5)

Imprint: Central, left-hand margin

Quantities sold: No. 659, 361,667; No. 660, 365,169; No. 661, 377,546; No. 662, 367,033; No. 663, 229,455; No. 664, 226,520

Withdrawn: 30.6.95

635 Sailing

636 Rifle Shooting

637 Hurdling

638 Swimming

639 Hockey

Centenary of International Olympic Committee

(Des A. Theobald. Litho Questa)

1994 (6 JUNE). Perf 14 (C)

665	**635**	18p multicoloured	40	35
666	**636**	23p multicoloured	55	55
667	**637**	30p multicoloured	75	75
668	**638**	41p multicoloured	1·10	1·10
669	**639**	60p multicoloured	1·50	1·60
665/9		*Set of 5*	4·00	4·00
		First Day Cover		4·50
		Presentation Pack	4·50	

Plate Nos.: All values 1A (×4)

Sheets: 20 (5×4)

Imprint: Central, left-hand margin

Quantities sold: 18p 279,163; 23p 276,438; 30p 178,234; 41p 183,875; 60p 133,357

Withdrawn: 30.6.95

640 Strawberry Anemone   **641** Hermit Crab and Parasitic Anemone

642 Velvet Swimming Crab   **643** Common Jellyfish

Marine Life

(Des W. Oliver. Litho Cartor)

1994 (2 AUG). Perf 13½ (C)

670	**640**	18p multicoloured	40	45
671	**641**	23p multicoloured	60	65
672	**642**	41p multicoloured	1·20	1·40
673	**643**	60p multicoloured	1·60	1·60
670/3		*Set of 4*	3·50	3·75
		First Day Cover		4·25
		Presentation Pack	4·50	

Plate Nos.: All values 1A, 1B, 1C, 1D (each ×4)

Sheets: 20 (4×5)

Imprint: Central, left-hand margin

Quantities sold: 18p 465,890; 23p 453,750; 41p 171,459; 60p 175,656

Withdrawn: 31.8.95

644 *Condor 10* (catamaran)   **645** Map of Jersey and Pillar Box

646 Vicker's Type 953 Vanguard of B.E.A.

647 Short 360 of Aurigny Air Services

648 *Caesarea* (Sealink ferry)

25th Anniversary of Jersey Postal Administration

(Des A. Copp. Litho Questa)

1994 (1 OCT). Perf 14 (C)

674	**644**	18p multicoloured	50	45
675	**645**	23p multicoloured	60	50
676	**646**	35p multicoloured	85	85
677	**647**	41p multicoloured	1·10	1·00
678	**648**	60p multicoloured	1·60	1·50
674/8		*Set of 5*	4·25	4·00
		First Day Cover		4·50
		Presentation Pack	5·00	
MS679		150×100 mm. Nos. 674/8	4·50	4·50
		First Day Cover		5·25
		Presentation Pack	4·75	

Plate Nos.: All values 1A (×5)

Sheets: 20 (5×4)

Imprint: Central, left-hand margin

Quantities sold: 18p 473,837; 23p 472,468; 35p 184,871; 41p 186,653; 60p 182,108; miniature sheet 76,623

Withdrawn: 31.10.95

649 'Away in a Manger'

650 'Hark! the Herald Angels Sing'

651 'While Shepherds watched'

652 'We Three Kings of Orient Are'

Christmas. Carols

(Des A. Copp. Litho Questa)

1994 (8 NOV). Perf 14 (C)

680	**649**	18p multicoloured	40	40
681	**650**	23p multicoloured	50	50
682	**651**	41p multicoloured	1·20	1·20
683	**652**	60p multicoloured	1·50	1·50
680/3		*Set of 4*	3·25	3·25
		First Day Cover		4·25
		Presentation Pack	4·25	

Plate Nos.: All values 1A, 1B (each ×4)

Sheets: 20 (5×4)

Imprint: Central, left-hand margin

Quantities sold: 18p 981,010; 23p 883,715; 41p 174,413; 60p 179,888

Withdrawn: 30.11.95

Post Office Yearbook

1994 (8 NOV). *Comprises Nos.* **MS**248 *and* 644/83

Yearbook . . . . 32·00

Sold out: By 2.2000

653 Dog and 'GOOD LUCK'

654 Rose and 'WITH LOVE'

655 Chick and 'CONGRAT-ULATIONS'

656 Bouquet of Flowers and 'THANK YOU'

657 Dove with Letter and 'WITH LOVE'

658 Cat with 'GOOD LUCK'

659 Carnations and 'THANK YOU'

660 Parrot and 'CONGRATU-LATIONS'

661 Pig and 'HAPPY NEW YEAR'

Greetings Stamps

(Des A. Copp. Litho B.D.T.)

1995 (24 JAN). Perf 13 (C)

684	**653**	18p multicoloured	30	20
		a. Horiz strip of 4. Nos. 684/7 .	2·00	2·00
		b. Booklet pane of 9. Nos. 684/92	6·00	
685	**654**	18p multicoloured	30	20
686	**655**	18p multicoloured	30	20
687	**656**	18p multicoloured	30	20
688	**657**	23p multicoloured	45	25
		a. Horiz strip of 4. Nos. 688/91	2·40	2·40
689	**658**	23p multicoloured	45	25
690	**659**	23p multicoloured	45	25
691	**660**	23p multicoloured	45	25
692	**661**	60p multicoloured	1·50	1·50
684/92		Set of 9	5·50	5·50
		First Day Cover (Nos. 684/91)	6·00	
		First Day Cover (No. 692)	2·40	
		Presentation Pack	5·75	

No. 684a was available as a loose pane from the Philatelic Bureau and was also included in the presentation pack. No. 692 commemorates the Chinese New Year of the Pig.

Plate Nos.: All values 1A, 1B, 1C, 1D (each ×4)

Sheets: 60p 10 (5×2); others 20 (4×5) the four designs for each value printed together, se-tenant, in horizontal strips of 4 throughout the sheets

Imprint: Central, left-hand margin

Quantities sold: 18p 369,217; 23p 338,047; 60p 101,753

Withdrawn: 31.1.96 (sheets)

662 'Captain Rawes'

663 'Brigadoon'

664 'Elsie Jury'

665 'Augusto L'Gouveia Pinto'

666 'Bella Romana'

Camellias

(Des and litho Questa)

1995 (21 MAR). Perf 14½ (C)

693	**662**	18p multicoloured	55	50
694	**663**	23p multicoloured	80	70
695	**664**	30p multicoloured	90	85
696	**665**	35p multicoloured	1·10	1·20
697	**666**	41p multicoloured	1·20	1·30
693/7		Set of 5	4·25	4·25
		First Day Cover		4·50
		Presentation Pack	4·50	

Plate Nos.: All values 1A (×5)

Sheets: 20 (5×4)

Imprint: Central, left-hand margin

Quantities sold: 18p 398,810; 23p 480,040; 30p 187,651; 35p 160,765; 41p 133,208

Withdrawn: 31.3.96

667 'Liberation' (sculpture, Philip Jackson)

Europa. Peace and Freedom

(Des A. Theobald. Litho Cartor)

1995 (9 MAY). Perf 13½ (C)

698	**667**	23p black and dull violet-blue	55	55
699		30p black and rose-pink	70	95
698/9		Set of 2	1·20	1·50
		First Day Cover		2·20
		Presentation Pack	2·00	

Plate Nos.: Both values 1A, 1B, 1C (each ×4)

Sheets: 10 (5×2)

Imprint: Bottom margin

Quantities sold: 19p 251,352; 30p 278,162

Withdrawn: 31.5.96

668 Baliff and Crown Officers in Launch

669 *Vega* (Red Cross supply ship)

670 H.M.S. *Beagle* (destroyer)

671 British Troops in Ordnance Yard, St. Helier

672 King George VI and Queen Elizabeth in Jersey

673 Unloading Supplies from Landing Craft, St. Aubin's

674a Royal Family with Winston Churchill on Buckingham Palace Balcony, V.E. Day

(illustration reduced. Actual size 110×75 mm)

50th Anniversary of Liberation

(Des A. Theobald. Litho B.D.T.)

1995 (9 MAY). Perf 15×14 (C)

700	**668**	18p multicoloured	40	40
		a. Booklet pane. Nos. 700/1, each ×3, with margins all round	2·00	
701	**669**	18p multicoloured	40	40
702	**670**	23p multicoloured	60	60
		a. Booklet pane. Nos. 702/3, each ×3, with margins all round	2·75	
703	**671**	23p multicoloured	60	60
704	**672**	60p multicoloured	1·50	1·50
		a. Booklet pane. Nos. 704/5, each ×3, with margins all round	7·50	
705	**673**	60p multicoloured	1·50	1·50
700/5		Set of 6	4·50	4·50
		First Day Cover		5·25
		Presentation Pack	5·50	
MS706		110×75 mm. **674a** £1 multicoloured	2·75	2·75
		a. Booklet pane. As No. **MS**706 with additional margins all round showing arms, mace and inscriptions	2·50	
		First Day Cover		3·50
		Presentation Pack	3·50	

Plate Nos.: All values 1A, 1B (each ×4)

Sheets: 20 (4×5)

Imprint: Central, left-hand margin

Quantities sold: 18p (No. 700) 207,666; 18p (No. 701) 214,869; 23p (No. 702) 279,930; 23p (No. 703) 274,379; 60p (No. 704) 131,342; 60p (No. 705) 136,508; £1 122,855

Withdrawn: 31.5.96 (sheets)

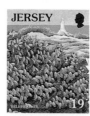

675 Bell Heather

676 Sea Campion

677 Spotted Rock-rose

678 Thrift

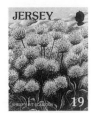

679 Sheep's-bit Scabious

680 Field Bind-weed

681 Common Bird's-foot Trefoil

682 Sea-holly

683 Common Centaury

684 Dwarf Pansy

European Nature Conservation Year. Wild Flowers

(Des N. Parlett. Litho B.D.T.)

1995 (4 JULY). Perf 13 (C)

707	**675**	19p multicoloured	40	20
		a. Horiz strip of 5. Nos. 707/11	3·00	3·00
708	**676**	19p multicoloured	40	20
709	**677**	19p multicoloured	40	20
710	**678**	19p multicoloured	40	20
711	**679**	19p multicoloured	40	20
712	**680**	23p multicoloured	50	25
		a. Horiz strip of 5. Nos. 712/16	3·50	3·50
713	**681**	23p multicoloured	50	25
714	**682**	23p multicoloured	50	25
715	**683**	23p multicoloured	50	25
716	**684**	23p multicoloured	50	25
707/16		Set of 10	6·00	6·00
		First Day Cover		6·25
		Presentation Pack	6·50	

Plate Nos.: Both values 1A, 1B (each ×4)

Sheets: 20 (5×4) the five designs for each value printed together, *se-tenant*, in horizontal strips of 5 throughout the sheets, the backgrounds forming composite designs

Imprint: Central, left-hand margin

Quantities sold: 19p 454,143; 23p 554,070

Withdrawn: 31.7.96

685 *Precis almana*

686 *Papilio palinurus*

687 *Catopsilia scylla*

688 *Papilio rumanzovia*

689 *Troides helena*

Butterflies

(Des W. Oliver. Litho Questa)

1995 (1 SEPT). Perf 14 (C)

717	**685**	19p multicoloured	50	55
718	**686**	23p multicoloured	55	60
719	**687**	30p multicoloured	80	85
720	**688**	41p multicoloured	1·00	1·10
721	**689**	60p multicoloured	1·60	1·70
717/21		Set of 5	4·00	4·25
		First Day Cover		4·75
		Presentation Pack	4·50	
MS722		150×100 mm. Nos. 720/1	2·40	2·50
		a. 41p value imperforate		
		First Day Cover		3·25
		Presentation Pack	3·25	

No. **MS**722 includes the 'Singapore '95' International Stamp Exhibition logo on the sheet margin and shows the two stamp designs without frames.

Plate Nos.: All values 1A (×4)

Sheets: 20 (5×4)

Imprint: Central, left-hand margin

Quantities sold: 19p 475,496; 23p 466,880; 30p 246,270; 41p 117,354; 60p 133,026; miniature sheet 76,062

Withdrawn: 30.9.96

690 Peace Doves and United Nations Anniversary Emblem

691 Symbolic Wheat and Anniversary Emblem

50th Anniversary of United Nations

(Des A. Copp. Litho Enschedé)

1995 (24 OCT). Perf 13×14½ (C)

723	**690**	19p cobalt and royal blue	60	50
724	**691**	23p turq-green & dp blue-green .	70	70
725		41p dp blue-green & turq-green .	1·20	1·20
726	**690**	60p royal blue and cobalt	1·50	1·50
723/6		Set of 4	3·50	3·50
		First Day Cover		4·50
		Presentation Pack	4·50	

Plate Nos.: 19p, 23p 1A, 1B (each ×2); others 1A (×2)

Sheets: 20 (5×4)

Imprint: Central, left-hand margin

Quantities sold: 19p 152,550; 23p 201,977; 41p 75,032; 60p 73,943

Withdrawn: 31.10.96

692 'Puss in Boots'

693 'Cinderella'

694 'Sleeping Beauty'

695 'Aladdin'

Christmas. Pantomimes

(Des V. Ambrus. Litho Cartor)

1995 (24 OCT). Perf 13½ (C)

727	**692**	19p multicoloured	50	40
728	**693**	23p multicoloured	55	45
729	**694**	41p multicoloured	1·00	1·00
730	**695**	60p multicoloured	1·60	1·50
727/30		Set of 4	3·25	3·00
		First Day Cover		4·25
		Presentation Pack	4·50	

Plate Nos.: All values 1A, 1B, 1C, 1D (each ×4)

Sheets: 20 (5×4)

Imprint: Central, left-hand margin

Quantities sold: 19p 986,299; 23p 716,510; 41p 118,699; 60p 131,497

Withdrawn: 31.10.96

Post Office Yearbook

1995 (24 OCT). Comprises Nos. 491c and 684/730

Yearbook . . . . 34·00

Sold out: 12.99

696a Rat with Top Hat

(illustration reduced. Actual size 110×75 mm)

Chinese New Year ('Year of the Rat')

(Des V. Ambrus. Litho Questa)

1996 (19 FEB). Sheet 110×75 mm. Perf 13½×14 (C)

MS731	**696a**	£1 multicoloured	2·50	2·50
		First Day Cover		3·25
		Presentation Pack	3·50	

Withdrawn: 28.2.97

697 African Child and Map

698 Children and Globe

699 European Child and Map

700 South American Child and Map

701 Asian Child and Map

702 South Pacific Child and Map

704 Elizabeth Garrett (first British woman doctor)

705 Emmeline Pankhurst (suffragette)

50th Anniversary of U.N.I.C.E.F.

(Des A. Copp. Litho Questa)

1996 (19 FEB). Perf 14½ (C)

732	**697**	19p multicoloured	45	40
733	**698**	23p multicoloured	55	45
734	**699**	30p multicoloured	70	65
735	**700**	35p multicoloured	90	95
736	**701**	41p multicoloured	1·00	1·10
737	**702**	60p multicoloured	1·50	1·60
732/7		Set of 6	4·50	4·50
		First Day Cover		5·25
		Presentation Pack	5·25	

Plate Nos.: All values 1A (×4)

Sheets: 20 (4×5)

Imprint: Central, left-hand margin

Quantities sold: 19p 464,379; 23p 413,906; 30p 152,043; 35p 84,359; 41p 86,886; 60p 90,074

Withdrawn: 28.2.97

703 Queen Elizabeth II (from photo by T. O.'Neill)

70th Birthday of Queen Elizabeth II

(Litho Questa)

1996 (21 APR). Perf 14×15 (C)

738	**703**	£5 multicoloured	10·00	10·00
		First Day Cover		12·00
		Presentation Pack	11·00	

No. 738 was retained as a definitive.

Plate Nos.: 1A (×5)

Sheets: 10 (2×5)

Imprint: Central, left-hand margin

Europa. Famous Women

(Des Jennifer Toombs. Litho B.D.T.)

1996 (25 APR). Perf 13½×14 (C)

739	**704**	23p multicoloured	60	60
740	**705**	30p multicoloured	90	90
739/40		Set of 2	1·50	1·50
		First Day Cover		2·00
		Presentation Pack	2·00	

Plate Nos.: 23p 1A, 1B, 1C (each ×4); 30p 1A, 1B, 1C, 1D, 1E (each ×4)

Sheets: 10 (5×2)

Imprint: Bottom margin

Quantities sold: 23p 245,907; 30p 432,935

Withdrawn: 30.4.97

706 Player shooting at Goal

707 Two Players chasing Ball

708 Player avoiding Tackle

709 Two players competing for Ball

710 Players heading Ball

European Football Championship, England

(Des A. Theobald. Litho B.D.T.)

1996 (25 APR). Perf 13½×14 (C)

741	**706**	19p multicoloured	50	40
742	**707**	23p multicoloured	60	50
743	**708**	35p multicoloured	95	90
744	**709**	41p multicoloured	1·00	1·00
745	**710**	60p multicoloured	1·60	1·60
741/5		Set of 5	4·25	4·00
		First Day Cover		4·50
		Presentation Pack	4·75	

Plate Nos.: 19p, 23p 1A, 1B (each ×4); others 1A (×4)

Sheets: 20 (5×4)

Imprint: Central, left-hand margin

Quantities sold: 19p 450,588; 23p 458,412; 35p 105,519; 41p 106,826; 60p 109,092

Withdrawn: 30.4.97

711 Rowing **712** Judo

713 Fencing **714** Boxing

715 Basketball

716a Olympic Torch and Stadium
(*illustration reduced. Actual size* 150×100 *mm*)

Sporting Anniversaries

(Des A. Theobald. Litho Questa)

1996 (8 JUNE). Perf 13½ (No. **MS**751) or 14 (others), both comb

746	**711**	19p multicoloured	50	40
747	**712**	23p multicoloured	60	50
748	**713**	35p multicoloured	95	95
749	**714**	41p multicoloured	1·00	1·00
750	**715**	60p multicoloured	1·60	1·60
746/50		Set of 5	4·25	4·25
		First Day Cover		5·00
		Presentation Pack	5·00	
MS751	150×100 mm. **716a** £1 mult		2·50	2·50
		First Day Cover		3·50
		Presentation Pack	3·50	

Anniversaries:—Nos. 746/8, 750/1, Centenary of Modern Olympic Games; No. 749, 50th anniversary of International Amateur Boxing Association.

No. **MS**751 also includes the 'CAPEX '96' International Stamp Exhibition logo.

Plate Nos.: All values 1A (×4)

Sheets: 20 (5×4)

Imprint: Central, left-hand margin

Withdrawn: 30.6.97

717 Bay on North Coast **718** Portelet Bay

719 Greve de Lecq Bay **720** Beauport Beach

721 Plemont Bay **722** St. Brelade's Bay

Tourism. Beaches

(Des A. Copp. Litho B.D.T.)

1996 (8 JUNE). Perf 14 (C)

752	**717**	19p multicoloured	50	50
		a. *Booklet pane. Nos. 752/3, each ×3, with margins all round*	2·50	
		b. *Booklet pane. Nos. 752/7, with margins all round*	4·25	
753	**718**	23p multicoloured	60	60
754	**719**	30p multicoloured	80	80
		a. *Booklet pane. Nos. 754/5, each ×3, with margins all round*	4·00	
755	**720**	35p multicoloured	95	95
756	**721**	41p multicoloured	1·10	1·10
		a. *Booklet pane. Nos. 756/7, each ×3, with margins all round*	6·00	
757	**722**	60p multicoloured	1·60	1·60
752/7		Set of 6	5·00	5·00
		First Day Cover		5·25
		Presentation Pack	5·25	
		Postcards (set of 6)	3·00	8·50

Plate Nos.: 19p, 23p 1A, 1B (each ×4); others 1A (×4)

Sheets: 20 (5×4)

Imprint: Central, left-hand margin

Withdrawn: 30.6.97 (sheets)

723 Drag Hunt

724 Pony and Trap

725 Training Racehorses on Beach

726 Show-jumping

727 Pony Club Event

728 Shire Mare and Foal

Horses

(Des P. Layton. Litho Enschedé)

1996 (13 SEPT). Perf 13½×14 (C)

758	**723**	19p multicoloured	50	50
759	**724**	23p multicoloured	60	60
760	**725**	30p multicoloured	80	80
761	**726**	35p multicoloured	95	95
762	**727**	41p multicoloured	1·10	1·10
763	**728**	60p multicoloured	1·60	1·60
758/63		Set of 6	5·00	5·00
		First Day Cover		5·25
		Presentation Pack	5·25	
		Postcards (set of 6)	3·00	8·50

Plate Nos.: All values 1A, 1B (each ×4)

Sheets: 20 (4×5)

Imprint: Central, left-hand margin

Withdrawn: 30.9.97

729 The Journey to Bethlehem

730 The Shepherds

731 The Nativity

732 The Three Kings

Christmas

(Des V. Ambrus. Litho Cartor)

1996 (12 NOV). Perf 13×13½ (C)

764	**729**	19p multicoloured	50	50
765	**730**	23p multicoloured	60	70
766	**731**	30p multicoloured	90	95
767	**732**	60p multicoloured	1·40	1·50
764/7		Set of 4	3·00	3·25
		First Day Cover		4·25
		Presentation Pack	4·25	

Plate Nos.: All values 1A, 1B, 1C (each ×4)

Sheets: 20 (4×5)

Imprint: Central, left-hand margin

Withdrawn: 28.11.97

Post Office Yearbook

1996 (12 NOV). Comprises Nos. **MS**731/67

Yearbook .... 38·00

Sold out: 12.99

733a Jersey Cow wearing Scarf
(*illustration reduced. Actual size* 110×75 *mm*)

Chinese New Year ('Year of the Ox')

(Des V. Ambrus. Litho Questa)

1997 (7 FEB). Sheet 110×74 *mm*. Perf 14×13½ (C)

MS768	**733a**	£1 multicoloured	3·25	3·75
		First Day Cover		4·50
		Presentation Pack	4·50	

Withdrawn: 28.2.98

'HONG KONG '97' International Stamp Exhibition

1997 (7 FEB). *No.* **MS**768 *optd with exhibition emblem in black and* 'JERSEY AT HONG KONG '97' *in red, both on sheet margin*

MS769	**733a**	£1 multicoloured	3·75	4·25
		First Day Cover		5·00
		Presentation Pack	5·00	

Withdrawn: 28.2.98

734 Lillie the Cow on the Beach

735 Lillie taking Photograph

736 Carrying Bucket and Spade

737 Eating Meal at Mont Orgueil

Tourism. 'Lillie the Cow'

(Des A. Copp. Litho B.D.T.)

1997 (12 FEB)–**99**. *Self-adhesive.* Perf 9½ (C)

770	**734**	(23p) multicoloured (*a*)	80	85
		a. With copyright symbol after date (bc)	4·50	4·50

771	**735**	(23p) multicoloured (*a*)	80	85
		a. With copyright symbol after date (bc)	4·50	4·50
772	**736**	(23p) multicoloured (*a*)	80	85
		a. With copyright symbol after date (bc)	4·50	4·50
773	**737**	(23p) multicoloured (*a*)	80	85
		a. With copyright symbol after date (bc)	4·50	4·50
770/3		Set of 4	2·75	3·00
770*a*/3*a*		Set of 4	16·00	16·00
		First Day Cover		4·50
		Presentation Pack	4·00	

Nos. 770/3, which are inscribed 'UK MINIMUM POSTAGE PAID', come, *se-tenant*, in strips of 4 or rolls of 100 with the surplus self-adhesive paper around each stamp removed. Nos. 770/3 were initially sold at 23p each; this was increased to 24p on 10 March 1997.

Initially released with "1997" imprint dates, Nos. 770*a*/3*a* were subsequently reissued inscribed "1999" (price per set, mint or used, £18) and "2000" (price £16).

Printings: (*a*) 12.2.97. Inscr '1997'; (*b*) 16.4.99. Inscr '1999'; (*c*) 9.12.00. Inscr '2000'

Sold out: By 5.2001

738 Red-breasted Merganser

739 Sanderling

740 Northern Gannet

741 Great Crested Grebe

742 Common Tern

743 Black-headed Gull

744 Dunlin

745 Sandwich Tern

746 Ringed Plover

747 Bar-tailed Godwit

758 Great Cormorant

759 Western Curlew

748 Atlantic Puffin

749 Brent Goose

760 Oystercatcher

761 Ruddy Turnstone

750 Grey Plover

751 Black Scoter

762 Herring Gull

763 Rock Pipit

752 Lesser Black-
backed Gull

753 Little Egret

764 Greater Black-
backed Gull

765 Pied Avocet

754 Fulmar

755 Golden Plover

766 Grey Heron

767 Common
Redshank

756 Common Greenshank

757 Little Grebe

768 Razorbill

769 Shag

371

Seabirds and Waders

(Des N. Parlett. Litho Questa)

1997 (12 Feb)–**99**. Perf 14½ (C)

774	**738**	1p multicoloured (a)	10	10
775	**739**	2p multicoloured (b)	10	10
776	**740**	4p multicoloured (d)	10	10
777	**741**	5p multicoloured (b)	10	15
778	**742**	10p multicoloured (a)	20	25
779	**743**	15p multicoloured (a)	30	35
780	**744**	20p multicoloured (a)	60	45
		a. With copyright symbol after date (c)	40	45
781	**745**	21p multicoloured (b)	40	45
782	**746**	22p multicoloured (d)	45	50
783	**747**	23p multicoloured (e)	45	50
784	**748**	24p multicoloured (a)	70	50
		a. With copyright symbol after date (c)	45	50
785	**749**	25p multicoloured (b)	50	55
786	**750**	26p multicoloured (d)	50	55
787	**751**	27p multicoloured (e)	55	60
788	**752**	28p multicoloured (e)	60	65
789	**753**	29p multicoloured (e)	60	65
790	**754**	30p multicoloured (b)	60	65
791	**755**	31p multicoloured (d)	60	65
792	**756**	32p multicoloured (d)	65	70
793	**757**	33p multicoloured (e)	65	70
794	**758**	34p multicoloured (e)	70	75
795	**759**	35p multicoloured (d)	70	75
796	**760**	37p multicoloured (a)	75	80
797	**761**	40p multicoloured (b)	80	85
798	**762**	44p multicoloured (d)	90	95
799	**763**	45p multicoloured (e)	90	95
800	**764**	50p multicoloured (d)	1·00	1·10
801	**765**	60p multicoloured (b)	1·20	1·40
802	**766**	65p multicoloured (e)	1·20	1·40
803	**767**	75p multicoloured (a)	2·00	2·10
804	**768**	£1 multicoloured (b)	2·50	2·50
805	**769**	£2 multicoloured (a)	5·00	5·25
774/805		Set of 32 .... 24·00		26·00
		First Day Covers (4)		30·00
		Presentation Packs (4) ..... 28·00		
		Postcards (set of 32) .... 13·00		40·00

MS806 Four sheets, each 136×130 mm. (a) Nos. 774, 778/80, 784, 796, 803 and 805 (a). (b) Nos. 775, 777, 781, 785, 790, 797, 801 and 804 (b). (c) Nos. 776, 782, 786, 791/2, 795, 798 and 800 (d). (d) Nos. 783, 787/9, 793/4, 799 and 802 (e)

	Set of 4 sheets .... 25·00		25·00
	First Day Covers (4)		40·00
	Souvenir Folders (4) .... 32·00		
	Complete series Souvenir Folder .... 28·00		

Printings: (a) 12.2.97. Inscr '1997' without copyright symbol; (b) 28.1.98. Inscr '1998' with copyright symbol; (c) 2.4.98. Inscr '1998' with copyright symbol; (d) 11.8.98. Inscr '1998' with copyright symbol; (e) 21.8.99. Inscr '1999' with copyright symbol

Plate Nos.: 1p, 2p, 22p, 25p, 26p, £2 1A, 1B, 1C, 1D (each ×4); 20p, 24p 1A, 1B, 1C, 1D (each ×4), 2A, 2B, 2C, 2D (each ×4) (Nos. 780a, 784a); 4p, 21p, 50p, 60p 1A, 1B, 1C, 1D, 1E, 1F, 1G, 1H (each ×4); **MS**806 1A (×4); others 1A, 1B (each ×4)

Sheets: 20 (4×5)

Imprint: Central, left-hand margin

Withdrawn: 31.12.2007

770 De Havilland D.H.95 Flamingo

771 Handley Page H.P.R.5 Marathon

772 De Havilland D.H.114 Heron

773 Boeing 737-236

774 Britten Norman Trislander

775 BAe 146-200

60th Anniversary of Jersey Airport

(Des A. Theobald. Litho Enschedé)

1997 (10 MAR). Perf 13½×14 (C)

807	**770**	20p multicoloured	45	40
808	**771**	24p multicoloured	55	40
809	**772**	31p multicoloured	65	65
810	**773**	37p multicoloured	95	95
811	**774**	43p multicoloured	1·10	1·10
812	**775**	63p multicoloured	1·70	1·70
807/12		Set of 6	5·00	5·00
		First Day Cover		5·25
		Presentation Pack .... 5·50		

Plate Nos.: All values 1A, 1B, 1C (each ×4)

Sheets: 20 (4×5)

Imprint: Central, left-hand margin

Withdrawn: 31.3.98

776 The Bull of St. Clement

777 The Black Horse of St. Ouen

778 The Black Dog of Bouley Bay

779 Les Fontaines des Mittes

Europa. Tales and Legends

(Des Jennifer Toombs. Litho B.D.T.)

1997 (15 APR). Perf 15×14 (C)

813	**776**	20p multicoloured	65	60
814	**777**	24p multicoloured	75	70
815	**778**	31p multicoloured	1·10	1·10
816	**779**	63p multicoloured	1·70	1·80
813/16		*Set of 4*	3·75	3·75
		First Day Cover		4·50
		Presentation Pack	4·50	

Nos. 814/15 include the 'EUROPA' emblem.

Plate Nos.: All values 1A, 1B (each ×5)

Sheets: 10 (5×2)

Imprint: Bottom margin

Withdrawn: 30.4.98

'Pacific 97' International Stamp Exhibition, San Francisco

1997 (29 May). *No.* **MS**806a *optd with exhibition emblem on sheet margin*

MS817   136×130 mm. Nos. 774, 778/80, 784, 796, 803 and 805 . . . .   7·50   8·50

Souvenir Folder . . . .   9·50

780 Cycling

781 Archery

782 Windsurfing

783 Gymnastics

784 Volleyball

785 Running

7th Island Games, Jersey

(Des A. Theobald. Litho B.D.T.)

1997 (28 JUNE). Perf 13½ (C)

818	**780**	20p multicoloured	55	55
		a. Booklet pane. Nos. 818/19, each ×3, with margins all round	2·50	
		b. Booklet pane. Nos. 818/23, with margins all round	5·25	
819	**781**	24p multicoloured	65	65
820	**782**	31p multicoloured	80	80
		a. Booklet pane. Nos. 820/1, each ×3, with margins all round	4·00	
821	**783**	37p multicoloured	1·00	1·00
822	**784**	43p multicoloured	1·10	1·10
		a. Booklet pane. Nos. 822/3, each ×3, with margins all round	6·25	
823	**785**	63p multicoloured	1·70	1·70
818/23		*Set of 6*	5·25	5·25
		First Day Cover		5·75
		Presentation Pack	6·00	

Plate Nos.: 20p, 24p 1A, 1B (each ×4); others 1A (×4)

Sheets: 20 (5×4)

Imprint: Central, left-hand margin

Withdrawn: 30.6.98 (sheets)

786 Mallorcan Midwife Toad

787 Aye-Aye

788 Mauritius Parakeet

789 Pigmy Hog

790 St. Lucia Whip-tail

791 Madagascar Teal

794 Beech

795 Sweet Chestnut

796 Hawthorn

797 Common Oak

Wildlife Preservation Trust (6th series)

(Des W. Oliver. Litho Cartor)

1997 (2 SEPT). Perf 13 (C)

824	**786**	20p multicoloured	. . . .	50	45
825	**787**	24p multicoloured	. . . .	60	50
826	**788**	31p multicoloured	. . . .	90	90
827	**789**	37p multicoloured	. . . .	1·00	1·10
828	**790**	43p multicoloured	. . . .	1·10	1·20
829	**791**	63p multicoloured	. . . .	1·70	1·80
824/9		*Set of* 6	. . . .	5·25	5·25
		First Day Cover	. . . .		5·50
		Presentation Pack	. . . .	6·00	

Plate Nos.: All values 1A, 1B (each ×4)

Sheets: 20 (5×4)

Imprint: Central, left-hand margin

Withdrawn: 30.9.98

Trees

(Des Norah Bryan. Litho Questa)

1997 (2 SEPT). Perf 14½ (C)

830	**792**	20p multicoloured	. . . .	50	45
831	**793**	24p multicoloured	. . . .	60	50
832	**794**	31p multicoloured	. . . .	90	90
833	**795**	37p multicoloured	. . . .	1·00	1·10
834	**796**	43p multicoloured	. . . .	1·10	1·20
835	**797**	63p multicoloured	. . . .	1·70	1·80
830/5		*Set of* 6	. . . .	5·25	5·25
		First Day Cover	. . . .		5·50
		Presentation Pack	. . . .	6·00	

Plate Nos.: 20p, 24p 1A, 1B (each ×4); others 1A (×4)

Sheets: 20 (5×4)

Imprint: Central, left-hand margin

Withdrawn: 30.9.98

792 Ash

793 Elder

798 Father Christmas and Reindeer outside Jersey Airport

799 Father Christmas with Presents, St. Aubin's Harbour

800 Father Christmas in Sleigh, Mont Orgueil Castle

801 Father Christmas with Children, Royal Square, St. Helier

Christmas

(Des Colleen Corlett. Litho B.D.T.)

1997 (11 NOV). Perf 14 (C)

836	**798**	20p multicoloured	60	60
837	**799**	24p multicoloured	70	70
838	**800**	31p multicoloured	1·00	1·00
839	**801**	63p multicoloured	1·90	1·90
836/9		Set of 4	3·75	3·75
		First Day Cover		4·50
		Presentation Pack	4·50	

Plate Nos.: 20p, 31p 1A, 1B (each ×5); others 1A, 1B (each ×4)

Sheets: 20 (4×5)

Imprint: Central, left-hand margin

Withdrawn: 30.11.98

802 Wedding Photograph, 1947

803 Queen Elizabeth and Prince Philip, 1997

804a Full-length Wedding Photograph, 1947
(*illustration reduced. Actual size* 150×100 *mm*)

Golden Wedding of Queen Elizabeth and Prince Philip

(Des G. Drummond. Litho Questa)

1997 (20 Nov). Perf 13½ (**MS**842) or 14½ (others), both comb

840	**802**	50p multicoloured	1·00	60
		a. Horiz pair. Nos. 840/1	3·00	3·00
841	**803**	50p multicoloured	1·00	60
840/1		Set of 2	3·00	3·00
		First Day Cover		3·75
		Presentation Pack	3·75	
MS842		150×100 mm. **804a** £1.50, mult . . .	4·50	4·50
		First Day Cover		5·00
		Presentation Pack	4·75	

Plate Nos.: 1A, 1B, 1C, 1D (each ×5)

Sheets: 20 (4×5). The two designs were printed together, *se-tenant*, in horizontal pairs throughout the sheets

Imprint: Central, left-hand margin

Withdrawn: 30.11.98

Year Pack 1997

1997 (20 NOV). Comprises Nos. **MS**768, 770/4, 778/80, 784, 796, 803, 805, 807/16 *and* 818/42

	Year Pack	45·00

Sold out: By 11.02

Post Office Yearbook

1997 (20 NOV). Comprises Nos. **MS**768, 770/4, 778/80, 784, 796, 803, 805, 807/16 *and* 818/42

	Yearbook	45·00

Sold out: By 7.04

805a Tiger wearing Scarf
(*illustration reduced. Actual size* 110×75 *mm*)

Chinese New Year ('Year of the Tiger')

(Des V. Ambrus. Litho Questa)

1998 (28 JAN). Sheet 110×75 mm. Perf 14×13½ (C)

MS843	**805a**	£1 multicoloured	2·50	2·75
		First Day Cover		3·75
		Presentation Pack	4·25	

Withdrawn: 30.1.99

806 J.M.T. Bristol 4 Tonner, 1923

807 Safety Coach Service Regent Double Decker, 1934

808 Slade's Dennis Lancet, *circa* 1936

809 Tantivy Leyland PLSC, Lion, 1947

810 J.B.S. Morris, *circa* 1958

811 J.M.T. Titan TD4 Double Decker, *circa* 1961

75th Anniversary of Jersey Motor Transport Company. Buses (1st series)

(Des A. Copp. Litho B.D.T.)

1998 (2 APR). Perf 14 (C)

844	**806**	20p multicoloured	55	50
		a. Booklet pane. Nos. 844/5, each ×3, with margins all round	2·50	
		b. Booklet pane. Nos. 844/9, with margins all round	4·50	
845	**807**	24p multicoloured	65	50
846	**808**	31p multicoloured	75	70
		a. Booklet pane. Nos. 846/7, each ×3, with margins all round	4·00	
847	**809**	37p multicoloured	1·00	1·00
848	**810**	43p multicoloured	1·10	1·10
		a. Booklet pane. Nos. 848/9, each ×3, with margins all round	6·50	
849	**811**	63p multicoloured	1·50	1·40
844/9		Set of 6	5·00	4·75
		First Day Cover		5·75
		Presentation Pack	5·75	

Plate Nos.: 20p, 24p 1A, 1B (each ×4); others 1A (×4)

Sheets: 20 (4×5)

Imprint: Central, left-hand margin

Withdrawn: 30.4.99 (sheets)

812 Creative Arts Festival

813 Jazz Festival

814 Good Food Festival

815 Floral Festival

Europa. National Festivals

(Des A. Copp. Litho Enschedé)

1998 (2 APR). Perf 14×13½ (C)

850	**812**	20p multicoloured	65	45
851	**813**	24p multicoloured	70	55
852	**814**	31p multicoloured	90	1·00
853	**815**	63p multicoloured	1·70	1·90
850/3		Set of 4	3·50	3·50
		First Day Cover		4·00
		Presentation Pack	4·00	

Nos. 851/2 include the 'EUROPA' emblem.

Plate Nos.: All values 1A, 1B (each ×4)

Sheets: 10 (5×2)

Imprint: Bottom, left-hand corner margin

Withdrawn: 30.4.99

816 Hobie Cat and *Duke of Normandy* (launch)

817 Hobie Cat with White, Yellow, Red and Green Sails

818 Hobie Cats with Pink, Purple and Orange Sails

819 Bow of Hobie Cat with Yellow, Blue and Purple Sail

820 Hobie Cat Heeling

821 Yacht with Red, White and Blue Spinnaker

822 Yacht with Pink Spinnaker

823 Yacht with Two White Sails

824 Trimaran

825 Yacht with Blue, White and Yellow Spinnaker in Foreground

Jersey Yachting (1st issue). Opening of Elizabeth Marina, St. Helier

(Des A. Theobald. Litho Cartor)

1998 (15 MAY). Perf 13 (C)

854	**816**	20p multicoloured	40	20
		a. *Horiz strip of 5. Nos. 854/8* .	2·50	2·50
855	**817**	20p multicoloured	40	20
856	**818**	20p multicoloured	40	20
857	**819**	20p multicoloured	40	20
858	**820**	20p multicoloured	40	20
859	**821**	24p multicoloured	45	25
		a. *Horiz strip of 5. Nos. 859/63*	3·00	3·00
860	**822**	24p multicoloured	45	25
861	**823**	24p multicoloured	45	25
862	**824**	24p multicoloured	45	25
863	**825**	24p multicoloured	45	25
854/63		*Set of 10*	5·00	5·00
		First Day Cover		6·00
		Presentation Pack	6·00	

Plate Nos.: Both values 1A (×4)

Sheets: 20 (5×4), the designs were each printed together, *se-tenant*, in horizontal strips of five throughout the sheets, each strip forming a composite design

Imprint: Central, left-hand margin

Withdrawn: 31.5.99

826 Bass

827 Red Gurnard

828 Skate

829 Mackerel

830 Tope

831 Cuckoo Wrasse

377

International Year of the Ocean. Fishes

(Des W. Oliver. Litho B.D.T.)

1998 (11 AUG). Perf 15×14 (C)

864	**826**	20p multicoloured	....	50	50
865	**827**	24p multicoloured	....	65	65
866	**828**	31p multicoloured	....	80	80
867	**829**	37p multicoloured	....	1·00	1·00
868	**830**	43p multicoloured	....	1·10	1·10
869	**831**	63p multicoloured	....	1·50	1·50
864/9		Set of 6	....	5·00	5·00
		First Day Cover	....		6·00
		Presentation Pack	....	6·00	

Plate Nos.: 20p, 24p 1A, 1B (each ×4); others 1A (×4)

Sheets: 20 (4×5)

Imprint: Central, left-hand margin

Withdrawn: 31.8.99

832 Cider-making

833 Potato Barrels on Cart

834 Collecting Seaweed for Fertiliser

835 Milking Jersey Cows

Days Gone By

(Des A. Copp. Litho SNP Cambec, Melbourne)

1998 (11 AUG). *Self-adhesive. With copyright symbol after date.* Perf 11½×11 (Die-cut)

870	**832**	(20p) multicoloured (abcde)	.....	90	90
871	**833**	(20p) multicoloured (abcde)	.....	90	90
872	**834**	(20p) multicoloured (abcde)	.....	90	90
873	**835**	(20p) multicoloured (abcde)	.....	90	90
870/3		Set of 4	....	3·25	3·25
		First Day Cover	....		3·50
		Presentation Pack	....	3·25	

Nos. 870/3, which are inscribed 'BAILIWICK MINIMUM POSTAGE PAID' and were initially sold at 20p each, come, *se-tenant*, in strips of 4 or rolls of 100 with the surplus self-adhesive paper around each stamp removed.

Initially released with "1998" imprint dates, Nos. 870/3 were subsequently reissued inscribed "1999" (price per set, unused or used, £18), "2000" (price £16), 2001 (price £10) and 2003 (price £6).

Printings: (a) 11.8.98, Inscr '1998'; (b) 16.7.99. Inscr '1999'; (c) 3.11.2000. Inscr '2000'; (d) 19.11.2001. Inscr '2001'; (e) 4.4.2003. Inscr '2003'

836 Irises

837 Carnations

838 Chrysanthemums

839 Pinks

840 Roses

841 Lilies

842a Lilium 'Star Gazer'
(illustration reduced. Actual size 150×100 mm)

Flowers

(Des Wendy Tait. Litho Questa)

1998 (23 OCT). Perf 14×13½ (No. **MS**880) or 14½ (others), both comb

874	**836**	20p multicoloured	....	50	40
875	**837**	24p multicoloured	....	60	50
876	**838**	31p multicoloured	....	75	70
877	**839**	37p multicoloured	....	90	90

878	**840**	43p multicoloured	1·00	1·10
879	**841**	63p multicoloured	1·40	1·50
874/9		Set of 6	4·75	4·75
		First Day Cover		5·50
		Presentation Pack	5·50	
MS880	150×100 mm. **842a** £1.50, mult . . .		3·25	3·75
		First Day Cover		4·50
		Presentation Pack	4·50	

No. **MS**880 includes the 'ITALIA '98' stamp exhibition emblem on the margin.

Plate Nos.: 20p, 24p 1A, 1B (each ×4); 31p, 37p 1A (×4); 43p, 63p 1A, 1B, 1C (each ×4)

Sheets: 20 (4×5)

Imprint: Central, left-hand margin

Withdrawn: 30.10.99

843 Central Market Crib

844 St. Thomas's Church Crib

845 Trinity Parish Church Crib

846 Royal Square Crib

Christmas. Cribs

(Des Colleen Corlett. Litho Cartor)

1998 (10 NOV). Perf 13 (C)

881	**843**	20p multicoloured	40	40
882	**844**	24p multicoloured	50	55
883	**845**	31p multicoloured	65	65
884	**846**	63p multicoloured	1·50	1·60
881/4		Set of 4	2·75	3·00
		First Day Cover		4·00
		Presentation Pack	4·00	

Plate Nos.: All values 1A (×4)

Sheets: 20 (4×5)

Imprint: Central, left-hand margin

Withdrawn: 30.11.99

Year Pack 1998

1998 (10 NOV). *Comprises Nos. 775/7, 781/2, 785/6, 790/2, 795, 797/8, 800/1, 804 and* **MS**843/84

Year Pack . . . . 45·00

Sold out: By 7.04

Post Office Yearbook

1998 (10 NOV). *Comprises Nos. 775/7, 781/2, 785/6, 790/2, 795, 797/8, 800/1, 804 and* **MS**843/84

Yearbook . . . . 45·00

Sold out: By 7.04

847a Rabbit
(*illustration reduced. Actual size* 110×75 *mm*)

Chinese New Year ('Year of the Rabbit')

(Des V. Ambrus. Litho Questa)

1999 (16 FEB). *Sheet* 110×75 *mm. Perf* 14×13½ (C)

MS885	**847a**	£1 multicoloured	2·50	2·75
		First Day Cover		4·00
		Presentation Pack	3·75	

Withdrawn: 29.2.2000

848 Jersey Eastern Railway Mail Train

849 *Brighton* (paddle-steamer)

850 De Havilland D.H.86 Dragon Express at Jersey Airport

851 Jersey Postal Service Morris Minor Van

125th Anniversary of Universal Postal Union

(Des A. Theobald. Litho B.D.T.)

1999 (16 FEB). Perf 14 (C)

886	**848**	20p multicoloured	....	55	50
887	**849**	24p multicoloured	....	65	60
888	**850**	43p multicoloured	....	95	1·10
889	**851**	63p multicoloured	....	1·40	1·70
886/9		Set of 4	....	3·25	3·50
		First Day Cover	....		4·50
		Presentation Pack	....	4·50	

Plate Nos.: All values 1A (×4)

Sheets: 20 (4×5)

Imprint: Central, left-hand margin

Withdrawn: 29.2.2000

852 Jessie Eliza, St.
Catherine

853 Alexander Coutanche,
St. Helier

175th Anniversary of Royal National Lifeboat Institution

(Litho Questa)

1999 (16 FEB). Perf 14½ (C)

890	**852**	75p multicoloured	....	2·00	80
		a. Horiz pair. Nos. 890/1	......	4·50	4·50
891	**853**	£1 multicoloured	....	2·50	1·00
890/1		Set of 2	....	4·50	4·50
		First Day Cover	....		5·00
		Presentation Pack	....	5·00	

Plate Nos.: 1A, 1B (each ×7)

Sheets: 20 (4×5), the two values printed together, *se-tenant*, in horizontal pairs throughout the sheet

Imprint: Central, left-hand margin

Withdrawn: 29.2.2000

854 Cymbidium
Maufant
'Jersey'

855 Miltonia
Millbrook
'Jersey'

856 Paphiopedilum
Transvaal

857 Paphiopedilum
Elizabeth
Castle

858 Calanthe Five
Oaks

859 Cymbidium
Icho Tower
'Trinity'

860a Miltonia Portelet
(*illustration reduced. Actual size 150×100 mm*)

Jersey Orchids (4th series)

(Litho Enschedé)

1999 (19 MAR). Perf 13½ (No. **MS**898) or 14×13, both comb

892	**854**	21p multicoloured	....	55	50
893	**855**	25p multicoloured	....	55	50
894	**856**	31p multicoloured	....	75	70
895	**857**	37p multicoloured	....	85	80
896	**858**	43p multicoloured	....	90	90
897	**859**	63p multicoloured	....	2·00	2·00
892/7		Set of 6	....	5·00	5·00
		First Day Cover	....		5·50
		Presentation Pack	....	5·50	

MS898 150×100 mm. **860a** £1.50, mult . . . 4·00   4·50
     First Day Cover . . . .   6·00
     Presentation Pack . . . . 4·50

No. **MS**898 also includes the 'Australia '99' World Stamp Exhibition, Melbourne, emblem on the margin at top left.

Plate Nos.: 21p, 25p 1A, 1B (each ×5); others 1A (×5)

Sheets: 20 (5×4)

Imprint: Central, left-hand margin

Withdrawn: 31.3.2000

861 Howard Davis Park

862 Sir Winston Churchill Memorial Park

863 Coronation Park

864 La Collette Gardens

Europa. Parks and Gardens

(Des Ariel Luke. Litho Cartor)

1999 (27 APR). Perf 13×13½ (C)

899	**861**	21p multicoloured	50	50
900	**862**	25p multicoloured	70	70
901	**863**	31p multicoloured	1·00	1·00
902	**864**	63p multicoloured	2·00	2·00
899/902		*Set of 4*	4·00	4·00
		First Day Cover		4·50
		Presentation Pack . . . . 4·50		

Nos. 900/1 include the 'EUROPA' logo at top left and all four values show the 'ibra '99' International Stamp Exhibition, Nuremberg, emblem at top right.

Plate Nos.: All values 1A (×4)

Sheets: 10 (2×5)

Imprint: Central, left-hand margin

Withdrawn: 29.4.2000

865 Prince Edward and Miss Sophie Rhys-Jones

Royal Wedding

(Des A. Copp. Litho Questa)

1999 (19 JUNE). Perf 14½ (C)

903	**865**	35p mult (yellow background) . . .	60	35
		a. Pair. Nos. 903/4	2·20	2·20
904		35p mult (blue background)	60	35
903/4		*Set of 2*	2·20	2·20
		First Day Cover		2·75
		Presentation Pack . . . . 3·00		

Plate Nos.: 1A, 1B, 1C, 1D (each ×4)

Sheets: 20 (4×5) with the two designs printed together, *se-tenant*, in horizontal or vertical pairs throughout the sheet

Imprint: Central, left-hand margin

Withdrawn: 30.6.2000

866 Jersey-built Benz, 1899

867 Star Tourer, 1910

868 Citroen 'Traction Avant', 1938

869 Talbot BG110 Tourer, 1937

870 Morris Cowley Six Special Coupé, 1934

871 Ford Anglia Saloon, 1946

Vintage Cars (3rd series). Centenary of Motoring in Jersey

(Des A. Copp. Litho B.D.T.)

1999 (2 JULY). Perf 14 (C)

905	**866**	21p multicoloured	45	45
		a. Booklet pane. Nos. 905/6,		
		each ×3, with margins all		
		round	2·75	
		b. Booklet pane. Nos. 905/10,		
		with margins all round	5·00	

906	**867**	25p multicoloured	. . . .	55	55
907	**868**	31p multicoloured	. . . .	65	65
		a. Booklet pane. Nos. 907/8, each ×3, with margins all round	. . . .	5·00	
908	**869**	37p multicoloured	. . . .	1·00	1·00
909	**870**	43p multicoloured	. . . .	1·20	1·20
		a. Booklet pane. Nos. 909/10, each ×3, with margins all round	. . . .	8·00	
910	**871**	63p multicoloured	. . . .	1·50	1·50
905/10		Set of 6	. . . .	5·00	5·00
		First Day Cover	. . . .		5·50
		Presentation Pack	. . . .	5·50	

Nos. 905a/b, 907a and 909a also include the 'PhilexFrance 99' International Stamp Exhibition emblem on the margins at top right.

Plate Nos.: 21p, 25p 1A, 1B (each ×4); others 1A (×4)

Sheets: 20 (4×5)

Imprint: Central, left-hand margin

Withdrawn: 31.7.2000 (sheets)

Small Mammals

(Des W. Oliver. Litho Cartor)

1999 (21 AUG). Perf 13½×13 (C)

911	**872**	21p multicoloured	. . . .	45	45
912	**873**	25p multicoloured	. . . .	55	55
913	**874**	31p multicoloured	. . . .	65	65
914	**875**	37p multicoloured	. . . .	1·00	1·10
915	**876**	43p multicoloured	. . . .	1·00	1·10
916	**877**	63p multicoloured	. . . .	2·00	2·20
911/16		Set of 6	. . . .	5·25	5·50
		First Day Cover	. . . .		6·00
		Presentation Pack	. . . .	6·00	

No. 913 is inscribed 'Pipestrelle' in error.

Plate Nos.: All values 1A (×4)

Sheets: 20 (4×5)

Imprint: Central, left-hand margin

Withdrawn: 31.8.2000

872 West European Hedgehog

873 Eurasian Red Squirrel

874 Nathusius Pipistrelle

875 Jersey Bank Vole

876 Lesser White-toothed Shrew

877 Common Mole

878 Gorey Pierhead Light

879 La Corbiere

880 Noirmont Point

881 Demie de Pas

882 Greve d'Azette

883 Sorel Point

150th Anniversary of First Lighthouse on Jersey (First Series)

(Des A. Copp. Litho Walsall)

1999 (5 OCT). Perf 14 (C)
917	**878**	21p multicoloured	45	45
918	**879**	25p multicoloured	55	55
919	**880**	34p multicoloured	75	75
920	**881**	38p multicoloured	1·00	1·00
921	**882**	44p multicoloured	1·20	1·20
922	**883**	64p multicoloured	2·00	2·00
917/22		Set of 6	5·50	5·50
		First Day Cover		6·00
		Presentation Pack	6·00	

Plate Nos.: All values 1A, 1B (each ×4)

Sheets: 20 (5×4)

Imprint: Central, left-hand margin

Withdrawn: 31.10.2000

See also Nos. 1086/91

884 Mistletoe

885 Holly

886 Ivy

887 Christmas Rose

Christmas. Festive Foliage

(Des Colleen Corlett. Litho B.D.T.)

1999 (9 NOV). Perf 14 (C)
923	**884**	21p multicoloured	45	45
924	**885**	25p multicoloured	55	55
925	**886**	34p multicoloured	1·10	75
926	**887**	64p multicoloured	1·60	2·00
923/6		Set of 4	3·50	3·50
		First Day Cover		4·50
		Presentation Pack	4·50	

Plate Nos.: All values 1A, 1B (each ×4)

Sheets: 20 (5×4)

Imprint: Central, left-hand margin

Withdrawn: 30.11.2000

Year Pack 1999

1999 (1 DEC). *Comprises Nos. 783, 787/9, 793/4, 799, 802 and* **MS**885/926

Year Pack .... 48·00

Post Office Yearbook

1999 (1 DEC). *Comprises Nos. 783, 787/9, 793/4, 799, 802 and* **MS**885/926

Yearbook .... 50·00

Sold out: By 11.03

888 Jersey Crest

New Millennium

(Des A. Copp. Litho, die-stamped and embossed Cartor)

2000 (1 JAN). Perf 13½ (C)
927	**888**	£10 gold, bright red and deep carmine	20·00	20·00
		First Day Cover		23·00
		Presentation Pack	21·00	

The printing of No. 927 incorporates metallic die-stamping and embossing using 22 carat gold.

No. 927 was retained in use as a definitive stamp.

Plate Nos.: 1A (×3)

Sheets: 10 (5×2)

Imprint: Upper left-hand margin

889a Dragon
(*illustration reduced. Actual size* 110×75 mm)

Chinese New Year ('Year of the Dragon')

(Des V. Ambrus. Litho Questa)

2000 (5 FEB). *Sheet* 110×75 *mm.* Perf 14½×13½ (C)

MS928	889a	£1 multicoloured	3·00	3·00
		First Day Cover		4·00
		Presentation Pack	4·00	

Withdrawn: 29.2.2001

890 'Ocean Adventure' (Gemma Carré)

891 'Solar Power' (Chantal Varley-Best)

892 'Floating City and Space Cars' (Nicola Singleton)

893 'Conservation' (Carly Logan)

'Stampin' the Future' (children's stamp design competition) Winners

(Litho Questa)

2000 (9 MAY). Perf 14 (C)

929	890	22p multicoloured	65	65
930	891	22p multicoloured	65	65
931	892	22p multicoloured	65	65
932	893	22p multicoloured	65	65
929/32		Set of 4	2·40	2·40
		First Day Cover		3·50
		Presentation Pack	3·50	
MS933		150×100 mm. Nos. 929/32	3·00	3·50
		First Day Cover		5·00
		Presentation Pack	5·00	

Plate Nos.: All designs 1A (×4)

Sheets: 10 (2×5)

Imprint: Central, left-hand margin

Withdrawn: 31.5.2001

894 'Jersey in Europe'

895 'Building Europe'

Europa

(Des A. Copp (26p), J.-P. Cousin (34p). Litho Cartor)

2000 (9 MAY). Perf 13½×13 (C)

934	894	26p multicoloured	2·00	2·00
935	895	34p multicoloured	3·00	3·50
934/5		Set of 2	4·50	4·75
		First Day Cover		6·00
		Presentation Pack	5·50	

Plate Nos.: Both values 1A (×4)

Sheets: 10 (2×5) 26p; (5×2) 34p

Imprint: Central, left-hand margin (26p); upper left-hand margin (34p)

Withdrawn: 31.5.2001

896 Roman Merchant Ship

897 Viking Longship

898 13th-century Warship

899 14th–15th century Merchant Ship

900 Tudor Warship

901 17th-century Warship

902 18th-century Naval Cutter

903 19th-century Barque

904 19th-century Oyster Cutter

905 20th-century Ketch

'The Stamp Show 2000' International Stamp Exhibition, London. Maritime Heritage

(Des A. Theobald. Litho B.D.T.)

2000 (22 MAY). Perf 14×13½ (C)

936	**896**	22p multicoloured	45	25
		a. Horiz strip of 5. *Nos.* 936/40	3·00	3·00
		b. Booklet pane. Nos. 936/9 *and* 941/4	4·50	
		c. Booklet pane. Nos. 936/7, 939/41 *and* 943/5	4·50	
		d. Booklet pane. Nos. 936, 938/42 *and* 944/5	4·50	
		e. Booklet pane. Nos. 936/8, 940/3 *and* 945	4·50	
937	**897**	22p multicoloured	45	25
		a. Booklet pane. Nos. 937/40 *and* 942/5	4·50	
938	**898**	22p multicoloured	45	25
939	**899**	22p multicoloured	45	25
940	**900**	22p multicoloured	45	25
941	**901**	26p multicoloured	50	30
		a. Horiz strip of 5. *Nos.* 941/5 .	3·25	3·25
942	**902**	26p multicoloured	50	30
943	**903**	26p multicoloured	50	30
944	**904**	26p multicoloured	50	30
945	**905**	26p multicoloured	50	30
936/45		*Set of* 10	6·00	6·00
		First Day Cover		6·50
		First Day Covers (set of 5 *booklet panes)*		31·00
		Presentation Pack	6·50	
		Souvenir Folder	13·00	
MS946		174×104 mm. Nos. 936/45	6·00	6·00
		First Day Cover		7·00
		Presentation Pack	7·00	
		a. With 'The Stamp Show 2000' logo added to top margin	6·00	6·00
		First Day Cover		7·00
		Presentation Pack	7·00	

Plate Nos.: Both values and miniature sheet 1A (×5)

Sheet: 10 (5×2). The five designs for each value printed together, *se-tenant*, in horizontal strips of 5 throughout the sheets, with 'The Stamp Show 2000' logo on the bottom sheet margin

Withdrawn: 31.5.2001 (sheets)

906 Bottle-nosed Dolphins

907 Long-finned Pilot Whales

908 Common Porpoises

909 Grey Seals

910 Risso's Dolphins

911 White-beaked Dolphin

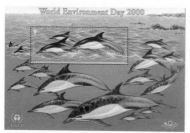

912a Common Dolphins
(illustration reduced. Actual size 150×100 mm)

World Environment Day. Marine Mammals

(Des W. Oliver. Litho B.D.T.)

2000 (5 JUNE). Perf 15×14 (C)

947	**906**	22p multicoloured	50	55
948	**907**	26p multicoloured	55	60
949	**908**	34p multicoloured	80	85
950	**909**	38p multicoloured	1·00	1·10
951	**910**	44p multicoloured	1·10	1·20
952	**911**	64p multicoloured	1·50	1·70
947/52		*Set of 6*	5·00	5·50
		First Day Cover		6·00
		Presentation Pack	6·50	
MS953		150×100 mm. **912a** £1·50, multicoloured	4·00	4·50
		First Day Cover		6·00
		Presentation Pack	6·00	

Plate Nos.: All values 1A, 1B, 1C (each ×4)

Sheets: 10 (2×5)

Imprint: Central, left-hand margin

Withdrawn: 30.6.2001

913 Prince William and Alps

914 Prince William and Polo Player

915 Prince William and Beaumaris Castle

916 Prince William and Fireworks

18th Birthday of Prince William

(Des W. Wall. Litho Questa)

2000 (21 JUNE). Perf 14½ (C)

954	**913**	75p multicoloured	1·50	1·50
955	**914**	75p multicoloured	1·50	1·50
956	**915**	75p multicoloured	1·50	1·50
957	**916**	75p multicoloured	1·50	1·50
954/7		*Set of 4*	6·00	6·00
		First Day Cover		7·00
		Presentation Pack	6·75	

Plate Nos.: All designs 1A (×4)

Sheets: 10 (2×5)

Imprint: Central, left-hand margin

Withdrawn: 30.6.2001

'World Stamp Expo 2000', Anaheim, U.S.A.

(Litho B.D.T.)

2000 (7 JULY). *As No.* MS953, *but with multicoloured exhibition logo added to top left corner of sheet margin.* Perf 15×14 (C)

MS958	150×100 mm. **912a** £1·50, multicoloured	4·00	4·00
	First Day Cover		6·00

Withdrawn: 31.7.2001

917 Queen Elizabeth the Queen Mother with Roses

918 Queen Elizabeth the Queen Mother with Daisies

Queen Elizabeth the Queen Mother's 100th Birthday

(Des Colleen Corlett. Litho and die-stamped Questa)

2000 (4 AUG). Perf 14½ (C)

959	**917**	50p multicoloured	1·20	1·20
960	**918**	50p multicoloured	1·20	1·20
959/60		*Set of 2*	2·50	2·50
		First Day Cover		3·25
		Presentation Pack	3·25	
MS961		150×100 mm. Nos. 959/60	2·50	3·00
		First Day Cover		4·50
		Presentation Pack	3·50	
		Souvenir Folder (containing **MS**961, *first day cover and presentation pack)*	16·00	

Plate Nos.: Both designs 1A (×6)

Sheets: 10 (5×2)

Imprint: Bottom margin

Withdrawn: 31.8.2001

919 Supermarine Spitfire
Mk Ia

920 Hawker Hurricane
Mk I

921 Bristol Blenheim
Mk IV

922 Vickers Wellington
Mk Ic

923 Boulton Paul Defiant
Mk I

924 Short Sunderland
Mk I

60th Anniversary of Battle of Britain

(Des A. Theobald. Litho Questa B.D.T.)

2000 (15 SEPT). Perf 14 (C)

962	**919**	22p multicoloured	50	55
963	**920**	26p multicoloured	60	65
964	**921**	36p multicoloured	80	85
965	**922**	40p multicoloured	90	95
966	**923**	45p multicoloured	1·00	1·10
967	**924**	65p multicoloured	1·50	1·60
962/7		Set of 6	4·75	5·00
		First Day Cover		5·50
		Presentation Pack	6·00	

Plate Nos.: All values 1A

Sheets: 10 (2×5)

Imprint: Bottom margin

Withdrawn: 29.9.2001

925 Virgin Mary

926 Shepherd

927 Angel

928 Magi with Gift

Christmas. Children's Nativity Play

(Des F. Venton. Litho Cartor)

2000 (7 NOV). Perf 13 (C)

968	**925**	22p multicoloured	55	55
969	**926**	26p multicoloured	65	65
970	**927**	36p multicoloured	1·00	1·00
971	**928**	65p multicoloured	1·60	1·60
968/71		Set of 4	3·50	3·50
		First Day Cover		4·50
		Presentation Pack	4·50	

Plate Nos.: All values 1A (each ×4)

Sheets: 10 (5×2)

Imprint: Bottom margin

Withdrawn: 30.11.2001

Year Pack 2000

2000 (1 DEC). *Comprises Nos.* 927/32, 934/45, 947/57 and 959/71

Year Pack .... 50·00

Sold out: By 4.05

Post Office Yearbook

2000 (1 DEC). *Comprises Nos.* 927/32, 934/45, 947/57 and 959/71

Yearbook .... 55·00

Sold out: By 8.05

929a Snake
(illustration reduced. Actual size 110×75 mm)

Chinese New Year ('Year of the Snake')

(Des V. Ambrus. Litho Questa)

2001 (24 JAN). *Sheet* 110×75 *mm. Perf* 14×13½ (C)
MS972 **929a** £1 multicoloured .... 2·75 3·00
First Day Cover .... 4·50
Presentation Pack .... 4·75

Withdrawn: 31.1.2002

930 *Rose* (1851–61)

931 *Comete* (1856–67)

932 *Cygne* (1894–1912)

933 *Victoria* (1896–1918)

934 *Attala* (1920–25)

935 *Brittany* (1933–62)

Maritime Links with France. Mail Packet Ships

(Des I. Boyd. Litho Cartor)

2001 (24 JAN). Perf 13×13½ (C)

973	**930**	22p multicoloured		50	55
974	**931**	26p multicoloured		60	65
975	**932**	36p multicoloured		80	85
976	**933**	40p multicoloured		90	95
977	**934**	45p multicoloured		1·20	1·30
978	**935**	65p multicoloured		1·70	1·80
973/8		Set of 6		5·25	5·50
		First Day Cover			6·00
		Presentation Pack	6·00		

Plate Nos.: All values 1A (×4)

Sheets: 10 (2×5)

Imprint: Central, left-hand margin

Withdrawn: 31.1.2002

936 H.H.S. *Jersey* (4th Rate), 1654–91

937 H.M.S. *Jersey* (6th Rate), 1694–98

938 H.M.S. *Jersey* (4th Rate), 1698–1731

939 H.M.S. *Jersey* (4th Rate), 1736–83

940 H.M.S. *Jersey* (cutter), 1860–73

941 H.M.S. *Jersey* (destroyer), 1938–41

Jersey Naval Connections (1st series). Royal Navy Ships named after Jersey

(Des A. Theobald. Litho B.D.T.)

2001 (3 APR). Perf 14 (C)

979	**936**	23p multicoloured		50	55
980	**937**	26p multicoloured		60	65
981	**938**	37p multicoloured		80	85

982	**939**	41p multicoloured	. . . .	1·00	95
983	**940**	46p multicoloured	. . . .	1·20	1·10
984	**941**	66p multicoloured	. . . .	1·50	1·60
979/84		*Set of* 6	. . . .	5·00	5·00
		First Day Cover	. . . .		6·00
		Presentation Pack	. . . .	5·50	

Plate Nos.: 23p, 26p 1A, 1B (each ×4); others 1A (×4)

Sheets: 10 (2×5)

Imprint: Bottom, left-hand corner margin

Withdrawn: 30.4.2002

942 Jersey Cows

943 Potatoes

944 Tomatoes

945 Cauliflower and Purple-sprouting Broccoli

946 Peppers and Courgettes

Jersey Cows and Farm Produce

(Des Colleen Corlett. Litho SNP Ausprint, Melbourne)

2001 (3 APR). *Self-adhesive.* Perf 11½ (C)

985	**942**	(26p) multicoloured (*abcd*)	. . . . . .	1·80	1·80
986	**943**	(26p) multicoloured (*abcd*)	. . . . . .	1·80	1·80
987	**944**	(26p) multicoloured (*abcd*)	. . . . . .	1·80	1·80
988	**945**	(26p) multicoloured (*abcd*)	. . . . . .	1·80	1·80
989	**946**	(26p) multicoloured (*abcd*)	. . . . . .	1·80	1·80
985/9		*Set of* 5	. . . .	9·00	9·00
		First Day Cover	. . . .		9·00
		Presentation Pack	. . . .	11·00	

Nos. 985/9, which are inscribed 'UK MINIMUM POSTAGE PAID' and were initially sold at 26p each, come, *se-tenant*, in strips of 5 or rolls of 100 with the surplus self-adhesive paper around each stamp removed.

Initially released with "2001" imprint dates (price per set, £10 unused, £11 used), Nos. 985/9 were subsequently reissued inscribed "2002" (price, unused or used, £9), "2003" (price, unused or used, £8) and "2005" (price £7).

Printings: (*a*) 3.4.2001. Inscr '2001'; (*b*) 4.10.2002. Inscr '2002'; (*c*) 4.4.2003. Inscr '2003'; (*d*) 21.10.2005. Inscr '2005'

947 Queen Elizabeth II

75th Birthday of Queen Elizabeth II

(Des W. Wall. Litho Questa)

2001 (21 APR). Perf 14×15 (C)

990	**947**	£3 multicoloured	. . . .	6·00	6·50
		First Day Cover	. . . .		7·00
		Presentation Pack	. . . .	7·00	

No. 990 was retained in use as part of the current definitive series.

Plate Nos.: 1A, 1B, 1C, 1D, 1E, 1F (each ×4)

Sheets: 10 (2×5)

Imprint: Bottom margin

Withdrawn: 30.11.2008

948 Agile Frog

949 Trout

950 White Water-Lily

951 Common Blue Damselfly

952 Palmate Newt

953 Tufted Duck

389

954a Common Kingfisher
(*illustration reduced. Actual size* 150×100 *mm*)

Europa. Water, a Natural Treasure. Pond Life

(Des N. Parlett. Litho B.D.T.)

2001 (22 MAY). Perf 14 (No. **MS**997) or 14½×14 (others), both comb

991	**948**	23p multicoloured	60	65
992	**949**	26p multicoloured	70	75
993	**950**	37p multicoloured	1·00	1·10
994	**951**	41p multicoloured	1·10	1·20
995	**952**	46p multicoloured	1·20	1·40
996	**953**	66p multicoloured	2·00	2·20
991/6		Set of 6	6·00	6·50
		First Day Cover		7·00
		Presentation Pack	7·00	
MS997		150×100 mm. **954a** £1.50, multi-coloured	5·00	5·00
		First Day Cover		5·50
		Presentation Pack	5·25	

The 26p and 37p values include the 'EUROPA' emblem.

Plate Nos.: All values 1A, 1B (each ×4)

Sheets: 10 (2×5)

Imprint: Central, left-hand margin

Withdrawn: 31.5.2002

955 Long-eared Owl

956 Peregrine Falcon

957 Short-eared Owl

958 Western Marsh Harrier

959 Northern Sparrow Hawk

960 Tawny Owl

'Belgica 2001' International Stamp Exhibition, Brussels

(Litho B.D.T.)

2001 (9 JUNE). *No.* **MS**997 *optd* 'JERSEY AT BELGICA 2001' *on sheet margin.* Perf 14 (C)

MS998	**954a**	£1.50, multicoloured	5·00	4·50
		First Day Cover		5·50
		Presentation Pack	5·50	

Withdrawn: 29.6.2002

961a Barn Owl
(*illustration reduced. Actual size* 110×75 *mm*)

Birds of Prey

(Des M. Chester. Litho Cartor)

2001 (3 JULY). Perf 13½×13 (C)

999	**955**	23p multicoloured	50	55
		a. Booklet pane. Nos. 999/ 1004	3·75	
		b. Booklet pane. Nos. 999, 1001 and 1004, each ×2 . .	4·25	
		c. Booklet pane. Nos. 999 ×2, 1000/1 and 1003 ×2	3·25	
		d. Booklet pane. Nos. 999/ 1001, 1002 ×2 and 1004 .	4·00	
1000	**956**	26p multicoloured	60	65
1001	**957**	37p multicoloured	80	85
1002	**958**	41p multicoloured	1·00	95
1003	**959**	46p multicoloured	1·20	1·10
1004	**960**	66p multicoloured	1·50	1·60
999/1004		Set of 6	5·00	5·00
		First Day Cover		6·00
		Presentation Pack	5·75	
MS1005		110×75 mm. **961a** £1.50, multi-coloured	5·00	5·00
		a. Booklet pane. As No. **MS**1005, but 153×100 mm with line of roulettes at left	9·00	9·50
		First Day Cover		6·50
		Presentation Pack	6·50	

Nos. 999a/d each have margins all round and a bird illustration on the tab at left.

No. **MS**1005a also differs from the normal miniature sheet by the owl on the post being centred on the stamp. No. **MS**1005 shows the '£1.5' of the face value across the post, but on the booklet pane the figures are to the right of the post.

Plate Nos.: All values 1A (×4)

Sheets: 10 (5×2)

Imprint: Bottom margin

Withdrawn: 31.7.2002 (sheets)

962a *Jersey Clipper* (yacht)
(*illustration reduced. Actual size* 150×100 *mm*)

The Times Clipper 2000 Round the World Yacht Race

(Des B. Ozard. Litho Questa)

2001 (17 SEPT). *Sheet* 150×100 *mm*. Perf 13½×14 (C)

MS1006	**962a**	£1.50, multicoloured	4·00	5·00
		First Day Cover		6·00
		Presentation Pack	5·50	

Withdrawn: 30.9.2002

963 Tilley 26 Manual Fire Engine, *circa* 1845   **964** Albion Merryweather, *circa* 1935

965 Dennis Ace, *circa* 1940   **966** Dennis F8 Pump Escape, *circa* 1952

967 Landrover Merry-weather, *circa* 1968   **968** Dennis Carmichael, *circa* 1989

Centenary of Jersey Fire and Rescue Service. Fire Engines

(Des A. Copp. Litho Cartor)

2001 (25 SEPT). Perf 13×13½ (C)

1007	**963**	23p multicoloured	50	55
1008	**964**	26p multicoloured	60	65
1009	**965**	37p multicoloured	80	85
1010	**966**	41p multicoloured	90	95
1011	**967**	46p multicoloured	1·00	1·10
1012	**968**	66p multicoloured	1·50	1·60
1007/12		Set of 6	4·75	5·00
		First Day Cover		6·00
		Presentation Pack	6·00	

Plate Nos.: All values 1A (×4)

Sheets: 10 (2×5)

Imprint: Central, left-hand margin

Withdrawn: 30.9.2002

'Hafnia 01' International Stamp Exhibition, Copenhagen

(Litho Cartor)

2001 (16 OCT). *As No.* **MS**1005, *but with brown-red exhibition logo added to bottom left corner of sheet margin and additionally inscr* 'Jersey visits Hafnia 01 Denmark'. Perf 13½×13 (C)

MS1013	**961a**	£1.50, multicoloured	3·75	3·75
		First Day Cover		4·50
		Presentation Pack	4·50	

Withdrawn: 31.10.2002

969 Nativity

970 Street Decorations

971 Carol Singers with Hand Bells

972 Father Christmas

973 Christmas Tree Decorations

974 Adoration of the Shepherds

975 Carol Singers and Father Christmas in Sleigh

976 Paper Bell, Chains and Christmas Tree

977 Church Bells ringing

978 Christmas Cracker

Christmas. Bells

(Des M. Pollard. Litho SNP Ausprint, Melbourne)

2001 (6 NOV). *Self-adhesive.* Perf 11×11½ (die-cut)

1014	**969**	(23p) multicoloured (*abc*)	60	60
		a. Booklet pane. Nos. 1014, 1016/18, 1019/20 *and* 1022/3, *each* ×2 (*a*)	9·00	
1015	**970**	(23p) multicoloured (*abc*)	75	75
1016	**971**	(23p) multicoloured (*abc*)	60	60
1017	**972**	(23p) multicoloured (*abc*)	60	60
1018	**973**	(23p) multicoloured (*abc*)	60	60
1019	**974**	(26p) multicoloured (*ab*)	60	60
1020	**975**	(26p) multicoloured (*ab*)	60	60
1021	**976**	(26p) multicoloured (*ab*)	75	75
1022	**977**	(26p) multicoloured (*ab*)	60	60
1023	**978**	(26p) multicoloured (*ab*)	60	60
1014/23		Set of 10	6·00	6·00
		First Day Cover		7·00
		Presentation Pack	7·00	

Nos. 1014/18 are inscribed 'JERSEY MINIMUM POSTAGE PAID' and were initially sold for 23p, and Nos. 1019/23 are inscribed 'U.K. MINIMUM POSTAGE PAID' and were initially sold for 26p. The 5 designs for each value were printed together, *se-tenant*, in strips of 5 or rolls of 100. Nos. 1014, 1016/20 and 1022/3 also come from £3.92 booklets, containing pane No. 1014*a* on which the surplus self-adhesive paper was retained.

Initially released with "2001" imprint dates Nos. 1014/23 were subsequently reissued inscribed "2002" and 2003 (all the same price).

Printings: (*a*) 6.11.2001. Inscr '2001'; (*b*) 23.11.2002. Inscr '2002'; (*c*) 10.11.2003. Inscr '2003'

Sold out: By 6.2003 (booklets) or by end of 2005 (coils)

Post Office Yearbook

2001 (1 DEC). *Comprises Nos.* **MS**972/97, 999/1012 *and* 1014/23

	Yearbook	55·00

Sold out: By 7.1.2008

979 *Duchess of Normandy* (launch)

980 *Duke of Normandy* (tug)

981 *Challenger* (customs patrol boat)

982 *Le Fret* (pilot boat)

983 *Norman le Brocq* (fisheries protection vessel)

States Vessels

(Des A. Theobald. Litho Cartor)

2002 (22 JAN). Perf 13×13½ (C)

1024	**979**	23p multicoloured	50	55
1025	**980**	29p multicoloured	65	70
1026	**981**	38p multicoloured	80	85
1027	**982**	47p multicoloured	1·20	1·30
1028	**983**	68p multicoloured	1·70	1·90
1024/8		Set of 5	4·50	4·75
		First Day Cover		5·75
		Presentation Pack	5·75	

Plate Nos.: All values 1A (×4)
Sheets: 10 (2×5)
Imprint: Bottom, left-hand margin
Withdrawn: 31.1.2003

984 Queen Elizabeth in Coronation Robes (after Cecil Beaton)

Golden Jubilee

(Litho with gold and silver embossing Cartor)

2002 (6 FEB). Perf 13½ (C)

1029	**984**	£3 multicoloured	6·25	6·50
		First Day Cover		7·50
		Presentation Pack	6·75	

Plate Nos.: 1A (×5)
Sheets: 4 (2×2)
Imprint: Upper left-hand margin
Withdrawn: 28.2.2003

985a Horse
(*illustration reduced. Actual size* 110×75 *mm*)

Chinese New Year ('Year of the Horse')

(Des V. Ambrus. Litho Questa)

2002 (12 FEB). *Sheet* 110×75 *mm.* Perf 14×13½ (C)

MS1030	**985a**	£1 multicoloured	2·20	2·50
		First Day Cover		4·50
		Presentation Pack	4·50	

Withdrawn: 28.2.2003

986 Elephant Float, Parish of St. John, 1980

987 Clown with Red Hair, Grouville, 1996

988 Clown with White Hat, Optimists, 1988

989 Performing Seal, Grouville, 1996

Europa. Circus. Carnival Floats

(Des N. Shewring. Litho B.D.T.)

2002 (12 MAR). Perf 14 (C)

1031	**986**	23p multicoloured	50	55
1032	**987**	29p multicoloured	65	70

1033	**988**	38p multicoloured	....	1·00	1·10
1034	**989**	68p multicoloured	....	1·70	2·00
1031/4		Set of 4	....	3·50	4·00
		First Day Cover	....		4·50
		Presentation Pack	....	4·50	

The 29p and 38p values include the 'EUROPA' emblem.

Plate Nos.: All values 1A, 1B (each ×4)

Sheets: 10 (5×2)

Imprint: Bottom margin, right-hand side

Withdrawn: 31.3.2003

990 Aubrey Boomer   **991** Harry Vardon

992 Sir Henry Cotton   **993** Diagram of Golf Swing

994 Putting

Centenary of La Moye Golf Club

(Des Jennifer Toombs. Litho Questa)

2002 (16 APR). Perf 14 (C)

1035	**990**	23p multicoloured	....	50	55
1036	**991**	29p multicoloured	....	65	70
1037	**992**	38p multicoloured	....	80	85
1038	**993**	47p multicoloured	....	1·00	1·10
1039	**994**	68p multicoloured	....	1·50	1·70
1035/9		Set of 5	....	4·00	4·50
		First Day Cover	....		5·50
		Presentation Pack	....	5·50	

Plate Nos.: 23p, 29p 1A, 1B, 1C, 1D, 1E, 1F (each ×7); 38p 1A, 1B, 1C, 1D, 1E, 1F, 1G, 1H, 1J (each ×7); 47p, 68p 1A, 1B, 1C (each ×7)

Sheets: 10 (2×5) with enlarged illustrated right margins

Imprint: Lower left-hand margin

Withdrawn: 30.4.2003

995 Vauxhall 12, 1952   **996** Jaguar 2.4 MkII, 1959–60

997 Austin 1800 1972–73   **998** Ford Cortina MkIV, 1978

999 Honda ST 1100 Motorcycle, 1995–2000   **1000** Vauxhall Vectra, 1998–2000

50th Anniversary of States of Jersey Police. Patrol Vehicles

(Des A. Copp. Litho Cartor)

2002 (24 MAY). Perf 13 (C)

1040	**995**	23p multicoloured	....	50	55
1041	**996**	29p multicoloured	....	65	70
1042	**997**	38p multicoloured	....	80	85
1043	**998**	40p multicoloured	....	85	90
1044	**999**	47p multicoloured	....	1·00	1·10
1045	**1000**	68p multicoloured	....	1·50	1·70
1040/5		Set of 6	....	5·00	5·25
		First Day Cover	....		6·25
		Presentation Pack	....	6·00	

Plate Nos.: All values 1A (each ×4)

Sheets: 10 (2×5)

Imprint: Bottom, left-hand margin

Withdrawn: 31.5.2003

1001 Honey Bee   **1002** Seven-spot Ladybird

1003 Great Green Bush-cricket

1004 Greater Horn-tail

1005 Emperor Dragonfly

1006 Hawthorn Shield Bug

Insects (1st series)

(Des W. Oliver. Litho B.D.T.)

2002 (18 JUNE). Perf 15×14 (C)

1046	**1001**	23p multicoloured	. . . .	50	55
1047	**1002**	29p multicoloured	. . . .	65	70
1048	**1003**	38p multicoloured	. . . .	80	85
1049	**1004**	40p multicoloured	. . . .	85	90
1050	**1005**	47p multicoloured	. . . .	1·10	1·20
1051	**1006**	68p multicoloured	. . . .	1·50	1·70
1046/51		Set of 6	. . . .	4·75	5·50
		First Day Cover	. . . .		6·50
		Presentation Pack	. . . .	6·00	

Plate Nos.: All values 1A, 1B (each ×4)

Sheets: 10 (2×5)

Imprint: Bottom margin, left-hand corner

Withdrawn: 30.6.2003

1007 Queen Elizabeth the Queen Mother in 1910, 1923 and 2002

Queen Elizabeth the Queen Mother Commemoration

(Des W. Wall. Litho Questa)

2002 (4 AUG). Perf 14×15 (C)

1052	**1007**	£2 multicoloured	. . . .	4·25	4·50
		First Day Cover	. . . .		5·50
		Presentation Pack	. . . .	5·50	

Plate Nos.: 1A, 1B, 1C, 1D, 1E, 1F (each ×4)

Sheets: 10 (2×5)

Imprint: Lower left-hand margin

Withdrawn: 30.8.2003

1008 Hydrangeas

1009 Chrysanthemums

1010 Hare's Tails and Pampas Grasses

1011 Asters

1012 Carnations

1013 Gladioli

1014a 'Zanzibar' Float (winner of Prix d'Honneur, 1999)
(*illustration reduced. Actual size 150×100 mm*)

Centenary of 'Battle of Flowers' Parade

(Des M. Pollard. Litho Cartor)

2002 (8 AUG). Perf 13 (C)

1053	**1008**	23p multicoloured	. . . .	50	55
		a. Booklet pane. Nos. 1053/8, with margins all round	. . . .	5·25	
1054	**1009**	29p multicoloured	. . . .	65	70
1055	**1010**	38p multicoloured	. . . .	80	85
1056	**1011**	40p multicoloured	. . . .	85	90
1057	**1012**	47p multicoloured	. . . .	1·00	1·10

1058	**1013**	68p multicoloured	1·50	1·70
1053/8		Set of 6	4·75	5·25
		First Day Cover		6·00
		Presentation Pack	6·00	

MS1059 150×100 mm. **1014a** £2 multicoloured .... 4·25 4·50
> a. Booklet pane. As No.
> **MS**1059, but with line of
> roulettes at left .... 4·25
> First Day Cover .... 5·00
> Presentation Pack .... 5·00

Booklet pane No. 1053a exists in three versions which differ in the order of the stamps within the block of six.

Plate Nos.: All values 1A (×4)

Sheets: 10 (2×5)

Imprint: Central, left-hand margin

Withdrawn: 30.8.2003 (sheets)

1015 British Dilute
Tortoiseshell

1016 Cream Persian

1017 Blue Exotic Shorthair

1018 Black Smoke Devon
Rex

1019 British Silver Tabby

1020 Usual Abyssinian

1021a British Cream/White Bi-colour Cross
(*illustration reduced. Actual size* 110×75 *mm*)

25th Anniversary of Caesarea Cat Club

(Des G. Vasarhelyi. Litho B.D.T.)

2002 (12 OCT). Perf 14 (No. **MS**1066) or 15×14 (others), both comb

1060	**1015**	23p multicoloured	50	55
1061	**1016**	29p multicoloured	65	70
1062	**1017**	38p multicoloured	80	85
1063	**1018**	40p multicoloured	85	90
1064	**1019**	47p multicoloured	1·00	1·10
1065	**1020**	68p multicoloured	1·50	1·70
1060/5		Set of 6	4·75	5·25
		First Day Cover		6·00
		Presentation Pack	5·75	

MS1066 110×75 mm. **1021a** £2 multicoloured .... 4·25 4·50
> First Day Cover .... 6·00
> Presentation Pack .... 5·50

Plate Nos.: All values 1A, 1B (each ×4)

Sheets: 10 (2×5)

Imprint: Lower left-hand margin

Withdrawn: 31.10.2003

1022 Victorian Pillar Box in
Central Market

1023 Edward VII Wall Box,
Colomberie

1024 George V Wall Box, St. Clement's Inner Road

1025 George V 'Boite Mobile' Ship Box

1026 Elizabeth II Pillar Box, Parade

1027 Modern Pillar Boxes, La Collette

1028a Posting Letter in First Pillar Box, David Place
(*illustration reduced. Actual size* 150×100 *mm*)

Jersey Postal History (1st series). 150th Anniversary of the First Pillar Box

(Des Colleen Corlett. Litho Questa)

2002 (23 NOV). Perf 14½ (No. **MS**1073) or 14½×14 (others), both comb

1067	**1022**	23p multicoloured	....	50	55
1068	**1023**	29p multicoloured	....	65	70
1069	**1024**	38p multicoloured	....	80	85
1070	**1025**	40p multicoloured	....	85	90
1071	**1026**	47p multicoloured	....	1·00	1·10
1072	**1027**	68p multicoloured	....	1·50	1·60
1067/72		Set of 6	....	4·75	5·25
		First Day Cover	....		6·00
		Presentation Pack	....	5·75	
MS1073		150×100 mm. **1028a** £2 multi-			
coloured		....		4·25	4·50
		First Day Cover	....		6·00
		Presentation Pack	....	5·50	

See also Nos. 1286/92.

Plate Nos.: All values 1A (×5)

Sheets: 10 (5×2)

Imprint: Bottom, right-hand corner margin

Withdrawn: 31.10.2003

Post Office Yearbook

2002 (2 DEC). *Comprises Nos.* 1024/73
Yearbook .... 65·00

Sold out

1029 Sanchez-Besa Hydroplane

1030 Supermarine S.6B Seaplane

1031 De Havilland DH84 Dragon

1032 De Havilland DH89a Rapide

1033 Vickers 701 Viscount

1034 BAC One Eleven

1035a Jacob Ellehammer's *Biplane*, 1906
(*illustration reduced. Actual size* 112×76 *mm*)

Centenary of Powered Flight

(Des T. Theobald. Litho Cartor)

2003 (21 JAN). Perf 13½×13 (No. **MS**1080) or 13×13½ (others), both comb

1074	**1029**	23p multicoloured	50	55
		a. Booklet pane. Nos. 1074/9 with margins all round	4·75	
1075	**1030**	29p multicoloured	65	70
1076	**1031**	38p multicoloured	80	85
1077	**1032**	40p multicoloured	85	90
1078	**1033**	47p multicoloured	1·00	1·10
1079	**1034**	68p multicoloured	1·50	1·60
1074/9		Set of 6	4·75	5·25
		First Day Cover		6·75
		Presentation Pack	6·75	
MS1080		112×76 mm. **1035a** £2 multicoloured	4·25	4·50
		a. Booklet pane. As No. **MS**1080, but 153×100 mm with line of roulettes at left	6·00	
		First Day Cover		5·50
		Presentation Pack	4·75	

No. 1074a comes with three different illustrations on the margins.

The stamp in booklet pane No. **MS**1080a differs from that in the normal miniature sheet by having the imprint date centred, rather than ranged to the left.

Plate Nos.: All values 1A (×4)

Sheets: 10 (2×5)

Imprint: Bottom, right-hand corner margin

Withdrawn: 31.1.2004

1036 Ram
(Illustration reduced. Actual size 110×75 mm)

Chinese New Year ('Year of the Ram')

(Des V. Ambrus. Litho Questa)

2003 (1 FEB). Sheet 110×75 mm. Perf 14×13½ (C)

MS1081	**1036**	£1 multicoloured	2·50	2·75
		First Day Cover		3·50
		Presentation Pack	3·25	

Withdrawn: 28.2.2004

1037 'Portelet' (Adrian Allinson)

1038 'Jersey' (Lander)

1039 'Channel Islands Map'

1040 'Jersey, the Sunny Channel Island' (A. Allinson)

Europa. Poster Art. Travel Posters

(Des N. Shewring. Litho Cartor)

2003 (11 MAR). Perf 13½ (C)

1082	**1037**	23p multicoloured	50	55
1083	**1038**	29p multicoloured	80	80
1084	**1039**	38p multicoloured	1·00	1·00
1085	**1040**	68p multicoloured	1·70	1·80
1082/5		Set of 4	3·75	3·75
		First Day Cover		5·00
		Presentation Pack	5·00	

The 29p and 38p values include the 'EUROPA' emblem.

Plate Nos.: All values 1A (×4)

Sheets: 10 (2×5) 23p, 68p; (5×2) 29p, 38p

Imprint: Lower left-hand margin

Withdrawn: 31.3.2004

1041 Violet Channel Light Buoy

1042 St. Catherine's Breakwater Light

1043 Frouquie Aubert
Light Buoy

1044 Mont Ube
Lighthouse

1045 Banc des Ormes
Light Buoy

1046 Gronez Point
Lighthouse

Jersey Lighthouses (2nd series)

(Des A. Copp. Litho B.D.T.)

2003 (15 APR). Perf 13½ (C)

1086	**1041**	29p multicoloured	50	30
		a. Pair. Nos. 1086/7	1·30	1·30
1087	**1042**	29p multicoloured	50	30
1088	**1043**	30p multicoloured	55	35
		a. Pair. Nos. 1088/9	1·30	1·30
1089	**1044**	30p multicoloured	55	35
1090	**1045**	48p multicoloured	85	50
		a. Pair. Nos. 1090/1	2·00	2·10
1091	**1046**	48p multicoloured	85	50
1086/91		Set of 6	4·25	4·50
		First Day Cover		5·50
		Presentation Pack	5·50	

The two designs for each value were printed together, *se-tenant*, both horizontally and vertically in sheets of ten stamps.

Plate Nos.: All values 1A (×4)

Sheets: 10 (5×2)

Imprint: Lower left-hand margin

Withdrawn: 30.4.2004

1047 Southern-marsh
Orchid

1048 Loose-flowered
Orchid

1049 Spotted
Orchid

1050 Autumn Ladies
Tresses

1051 Green-winged
Orchid

1052 Pyramidal
Orchid

1053a Loose-flowered Orchid
(*illustration reduced. Actual size* 110×75 *mm*)

Wild Orchids

(Des B. Ozard. Litho Cartor)

2003 (13 MAY). Perf 13 (C)

1092	**1047**	29p multicoloured	60	65
1093	**1048**	30p multicoloured	60	65
1094	**1049**	39p multicoloured	80	85
1095	**1050**	50p multicoloured	1·00	1·10
1096	**1051**	53p multicoloured	1·10	1·20
1097	**1052**	69p multicoloured	1·40	1·50
1092/7		Set of 6	5·25	5·75
		First Day Cover		6·50
		Presentation Pack	6·50	
MS1098		110×75 mm. **1053a** £2 multi-coloured	4·00	4·25
		First Day Cover		5·25
		Presentation Pack	5·25	

Plate Nos.: All values 1A (×4)

Sheets: 10 (5×2)

Imprint: Lower left-hand margin

Withdrawn: 31.5.2004

1054 Sovereign's Orb

1055 St. Edward's Crown

1056 Sceptre with Cross

1057 Ampulla and Spoon

1058 Sovereign's Ring

1059 Armills

50th Anniversary of Coronation. Coronation Regalia

(Des Jennifer Toombs. Litho and die-stamped B.D.T.)

2003 (2 JUNE). Perf 15×14 (C)

1099	**1054**	29p multicoloured	....	60	65
1100	**1055**	30p multicoloured	....	60	65
1101	**1056**	39p multicoloured	....	80	85
1102	**1057**	50p multicoloured	....	1·00	1·10
1103	**1058**	53p multicoloured	....	1·00	1·10
1104	**1059**	69p multicoloured	....	1·40	1·50
1099/1104		Set of 6	....	5·25	5·75
		First Day Cover	....		6·50
		Presentation Pack	....	6·50	
MS1105	150×100 mm. Nos. 1099/1104 ...			5·25	5·75
		First Day Cover	....		6·50
		Presentation Pack	....	6·50	

Nos. 1099/1104 were each printed in sheets of 10 (2×5) with enlarged illustrated right-hand margins.

Plate Nos.: All values 1A (×6)

Sheets: 10 (2×5) with enlarged illustrated right-hand margins

Imprint: Lower left-hand margin

Withdrawn: 30.6.2004

1060a Prince William, Prince Charles and Queen Elizabeth (*illustration reduced. Actual size* 110×75 *mm*)

Royal Links

(Des The Partnership. Litho Questa)

2003 (21 JUNE). *Sheet* 110×75 *mm. Perf* 14×13½ (C)

MS1106	**1060a**	£2 multicoloured	4·00	4·25
		First Day Cover		5·25
		Presentation Pack	5·25	

Withdrawn: 30.6.2004

1061 Rock Samphire and Paternosters

1062 Bluebells and Les Ecrehous

1063 Tree-mallow and Les Ecrehous

1064 Smooth Sow-thistle and Les Minquiers

1065 Thrift and Les Minquiers

Offshore Reefs

(Des Colleen Corlett. Photo Questa)

2003 (5 AUG). *Self-adhesive*. Perf 11 (die-cut)

1107	**1061**	(29p) multicoloured	90	90
1108	**1062**	(29p) multicoloured	90	90
1109	**1063**	(29p) multicoloured	90	90
1110	**1064**	(29p) multicoloured	90	90
1111	**1065**	(29p) multicoloured	90	90
1107/11		*Set of* 5	4·50	4·50
		First Day Cover		5·00
		Presentation Pack	5·00	

Nos. 1107/11, which are inscribed 'JERSEY MINIMUM POSTAGE PAID' and were initially sold at 29p each, come *se-tenant* in strips of 5 or rolls of 100 with the surplus self-adhesive paper around each stamp removed.

Nos. 1107/11 are inscr '2003' with copyright symbol before date.

For designs as Nos. 1107/11 printed in lithography by Sprintpak see Nos. 1180/4.

1066 Albino Rex Rabbit

1067 Black Labrador Puppy

1068 Canary and Budgerigar

1069 Hamster

1070 Guinea Pig

1071a Border Collie
(*illustration reduced. Actual size* 150×100 *mm*)

Pets

(Des N. Parlett. Litho B.D.T.)

2003 (9 SEPT). Perf 13×13½ (No. **MS**1117) or 13½ (others), both comb

1112	**1066**	29p multicoloured	95	95
1113	**1067**	30p multicoloured	95	95
1114	**1068**	38p multicoloured	1·20	1·20
1115	**1069**	53p multicoloured	1·70	1·70
1116	**1070**	69p multicoloured	2·20	2·20
1112/16		*Set of* 5	7·00	7·00
		First Day Cover		9·25
		Presentation Pack	9·25	
MS1117		150×100 mm. **1071a** £2 Border collie	6·50	6·50
		First Day Cover		8·50
		Presentation Pack	8·50	

Plate Nos.: All values 1A (×4)

Sheets: 10 (2×5)

Imprint: Central, bottom margin

Withdrawn: 30.9.2004

'Bangkok 2003' International Stamp Exhibition

2003 (4 OCT). No. **MS**1098 optd with 'Jersey at Bangkok 2003' and emblem on sheet margin. Perf 13 (C)

MS1118	110×75 mm. £2 multicoloured . . .	6·50	6·50
	First Day Cover		8·50
	Presentation Pack	8·50	

Withdrawn: 31.10.2004

1072 Japanese Quince

1073 Winter Jasmine

1074 Snowdrop

1075 Winter Heath

1076 Chinese Witch-hazel

1077 Winter Daphne

1080 Bishop

1081 Pawn

1082 Queen

1083 King

Winter Flowers

(Des Wendy Tait. Litho Questa)

2003 (10 NOV). Perf 14½ (C)

1119	**1072**	29p multicoloured	....	60	65
1120	**1073**	30p multicoloured	....	60	65
1121	**1074**	39p multicoloured	....	80	85
1122	**1075**	48p multicoloured	....	95	1·00
1123	**1076**	53p multicoloured	....	1·00	1·10
1124	**1077**	69p multicoloured	....	1·40	1·50
1119/24		Set of 6	....	5·25	5·75
		First Day Cover	....		6·75
		Presentation Pack	....	6·50	

Plate Nos.: 29p 1A, 1B, 1C, 1D; 30p 1A, 1B, 1C, 1D, 1E, 1F; others 1A, 1B (each ×5)

Sheets: 10 (5×2)

Imprint: Right-hand side, bottom margin

Withdrawn: 30.11.2004

Post Office Yearbook

2003 (1 DEC). *Comprises Nos.* 1074/1104 *and* **MS**1106/17 *and* 1119/24

	Yearbook	....	65·00

Sold out: By 11.04

Jersey Festivals (1st issue). Festival of Chess

(Des Jennifer Toombs. Litho BDT)

2004 (22 JAN). Perf 14×13½ (C)

1125	**1078**	29p multicoloured	....	95	95
1126	**1079**	30p multicoloured	....	1·00	1·00
1127	**1080**	39p multicoloured	....	1·30	1·30
1128	**1081**	48p multicoloured	....	1·60	1·60
1129	**1082**	53p multicoloured	....	1·70	1·70
1130	**1083**	69p multicoloured	....	2·20	2·20
1125/30		Set of 6	....	8·75	8·75
		First Day Cover	....		11·00
		Presentation Pack	....	11·00	

Plate Nos.: All values 1A (×5)

Sheets: 10 (5×2)

Imprint: Bottom margin

Withdrawn: 31.1.2005

1078 Rook

1079 Knight

1084a Monkey
(*illustration reduced. Actual size* 110×75 mm)

Chinese New Year ('Year of the Monkey')

(Des V. Ambrus. Litho Questa)

2004 (22 JAN). *Sheet* 110×75 *mm.* Perf 14×13½ (C)

MS1131 1084a   £1 multicoloured . . . . 3·25   3·25
                First Day Cover . . . .   5·25
                Presentation Pack . . . . . . 5·25

1085 St. Aubin's Harbour

1086 Mont Orgueil Castle

1087 Corbiere Lighthouse

1088 Rozel Harbour

Europa. Holidays

(Des A. Copp. Litho Cartor)

2004 (9 MAR). Perf 13×13½ (C)

1132 **1085** 29p multicoloured 95   95
1133 **1086** 30p multicoloured 95   95
1134 **1087** 39p multicoloured . . . . 1·30 1·30
1135 **1088** 69p multicoloured . . . . 2·30 2·30
1132/5   Set of 4 . . . . 5·50 5·50
                 First Day Cover . . . .   7·50
                 Presentation Pack . . . . 7·50

The 30p and 39p values include the 'EUROPA' emblem.

Plate Nos.: All values 1A (×4)

Sheets: 10 (2×5)

Imprint: Upper left-hand margin

Withdrawn: 31.3.2005

1089 Green-winged Teal
('Eurasian Teal')

1090 Mute Swan

1091 Northern Shoveler

1092 Common Pochard

1093 Black Swan

1094 European Wigeon
('Eurasian Wigeon')

1095a Mallard
(*illustration reduced. Actual size* 150×100 *mm*)

Ducks and Swans

(Des N. Parlett. Litho BDT)

2004 (6 APR). Perf 15×14 (C)

1136 **1089** 32p multicoloured . . . . 1·00   1·00
1137 **1090** 33p multicoloured . . . . 1·10   1·10
1138 **1091** 40p multicoloured . . . . 1·30   1·30
1139 **1092** 49p multicoloured . . . . 1·60   1·60
1140 **1093** 62p multicoloured . . . . 2·00   2·00
1141 **1094** 70p multicoloured . . . . 2·30   2·30
1136/41   Set of 6 . . . . 9·25   9·25
                 First Day Cover . . . .   11·25
                 Presentation Pack . . . . . . 11·25
MS1142   150×100 mm. **1095a** £2 multi-
         coloured. Perf 14 . . . . 6·50   6·50
                 First Day Cover . . . .   8·50
                 Presentation Pack . . . . . . 8·50

Plate Nos.: All values 1A (×4)

Sheets: 10 (2×5)

Imprint: Central, left-hand margin

Withdrawn: 30.4.2005

1096 *Cymbidium*
lowianum
'Concolor'

1097 *Phragmipedium*
besseae var.
flavum

1098 *Peristeria elata*

1099 *Cymbidium*
tracyanum

1100 *Paphiopedilum*
Victoria Village 'Isle
of Jersey'

1101 *Paphiopedilum*
hirsutissimum

1102a *Phragmipedium 'Jason Fischer'*
(illustration reduced. Actual size 110×75 mm)

Jersey Orchids (5th series)

(Des S. Giovinazzi. Litho Cartor)

2004 (25 MAY). Perf 13×13½ (C)

1143	**1096**	32p multicoloured	....	1·00	1·00
		a. *Booklet pane. Nos. 1143/8*			
		with margins all round	....	9·50	
1144	**1097**	33p multicoloured	....	1·10	1·10
1145	**1098**	40p multicoloured	....	1·30	1·30

1146	**1099**	54p multicoloured	....	1·80	1·80
1147	**1100**	62p multicoloured	....	2·00	2·00
1148	**1101**	70p multicoloured	....	2·30	2·30
1143/8		*Set of 6*		9·50	9·50
		First Day Cover			11·75
		Presentation Pack	......	11·75	

MS1149	110×75 mm. **1102a** £2 multi-			
	coloured	....	6·50	6·50
	a. *Booklet pane. No.* **MS**1149,			
	but 151×100 mm with line			
	of roulettes at left	......	6·50	
	First Day Cover	....		8·75
	Presentation Pack	......	7·50	

Booklet pane No. 1143a exists in three versions which
differ in the order of the stamps within the block of six.

Plate Nos.: All values 1A (×5)

Sheets: 10 (2×5)

Imprint: Lower left-hand margin

Withdrawn: 31.5.2005

1103a Invasion Map
(illustration reduced. Actual size 110×75 mm)

60th Anniversary of D-Day

(Des A. Theobald. Litho Cartor)

2004 (6 JUNE). *Sheet* 110×75 mm. Perf 13 (C)

MS1150	**1103a**	£2 multicoloured	....	6·50	6·50
		First Day Cover	....		8·75
		Presentation Pack	....	7·50	

Withdrawn: 30.6.2005

1104 Mont Orgueil Castle in 13th
Century

1105 King John,
c. 1204

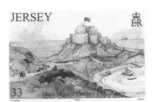

1106 Mont Orgueil Castle in 17th Century

1107 King Charles II, c. 1684

1108 Mont Orgueil Castle Castle, 2004

1109 Queen Elizabeth II, 2002

(Des V. Ambrus. Litho Questa)

Jersey—'A Peculiar of the Crown'

2004 (25 JUNE). Perf 14½×15 (C)

1151	**1104**	32p multicoloured	60	35
		a. Horiz pair. Nos. 1151/2 ...	2·00	2·00
1152	**1105**	32p multicoloured	60	35
1153	**1106**	33p multicoloured	60	35
		a. Horiz pair. Nos. 1153/4 ...	2·00	2·00
1154	**1107**	33p multicoloured	60	35
1155	**1108**	40p multicoloured	80	45
		a. Horiz pair. Nos. 1155/6 ...	2·50	2·50
1156	**1109**	40p multicoloured	80	45
1151/6		Set of 6	6·50	6·50
		First Day Cover		8·75
		Presentation Pack	7·50	

Plate Nos.: All values 1A (×4)

Sheets: 10 (2×5). Nos. 1151/2, 1153/4 and 1155/6 were each printed together, *se-tenant*, in horizontal pairs

Imprint: Upper left-hand margin (32p, 33p) or central, left-hand margin (40p)

Withdrawn: 30.6.2005

Salon du Timbre Stamp Exhibition, Paris

2004 (26 JUNE). As No. **MS**1149, *but optd with* "Jersey at Le Salon du Timbre 2004" *at top left corner of sheet margin.* Perf 13×13½ (C)

MS1157 110×75 mm. **1102a** £2 multicoloured	6·50	6·50
First Day Cover		8·75
Presentation Pack	7·50	

Withdrawn: 30.6.2005

1110 Wall Lizard

1111 Ant Lion

1112 Field Cricket

1113 Dartford Warbler

Endangered Species of Jersey

(Des W. Oliver. Litho BDT)

2004 (27 JULY). Perf 15×14 (C)

1158	**1110**	32p multicoloured	1·00	1·00
1159	**1111**	33p multicoloured	1·10	1·10
1160	**1112**	49p multicoloured	1·60	1·60
1161	**1113**	70p multicoloured	2·30	2·30
1158/61		Set of 4	6·00	6·00
		First Day Cover		8·25
		Presentation Pack	7·50	
MS1162	141×174 mm. Nos. 1158/61 each			
×2	....	12·00	12·00

Plate Nos.: All values 1A (×4)

Sheets: 10 (2×5)

Imprint: Bottom margin

Withdrawn: 30.7.2005

1114 Dead Man's Fingers

1115 Devonshire Cup

1116 White Sea Fan

1117 Pink Sea Fan

1118 Sunset Cup   **1119** Red Fingers

Corals

(Des Colleen Corlett. Litho Cartor)

2004 (28 SEPT). Perf 13×13½ (C)

1163	**1114**	32p multicoloured	....	1·00	1·00
1164	**1115**	33p multicoloured	....	1·10	1·10
1165	**1116**	40p multicoloured	....	1·30	1·30
1166	**1117**	54p multicoloured	....	1·80	1·80
1167	**1118**	62p multicoloured	....	2·00	2·00
1168	**1119**	70p multicoloured	....	2·30	2·30
1163/8		*Set of 6*	....	9·50	9·50
		First Day Cover	....		11·50
		Presentation Pack	....	10·50	
MS1169	150×100 mm. Nos. 1166/8		......	6·00	6·00
		First Day Cover	....		8·25
		Presentation Pack	....	7·00	

Plate Nos.: All values 1A (×4)

Sheets: 10 (2×5)

Imprint: Lower left-hand margin

Withdrawn: 30.9.2005

1120 Nativity Scene   **1121** Fairy Lights over Busy Street

1122 Santa Claus, Children and Christmas Tree   **1123** Candles in Church

1124 Three Candles and Holly   **1125** Mary and Jesus

1126 Stockings and Candle on Mantlepiece   **1127** Five Candles

1128 Angel and Candle   **1129** Candles in Window

Christmas Illuminations

(Des M. Pollard. Litho SNP Sprint)

2004 (2 NOV). *Self-adhesive.* Perf 11½ (die-cut)

1170	**1120**	(32p) multicoloured (*abc*)	.....	1·00	1·00
1171	**1121**	(32p) multicoloured (*abc*) (×4)		1·00	1·00
1172	**1122**	(32p) multicoloured (*abc*)	.....	1·00	1·00
1173	**1123**	(32p) multicoloured (*abc*)	.....	1·00	1·00
1174	**1124**	(32p) multicoloured (*abc*)	.....	1·00	1·00
1175	**1125**	(33p) multicoloured (*abc*)	.....	1·10	1·10
1176	**1126**	(33p) multicoloured (*abc*)	.....	1·10	1·10
1177	**1127**	(33p) multicoloured (*abc*)	.....	1·10	1·10
1178	**1128**	(33p) multicoloured (*abc*)	.....	1·10	1·10
1179	**1129**	(33p) multicoloured (*abc*)	.....	1·10	1·10
1170/9		*Set of 10*	....	10·50	10·50
		First Day Cover	....		12·75
		Presentation Pack	.....	12·75	

Nos. 1170/4, which are inscribed 'JERSEY MINIMUM POSTAGE PAID' and Nos. 1175/9, inscribed 'U.K. MINIMUM POSTAGE PAID' were sold at 32p and 33p respectively and were available in strips of 5 and rolls of 100 with the surplus self-adhesive paper around each stamp removed.

Initially released with "2004" imprint dates, Nos. 1170/9 were subsequently reissued inscribed "2005" and "2006" (all prices the same).

Printings: (*a*) 2.11.2004. Inscr '2004'; (*b*) 21.10.2005. Inscr '2005'; (c) 31.10.2006. Inscr '2006'

(Litho SNP Sprint, Australia)

2004 (3 NOV). *Designs as Nos. 1107/11 (Offshore Reefs). Self-adhesive.* Perf 11½ (die-cut)

1180	**1061**	(32p) multicoloured (*ab*)	......	65	70
1181	**1062**	(32p) multicoloured (*ab*)	......	65	70
1182	**1063**	(32p) multicoloured (*ab*)	......	65	70
1183	**1064**	(32p) multicoloured (*ab*)	......	65	70
1184	**1065**	(32p) multicoloured (*ab*)	......	65	70
1180/4		*Set of 5*	....	3·25	3·50

Nos. 1180/4, which are inscribed 'JERSEY MINIMUM POSTAGE PAID' and were initially sold at 32p each, come se-tenant in strips of 5 or rolls of 100 with the surplus self-adhesive paper around each stamp removed.

Nos. 1180/4 are inscr '2004' or '2006' with copyright symbol after date.

Initially released with "2004" imprint dates, Nos. 1180/4 were subsequently reissued inscribed "2006" (prices the same).

Printings: (a) 3.11.2004. Inscr '2004'; (b) 16.11.2006. Inscr '2006'

Post Office Yearbook

2004 (1 DEC). *Comprises Nos.* 1125/56, 1158/61, 1163/8 *and* 1170/9

Yearbook .... 65·00

Sold out

1130 C 1 Air Search Aircraft

1131 Burby Helicopter

1132 Beach Lifeguard Service

1133 Fire Rescue Inflatable

1134 RAF Sea King Helicopter

Rescue Craft

(Des A. Theobald. Litho Cartor)

2005 (18 JAN). Perf 13×13½ (C)

1185	**1130**	32p multicoloured	65	70
1186	**1131**	33p multicoloured	65	70
1187	**1132**	40p multicoloured	80	85
1188	**1133**	49p multicoloured	1·00	1·10
1189	**1134**	70p multicoloured	1·40	1·50
1185/9		Set of 5	4·50	4·75
		First Day Cover		5·75
		Presentation Pack	5·75	

Plate Nos.: All values 1A (×4)

Sheets: 10 (2×5)

Imprint: Right-hand side, bottom margin

Withdrawn: 31.1.2006

1135 Rooster
(*illustration reduced. Actual size* 110×75 mm)

Chinese New Year ('Year of the Rooster')

(Des V. Ambrus. Litho BDT)

2005 (9 FEB). *Sheet* 110×75 mm. Perf 14½ (C)

MS1190	**1135**	£1 multicoloured	2·50	2·75
		First Day Cover		3·50
		Presentation Pack	3·50	

Withdrawn: 28.2.2006

1136 Conger Eel Soup

1137 Oysters

1138 Bean Crock

1139 Bourdélots with Black Butter

Europa. Gastronomy

(Des Jennifer Toombs. Litho BDT)

2005 (8 MAR). Perf 14 (C)

1191	**1136**	32p multicoloured	65	70
1192	**1137**	33p multicoloured	65	70
1193	**1138**	40p multicoloured	80	85
1194	**1139**	70p multicoloured	1·40	1·50
1191/4		Set of 4	3·50	3·75
		First Day Cover		5·50
		Presentation Pack	5·00	

The 33p and 40p values include the 'EUROPA' emblem.

Plate Nos.: All values 1A (×5)
Sheets: 10 (5×2)
Imprint: Right-hand side, bottom margin
Withdrawn: 31.3.2006

1140 *Little Red Riding Hood*

1141 *The Little Mermaid*

1142 *Beauty and the Beast*

1143 *Rumpelstiltskin*

1144 *Goose that laid the Golden Egg*

1145 *The Ugly Duckling*
(*illustration reduced. Actual size* 110×75 *mm*)

Fairy Tales

(Des M. Pollard. Litho Cartor)

2005 (2 APR). Perf 13×13½ (C)

1195	**1140**	33p multicoloured	65	70
1196	**1141**	34p multicoloured	70	75
1197	**1142**	41p multicoloured	80	85
1198	**1143**	50p multicoloured	1·00	1·10
1199	**1144**	73p multicoloured	1·50	1·60

1195/9	*Set of 5*	4·50	5·00
	First Day Cover		5·75
	Presentation Pack	5·50	

MS1200   110×75 mm. **1145** £2 multi-coloured. Perf 13½ (C)

		4·00	4·25
	First Day Cover		5·50
	Presentation Pack	5·50	

Nos. 1195/**MS**1200 commemorate the birth bicentenary of Hans Christian Andersen.

Plate Nos.: All values 1A (×4)
Sheets: 10 (2×5)
Imprint: Lower left-hand margin
Withdrawn: 30.4.2006

1146 Muratti Vase Medal
(*illustration reduced. Actual size* 110×75 *mm*)

Centenary of Jersey Football Association and Muratti Vase

(Des A. Robinson. Litho Cartor)

2005 (27 APR). Sheet 110×75 mm. Perf 14½ (C)

MS1201   **1146**   £2 brown-ochre, black and orange-brown

		4·00	4·25
	First Day Cover		5·50
	Presentation Pack	5·50	

Withdrawn: 29.4.2006

1147 Peace Dove
(*illustration reduced. Actual size* 110×75 *mm*)

60th Anniversary of Liberation of Channel Islands. Peace and Reconciliation

(Des A. Robinson. Litho BDT)

2005 (9 MAY). *Sheet* 110×75 *mm*. Perf 14½ (C)

MS1202	**1147**	£2 multicoloured	4·00	4·25
		First Day Cover		5·50
		Presentation Pack	5·50	

Withdrawn: 31.5.2006

'Nordia 2005' Stamp Exhibition, Göteborg, Sweden

2005 (26 MAY). *No.* **MS**1200 *optd* 'Jersey at Nordia 2005' *in blue and* 'Göteborg 26–29 mai SVENSKA FRIMÄRKET 150 ÅR' *in black on bottom sheet margin.* Perf 13½ (C)

MS1203		110×75 mm. **1147** £2 multi-		
coloured		....	4·00	4·25

Withdrawn: 31.5.2006

1148 MGB GT

1149 Mini Cooper

1150 Citröen DS

1151 Jaguar E Type

1152 Volkswagen Beetle   **1153** Aston Martin DB5

Jersey Festivals (2nd issue). Motor Festival. Classic Cars

(Des A. Copp. Litho Cartor)

2005 (6 JUNE). Perf 13×13½ (C)

1204	**1148**	33p multicoloured	65	70
		a. Booklet pane. Nos. 1204/9	5·75	
1205	**1149**	34p multicoloured	70	75
1206	**1150**	41p multicoloured	80	85
1207	**1151**	50p multicoloured	1·00	1·10
1208	**1152**	56p multicoloured	1·10	1·20
1209	**1153**	73p multicoloured	1·50	1·60
1204/9		Set of 6	5·75	6·00
		First Day Cover		7·00
		Presentation Pack	7·00	

Booklet pane No. 1204a exists in three versions which differ in the order of the stamps within the block of six.

Plate Nos.: All values 1A (×4)

Sheets: 10 (2×5)

Imprint: Lower left-hand margin

Withdrawn: 30.6.2006 (sheets)

1154 Yellow Bartsia

1155 Scarlet Pimpernel

1156 Wild Angelica

1157 Common Knapweed

1158 Marsh St. Johnswort

1159 Black Bryony

1160 Bog Pimpernel

1161 Greater Stitchwort

1162 Horseshoe Vetch

1163 Common Mallow

1164 English Stonecrop

1165 White Campion

1166 Tutsan

1167 Common Dog-violet

1168 Ox Eye Daisy

1169 Rock Sea Spurrey

1170 Herb-Robert

1171 Ragged Robin

1172 Brooklime

1173 Mouse Ear Hawkweed

1174 Cuckoo Flower

1175 Yellow Iris

1176 Three-cornered Garlic

1177 Devil's-bit Scabious

Wild Flowers

(Des N. Parlett. Litho Cartor)

2005 (19 JULY)–**2007**. Perf 13½ (C)

1210	**1154**	1p multicoloured (b)		10	10
1211	**1155**	2p multicoloured (a)		10	10
1212	**1156**	3p multicoloured (b)		10	10
1213	**1157**	4p multicoloured (a)		10	10
1214	**1158**	5p multicoloured (b)		10	15
1215	**1159**	10p multicoloured (c)		30	30
1216	**1160**	15p multicoloured (b)		30	35
1217	**1161**	20p multicoloured (a)		40	45
1218	**1162**	25p multicoloured (c)		75	75
1219	**1163**	30p multicoloured (a)		60	65
1220	**1164**	35p multicoloured (c)		1·00	1·00
1221	**1165**	40p multicoloured (a)		80	85
1222	**1166**	45p multicoloured (c)		1·30	1·30
1223	**1167**	50p multicoloured (a)		1·00	1·10
1224	**1168**	55p multicoloured (c)		1·60	1·60
1225	**1169**	60p multicoloured (c)		1·80	1·80
1226	**1170**	65p multicoloured (a)		1·30	1·40
1227	**1171**	70p multicoloured (b)		1·40	1·50
1228	**1172**	75p multicoloured (b)		1·50	1·60
1229	**1173**	80p multicoloured (c)		2·30	2·30
1230	**1174**	85p multicoloured (b)		1·70	1·80
1231	**1175**	90p multicoloured (b)		1·80	1·90
1232	**1176**	£1 multicoloured (a)		2·00	2·10
1233	**1177**	£1.50 multicoloured (c)		4·50	4·50

1210/33		Set of 24	25·00	26·00
		First Day Covers (3)		29·00
		Presentation Packs (3) ..	29·00	

MS1234 Three sheets, each 150×100 mm.
(a)   Nos. 1211, 1213, 1217, 1219, 1221,
1223, 1226 and 1232 (a). (b) Nos. 1210,
1212, 1214, 1216, 1227/8 and 1230/1 (b). (c)
Nos. 1215, 1218, 1220, 1222, 1224/5, 1229
and 1233 (c)   Set of 3 sheets .... 26·00 27·00
| | | First Day Covers (3) .... | | 29·00 |
| | | Presentation Packs (3) .. | 29·00 | |

Printings: (a) 19.7.2005. Inscr '2005' with copyright symbol. (b) 26.9.2006. Inscr '2006' with copyright symbol. (c) 25.7.2007. Inscr '2007' with copyright symbol

Plate Nos.: 1p to 5p, 15p, 20p, 30p, 40p, 50p, 65p to 75p, 85p to £1 1A (×4); 10p, 25p, 35p, 45p, 55p, 60p, 80p, £1.50 1A (×5)

Sheets: 10 (5×2)

Imprint: Right-hand side, bottom margin

1178 Le Hocq Tower

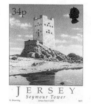

1179 Seymour Tower

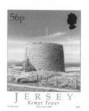

1180 Archirondel Tower

1181 Kempt Tower

1182 Le Rocco Tower

Coastal Towers

(Des N. Shewring. Litho BDT)

2005 (9 AUG). Perf 14 (C)

1235	**1178**	33p multicoloured	65	70
1236	**1179**	34p multicoloured	70	75
1237	**1180**	41p multicoloured	80	85
1238	**1181**	56p multicoloured	1·10	1·20
1239	**1182**	73p multicoloured	1·50	1·60
1235/9		Set of 5	4·75	5·00
		First Day Cover		6·25
		Presentation Pack	6·25	

Plate Nos.: All values 1A (×4)

Sheets: 10 (5×2)

Imprint: Upper left-hand margin

Withdrawn: 31.8.2006

1189 *Marasmius oreades*
(*illustration reduced. Actual size* 150×100 *mm*)

Fungi

(Des W. Oliver. Litho BDT)

2005 (13 SEPT). Perf 14 (C)

1240	**1183**	33p multicoloured	65	70
1241	**1184**	34p multicoloured	70	75
1242	**1185**	41p multicoloured	80	85
1243	**1186**	50p multicoloured	1·00	1·10
1244	**1187**	56p multicoloured	1·10	1·20
1245	**1188**	73p multicoloured	1·50	1·60
1240/5		Set of 6	5·75	6·00
		First Day Cover		7·50
		Presentation Pack	5·00	
MS1246		150×100 mm. **1189** £2 *Marasmius*		
		oreades. Perf 14½ (C)	4·00	4·25
		First Day Cover		7·50
		Presentation Pack	5·00	

Plate Nos.: All values 1A (×4)

Sheets: 10 (5×2)

Imprint: Upper left-hand margin

Withdrawn: 30.9.2006

1183 *Hygrocybe calyptriformis*

1184 *Boletus erythropus*

1185 *Inocybe godeyi*

1186 *Myriostoma coliforme*

1187 *Helvella crispa*

1188 *Hygrocybe coccinea*

1190 H.M.S. *Belleisle*

1191 H.M.S. *Royal Sovereign*

1192 H.M.S. *Neptune*

1193 H.M.S. *Euryalus*

411

1194 H.M.S. *Mars*

1195 H.M.S. *Victory*
(*illustration reduced. Actual size* 110×75 *mm*)

1196 Royal Jersey
Regiment, *c.* 1830

1197 Royal Jersey
Regiment, *c.* 1844

1198 Royal Jersey
Artillery, *c.* 1881

1199 Royal Jersey Light
Infantry, *c.* 1890

1200 Royal Engineers (modern)

Bicentenary of the Battle of Trafalgar

(Des A. Theobald. Litho BDT)

2005 (21 OCT). Perf 14 (C)

1247	**1190**	33p multicoloured	65	70
1248	**1191**	34p multicoloured	70	75
1249	**1192**	41p multicoloured	80	95
1250	**1193**	50p multicoloured	1·20	1·50
1251	**1194**	73p multicoloured	1·80	2·00
1247/51		Set of 5	5·00	5·75
		First Day Cover		6·50
		Presentation Pack	6·50	
MS1252		110×75 mm. **1195** £2 multi-		
coloured		. . . .	4·50	5·00
		First Day Cover		6·50
		Presentation Pack	6·50	

Plate Nos.: All values 1A (×4)

Sheets: 10 (2×5)

Imprint: Lower left-hand margin

Withdrawn: 31.10.2006

Post Office Yearbook

2005 (1 DEC). *Comprises Nos.* 1185/**MS**1202, 1204/9, 1211,
1213, 1217, 1219, 1221, 1223, 1226, 1232 *and* 1235/52
Yearbook . . . . 75·00

Royal Jersey Militia (2nd series)

(Des A. Robinson. Litho Enschedé)

2006 (6 JAN). Perf 13½×14 (C)

1253	**1196**	33p multicoloured	65	70
1254	**1197**	34p multicoloured	70	75
1255	**1198**	41p multicoloured	80	85
1256	**1199**	50p multicoloured	1·10	1·20
1257	**1200**	73p multicoloured	1·90	1·90
1253/7		Set of 5	5·00	5·25
		First Day Cover		6·25
		Presentation Pack	6·25	

Plate Nos.: All values 1A, 1B (each ×4)

Sheets: 10 (2×5)

Imprint: Bottom, left-hand corner margin

Withdrawn: 31.1.2007

1201 Victoria Cross
(illustration reduced. Actual size 110×75 mm)

150th Anniversary of the Victoria Cross

(Des A. Robinson. Litho Enschedé)

2006 (29 JAN). *Sheet* 110×75 *mm.* Perf 13½×14 (C)

MS1258	**1201** £2 multicoloured	....	4·25	5·00
	First Day Cover	....		5·50
	Presentation Pack	....	5·50	

Withdrawn: 31.1.2007

1202 Dog
(illustration reduced. Actual size 110×75 mm)

Chinese New Year ("Year of the Dog)

(Des V. Ambrus. Litho BDT)

2006 (29 JAN). *Sheet* 110×75 *mm.* Perf 14½ (C)

MS1259	**1202** £1 multicoloured	....	3·50	3·75
	First Day Cover	....		4·00
	Presentation Pack	....	4·00	

1203 Chinese National
Costumes and Mask
(Elliott Grimes)

1204 Portuguese Fado
Music Festival
(Liam Reynolds)

1205 Polish Pisanki
painted Easter Egg
Design (Kelly
Reynolds)

1206 Indian National
Costumes (Olivia
Grimes)

Europa. Winning Entries in Children's Stamp Design Competition

(Adapted A. Copp. Litho BDT)

2006 (7 MAR). Perf 14 (C)

1260	**1203**	33p multicoloured	....	65	70
1261	**1204**	34p multicoloured	....	70	75
1262	**1205**	41p multicoloured	....	1·50	1·50
1263	**1206**	73p multicoloured	....	2·00	2·25
1260/3		*Set of 4*	....	4·00	5·00
		First Day Cover	....		6·50
		Presentation Pack	....	6·50	

Plate Nos.: All values 1A (×4)

Sheets: 10 (2×10) with enlarged illustrated margins

Imprint: Lower left-hand margin

Withdrawn: 31.3.2007

1207 Flat Periwinkle

1208 Painted Top Shell

1209 Dog Cockle

1210 Variegated Scallop

1211 Blue Rayed Limpet

1212 European Cowrie

413

1213 Ormer Shell
(*illustration reduced. Actual size* 150×100 *mm)*

Sea Shells

(Des N. Parlett. Litho (with thermography (Nos. 1264/9) or embossing (**MS**1270)) Cartor)

2006 (4 APR). Perf 13×13½ (C)

1264	**1207**	34p multicoloured	70	75
1265	**1208**	37p multicoloured	75	80
1266	**1209**	42p multicoloured	85	90
1267	**1210**	51p multicoloured	1·00	1·10
1268	**1211**	57p multicoloured	1·10	1·20
1269	**1212**	74p multicoloured	1·50	1·60
1264/9		Set of 6	5·75	6·25
		First Day Cover		7·75
		Presentation Pack	7·75	
MS1270		150×100 mm. **1213** £2 multi- coloured. Perf 13½	4·00	4·25
		First Day Cover		5·25
		Presentation Pack	5·25	

Plate Nos.: All values 1A (×4)
Sheets: 10 (2×5) with enlarged illustrated margins
Imprint: Lower left-hand margin
Withdrawn: 30.4.2007

1214 Wedding Photograph

First Wedding Anniversary of Prince Charles and Duchess of Cornwall

(Des A. Robinson. Litho Cartor)

2006 (9 APR). Perf 13½ (C)

1271	**1214**	£2 multicoloured	4·00	4·50
		First Day Cover		5·50
		Presentation Pack	5·50	

No. 1271 was retained in use as a definitive stamp.

Plate Nos.: 1A (×5)
Sheets: 4 (2×2)
Imprint: Lower left-hand margin

1215 Queen Elizabeth II

1216 Queen Elizabeth II (£5; New Zealand $5)
(*illustration reduced. Actual size* 150×100 *mm)*

80th Birthday of Queen Elizabeth II

(Litho and embossed Cartor)

2006 (21 APR). Perf 13½ (C)

1272	**1215**	£5 multicoloured	10·00	10·50
		First Day Cover		13·00
		Presentation Pack	13·50	
MS1273		150×100 mm. **1216** £5 multi- coloured; New Zealand $5 multicoloured (sold at £7) .	15·00	15·00
		First Day Cover		17·00
		Presentation Pack	17·00	

The background colour of the sheet stamp, No. 1272, is deep ultramarine, but both the stamps in the miniature sheet have a deep turquoise-blue background.

The miniature sheet contains a £5 Jersey stamp and a $5 New Zealand stamp. The same miniature sheet and a stamp in a similar design to No. 1272 was also issued by New Zealand. The sheet is known with the silver foil (country names, values and borders) omitted (Price £2750).

No. 1272 was retained in use as a definitive stamp.

Plate Nos.: 1A (×6)

Sheets: 4 (2×2)

Imprint: Upper left-hand margin

1217 Football and World Cup Trophy
(illustration reduced. Actual size 110×75 *mm)*

World Cup Football Championship, Germany

(Des N. Shewring. Litho BDT)

2006 (9 JUNE). *Sheet* 110×75 *mm. Perf* 14½ (C)

MS1274	**1217**	£2 multicoloured	4·75	5·00
		First Day Cover		5·50
		Presentation Pack	5·50	

Withdrawn: 30.6.2007

1218 Greve de Lecq

1219 La Rocque

1220 Portelet

1221 St. Brelade's Bay

Island Views

(Des Colleen Corlett. Litho SEP Sprint, Australia)

2006 (11 JULY). *Self-adhesive. Perf* 11½ (die-cut)

1275	**1218**	(37p) multicoloured	75	80
1276	**1219**	(37p) multicoloured	75	80
1277	**1220**	(37p) multicoloured	75	80
1278	**1221**	(37p) multicoloured	75	80
1275/8		*Set of 4*	4·00	4·00
		First Day Cover		5·00
		Presentation Pack	4·50	

Nos. 1275/8, which are inscribed "UK MINIMUM POSTAGE PAID" and were initially sold at 37p each, come *se-tenant* in strips of 4 or rolls of 100 with the surplus self-adhesive paper around each stamp removed.

1222 Red Underwing Moth

1223 Comma Butterfly

1224 Black Arches Moth

1225 Small Copper Butterfly

1226 Holly Blue Butterfly

1227 Orange-tip Butterfly

Butterflies and Moths

(Des W. Oliver. Litho BDT)

2006 (1 AUG). *Perf* 15×14 (C)

1279	**1222**	34p multicoloured	70	75
1280	**1223**	37p multicoloured	75	80
1281	**1224**	42p multicoloured	85	90
1282	**1225**	51p multicoloured	1·00	1·10
1283	**1226**	57p multicoloured	1·10	1·20
1284	**1227**	74p multicoloured	1·50	1·60
1279/84		*Set of 6*	5·75	6·25
		First Day Cover		7·75
		Presentation Pack	7·75	
MS1285		150×100 mm. Nos. 1282/4	3·75	4·50
		First Day Cover		5·25
		Presentation Pack	5·25	

Stamps from **MS**1285 have no white borders.

Plate Nos.: All values 1A (×4)

Sheets: 10 (2×5) with enlarged illustrated margins.

Imprint: Lower left-hand margin

Withdrawn: 31.8.2007

1228 LDV Luton Van,
c. 2004

1229 Renault Kangoo,
1999–2004

1230 LDV Pilot,
1994–2004

1231 Ford Transit, Luton
Body, 1988–96

1232 Morris Marina,
440/575, c. 1978

1233 Morris Minor,
c. 1969

Jersey Postal History (2nd series). Postal Vehicles

(Des A. Theobald. Litho Cartor)

2006 (31 OCT). Perf 13×13½ (C)

1286	**1228**	34p multicoloured	70	75
		a. Booklet pane. Nos. 1286/91		
		with margins all round	5·75	
1287	**1229**	37p multicoloured	75	80
1288	**1230**	42p multicoloured	85	90
1289	**1231**	51p multicoloured	1·00	1·10
1290	**1232**	57p multicoloured	1·10	1·20
1291	**1233**	74p multicoloured	1·50	1·60
1286/91		Set of 6	5·75	6·25
		First Day Cover		7·75
		Presentation Pack	7·75	
MS1292		150×100 mm. Nos. 1289/91	4·00	4·75
		a. Booklet pane. No. **MS**1292,		
		but with line of roulettes at		
		left	4·00	
		First Day Cover		5·25
		Presentation Pack	5·25	

Booklet pane No. 1286a exists in three versions which
differ in the order of the stamps within the block of six.

Plate Nos.: All values 1A (×4)

Sheets: 10 (2×5)

Imprint: Right-hand side, bottom margin

Withdrawn: 31.10.2007

Belgica '06 International Stamp Exhibition, Brussels

2006 (16 NOV). No. **MS**1270 optd with "Jersey at" and Belgica
emblem on bottom left sheet margin.

MS1293	150×100 mm. **1213** £2 multi-			
	coloured	4·50	5·50
	First Day Cover		6·00
	Presentation Pack	6·00	

Withdrawn: 31.10.2007

Post Office Yearbook

2006 (1 DEC). Comprises Nos. 1210, 1212, 1214, 1216,
1227/8, 1230/1, 1253/72, **MS**1274/84 and 1286/91

Yearbook . . . . 80·00

1234 Molybdenite

1235 Muscovite in
Pegmatite Vein,
Feldspar+Quartz

1236 Orthoclase and
Plagioclase

1237 Quartz coated with
Manganese Oxide

1238 Smoky Quartz

Mineralogy

(Des Jennifer Toombs. Litho Cartor)

2007 (23 JAN). Perf 13×13½ (C)

1294	**1234**	34p multicoloured	1·00	1·00
1295	**1235**	37p multicoloured	1·10	1·10
1296	**1236**	42p multicoloured	1·20	1·20
1297	**1237**	51p multicoloured	1·50	1·50

1298	**1238**	74p multicoloured	2·20	2·20
1294/8		Set of 5	7·00	7·00
		First Day Cover		7·50
		Presentation Pack	7·50	

Plate Nos.: All values 1A (×5)

Sheets: 10 (2×5) with enlarged illustrated margins

Imprint: Lower left-hand margin

Withdrawn: 31.1.2008

1239 Pig
(*illustration reduced. Actual size* 110×75 *mm*)

Chinese New Year ('Year of the Pig')

(Des V. Ambrus. Litho BDT)

2007 (18 FEB). *Sheet* 110×75 *mm.* Perf 14½ (C)

MS1299	**1239**	£1 multicoloured	3·00	3·00
		First Day Cover		3·75
		Presentation Pack	3·75	
		Omnibus Folder (containing Nos. **MS**731, **MS**768, **MS**843, **MS**885, **MS**928, **MS**972, **MS**1030, **MS**1081, **MS**1131, **MS**1190, **MS**1259, **MS**1299	32·00	

Withdrawn: 29.2.2008

1240 Windsurfing, canoeing and land yachting ('Adventure')

1241 Scouts playing Trumpets and National Flags ('International Friendship')

1242 Climbing and go-karting ('Developing Young People')

1243 Scouts and Badges ('Changing the World for Good')

Europa. Centenary of Scouting

(Des Colleen Corlett. Litho Austrian State Ptg Wks, Vienna)

2007 (6 MAR). Perf 14 (C)

1300	**1240**	34p multicoloured	1·00	1·00
1301	**1241**	37p multicoloured	1·10	1·10
1302	**1242**	42p multicoloured	1·20	1·20
1303	**1243**	74p multicoloured	2·20	2·20
1300/3		Set of 4	5·50	5·50
		First Day Cover		6·00
		Presentation Pack	6·00	

Plate Nos.: All values 1A (×4)

Sheets: 10 (2×5) with enlarged illustrated margins

Imprint: Lower left-hand margin

Withdrawn: 31.3.2008

1244 Long-tailed Field Mouse

1245 Rabbits

1246 Polecat

1247 Common Shrew

1248 Stoat

1249 Brown Rat

417

Countryside Animals

(Des W. Oliver. Litho BDT)

2007 (10 APR). Perf 15×14 (C)

1304	**1244**	34p multicoloured	1·00	1·00
1305	**1245**	37p multicoloured	1·10	1·10
1306	**1246**	42p multicoloured	1·30	1·30
1307	**1247**	51p multicoloured	1·50	1·50
1308	**1248**	57p multicoloured	1·70	1·70
1309	**1249**	74p multicoloured	2·20	2·20
1304/9		Set of 6	8·75	8·75
		First Day Cover		9·25
		Presentation Pack	9·25	
MS1310		150×100 mm. As Nos. 1307/9	5·25	5·25
		First Day Cover		5·75
		Presentation Pack	5·75	

Stamps from **MS**1310 have no white borders.

Plate Nos.: All values 1A (×4)

Sheets: 10 (2×5) with enlarged illustrated margins

Imprint: Lower left-hand margin

Withdrawn: 30.4.2008

1250 House Sparrow

1251 Chaffinch

1252 Blue Tit

1253 Blackbirds (pair)

1254 Magpie

1255 Great Tit

Jersey Birdlife (1st series). Garden Birds

(Des Nick Parlett. Litho Cartor)

2007 (19 JUNE). Perf 13×13½ (C)

1311	**1250**	34p multicoloured	1·00	1·00
1312	**1251**	37p multicoloured	1·10	1·10
1313	**1252**	42p multicoloured	1·30	1·30
1314	**1253**	51p multicoloured	1·50	1·50
1315	**1254**	57p multicoloured	1·70	1·70
1316	**1255**	74p multicoloured	2·20	2·20

1311/16		Set of 6	8·75	8·75
		First Day Cover		9·25
		Presentation Pack	9·25	
MS1317		150×100 mm. As Nos. 1314/16	5·25	5·25
		First Day Cover		5·75
		Presentation Pack	5·75	
MS1318		150×100 mm. Nos. 1311/16	8·75	8·75
		First Day Cover		9·25
		Presentation Pack	9·25	

Stamps from **MS**1317 have no white borders.

Plate Nos.: All values 1A (×5)

Sheets: 10 (2×5) with enlarged illustrated margins

Imprint: Lower left-hand margin

Withdrawn: 30.6.2008 (except **MS**1318)

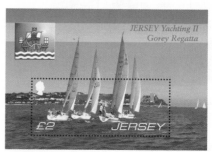

1256 Gorey Regatta
(*illustration reduced. Actual size* 110×75 *mm*)

Jersey Yachting (2nd issue). 150th Anniversary of Gorey Regatta

(Des Andrew Robinson. Litho Enschedé)

2007 (22 JUNE). *Sheet* 110×75 mm. Perf 13×13½ (C)

MS1319	**1256**	£2 multicoloured	6·00	6·00
		First Day Cover		6·50
		Presentation Pack	6·50	

Withdrawn: 30.6.2008

1257 Clematis 'Nelly Moser' and 'The President'

1258 Rose 'Just Joey'

1259 Honeysuckle
Lonicera × americana

1260 Fuchsia 'Swingtime'

1261 Sweet Peas

1262 Lilac

Summer Flowers

(Des Wendy Tait. Litho Enschedé)

2007 (25 JULY). Perf 13½ (C)

1320	**1257**	34p multicoloured	....	1·00	1·00
1321	**1258**	37p multicoloured	....	1·10	1·10
1322	**1259**	42p multicoloured	....	1·30	1·30
1323	**1260**	51p multicoloured	....	1·50	1·50
1324	**1261**	57p multicoloured	....	1·70	1·70
1325	**1262**	74p multicoloured	....	2·20	2·20
1320/5		Set of 6	....	8·75	8·75
		First Day Cover	....		9·25
		Presentation Pack	....	9·25	

Plate Nos.: 34p, 37p 1A, 1B; others 1A (each ×5)

Sheets: 10 (5×2)

Imprint: Bottom margin

Withdrawn: 31.7.2008

1263 Dornier Do 24 ATT

1264 Avro Vulcan B.2

1265 Junkers Ju 52

1266 Sukhoi Su-27 'Flanker'

1267 Boeing B-52 Stratofortress

1268 Anglo French Concorde

1269 Red Arrows
(*illustration reduced. Actual size 110×75 mm*)

60th Anniversary of Jersey International Air Display

(Des Tony Theobald. Litho Cartor)

2007 (13 SEPT). Perf 13×13½ (C)

1326	**1263**	34p multicoloured	....	1·00	1·00
		a. Booklet pane. Nos. 1326/31 *with margins all round*	....	6·00	
1327	**1264**	37p multicoloured	....	1·10	1·10
1328	**1265**	42p multicoloured	....	1·30	1·30
1329	**1266**	51p multicoloured	....	1·50	1·50
1330	**1267**	57p multicoloured	....	1·70	1·70
1331	**1268**	74p multicoloured	....	2·20	2·20
1326/31		Set of 6	....	8·75	8·75
		First Day Cover	....		9·25
		Presentation Pack	....	9·25	
MS1332		110×75 mm. **1269** £2·50 multicoloured. Perf 13½×13	....	7·25	7·25
		a. Booklet pane. No. **MS**1332 but 150×100 mm with line of roulettes at left	....	5·00	
		First Day Cover			7·75
		Presentation Pack	....	7·75	

Booklet pane No. 1326a exists in three versions which differ in the order of the stamps within the block of six.

Plate Nos.: All values 1A (×4)

Sheets: 10 (2×5) with enlarged illustrated margins

Imprint: Lower left-hand margin

Withdrawn: 30.9.2008 (sheets)

1270 Queen's Valley Reservoir

1271 Mont Orgueil Castle

1272 Bonne Nuit Harbour

1273 La Hougue Bie

1274 Bouley Bay

1275 La Corbiere Lighthouse

Jersey Scenery (1st series)

(Des Andrew Robinson. Litho Enschedé)

2007 (1 OCT). Perf 14×13½ (C)

1333	**1270**	34p multicoloured	1·00	1·00
1334	**1271**	37p multicoloured	1·10	1·10
1335	**1272**	42p multicoloured	1·30	1·30
1336	**1273**	51p multicoloured	1·50	1·50
1337	**1274**	57p multicoloured	1·70	1·70
1338	**1275**	74p multicoloured	2·20	2·20
1333/8		Set of 6	8·75	8·75
		First Day Cover		9·25
		Presentation Pack	9·25	

The 42p value No. 1335 is inscr 'sepac' and was also available in a souvenir folder with ten other Sepac logo stamps issued by other administrations.

Plate Nos.: 34p, 37p 1A, 1B, 1C; 42p, 74p 1A, 1B; 51p, 57p 1A (each ×4)

Sheets: 10 (2×5) with enlarged illustrated margins

Imprint: Lower left-hand margin

Withdrawn: 31.10.2008

1276 'Minuit Chrétiens'

1277 'While Shepherds Watched'

1278 'O Come All Ye Faithful'

1279 'O Christmas Tree'

1280 'Jingle Bells'

1281 'Hark the Herald Angels Sing'

1282 'We Three Kings'

1283 'Ding Dong Merrily on High'

1284 'Holly and the Ivy'

1285 'Good King Wenceslas'

420

Christmas Carols

(Des Michael Pollard. Litho SNP Sprint, Australia)

2007 (7 NOV). *Self-adhesive.* Perf 11½ (die-cut)

1339	**1276**	(35p) multicoloured (ab)	1·00	1·00
1340	**1277**	(35p) multicoloured (ab)	1·00	1·00
1341	**1278**	(35p) multicoloured (ab)	1·00	1·00
1342	**1279**	(35p) multicoloured (ab)	1·00	1·00
1343	**1280**	(35p) multicoloured (ab)	1·00	1·00
1344	**1281**	(39p) multicoloured (ab)	1·20	1·20
1345	**1282**	(39p) multicoloured (ab)	1·20	1·20
1346	**1283**	(39p) multicoloured (ab)	1·20	1·20
1347	**1284**	(39p) multicoloured (ab)	1·20	1·20
1348	**1285**	(39p) multicoloured (ab)	1·20	1·20
1339/48		Set of 10	11·00	11·00
		First Day Cover		12·00
		Presentation Pack	12·00	

Nos. 1339/43 which are inscribed 'JERSEY MINIMUM POSTAGE PAID' were sold for 35p., and Nos. 1344/8 which are inscribed 'U.K. MINIMUM POSTAGE PAID' were sold for 39p. Nos. 1339/43 and 1344/8 were each printed together, se-tenant, in strips of 5 from rolls of 100, from which the surplus self-adhesive backing paper around each stamp was removed.

Initially released with '2007' imprint dates, Nos. 1339/43 were subsequently re-issued inscribed '2008'.

Printings: (a) 7.11.2007. Inscr '2007'; (b) 14.11.2008. Inscr '2008'

1286 Queen Elizabeth II and Duke of Edinburgh

Diamond Wedding of Queen Elizabeth II and Duke of Edinburgh

(Des Andrew Robinson. Litho Cartor)

2007 (20 NOV). Perf 13½ (C)

1349	**1286**	£3 multicoloured	8·75	8·75
		First Day Cover		9·25
		Presentation Pack	9·25	

No. 1349 was retained in use as a definitive stamp.

Plate Nos.: 1A (×5)

Sheets: 4 (2×2)

Imprint: Lower left-hand margin

Post Office Yearbook

2007 (1 DEC). *Comprises Nos.* 1215, 1218, 1220, 1222, 1224/5, 1229, 1233, 1294/309, 1311/16 *and* **MS**1319/49

	Yearbook	82·00

1287 Sunshine

1288 Strong Wind Signals

1289 Weather Signals

1290 Temperature

1291 Tides and Wave Signals

300th Anniversary of Jersey Signal Station

(Des Nick Shewring. Litho Austrian State Ptg Wks, Vienna)

2008 (15 JAN). Perf 14 (C)

1350	**1287**	35p multicoloured	1·00	1·00
1351	**1288**	39p multicoloured	1·20	1·20
1352	**1289**	43p multicoloured	1·30	1·30
1353	**1290**	58p multicoloured	1·70	1·70
1354	**1291**	76p multicoloured	2·30	2·30
1350/4		Set of 5	7·50	7·50
		First Day Cover		10·00
		Presentation Pack	10·00	

Plate Nos.: All values 1A (each ×4)

Sheets: 10 (2×5) with enlarged illustrated margins

Imprint: Lower left-hand margin

Withdrawn: 31.1.2009

1292 Thank You Letter

1293 Love Letter

1294 Letter to Santa Claus   **1295** Family Letter

Europa. The Letter

(Des Jennifer Toombs. Litho Enschedé)

2008 (14 FEB). Perf 13½×14 (C)

1355	**1292**	35p multicoloured	....	1·00	1·00
1356	**1293**	39p multicoloured	....	1·20	1·20
1357	**1294**	43p multicoloured	....	1·30	1·30
1358	**1295**	76p multicoloured	....	2·30	2·30
1355/8		Set of 4	....	5·75	5·75
		First Day Cover	....		8·25
		Presentation Pack	....	8·25	

The 39p and 43p values include the 'EUROPA' emblem.

Plate Nos.: 35p, 39p 1A, 1B; 43p, 76p 1A (each ×6)

Sheets: 10 (2×5) with enlarged inscribed margins

Imprint: Lower left-hand margin

Withdrawn: 28.2.2009

1296 Arts and Crafts   **1297** Dance and Drama

1298 Speech   **1299** Films and Photography

1300 Music

Jersey Festivals (3rd issue). Centenary of Jersey Eisteddfod

(Des Jennifer Toombs. Litho Austrian State Ptg Wks, Vienna)

2008 (3 MAR). Perf 14 (C)

1359	**1296**	35p multicoloured	....	1·00	1·00
1360	**1297**	39p multicoloured	....	1·20	1·20
1361	**1298**	43p multicoloured	....	1·30	1·30
1362	**1299**	58p multicoloured	....	1·70	1·70
1363	**1300**	76p multicoloured	....	2·30	2·30
1359/63		Set of 5	....	7·50	7·50
		First Day Cover	....		10·00
		Presentation Pack	....	10·00	

Plate Nos.: All values 1A (each ×4)

Sheets: 10 (2×5) with enlarged illustrated margins

Imprint: Lower left-hand margin

1301 Grey Bus Services Daimler CB, c. 1920   **1302** SCS Ex LGOC 'K' Single Decker, c.1930

1303 JMT Town Bus Service, c. 1941   **1304** JMT Leyland Lion Charcoal Burner, c. 1941

1305 JBS Bedford WLB, c. 1956   **1306** JMT Commer Commando, c. 1963

1307 JMT Ford Willowbrook, c. 1977
(*illustration reduced. Actual size* 110×75 *mm*)

Jersey Transport. Buses (2nd series)

(Des Alan Copp. Litho Enschedé)

2008 (8 APR). Perf 14 (C)

1364	**1301**	35p multicoloured	85	85
1365	**1302**	39p multicoloured	95	95
1366	**1303**	43p multicoloured	1·00	1·00
1367	**1304**	52p multicoloured	1·30	1·30
1368	**1305**	58p multicoloured	1·40	1·40
1369	**1306**	76p multicoloured	1·80	1·80
1364/9		Set of 6	7·25	7·25
		First Day Cover		11·50
		Presentation Pack	11·50	

MS1370 110×75 mm. **1307** £2.50 multicoloured. Perf 13½×14 (C) .... 7·25   7·25
           First Day Cover ....   10·00
           Presentation Pack .... 10·00

Plate Nos.: 35p, 39p, 43p 1A, 1B, 1C; 52p, 58p, 76p 1A (each ×5)

Sheets: 10 (2×5) with enlarged illustrated margins

Imprint: Lower left-hand margin

1308 Jersey Bull 'Mermaid's Warrior Count'
(*illustration reduced. Actual size* 110×75 *mm*)

18th World Jersey Cattle Bureau Conference, Jersey

(Des William Oliver. Litho Cartor)

2008 (18 MAY). *Sheet* 110×75 *mm.* Perf 13×13½ (C)
MS1371   **1308** £2 multicoloured .... 5·75   5·75
           First Day Cover ....   8·50
           Presentation Pack ...... 8·50

1309 *Cymbidium*   **1310** *Miltonia* 'Tesson Mill'
Averanches 'Victoria
Village'

1311 *Anguloa* Victoire   **1312** *Phragmipedium* La
'Trinity'   Hougette

1313 *Phragmipedium*   **1314** *Paphiopedilum* Rolfei
Havre de Pas   'Trinity'
'Jersey'

1315 *Paphiopedilum* Rocco Tower
(*illustration reduced. Actual size* 110×75 *mm*)

Jersey Orchids (6th series)

(Des Andrew Robinson. Litho Cartor)

2008 (20 MAY). Perf 13×13½ (C)

1372	**1309**	35p multicoloured	1·00	1·00
1373	**1310**	39p multicoloured	1·20	1·20
1374	**1311**	43p multicoloured	1·30	1·30
1375	**1312**	52p multicoloured	1·50	1·50
1376	**1313**	58p multicoloured	1·70	1·70
1377	**1314**	76p multicoloured	2·30	2·30
1372/7		Set of 6	9·00	9·00
		First Day Cover		11·50
		Presentation Pack	11·50	

MS1378   110×75 mm. **1315** £2.50 multicoloured   7·25   7·25

First Day Cover   10·00
Presentation Pack   10·00

Plate Nos.: All values 1A (each ×5)

Sheets: 10 (2×5) with enlarged illustrated margins.

Imprint: Lower left-hand margin

1316 Jersey Cricket Board Ball hitting Stumps
(*illustration reduced. Actual size* 110×75 *mm*)

World Cricket League Division 5 Tournament, Jersey

(Des Andrew Robinson. Litho Cartor)

2008 (23 MAY). *Sheet* 110×75 *mm.* Perf 13×13½ (C)
MS1379   **1316** £2 multicoloured   5·75

First Day Cover   8·50
Presentation Pack   8·50

1317 HMS *Roebuck*

1318 HMS *Monmouth*

1319 HMS *Edinburgh*

1320 HMS *Express*

1321 HMS *Severn*

1322 HMS *Cottesmore*

1323 HMY Britannia
(*illustration reduced. Actual size* 110×75 *mm*)

Jersey Naval Connections (2nd series). Visiting Naval Vessels

(Des Tony Theobald. Litho Cartor)

2008 (24 JUNE). Perf 13×13½ (C)

1380	**1317**	35p multicoloured	1·00	1·00
		a. Booklet pane. Nos. 1380/5 with margins all round	9·00	
1381	**1318**	39p multicoloured	1·20	1·20
1382	**1319**	43p multicoloured	1·30	1·30
1383	**1320**	52p multicoloured	1·50	1·50
1384	**1321**	58p multicoloured	1·70	1·70
1385	**1322**	76p multicoloured	2·30	2·30
1380/5		Set of 6	9·00	9·00
		First Day Cover		11·50
		Presentation Pack	11·50	

MS1386   110×75 mm. **1323** £2.50 multicoloured. Perf 13½×13 (C)   7·25   7·25

a. Booklet pane. No. **MS**1386,
but 150×100 mm with line
of roulettes at left   7·25
First Day Cover   10·00
Presentation Pack   10·00

Booklet pane No. 1380a exists in three versions which differ in the order of the stamps within the block of six.

Plate Nos.: All values 1A (each ×4)

Sheets: 10 (2×5) with enlarged illustrated margins

Imprint: Lower left-hand margin

1324 Daimler Dart
(*illustration reduced. Actual size 110×75 mm*)

Jersey Festival of Speed

(Des Alan R. Copp. Litho Cartor)

2008 (23 AUG). *Sheet* 110×75 *mm. Perf* 13×13½ (C)
MS1387 **1324** £2.50 multicoloured . . . . 7·25   7·25
         First Day Cover . . . .   10·00
         Presentation Pack . . . . 10·00

1325 Cockerel, Hen and Chicks

1326 Ewe and Lambs

1327 Sow and Piglets

1328 Geese and Goslings

1329 Jersey Cows and Calf

Farm Animals

(Des Colleen Corlett. Litho SEP Sprint, Australia)

2008 (26 AUG). *Self-adhesive. Perf* 11½ (die-cut).
1388 **1325** (35p) multicoloured . . . . 1·00   1·00
1389 **1326** (35p) multicoloured . . . . 1·00   1·00
1390 **1327** (35p) multicoloured . . . . 1·00   1·00
1391 **1328** (35p) multicoloured . . . . 1·00   1·00
1392 **1329** (35p) multicoloured . . . . 1·00   1·00
1388/92   *Set of* 5 . . . . 5·00   5·00
                First Day Cover . . . .   7·75
                Presentation Pack . . . . . 7·75

Nos. 1388/92 are inscribed 'JERSEY MINIMUM POSTAGE PAID' and were sold for 35p. each. They were printed together, *se-tenant*, in strips of five from rolls of 100, from which the surplus self-adhesive backing paper around each stamp was removed.

Nos. 1388/92 commemorate the 175th anniversary of the Royal Jersey Agricultural and Horticultural Society.

1330 Carpenter Bee

1331 Buff-tailed Bumblebee

1332 Clown-faced Bug

1333 Large Migrant Hoverfly

1334 Ruby-tailed Wasp

1335 22-spot Ladybird

Insects (2nd series)

(Des William Oliver. Litho Cartor)

2008 (8 SEPT). *Perf* 13×13½ (C)
1393 **1330** 35p multicoloured . . . . 1·00   1·00
1394 **1331** 39p multicoloured . . . . 1·20   1·20
1395 **1332** 43p multicoloured . . . . 1·30   1·30
1396 **1333** 52p multicoloured . . . . 1·50   1·50
1397 **1334** 58p multicoloured . . . . 1·70   1·70
1398 **1335** 76p multicoloured . . . . 2·30   2·30

1393/8		Set of 6	9·00	9·00
		First Day Cover		11·50
		Presentation Pack	11·50	

Plate Nos.: All values 1A (each ×4)

Sheets: 10 (2×5) with enlarged illustrated margins

Imprint: Lower left-hand margin

Wipa08 International Stamp Exhibition, Vienna

2008 (18 SEPT). *No.* **MS**1370 *optd* 'Jersey at WIPA08' *on bottom right sheet margin.*
MS1399   110×75 mm. **1307** £2.50 multi-coloured. Perf 13½×14 (C) ....   7·25   7·25

1336 Northern Wheatear

1337 Whinchat

1338 Pied Flycatcher

1339 Yellow Wagtail

1340 Ring Ouzel

1341 Common Redstart

Jersey Birdlife (2nd series). Migrating Birds

(Des Nick Parlett. Litho Cartor)

2008 (21 OCT). Perf 13×13½ (C)

1400	**1336**	35p multicoloured	....	1·00	1·00
1401	**1337**	39p multicoloured	....	1·20	1·20
1402	**1338**	43p multicoloured	....	1·30	1·30
1403	**1339**	52p multicoloured	....	1·50	1·50
1404	**1340**	58p multicoloured	....	1·70	1·70
1405	**1341**	76p multicoloured	....	2·30	2·30
1400/5		Set of 6		9·00	9·00
		First Day Cover			11·50
		Presentation Pack		11·50	

MS1406	150×100 mm. Nos. 1400/5	9·00	9·00
	First Day Cover		11·50
	Presentation Pack	11·50	
MS1407	150×100 mm. Nos. 1403/5	5·50	5·50
	First Day Cover		8·00
	Presentation Pack	8·00	

Stamps from **MS**1407 have no white borders.

Plate Nos.: All values 1A (each ×5)

Sheets: 10 (2×5) with enlarged illustrated margins

Imprint: Lower left-hand margin

1342 Prince Charles

60th Birthday of Prince Charles

(Des Andrew Robinson. Litho Cartor)

2008 (14 NOV). Perf 13½ (C)

1408	**1342**	£4 multicoloured	....	12·00	12·00
		First Day Cover			14·50
		Presentation Pack		14·50	
MS1409		150×100 mm. No. 1408		12·00	12·00
		First Day Cover			14·50
		Presentation Pack		14·50	

Plate Nos.: 1A (×5)

Sheets: 4 (2×2)

Imprint: Lower left-hand margin

Post Office Yearbook

2008 (1 DEC). *Comprises Nos.* 1350/98, 1400/5 *and* 1408
Yearbook .... 95·00

COMMEMORATIVE POSTAL STATIONERY ENVELOPE

40th Anniversary of Liberation

1985 (7 MAY). *Cover showing imprinted stamp design as No. 36. Sold at 25p*
PS1   13p multicoloured . . . .   1·00   2·00

Quantity sold: 79,744

Sold out: 6.85

POSTAGE DUE STAMPS

D **1**   D **2** Map   D **3** Map

(Des F. Guenier. Litho Bradbury, Wilkinson)

1969 (1 OCT). Perf 14×13½ (C)

D1	D **1**	1d bluish violet (*ab*)	65	1·10
D2		2d sepia (*ad*)	90	1·10
D3		3d magenta (*ad*)	1·00	1·10
D4	D **2**	1s bright emerald (*acd*)	5·50	5·00
D5		2s6d olive-grey (*acd*)	13·00	14·00
D6		5s vermilion (*ad*)	15·00	16·00
D1/6		*Set of 6*	32·00	35·00

Sheets: 120 (2 panes 6×10)

Imprint: Central, bottom margin

Printings: (*a*) 1.10.69; (*b*) 16.12.69; (*c*) 18.2.70; (*d*) 6.6.70

Quantities sold: 1d 98,535; 2d 181,601; 3d 155,832; 1s 174,599; 2s6d 205,962; 5s 200,698

Withdrawn and invalidated: 14.2.72

Decimal Currency

(Des F. Guenier. Litho Bradbury, Wilkinson)

1971 (15 FEB)–**75**. Perf 14×13½ (C)

D7	D **3**	½p black (*a*)	10	10
D8		1p violet-blue (*a*)	10	10
D9		2p olive-grey (*a*)	10	10
D10		3p reddish purple (*a*)	10	10
D11		4p pale red (*a*)	10	10
D12		5p bright emerald (*a*)	10	10
D13		6p yellow-orange (*b*)	10	10
D14		7p bistre-yellow (*a*)	10	10
D15		8p light greenish blue (*c*)	15	20
D16		10p pale olive-grey (*a*)	15	20
D17		11p ochre (*c*)	30	35
D18		14p violet (*c*)	40	50
D19		25p myrtle-green (*b*)	45	90
D20		50p dull purple (*c*)	1·10	1·70
D7/20		*Set of 14*	3·00	4·50
		Presentation Pack	5·00	

Printings: (*a*) 15.2.71; (*b*) 12.8.74; (*c*) 1.5.75

Plate Nos.: 3p 1*a*, 1*d*; 8, 25p 1*b*, 1*c*, 1*d*; 11p 1*a*, 1*b*, 1*d*; others 1*a*, 1*b*, 1*c*, 1*d*

Sheets: 50 (5×10)

Quantities sold: ½p 313,604; 1p 281,598; 2p 205,263; 3p 183,353; 4p 180,948; 5p 199,771; 6p 161,580; 7p 156,534; 8p 154,904; 10p 198,530; 11p 151,638; 14p 147,075; 25p 158,663; 50p 146,602

Imprint: Central, bottom margin

Withdrawn: 31.1.79

D **4** Arms of St. Clement and Dovecote at Samares

D **5** Arms of St. Lawrence and Handois Reservoir

D **6** Arms of St. John and Sorel Point

D **7** Arms of St. Ouen and Pinnacle Rock

D **8** Arms of St. Peter and Quetivel Mill

D **9** Arms of St. Martin and St. Catherine's Breakwater

D **10** Arms and Harbour of St. Helier

D **11** Arms of St. Saviour and Highlands College

D **12** Arms of St. Brelade and Beauport Bay

D **13** Arms of Grouville and La Hougue Bie

D **14** Arms of St. Mary and Perry Farm

D **15** Arms of Trinity and Bouley Bay

427

Parish Arms and Views

(Des G. Drummond. Litho Questa)

1978 (17 JAN). Perf 14 (C)

D21	D **4**	1p blue-green and black	10	10
D22	D **5**	2p orange-yellow and black ...	10	10
D23	D **6**	3p lake-brown and black	10	10
D24	D **7**	4p orange-vermilion and black .	10	10
D25	D **8**	5p ultramarine and black	10	10
D26	D **9**	10p brown-olive and black	10	10
D27	D **10**	12p greenish blue and black	15	10
D28	D **11**	14p red-orange and black	20	15
D29	D **12**	15p bright magenta and black ..	25	30
D30	D **13**	20p yellow-green and black	30	40
D31	D **14**	50p deep brown and black	90	80
D32	D **15**	£1 chalky blue and black	1·40	1·40
D21/32		Set of 12	3·25	3·25
		Presentation Pack	3·75	

Plate Nos.: All values 1A–1A, 1B–1B, 1C–1C, 1D–1D, 1E–1E, 1F–1F

Sheets: 50 (10×5)

Imprint: Right-hand corner, bottom margin

Withdrawn: 30.9.83

D **16** St. Brelade   D **17** St. Aubin   D **18** Rozel

D **19** Greve de Lecq   D **20** Bouley Bay   D **21** St. Catherine

D **22** Gorey   D **23** Bonne Nuit   D **24** La Rocque

D **28** Elizabeth Castle   D **29** Upper Harbour Marina

Jersey Harbours

(Des G. Drummond. Litho Questa)

1982 (7 SEPT). Perf 14 (C)

D33	D **16**	1p brt turquoise-green & black .	10	10
D34	D **17**	2p chrome yellow and black ...	10	10
D35	D **18**	3p lake-brown and black	10	10
D36	D **19**	4p red and black	10	10
D37	D **20**	5p bright blue and black	10	10
D38	D **21**	6p yellow-olive and black	10	15
D39	D **22**	7p reddish mauve and black ...	15	20
D40	D **23**	8p bright orange-red and black .	15	20
D41	D **24**	9p bright green and black	20	20
D42	D **25**	10p turquoise-blue and black ...	20	20
D43	D **26**	20p apple-green and black	40	40
D44	D **27**	30p bright purple and black	60	60
D45	D **28**	40p dull orange and black	80	80
D46	D **29**	£1 bright reddish violet & black	2·00	2·00
D33/46		Set of 14	4·50	4·50
		Presentation Pack	4·75	

Plate Nos.: All values 1A, 1B, 1C, 1D, 1E, 1F, 1G, 1H (each ×2)

Sheets: 50 (10×5)

Imprint: Right-hand corner, bottom margin

Sold out: By 10.2005

D **25** St. Helier   D **26** Ronez   D **27** La Collette

STAMP BOOKLETS

PRICES given are for complete booklets. All booklets are stitched unless otherwise stated.

Contents 5at4d 4at1d   B **1** Map

1969 (1 OCT)–**70.**

2s Booklet. Blue cover as Type B **1**
SB1   Containing 5×4d (No. 19*a*), 4×1d (No. 16*a*), all in panes of one with wide margins ......   2·00

Contents
12at4d 6at5d 6at1d   B **2** Arms and Royal Mace

7s Booklet. Yellow cover as Type B **2**
SB2   Containing 12×4d (No. 19), 6×5d (No. 20), 6×1d (No. 16*b*). all in vertical pairs ....   13·00
SB2*a* Containing 12×4d (No. 19*b*). 6×5d (No. 20*a*), 6×1d (No. 16), all in vertical pairs (5.5.70) ...   £130

10s Booklet. Pink cover as Type B **2** *showing Mont Orgueil Castle*
SB3   Containing 14×4d (No. 19), 12×5d (No. 20), 4×1d (No. 16*b*), all in vertical pairs ....   10·00
SB3*a* Containing 14×4d (No. 19*b*). 12×5d (No. 20*a*), 4×1d (No. 16), all in vertical pairs (5.5.70) ...   40·00

Special printings in sheets of 48 were made for manufacturing the 2s. booklets, but the 7s. and 10s. booklets were made up from ordinary sheets, using vertical pairs with stitching through the side margins. Stamps from both sides of the sheet were utilised so that the panes come either upright or inverted.

Decimal Currency

1971 (15 FEB).

10p Booklet. Blue cover as Type B **1** *showing Martello Tower*
SB4   Containing 2×½p (No. 42*a*), 2×2p (No. 45*a*) and 2×2½p (No. 46*a*). Each stamp with wide margin at bottom ....   1·00
SB4*a* Containing 2×½p (No. 42*a*), 2×2p (No. 45*a*) and 2×2½p (No. 46*a*). Each stamp with wide margin at top ....   2·75

35p Booklet. Yellow cover as Type B **2** *showing The Royal Court*
SB5   Containing 10×2p (No. 45) and 6×2½p (No. 46) ....   1·20

50p Booklet. Pink cover as Type B **2** *showing Elizabeth Castle*
SB6   Containing 10×2p (No. 45) and 12×2½p (No. 46) ....   1·70

The panes for Nos. SB4/*a* were produced in sheets of 48, of which half were *tête-bêche*. In consequence, half the booklets have the blank margin at the bottom (SB4), and the other half at the top (SB4*a*).

Owing to the postal information printed in the booklets being out of date, supplies of Nos. SB4/*a* dispensed from machines between 10 July and early September 1972 bore an adhesive label on the front with the words 'RATE TO UNITED KINGDOM LETTERS up to 4 ozs. and postcards 3p' in two lines. They were primarily to warn holiday-makers of the new rate and were issued only through the machines. Of these about 52,000 were sold.

Quantities sold: SB4/*a* 244,544; SB5 20,875; SB6 17,638

1972 (15 MAY).

20p Booklet. Green cover as Type B **2** *showing Jersey Cow*
SB7   Containing 8×2½p (No. 46), all in vertical pairs   2·20

30p Booklet. Yellow cover as Type B **2** *showing Portelet Bay*
SB8   Containing 10×3p (No. 47), all in vertical pairs   25·00

50p Booklet. Pink cover as Type B **2** *showing La Corbière Lighthouse*
SB9   Containing 8×2½p (No. 46) and 10×3p (No. 47), all in vertical pairs ....   1·70

1972 (1 DEC).

10p Booklet. Orange cover as Type B **1** *showing Legislative Chamber*
SB10   Containing 3×½p (No. 42*a*), 1×2½p (No. 45*a*) and 2×3p (No. 47*a*). Each stamp with wide margin *at bottom*   90
SB10*a* As SB10 but with margin *at top*   90

Quantity sold: 126,877

1973 (1 JUNE).

10p Booklet. Green cover as Type B **1** showing Mont Orgueil by night
SB11   Contents as No. SB10. Each stamp with wide
      margin *at bottom*   90
SB11*a* As SB11 but with margin *at top*   90

  Quantity sold: 109,129

1973 (10 SEPT).

20p Booklet. Green cover as Type B **2** showing Jersey Wildlife Preservation Trust species
SB12   Containing 8×2½p (No. 46) ....   3·00

30p Booklet. Buff cover as Type B **2** showing Jersey Wild Flowers
SB13   Containing 10×3p (No. 47) ....   2·50

50p Booklet. Blue cover as Type B **2** showing 'English Fleet in the Channel' by Peter Monamy
SB14   Containing 8×2½p (No. 46) and 10×3p (No. 47)   2·00

  Quantites sold: SB12 8,790; SB13 11,450; SB14 14,145

1974 (7 JAN). Jersey Wildlife Preservation Trust

20p Booklet. Green cover as Type B **2** showing Spectacled Bear
SB15   Containing 8×2½p (No. 46) ....   1·50

30p Booklet. Yellow cover as Type B **2** showing White Eared-Pheasant
SB16   Containing 10×3p (No. 47) ....   1·50

50p Booklet. Red cover as Type B **2** showing Thick-billed Parrot
SB17   Containing 8×2½p (No. 46) and 10×3p (No. 47)   2·20

  Quantities sold: SB15 14,283; SB16 14,049; SB17 15,976

1974 (1 JULY).

10p Booklet. Orange cover as Type B **1** showing Jersey Airport
SB18   Containing 1×3p (No. 47*a*) and 2×3½p (No.
      48*a*). Each stamp with wide margin *at bottom* ..   60
SB18*a* As SB18 but with margin *at top*   60

  Quantity sold: 129,235

1974 (1 JULY). Jersey Wildlife Preservation Trust

60p Booklet. Pink cover as Type B **2** showing Ring-tailed Lemur
SB19   Containing 6×3p (No. 47) and 12×3½p (No. 48)   2·00

  Quantity sold: 22,274

1974 (1 OCT). Jersey Wildlife Preservation Trust

60p Booklet. Green cover as Type B **2** showing Tuatara Lizard
SB20   Contents as No. SB19 ....   2·00

  Quantity sold: 20,984

B **3** Artillery Shako

1975 (25 FEB). Military Headgear

10p Booklet. Grey cover as Type B **3**
SB21   Containing 1×½p (No. 42*a*), 2×3p (No. 47*a*)
      and 1×3½p (No. 48*a*). Each stamp with wide
      margin *at bottom*   50
SB21*a* As SB21 but with margin *at top*   50

20p Booklet. Rose cover as Type B **3** showing Shako, 2nd North Regt
SB22   Containnig 2×3p (No. 47*a*) and 4×3½p (No.
      48*a*). Each stamp with wide margin *at
      bottom*   60
SB22*a* As SB22 but with margin *at top*   50

  Quantities sold: SB21/*a* 37,849; SB22/*a* 38,854

STAMP SACHETS These are booklet covers with the stamps loose inside and contained in clear plastic sachets. They are noted but not priced as such items are outside the scope of this checklist.

B **4** Post Office Crest

1975 (1 APR). 20p Stamp Sachet. Red cover as Type B **4**
Containing 2×1p (No. 43), 2×4p (No. 49) and 2×5p (No. 50)

430

£1 Contents 8 at 1p 8 at 4p 12 at 5p

B **5** Astra Biplane
(*illustration reduced. Actual size 94×56 mm*)

1975 (21 APR). *Aviation History. Pale blue cover* (SB23) *or yellow cover* (SB24)

50p *Booklet as Type* B **2** *showing Supermarine Sea Eagle*
SB23   Containing 6×1p (No. 43), 6×4p (No. 49) and
4×5p (No. 50) . . . .   1·70

£1 *Booklet as Type* B **5**
SB24   Containing 8×1p (No. 43), 8×4p (No. 49) and
12×5p (No. 50) . . . .   3·00

Quantites sold: SB23 29,872; SB24 29,608

1976 (29 JAN). *20p Stamp Sachet. Blue cover as Type* B **4**
Containing 3×1p (No. 138), 2×5p (No. 139) and 1×7p (No. 141)

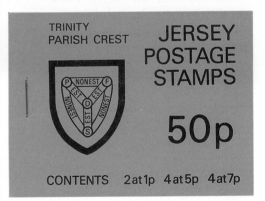

B **6** Trinity Parish Crest

1976 (5 APR). *Green cover* (SB25) *or magenta cover* (SB26) *as Type* B **6**

50p *Booklet. Trinity Parish Crest*
SB25   Containing booklet panes Nos. 138a, 139a
and 141a . . . .   1·50

£1 *Booklet. St. Ouen's Parish Crest*
SB26   Containing booklet panes Nos. 138b, 139a×2
and 141a×2 . . . .   3·00

Quantities sold: SB25 85,210; SB26 64,609

1976 (2 NOV). *20p Stamp Sachet. Green cover as Type* B **4**
Containing 3×1p, 2×5p and 1×7p (Nos. 138/9 and 141)

1977 (29 SEPT). *20p Stamp Sachet. Brown cover as Type* B **4**
Containing 3×1p, 2×5p and 1×7p (Nos. 138/9 and 141)

1978 (28 FEB). *Orange-red cover* (SB27) *or pale blue cover* (SB28) *as Type* B **6**

£1 *Booklet. Grouville Parish Arms*
SB27   Containing booklet panes Nos. 138b and 140a
×4 . . . .   3·00

£1 *Booklet. St. Saviour Parish Arms*
SB28   Containing booklet panes Nos. 138b and 142a
×3 . . . .   3·00

Quantities sold: SB27 43,446; SB28 45,015

1978 (1 MAY). *30p Stamp Sachet. Violet cover as Type* B **4**
Containing 2×1p, 2×6p and 2×8p (Nos. 138, 140 and 142)

1979 (13 AUG). *30p Stamp Sachet. Purple cover as Type* B **4**
Containing 2×1p, 2×6p and 2×8p (Nos. 138, 140 and 142)

B **7** Jersey Post Office Headquarters, Mont Millais, St. Helier
(*illustration reduced. Actual size 90×65 mm*)

1979 (1 OCT). *Bistre-brown on buff cover as Type* B **7**. *Stapled*
SB29   £1.20 booklet containing Nos. 138b, 140a and
142a each ×2 . . . .   4·00

Quantity sold: 82,738

1980 (6 MAY). *Black on red cover as Type* B **6** *showing St. Helier Parish Arms. Stapled*
SB30   £1.40 booklet containing Nos. 138*b*×3, 141*a*×2 and 143*a*×2 . . . .   4·50

Quantity sold: 29,900

1980 (6 MAY). *20p Stamp Sachet. Black on red cover as Type* B **4**
Containing 4×1p, 1×7p and 1×9p (Nos. 138, 141 and 143)

1981 (24 FEB). *Black on blue cover as Type* B **6**, *but* 82×65 *mm, showing De Bagot crest. Stapled*
SB31   £1.32 booklet containing Nos. 250*a*×2, 252*a*, 256*a* and 259*a* . . . .   4·50

Quantity sold: 49,486

1981 (24 FEB). *20p Stamp Sachet. Black on blue cover as Type* B **4** *Containing* 2×3p and 2×7p (Nos. 252 and 256)

1981 (1 DEC). *Black on green cover as Type* B **6**, *but* 82×65 *mm, showing Poingdestre Arms. Stapled*
SB32   £1.20 booklet containing Nos. 250*a*, 251*a*, 256*a* and 259*a* . . . .   4·00

Quantity sold: 43,434

B **8** Jean Martell
   (*illustration reduced. Actual size* 155×80 *mm*)

Martell Cognac

1982 (7 SEPT). *Multicoloured cover as Type* B **8**. *Booklet contains text and illustrations on labels attached to panes and on interleaving pages*
SB33   £3.08 booklet containing Nos. 293*b*, 295*b* and 297*b* each ×2 . . . .   8·00

Quantity sold: 54,654

1983 (19 APR). *Black on orange-red cover as Type* B **6**, *but* 82×65 *mm, showing Bisson crest. Stapled*
SB34   £1.32 booklet containing Nos. 250*a*, 251*a*, 257*a* and 260*a* . . . .   4·00

Quantity sold: 29,393

1983 (19 APR). *20p Stamp Sachet. Black on turquoise-green as Type* B **4** *Containing* 2×½p, 1×8p and 1×11p (Nos. 249, 257 and 260)

1984 (3 JAN). *30p Stamp Sachet. Black in pink cover as Type* B **4** *Containing* 2×9p and 1×12p (Nos. 258 and 261)

1984 (27 APR). *Black on rose-lilac cover as Type* B **6**, *but* 80×65 *mm, showing Robin crest. Stapled*
SB35   £2.16 booklet containing Nos. 252*ba*×2, 258*ab*×2 and 261*ab* . . . .   6·00

Quantity sold: 38,782

1985 (15 APR). *50p Stamp Sachet. Black on light green cover as Type* B **4** *Containing* 1×1p, 3×3p and 4×10p (Nos. 250, 252*b* and 259)

B **9** Cross of Lorraine
   (*illustration reduced. Actual size* 155×80 *mm*)

300th Anniversary of Huguenot Immigration

1985 (10 SEPT). *Multicoloured cover as Type* B **9**
SB36   £3.60 booklet containing Nos. 370*a*/5*a* . . . . .   10·00

Quantity sold: 31,042

1986 (1 APR). *Black on carmine cover as Type* B **6**, *but* 81×65 *mm, showing Messervy crest. Stapled*
SB37   £3.12 booklet containing Nos. 251*ba*, 259*ba* and 263*ab*, each ×2 . . . .   9·00

Quantity sold 23,729
Withdrawn: 31.3.91

B **10** Post Office Emblem

1986 (1 APR). 50p *Stamp Sachet. Black and orange-vermilion cover as Type* B **10** Containing 1×2p, 2×4p and 4×10p (Nos. 251*b*, 253*a* and 259)

1987 (6 APR). *Black on blue cover as Type* B **6**, *but* 81×65 *mm, showing Fiott crest. Stapled*
SB38   £3.60 booklet containing Nos. 253*ab*, 260*ba* and 264*ab*, each ×2 . . . .   8·50

Quantity sold: 23,647

Withdrawn: 31.3.91

1987 (6 APR). 50p *Stamp Sachet. Black and orange-vermilion cover as Type* B **10** Containing 1×2p, 1×3p, 3×4p and 3×11p (Nos. 251*b*, 252*b*, 253*a* and 260)

B **11** Vikings
   (*illustration reduced. Actual size* 168×80 *mm*)

900th Death Anniversary of William the Conqueror

1987 (16 OCT). *Multicoloured cover as Type* B **11**. *Booklet contains text and illustrations on labels attached to panes and on interleaving pages*
SB39   £5.50 booklet containing Nos. 422*a*/7*a* . . . . .   15·00

Quantity sold: 30,107

Sold out: 4.88

1988 (17 MAY). *Black on bright green cover as Type* B **6**, *but* 81×56 *mm, showing Malet crest. Stapled*
SB40   £3.84 booklet containing Nos. 253*ab*, 261*ab* and 265*a*, each ×2 . . . .   11·00

Quantity sold: 16,566

Withdrawn: 31.3.91

1988 (17 MAY). 50p *Stamp Sachet. Black and orange-vermilion cover as Type* B **10** Containing 1×2p, 3×4p and 3×12p (Nos. 251*b*, 253*a* and 261)

B **12** Chouan Rebels
   (*illustration reduced. Actual size* 155×80 *mm*)

Bicentenary of the French Revolution. Philippe D'Auvergne

1989 (7 JULY). *Multicoloured cover as Type* B **12**. *Booklet contains text on labels attached to panes and on interleaving pages*
SB41   £6 booklet containing Nos. 501*a*/6*a* . . . .   17·00

Quantity sold: 31,052

Sold out: 7.8.99

B **13** Flags of Jersey and Great Britain
   (*illustration reduced. Actual size* 108×63 *mm*)

'Stamp World London 90' International Stamp Exhibition

1990 (3 MAY). *Multicoloured cover as Type* B **13**
SB42   £4.20 booklet containing Nos. 470*a*, 474*a* and 478*a*, each ×2 . . . .   11·00

Withdrawn: 30.6.96

B **14**

1990 (3 MAY). *50p Stamp Sachet. Multicoloured cover as Type* B **14** *showing* 18p *stamp* (No. 478) *Containing* 2×4p *and* 3×14p (Nos. 470 and 474)

B **15** Elizabeth Castle
(*illustration reduced. Actual size* 108×63 *mm*)

1991 (12 FEB). *Jersey Scenes. Multicoloured cover as Type* B **15**
SB43 £4.80 booklet containing Nos. 471*a*, 475*a* and 480*a*, each ×2 . . . . 11·50

Withdrawn: 30.6.96

1992 (25 FEB). £1 *Stamp Sachet. Multicoloured cover as Type* B **14** *showing design of* 22p *stamp* (No. 480) *Containing* 1×2p, 2×16p, 3×22p (Nos. 467, 474 and 480)

B **16** William Mesny on Horseback
(*illustration reduced. Actual size* 155×80 *mm*)

Jersey Adventures (3rd series). 150th Birth Anniversary of William Mesny

1992 (25 FEB). *Multicoloured cover as Type* B **16**. *Booklet contains text on labels attached to panes and on interleaving pages*
SB44 £5.50 booklet containing Nos. 573*b*/8*a* . . . . . 12·00

Withdrawn: 30.6.96

B **17** Jersey Post Logo

1992 (25 MAY). *Covers as Type* B **17**. *Panes attached by selvedge*
SB45 £1.12 booklet (scarlet on white cover) containing No. 474*b* . . . . 2·75
SB46 £1.28 booklet (bright yellow on scarlet cover) containing No. 476*a* . . . . 3·50
SB47 £1.76 booklet (scarlet on bright yellow cover) containing No. 482*a* . . . . 4·50

Withdrawn: 30.6.96

1993 (26 JAN). *Covers as Type* B **17**. *Panes attached by selvedge*
SB48 (£1.36) booklet (bright yellow on green cover) containing pane No. 601*a* . . . . 5·00
SB49 (£1.84) booklet (scarlet on flesh cover) containing pane No. 605*a* . . . . 5·50
SB50 (£2.24) booklet (white on bright new blue cover) containing pane No. 609*a* . . . . 7·00

Face values quoted for each booklet are those at which they were initially sold. The price of No. SB48 was increased to £1.44 and that of No. SB50 to £2.40 on 10 January 1994. No. SB48 was sold at £1.52 from 4 July 1995. On 10 March 1997. No. SB48 was increased to £1.60, No. SB49 to £1.92 and No. SB50 to £2.48.

Withdrawn: 30.9.99

B **18** Invasion Map
(*illustration reduced. Actual size* 162×98 *mm*)

50th Anniversary of D-Day

1994 (6 JUNE). *Multicoloured cover as Type B* **18**. *Booklet contains text and illustrations on panes and interleaving pages*
SB51 £5.68 booklet containing Nos. 659a/b, 661a
and 663a .... 17·00

Sold out: 12.94

B **19** 'Greetings From JERSEY'
(*illustration reduced. Actual size* 152×75 *mm*)

Greetings Stamps

1995 (24 JAN). *Multicoloured cover as Type B* **19**. *Pane attached by selvedge*
SB52 £2.24 booklet containing pane No. 684b .... 6·50

Quantity sold: 65,810
Withdrawn: 30.9.99

B **20** Crowd Celebrating
(*illustration reduced. Actual size* 162×97 *mm*)

50th Anniversary of Liberation

1995 (9 MAY). *Multicoloured cover as Type B* **20**. *Booklet contains text and illustrations on panes and interleaving pages*
SB53 £7.06 booklet containing Nos. 700a, 702a,
704a and **MS**706a .... 14·00

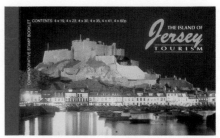

B **21** Mont Orgueil Castle, Gorey
(*illustration reduced. Actual size* 164×97 *mm*)

Tourism

1996 (8 JUNE). *Multicoloured cover as Type B* **21**. *Booklet contains text and illustrations on panes and interleaving pages*
SB54 £8.32 booklet containing Nos. 752a/b, 754a
and 756a .... 16·00

B **22** Island Sports
(*illustration reduced. Actual size* 163×98 *mm*)

7th Island Games, Jersey

1997 (28 JUNE). *Multicoloured cover as Type B* **22**. *Booklet contains text and illustrations on panes and interleaving pages*
SB55 £8.72 booklet containing Nos. 818a/b, 820a
and 822a .... 17·00

B **23** Buses in Royal Square, St. Helier
(*illustration reduced. Actual size* 164×98 *mm*)

75th Anniversary of Jersey Motor Transport Company. Buses

1998 (2 APR). *Multicoloured cover as Type B **23**. Booklet contains text and illustrations on panes and interleaving pages*

SB56 £8.72 booklet containing Nos. 844*a/b*, 846*a* and 848*a* . . . . 17·00

B **24** Four Vintage Humbers at the Weighbridge, 1905
(*illustration reduced. Actual size 164×98 mm*)

Centenary of Motoring in Jersey

1999 (2 JULY). *Multicoloured cover as Type B **24**. Booklet contains text and illustrations on panes and interleaving pages*

SB57 £8.80 booklet containing Nos. 905*a/b*, 907*a* and 909*a* . . . . 19·00

B **25** Full-rigged Sailing Ship
(*illustration reduced. Actual size 164×100 mm*)

'The Stamp Show 2000' International Stamp Exhibition, London. Maritime Heritage

2000 (22 MAY). *Multicoloured cover as Type B **25**. Booklet contains text and illustrations on interleaving pages. Stitched*

SB58 £9.60 booklet containing Nos. 936*b/e* and 937*a* . . . . 19·00

B **26** Two Tawny Owls on Gate
(*illustration reduced. Actual size 164×101 mm*)

Birds of Prey

2001 (3 JULY). *Multicoloured cover as Type B **26**. Booklet contains text and illustrations on panes and interleaving pages. Stitched*

SB59 £10.76 booklet containing Nos. 999*a/d* and **MS**1005*a* . . . . 21·00

Sold out: By 7.2007

B **27** Bells

Christmas

2001 (6 NOV). *Multicoloured cover as Type B **27**. Self-adhesive*

SB60 £3.92 booklet containing No. 1014*a* . . . . 9·00

Sold out: By 6.2003

B **28** Mickey Mouse Float
(*illustration reduced. Actual size 165×100 mm*)

Centenary of 'Battle of Flowers' Parade

2002 (8 AUG). *Multicoloured cover as Type B* **28**. *Booklet contains text and illustrations on panes and interleaving pages. Stitched*
SB61 £9.35 booklet containing Nos. 1053*a*×3 and
MS1059*a* . . . . 19·00

B **29** Ellehammer's *Biplane* and Space Shuttle
(*illustration reduced. Actual size 164×100 mm*)

Centenary of Powered Flight

2003 (21 JAN). *Multicoloured cover as Type B* **29**. *Booklet contains text and illustrations on panes and interleaving pages. Stitched.*
SB62 £9.35 booklet containing No. 1074*a*×3, with
different marginal illustrations, and **MS**1080*a* 18·00

B **30** *Paphiopedilum chamberlainianum*
(*illustration reduced. Actual size 165×100 mm*)

Jersey Orchids (5th series)

2004 (25 MAY). *Multicoloured cover as Type B* **30**. *Booklet contains text and illustrations on panes and interleaving pages. Stitched.*
SB63 £10.73 booklet containing No. 1143*a*×3 and
MS1149*a* . . . . 35·00

B **31** MG
(*illustration reduced. Actual size 165×100 mm*)

Jersey Festivals (2nd issue). Motor Festival. Classic Cars

2005 (6 JUNE). *Multicoloured cover as Type B* **31**. *Booklet contains text and illustrations on panes and interleaving pages. Stitched.*
SB64 £8.61 booklet containing No. 1204*a*×3 . . . . . 17·00

B **32** Jersey Post Vehicles
(*illustration reduced. Actual size 164×100 mm*)

Jersey Postal History (2nd series). Postal Vehicles

2006 (31 OCT). *Multicoloured cover as Type B* **32**. *Booklet contains text and illustrations on panes and interleaving pages. Stitched.*
SB65 £10.67 booklet containing No. 1286*a*×3
and **MS**1292*a* . . . . 20·00

B **33** Concorde
(*illustration reduced. Actual size 164×100 mm*)

60th Anniversary of Jersey International Air Display

2007 (13 SEPT). *Multicoloured cover as Type B* **33**. *Booklet contains text and illustrations on panes and interleaving pages. Stitched.*

SB66   £11.35 booklet containing Nos. 1326*a*×3 and
   MS1332*a* . . . .   21·00

B **34** HMS *Richmond*
   (*illustration reduced. Actual size* 165×100 *mm*)

Jersey Naval Connections (2nd series). Visiting Naval Vessels

2008 (24 JUNE). *Multicoloured cover as Type B* **34**. *Booklet contains text and illustrations on panes and interleaving pages. Stitched.*

SB67   £11.59   booklet   containing   panes   Nos.
   1380×3 and **MS**1386*a* . . . .   34·00

COLLECT
CHANNEL ISLANDS
AND ISLE OF MAN STAMPS

From Stanley Gibbons, THE WORLD'S LARGEST STAMP STOCK
Priority order form – Four easy ways to order

Phone:
020 7836 8444
Overseas: +44 (0)20 7836 8444

Fax:
020 7557 4499
Overseas: +44 (0)20 7557 4499

Email:
lmourne@stanleygibbons.co.uk

Post: Lesley Mourne,
Stamp Mail Order Department
Stanley Gibbons Ltd, 399 Strand
London, WC2R 0LX, England

Customer Details _____

Account Number _____

Name _____

Address _____

_____ Postcode _____

Country _____ Email _____

Tel No _____ Fax No _____

Payment details

Registered Postage & Packing   £3.60

I enclose my cheque/postal order for £ _____ in full payment.
Please make cheques/postal orders payable to Stanley Gibbons Ltd.
Cheques must be in £ sterling and drawn on a UK bank

Please debit my credit card for £ _____ in full payment.
I have completed the Credit Card section below.

Card Number

CVC Number

Start Date (Switch & Amex)   Expiry Date

Issue No (Switch)

Signature_____ Date _____

COLLECT
CHANNEL ISLANDS
AND ISLE OF MAN STAMPS

From Stanley Gibbons, THE WORLD'S LARGEST STAMP STOCK

Condition (mint/UM/used)	Country	SG No.	Description	Price	Office use only
			POSTAGE & PACKAGING	£3.60	
			GRAND TOTAL		

Minimum price. The minimum catalogue price quoted is 10p. For individual stamps, prices between 10p and 95p are provided as a guide for catalogue users. The lowest price charged for individual stamps or sets purchased from Stanley Gibbons Ltd is £1.00 and only complete commemorative sets sold

Please complete payment, name and address details overleaf